The Vulnerable Brain and Environmental Risks

Volume 2
Toxins in Food

The Vulnerable Brain and Environmental Risks

Volume 2
Toxins in Food

Edited by

Robert L. Isaacson

Binghamton University
Binghamton, New York

and

Karl F. Jensen

U. S. Environmental Protection Agency
Research Triangle Park, North Carolina

Plenum Press • New York and London

RC
347.5
.V85
1992
V.2

Library of Congress Cataloging-in-Publication Data

The Vulnerable brain and environmental risks / edited by Robert L.
Isaacson and Karl F. Jensen.
        p.   cm.
    Includes bibliographical references and index.
    Contents: v. 1. Malnutrition and hazard assessment -- v. 2. Toxins
in food.
    ISBN 0-306-44148-9 (v. 1). -- ISBN 0-306-44165-9 (v. 2)
    1. Neurotoxicology. 2. Neurotoxicology--Environmental aspects.
I. Isaacson, Robert L., 1928-   . II. Jensen, Karl F.
    [DNLM: 1. Environmental Exposure. 2. Nervous System Diseases-
-chemically induced. 3. Neurotoxins. 4. Protein-Energy
Malnutrition--complications.   WL 100 V991]
RC347.5.V85   1992
616.8--dc20
DNLM/DLC
for Library of Congress   92-49396
                                                               CIP

ISBN 0-306-44165-9

© 1992 Plenum Press, New York
A Division of Plenum Publishing Corporation
233 Spring Street, New York, N.Y. 10013

Printed in the United States of America

Contributors

Judy L. Aschner • Department of Pediatrics, Albany Medical College, Albany, New York 12208

Michael Aschner • Department of Pharmacology and Toxicology, Albany Medical College, Albany, New York 12208

Blaine L. Beaman • Department of Medical Microbiology and Immunology, University of California School of Medicine, Davis, California 95616

Stephen C. Bondy • Department of Community and Environmental Medicine, University of California, Irvine, California 72717

Richard G. Burright • Environmental Neuropsychology Laboratory, Department of Psychology, State University of New York, Binghamton, New York 13902

Steven J. Bursian • Department of Animal Science, Michigan State University, East Lansing, Michigan 48824

Louis W. Chang • Departments of Pathology, Pharmacology, and Toxicology, University of Arkansas for Medical Sciences, Little Rock, Arkansas 72205

Peter J. Donovick • Environmental Neuropsychology Laboratory, Department of Psychology, State University of New York, Binghamton, New York 13902

Per Eriksson • Department of Zoophysiology, Uppsala University, S-751 22 Uppsala, Sweden

Clayton P. Gillette • University of Virginia School of Law, Charlottesville, Virginia 22908

Harold K. Kimelberg • Division of Neurosurgery, Albany Medical College, Albany, New York 12208

James E. Krier • University of Michigan Law School, Ann Arbor, Michigan 48109

Carl P. LeBel • Alkermes, Cambridge, Massachusetts 02139

Ellen J. Lehning • Department of Animal Science, Michigan State University, East Lansing, Michigan 48824

Joan Massiah • Centre for Research in Neurodegenerative Diseases, University of Toronto, Toronto, Ontario, Canada M5S 1A8

D. R. McLachlan • Centre for Research in Neurodegenerative Diseases, University of Toronto, Toronto, Ontario, Canada M5S 1A8

Daniel Minnema • Hazleton Washington, Vienna, Virginia 22182

Herbert L. Needleman • University of Pittsburgh School of Medicine, Pittsburgh, Pennsylvania 15213

John R. O'Kusky • Department of Pathology, University of British Columbia, Vancouver, British Columbia, Canada V5Z 1M9

John W. Olney • Department of Psychiatry, Washington University Medical School, St. Louis, Missouri 63110

David H. Overstreet • Center for Alcohol Studies, Department of Psychiatry, University of North Carolina, Chapel Hill, North Carolina 27599

Julie A. Riess • University of Pittsburgh School of Medicine, Pittsburgh, Pennsylvania 15213

Grant D. Schiller • School of Biological Sciences, Flinders University, Adelaide, S.A. 5001 Australia

J. S. Schneider • Center for Neurological Research of the Department of Neurology, Hahnemann University School of Medicine, Philadelphia, Pennsylvania 19102

Richard F. Seegal • New York State Department of Health, Wadsworth Center for Laboratories and Research, Albany, New York 12201, and School of Public Health, State University of New York at Albany, Albany, New York 12203

William Shain • New York State Department of Health, Wadsworth Center for Laboratories and Research, Albany, New York 12201, and School of Public Health, State University of New York at Albany, Albany, New York 12203

Duke Tanaka, Jr. • Department of Anatomy, Michigan State University, East Lansing, Michigan 48824

Gijsbert B. van der Voet • Toxicology Laboratory, University Hospital, Leiden, The Netherlands

Charles F. Zorumski • Department of Psychiatry, Washington University Medical School, St. Louis, Missouri 63110

General Introduction

This series was undertaken because of our awareness that environmental pollution is adversely affecting brain function and behavior. The degree and nature of these effects in many instances remain uncertain but are active targets of investigation by scientists working in many domains of neuroscience. Different techniques, approaches, and conceptual frameworks are being used, many of a specialized nature. As a result, it is difficult for experts or for students in any one field to gain an overview of these various efforts and to be aware of points of convergence among investigations. We believe that the sharing of information among those using different approaches is necessary to a full understanding of the nature of the problems confronting the human species. We believe that gaining a more complete understanding of the effects of environmental toxins and pollutants is essential to world health.

As demonstrated in the chapters of these books, pollutants affect sensory, motor, and emotional functions, as well as learning, memory, and intellectual capacities. These effects can range from the subtle to the profound. Very little is known about the mechanisms by which pollutants affect the nervous system, and little is known about the number of compounds causing such effects. According to the U.S. Congress's Office of Technology Assessment, "The number of neurotoxic substances that pose a significant public health risk is unknown because the potential neurotoxicity of only a small number of chemicals has been evaluated adequately."*

There is an urgent need for understanding the effects of pollutants on the nervous system at every level of analysis. By bringing together contributions from scientists in both basic and applied neuroscience, we hope that investigators of all ages and disciplines, including graduate and undergraduate students, will become interested in these problems and their solutions. These books demonstrate the fruitfulness of using diverse methods to study the effects of environmental pollutants, and by so doing suggest new ways in which scientists of many persuasions can join in the attempt to understand the vulnerability of the brain and the behavioral sequelae of this vulnerability.

Unfortunately, almost all of the chapters assume some degree of familiarity with the topics being presented. With a few exceptions, the chapters have been written so as to be credible to those working in the field and may be difficult for the nonspecialist in some aspects. But how else can current science be presented in a faithful manner? We believe

---

*U.S. Congress, Office of Technology Assessment, 1990, *Neurotoxicity: Identifying and Controlling Poisons of the Nervous System*, OTA-BA-436 U.S. Government Printing Office, Washington, DC.

that it is wisest to present the best and most current information as seen by leaders in the field. Even though the books may be considered to be "samples of ideas and methods," we believe they sample the best.

These volumes reflect our belief that an adequate description of current risk from environmental pollutants requires full use of current knowledge of behavior, physiology, anatomy, biochemistry, and pharmacology to assess the integrity of the nervous system. Thus, for all types of toxins we have tried to put together an interdisciplinary body of information from closely related, but distinct, arenas of research. In a number of cases, we have intentionally selected topics or perspectives that are controversial, since it is controversy that often reveals the most interesting facets of scientific investigation.

We hope the reader, on finishing these books, will have a better understanding of a number of issues concerning the effects of nutrients and pollutants on brain and behavior, that is, the many substances in our environment that endanger our functional capabilities. The goal of adequately assessing large numbers of substances for potential effects on brain and behavior faces substantial challenges. These challenges can be addressed only by appropriately focused and interdisciplinary research efforts in neurotoxicology.

Robert L. Isaacson
Karl F. Jensen

Binghamton, New York
Research Triangle Park, North Carolina

Introduction to Volume 2

This second book of the series *The Vulnerable Brain and Environmental Risks* deals with the specific effects of common toxins, pollutants, and poisons on brain function and behavior. The chapters by Michael Aschner, Judy Aschner, and Harold Kimelburg, and John O'Kusky describe neurotoxic effects of methylmercury. The episode of methylmercury poisoning that occurred in Minamata Bay, Japan, in the 1950s is an example of an outbreak of neurotoxic disease resulting from food contaminants. Industrial refuse containing mercury was dumped directly into the bay. The most severely affected people were those for whom the fish and shellfish in the bay served as their primary food source. Over 121 people were sufficiently affected to be diagnosed as suffering from mercury toxicity. Forty-six people died. Many infants were born with nervous system damage, even though their mothers showed no obvious signs of poisoning. But neurological diseases caused by food contamination by metals are not limited to populations dependent on restricted, easily contaminated food sources.

With the increase in the average age of the population, there is a growing interest in neurodegenerative disorders that appear later in life. Of these, Alzheimer's dementia is one of the most frightening, primarily because it gradually diminishes the ability of a physically healthy individual to function in a day-to-day situation, eventually eliminating even the most basic cognitive and biological functions. The finding of high levels of aluminum in the brains of Alzheimer patients, as well as symptomatic similarities to dialysis encephalopathy produced by aluminum toxicity, has suggested a link between aluminum accumulation and this dementia. The factors that influence the uptake, distribution, and accumulation of aluminum by the nervous system are discussed by Gijsbert van der Voet, and the relationship between neurological disorders and aluminum neurotoxicity is presented by D.R. McLachlan and Joan Massiah.

Neurotoxic metals can have a variety of targets within neurons. Damage to some of these targets may transiently impair the function of the neuron, while damage to other targets may result in the death of the neuron.

Louis Chang points out that it is important to recognize when damage to certain regions of the nervous system may be indirect or secondary to the damage to another region of the nervous system (see also Chapter 10 by Balaban in Volume 1). Another

The material presented in this introduction has not been submitted to the Environmental Protection Agency's peer and administrative review; therefore, the views and opinions expressed are those of the editors and should not be construed to reflect the policy of the agency.

concept discussed by Chang is that toxic metals may produce some of their effects by displacing endogenous metals that are essential to normal cell functions. In support of this idea, he points out that the symptoms of some metal toxicities are very much like those produced by deficiencies of such essential elements.

In the following chapter, Daniel Minnema describes a number of such targets involved in the biochemical pathways by which signals between neurons are transduced. His emphasis is on the interruption of the indirect, second-messenger systems by toxic metals. Lead is an environmental pollutant to which the human nervous system is particularly vulnerable during prenatal and early postnatal development. Undoubtedly, it is the most common environmental cause of mental and physical impairments of children even today. Julie Riess and Herbert Needleman review the ongoing investigations that bear on the question of whether or not there can be a "safe" level of lead in our blood. One approach is to study cohorts of people with different levels of exposure using an epidemiological approach. As the sophistication of epidemiological studies increases, the level of lead in blood that is considered safe continues to decrease. The possibility exists that there may not be any safe level of lead, that is, a dose below which there are no adverse biological effects. But in spite of the long-standing and overwhelming evidence that lead exposure has and continues to retard the neurological development of millions of children, the problem persists.

Riess and Needleman also point out that there appears to be a significant interaction between malnutrition and lead exposure. Such an interaction may have its most devastating effects in our inner cities. While lead has now been banned from paints, leaded paint still remains a problem in older buildings, particularly in ghetto areas.

In the subsequent chapter, Peter Donovick and Richard Burright present arguments that the consumption of leaded paint chips may contribute to abnormal behavior, such as "pica." Pica is the eating of nonnutritional substances such as paint chips and dirt. Thus, the very lead consumed by children may predispose them to increase further their consumption of lead-containing paint chips and other hazardous substances. This increased intake of lead may compromise the immune system, reducing the body's defenses against parasitic, viral, and bacterial infections. The possibility that such infectious agents may also be involved in neurological syndromes such as Parkinson's disease is discussed by Blaine Beaman in his chapter on *Nocardia* infections of the brain. From a toxicological perspective, it is an intriguing observation that brain damage can be induced by a toxin produced by this bacterium. How many other bacteria or viral agents or fragments have the same capacity to generate neurotoxins?

Part II of this volume discusses the effects of toxicants on brain function and behavior. Each chapter will, to varying degrees, discuss the environmental sources of these agents, how they reach the nervous system, the patterns of damage seen, and the function deficits they produce.

The word *toxicant* may not be familiar to all readers. A brief summary of its use may be useful. Most dictionaries define *toxins* as poisons produced by living organisms. The term *toxicant* is often used when referring to agents that have been purposefully made to produce a desired effect, such as the elimination of agricultural pests. But the term *toxicant* can also be used in a broader sense to refer to all poisonous substances that are not produced by living organisms, including substances that occur naturally (e.g., lead), as well as those that do not [e.g., organophosphates, polychlorinated biphenyls (PCBs)]. In spite of these distinctions, both terms clearly refer to substances that act as poisons to the nervous system.

In this section of the book, toxicants not naturally originating in nature, and frequently agents formulated to kill unwanted animal or plant life, are considered. Since there are fundamental cellular and molecular similarities in the biological processes of both plants and animals, there are legitimate concerns about human exposure to plant-targeted toxicants. In fact, the degree of risk presented to the human by any level of exposure to most common toxicants—especially when presented for a long time at low levels—can be only poorly estimated. Information about the effects of prolonged exposure to low levels of common pesticides and herbicides is greatly needed. Making this a difficult undertaking is the likelihood that the effects of prolonged low-level exposure may not resemble those produced by an acute high-level dose. Furthermore, the latency to onset of obvious symptoms may be quite long. Be that as it may, many examples of common toxicants to which we are exposed will be discussed.

How substantial a risk do we face from exposure to neurotoxins commonly found in our environment? Of the neurotoxicants we currently know about, which ones present the greatest problem? Are there exposure levels to any toxicants that are so low that the effects produced on mind and body are insignificant? Are the methods currently used to assess risk accurate and appropriate for neurotoxins? These are extraordinarily difficult questions. Our ability to reduce risk from neurotoxic pollutants depends on understanding the relationship between exposure and effect.

Because of their wide variety of applications, PCBs are found throughout the industrialized world. Safe methods of disposal of these compounds are difficult to find, and PCB contamination of soil, water, and air is very common. This is alarming since PCBs damage the nervous system at low levels of exposure. These considerations underline the importance of the chapter by Richard Seegal and William Shain. In their chapter, information about the most notorious PCB, 2,3,7,8-tetrachlorodibenzo-*p*-dioxin (TCDD), sometimes improperly referred to as "dioxin," is provided. A variety of issues shroud any discussion of TCDD. In addition to its carcinogenicity and teratogenicity, numerous organs, including the brain, are deleteriously affected by TCDD. Industrial accidents, such as the one in Seveso, Italy, in 1976 and the contamination of herbicides such as Agent Orange used during the Vietnam War, have resulted in massive exposures to TCDD and related compounds. PCBs are an example of how the carcinogenic potential of toxicants can engender more concern than noncancer effects, such as teratogenicity or neurotoxicity, even if the latter may potentially pose greater hazards. Work is described that demonstrates how *in vivo* and *in vitro* studies can be effectively coordinated to gain insight into how such toxicants impair behavior.

Insecticides are another class of compounds well known for their deleterious effects on the nervous system. Of all known instances of human insecticide poisoning, cases involving the organophosphates have probably been the best documented. The most prominent acute effects result from the inhibition of cholinesterases, most notably acetylcholinesterase. The subsequent dramatic accumulation of acetylcholine in the nervous system results in a wide range of sensorimotor, cognitive, and autonomic effects that, if extreme, can be fatal. Various behavioral, physiological, and neurochemical consequences of exposure to organophosphates and their relation to the cholinergic systems of the nervous system are described by David Overstreet and Grant Shiller.

A number of organophosphates exhibit an additional neurotoxic property that is not dependent on the ability to inhibit cholinesterase. Exposure to such organophosphates produces the degeneration of axons in peripheral nerves and the spinal cord. Since this degeneration does not become apparent until 10–21 days after exposure, it has been referred to as organophosphate-induced delayed neuropathy (OPIDN). There have been several outbreaks of OPIDN in human populations. During Prohibition in the United States, thousands of cases of "Jake-Leg" paralysis were caused by the adulteration of

Jamaican ginger extract with tri-*ortho*-cresyl-phosphate. In 1959, over 10,000 people in Morocco were intoxicated by cooking oil adulterated with cresyl phosphates. Different species of animals exhibit widely varying sensitivities to cresyl phosphates. The chicken, rather than the rat or monkey, exhibits a sensitivity to the neurotoxic actions of the cresyl phosphates that is more comparable to that of humans. Duke Tanaka, Stephen Bursian, and Ellen Lehning describe species differences in the degree of structural damage induced by organophosphates. Their use of the Fink–Heimer silver stain to demonstrate the neural degeneration occurring in the central nervous system indicates that damage may be more widespread than previously thought (see also Chapter 10 by Balaban in Volume 1).

In comparison to organophosphates, organochlorine pesticides, such as DDT, are considered to be less toxic. But, because of their well-known persistence in the environment and in the body, they present a greater risk for chronic toxicity. As such, DDT is an example of how a compound and its metabolites can accumulate in the food chain by the process of biological concentration in the ecosystem. Acute exposure to DDT can result in neurologic symptoms, including paresthesia, hyperactivity, tremor, and even convulsions.

Pyrethrums are insecticidal compounds extractable from chrysanthemums. Synthetic pyrethroids may be preferred over organochlorine insecticides because of their rapid biodegradation and high insect–mammal toxicity ratio. Attempts have been made to relate the neurological symptoms of exposures to particular classes of pyrethoids or organochlorines to the actions on specific channels or receptors. Per Eriksson discusses in his chapter the effects of both DDT and pyrethroid insecticides on animals exposed early in life and in adulthood. His contribution is especially important because DDT is such a widely used contaminant of the food chain in many of the developing countries.

Our knowledge of a toxicant's actions depends on knowing the mechanisms by which it damages the nervous system. Because of the importance of knowing how toxicants work, the third part of this volume deals with investigations into such mechanisms.

On exposure to some toxicants, cells may accumulate certain materials in large quantities and may be damaged or killed by these substances. While many substances may accumulate in neurons, in most cases we do not know how most foreign agents or elements kill neurons. One established mechanism is discussed by Stephen Bondy and Carl LeBel in their chapter, namely, the accumulation of free radicals. Biochemical free radicals have many destructive interactions with cellular structures. For example, they can alter numerous activities of the cell by producing cross-linkages within and between proteins and nucleic acids. They also can destroy or damage the lipid membranes of the cells, breaking down the usual ion barriers. When great numbers of free radicals accumulate, the damage to the cell may be lethal.

Many of our foods contain chemicals purposefully added to preserve their "freshness" or to enhance their taste and appearance. Some of these additives are excitatory amino acids, or their analogs, often in large amounts. Charles Zorumski and John Olney describe the mechanisms of brain damage induced by excess amounts of glumate and glutamic acid. These excitatory amino acids reach the nervous system and excite (depolarize) those neurons that have receptors for excitatory amino acids. Excess amounts of these transmitters can cause neurons to be overly activated and can lead to cell death. Zorumski and Olney describe the potential contribution of such excitotoxins to several neurodegenerative diseases.

Another neurotoxicant, MPTP, has contributed significantly to our understanding of Parkinson's disease. MPTP is a contaminant produced during the synthesis of illicit, "street" drugs. Its effects were first identified in humans. In high doses, MPTP can damage and kill neurons in the nigrostriatal pathways of the brain. Damage to this region of the brain has been correlated with the motor symptoms associated with Parkinson's disease. In his chapter, Jay Schneider discusses two new and interesting aspects of the effects of the MPTP. He also presents evidence that MPTP not only disrupts motor functions but also interferes with cognitive activities. In addition, he reports that exposure to low doses for a prolonged period of time can produce effects similar to those observed after a higher acute dose. This is important because there are a number of environmental toxins that resemble MPTP, including phenylpyridines found in herbicides and in soot and ash resulting from the combustion of organic fuels and refuse. Some phenylpyridines may have effects on the nervous system similar to MPTP while other phenylpyridines may not. In the future it may be possible to identify chemical characteristics necessary to inflict MPTP-like damage to the nervous system. Until then, vigorous interdisciplinary assessments will be necessary before such pollutants can be either implicated or absolved of involvement in the production of neurodegenerative disorders.

The fourth and last part of Volume 2 is a chapter discussing the methods used in the United States for dealing with the risks associated with our food supplies and other sources of pollution to which we are exposed. The issue is how to arrive at effective and fair ways to protect the public from hazards associated with both new and existing technologies. How will products be regulated and inspected? How can regulations be enforced? What recourse should an individual have through the judicial system for compensation when harm is not prevented? In this chapter the advantages and disadvantages of our agencies and our courts in the roles of society's monitors and enforcers for the public and individual good are intelligently discussed by two eminent legal scholars, Clayton Gillette of the University of Virginia School of Law and James Krier of the University of Michigan Law School. The reader will gain new insights into how the complexities of our rapidly changing technological world force us to deal with the effects of constantly changing foods, food additives, food substitutes, and methods of food processing.

Robert L. Isaacson
Karl F. Jensen

Contents

Chapter 6
Neurotoxic Metals and Neuronal Signalling Processes
Daniel Minnema

Chapter 7
Cognitive, Neural, and Behavioral Effects of Low-Level Lead Exposure
Julie A. Riess and Herbert L. Needleman

Chapter 8
Lead Poisoning, Toxocariasis, and Pica: Links to Neurobehavioral Disorders
Peter J. Donovick and Richard G. Burright

Chapter 9
Nocardia: **An Environmental Bacterium Possibly Associated with Neurodegenerative Diseases in Humans**
Blaine L. Beaman

Part II. Toxicants

Chapter 10
Neurotoxicity of Polychlorinated Biphenyls: The Role of *Ortho*-Substituted Congeners in Altering Neurochemical Function
Richard F. Seegal and William Shain

Chapter 11
**Central Nervous System Plasticity and Pathology Induced
by Exposure to Organophosphate Pesticides**
David H. Overstreet and Grant D. Schiller

Chapter 12
**Silver Impregnation of Organophosphorus-Induced Delayed
Neuropathy in the Central Nervous System**
Duke Tanaka, Jr., Steven J. Bursian, and Ellen J. Lehning

Chapter 13
Neuroreceptor and Behavioral Effects of DDT and Pyrethroids in Immature and Adult Mammals
Per Eriksson

Part III. Selected Mechanisms of Action

Chapter 14
Formation of Excess Reactive Oxygen Species within the Brain
Stephen C. Bondy and Carl P. LeBel

Part IV. Legal Issues

Part I

Metals

Chapter 1

Methylmercury Neurotoxicity and Its Uptake Across the Blood– Brain Barrier

Michael Aschner, Judy L. Aschner, and *Harold K. Kimelberg*

1. INTRODUCTION

Metals are inextricably bound to many facets of modern human existence. While some metals are biologically essential (vanadium, manganese), others are extremely poisonous (lead, cadmium, mercury). Metals such as mercury (Hg) are likely to continue to contaminate the environment, because in addition to its natural emissions from the earth crust and oceans, anthropogenic sources continue to discharge Hg into the atmosphere. Many advances and notable contributions to daily life claim Hg as a significant contributor to their success. Consequently, perturbations of atmospheric Hg by recognized point sources are likely to continue to permeate the food chain and to pose increasingly greater risks to human health. As the scope of scientific investigation continues to broaden our understanding of Hg toxicity, we will be in a better position to understand the effects of Hg contamination on the health of the people, to identify populations at risk, and to identify the interactive effects of diet, nutrition, disease, and natural stresses on the uptake and toxicity of Hg to animal and marine populations, and ultimately to humans.

For the environmental health sciences, positioned at the juncture of toxicology and regulation, the ultimate question culminates in the estimation of risk. This is often based on extrapolation from the dose-response curve, and using this information many public health decisions are made. However, with the exception of catastrophic accidents or

Michael Aschner • Department of Pharmacology and Toxicology, Albany Medical College, Albany, New York 12208. *Judy L. Aschner* • Department of Pediatrics, Albany Medical College, Albany, New York 12208. *Harold K. Kimelberg* • Division of Neurosurgery, Albany Medical College, Albany, New York 12208.

The Vulnerable Brain and Environmental Risks, Volume 2: Toxins in Food, edited by Robert L. Isaacson and Karl F. Jensen. Plenum Press, New York, 1992.

unique circumstances of occupational exposure, it is chronic exposure at the lower end of the dose-response curve that poses the greatest threat to humankind and the greatest challenge to toxicologists. To assess the health implications of this type of exposure, mechanistic studies of toxicity are essential. The following review addresses the persistent issues of methylmercury (MeHg) toxicity from the vantage point of the biochemical and cellular mechanisms that contribute to MeHg's uptake and toxic effects in the CNS. For the purpose of this review, the effects of MeHg on the CNS will be limited to the adult CNS, acknowledging that these effects differ both quantitatively and qualitatively from the effects afflicted on the developing fetus and during the early postnatal period. The objectives of this chapter are (1) to identify the transport mechanism(s) of MeHg across the blood–brain barrier, under the assumption that the rate and extent of MeHg transport across the blood–brain barrier will affect its toxicity, (2) to review the role afforded by astrocytes in MeHg's toxicity, and (3) to summarize mechanisms implicated in adult MeHg neurotoxicity.

2. MERCURY: SOURCES OF HUMAN EXPOSURE

Hg, a ubiquitous metal, exists in a number of physical and chemical forms (Carty and Malone, 1979). Inorganic Hg exists in the metallic form (Hg^0), in the mercurous form (Hg^+), and in the mercuric form (Hg^{2+}). Both the mercurous and mercuric cations form a number of inorganic compounds that undergo methylation by aquatic microorganisms to produce organic species of Hg (CH_3Hg^+; Jensen and Jernelov, 1969; Wood *et al.*, 1968), which accumulate in the food chain. In addition, unlike most other metals, MeHg indisputably biomagnifies through the food chain (Fagerstrom and Larsson, unpublished report; Stokes and Wren, 1987), resulting in the highest Hg concentrations in those fish at the end of the food chain, such as the large carnivorous species, the same fish that are most palatable to our taste buds. Considered together with Hg's long residence in the atmosphere, it becomes clear that Hg exposure may be potentially serious, even to populations remote from point sources of emission. Furthermore, these biogeochemical properties suggest that any source of environmental Hg represents a potential for poisoning with organic Hg species, and with MeHg in particular. The acidification of freshwater streams and lakes in Northern Europe and North America, and the impoundment of water for large hydroelectric schemes, have led to further increases in MeHg concentrations in fish (Wren and Stokes, 1987), posing increasingly greater risk to human populations.

Consumption of fish and fish products represents the major pathway of environmental Hg exposure to the general population (WHO, 1976). In comparison, the exposure of Hg (both organic and inorganic) via inhalation or digestion of terrestrial diet and drinking water is negligible. Several conclusion can be drawn about Hg concentrations in fish (Inskip and Piotrowski, 1985):

1.   In general, Hg concentrations in most freshwater fish and marine fish do not exceed 200 μg/kg wet weight. Higher concentrations can be found, however, in polluted freshwater, with Hg concentrations reaching 20,000 μg/kg wet weight.
2.   The age, length, as well as the geographical location of the fish are important

determinants of Hg concentrations. For example, in the Mediterranean Sea, tuna fish have greater Hg concentrations compared with other geographical areas.

3. Hg in aquatic organisms is almost entirely in the methylated species.

The health consequences arising from consumption of MeHg are dependent upon the frequency and quantity consumed. The average daily consumption of MeHg varies greatly from country to country and is dependent upon the dietary habits of their respective populations. Accordingly, while a figure of 20 g of Hg is used to represent the average intake of those populations consuming one fish meal per week in the United States, two to three times higher intake is reported for Denmark, Sweden, and Spain, and a 10-fold greater intake is reported for the average population in Japan (National Academy of Sciences, 1978; UN Food and Agricultural Organization, 1977). The greatest risk of MeHg exposure is, however, to selected subpopulations who rely almost exclusively on dietary proteins from marine sources; these are mainly fishermen and their families. Even at Hg concentrations as low as 200 μg/kg wet weight, members of fishing communities who consume fish or its products two to three times daily can attain toxic MeHg concentrations (Piotrowski and Inskip, 1981).

As scientific investigations broaden our understanding of the natural vs. the anthropogenic fluxes of Hg in the atmosphere, identify trends in global deposition, and identify those populations at risk, we must increasingly recognize MeHg contamination as a widespread and serious threat to the human race and our ecosystem. Accordingly, we must define the neuropharmacology of MeHg, describing the extent to which it is transported into the CNS, its major target organ, and the degree of injury it afflicts on the brain. As a first step we must, therefore, consider MeHg transport processes across the restrictive blood–brain barrier, which protects the brain and the rest of the CNS from toxins and fluctuations present in the body.

3. THE BLOOD–BRAIN BARRIER

The concept of a blood–brain barrier arose late in the 19th century when the German bacteriologist, Paul Ehrlich (1906), observed that certain dyes administered intravenously to small animals stained all the organs with the exception of the brain. Although, Ehrlich's interpretation of these results was that the brain had a low affinity for these dyes, Edwin E. Goldmann (1913), who had studied under Ehrlich, proved his teacher wrong. Goldmann injected trypan blue directly into the CSF of rabbits and dogs. The dye readily stained the brain parenchyma but did not enter the bloodstream to stain other internal organs. Thus, Goldmann was the first to show that some kind of a barrier separates the CNS from the blood. This barrier is a specialized structure composed of endothelial cells. Unlike endothelial cells in other organs, those of the blood–brain barrier form a continuous layer characterized by tight junctions (Brightman and Reese, 1969), where adjoining cells physically merge, preventing most substances from entering the brain in between cells, and negating oncotic and osmotic forces that normally control blood–tissue exchange. In addition, astrocyte foot processes almost completely surround each capillary (Wolff, 1963), making contact and exerting modulatory effects on the capillary (Phelps, 1972). The functions of astrocytes have begun to be delineated only over the last 15 years (Fedoroff and Vernadakis, 1986; Kimelberg and Norenberg, 1989). The prevailing view that they exclusively function as a passive physical support for neurons is rapidly fading. It is now clear that to understand both the normal and abnormal brain we must also understand the roles assumed by astrocytes, for they function prominently not only in normal brain physiology and development, but also in the pathology of the nervous system (Kimelberg and Norenberg, 1989; Norenberg *et al.*, 1988) and as potential sites for neurotoxins (Aschner and Kimelberg, 1991).

Several factors determine how easily a compound will traverse the blood–brain barrier (Rapoport, 1976). For most substances, ease of passage across the blood–brain barrier is largely determined by their lipid solubility. Certain molecules needed for brain meta-bolism, however, cross this barrier more readily than their lipid solubility alone would suggest (Oldendorf, 1970). Such compounds are transported via specific carrier-mediated transport systems or facilitated diffusion. Some of these carriers are symmetrically dis-tributed both on the luminal and abluminal membranes of the endothelial cells, while others have an asymmetric distribution (Betz and Goldstein, 1978). For example, the carriers for the essential neutral amino acids that are required in the brain for neurotrans-mitter synthesis are localized on both luminal and abluminal membranes. In contrast, the carrier for glycine is located only on the abluminal membrane. This asymmetric distribu-tion functions to remove glycine from the CNS and to keep its concentration in the brain low. Similarly, the abluminal membrane contains more of the enzyme ATPase than does the luminal membrane (Betz and Goldstein, 1978). This enzyme forms the basis of a pump that simultaneously transports Na^+ out of the endothelium into the brain and K^+ out of the brain into the endothelium. Like glycine, K^+ has a potent effect on the transmission of nerve impulses and neuron firing, and it is desirable to keep its concentra-tion in the extracellular fluid of the CNS low (Kandel and Schwartz, 1985).

In human beings and other complex organisms, life itself depends on homeostasis, the maintenance of a constant internal milieu. Nowhere is this dependence more pro-nounced than in the brain (Goldstein and Betz, 1986). Elsewhere in the body the extra-cellular concentrations of hormones, amino acids, and ions such as potassium undergo frequent fluctuations, particularly after bouts of exercise or after a meal. If the brain were exposed to such fluctuations, the result might be uncontrolled nervous activity, because some hormones and amino acids serve as neurotransmitters and potassium ion influences the threshold for the firing of nerve cells. Therefore, the brain must be kept rigorously isolated from transient changes in the composition of the blood (Goldstein and Betz, 1986). Nonetheless, despite the inherent specialization of the blood–brain barrier and its "built in" safeguards, this highly restrictive barrier is incapable of preventing the ex-change of toxins from the blood to the brain when their transport is governed by the same physiologic properties that govern the exchange of nutrients, therapeutic agents, or hor-mones; namely, lipid solubility or the ability to substitute the naturally occurring com-pounds on any of the blood–brain barrier transporters.

4. MERCURY UPTAKE ACROSS THE BLOOD–BRAIN BARRIER

4.1. Transport Across Biological Membranes

Within the systemic circulation, the toxicity of mercurials is largely dependent upon their chemical and physical form. Changes in redox potential, i.e., removal of electrons, will influence the metal's chemical activity and will govern its distribution in the body and its availability for transport across biological membranes. This is exemplified by the pattern of distribution and organ toxicity of inorganic mercurials. The distribution of Hg in organs and tissues is generally similar after ingestion of inorganic salts and inhalation of metallic vapor (Hayes and Rothstein, 1962; Rothstein and Hayes, 1960). However, exposure to vapor leads to much higher concentrations of inorganic Hg in the CNS (Berlin *et al.*, 1966; Magos, 1967), culminating in neurotoxicity. Inhaled Hg vapor rapidly traverses the alveolar membrane because of its high lipophilicity (Magos, 1967). In the plasma, this monoatomic gas rapidly diffuses into erythrocytes, where it is oxidized to divalent ionic Hg (Hg^{2+}). Despite this rapid oxidation by red blood cells, some Hg vapor persists in the bloodstream sufficiently long to diffuse across the blood–brain barrier, where it is oxidized by the endogenous hydrogen peroxide catalase system to the divalent cation, Hg^{2+}. Although metallic Hg can pass through membranes in both directions, this last oxidation reaction results in fixation of Hg in the CNS by its binding to -SH-containing ligands. Thus, the enhanced brain accumulation of Hg in the CNS subsequent to exposure to the elemental form is related both to its lipid solubility and its rapid conversion to the nondiffusible divalent form (Magos *et al.*, 1973). Correspondingly, inorganic Hg salts in the ionic form (Hg^+ and Hg^{2+}) are largely protein bound in plasma. The exceptional polarizing power of mercuric ions (Hg^{2+}) lends considerable covalent character to the oxides, sulphides, and halides (Carty and Malone, 1979). These exhibit poor lipid solubility and pass the blood–brain barrier less freely than metallic Hg (Magos, 1976). Although their tissue distribution and pathway of excretion are similar to that of inhaled Hg, they do not appear to affect the CNS. It was previously assumed that MeHg formed lipid-soluble compounds in the body and therefore could passively diffuse across membranes. A lipid-soluble form is, in fact, only produced by the addition of concentrated hydrochloric acid to tissue homogenates in the process of MeHg extraction for analytical purposes (Gage, 1961) or by treating animals with large doses of sodium selenite, which results in the formation of bis-dimethyl Hg selenide (Magos *et al.*, 1979). All other studies (USEPA, 1983) have found MeHg to be associated with water-soluble molecules such as proteins, or thiol-containing amino acids or peptides. The very high chemical affinity of the MeHg cation (CH_3Hg^+) for -SH groups provides the theoretical basis for these findings (Carty and Malone, 1979).

Hughes (1957) was the first to draw attention to the remarkable affinity of MeHg for the anionic form of -SH groups and to suggest that the principal chemical reaction of MeHg is with thiols. Variations in the distribution and effects of MeHg seems to be principally dependent upon this reaction. The affinity of MeHg for the anionic form of -SH groups (log K, where K is the association constant) is extremely high, on the order of 15–23, whereas its affinity constants for oxygen-, chloride-, or nitrogen-containing ligands, such as carboxyl or amino groups, are about 10 orders of magnitude lower (Carty and Malone, 1979). Indeed, wherever a MeHg compound has been identified in biological media, it has been complexed to -SH-containing ligands. Complexes with cysteine and glutathione (GSH) have been identified in blood (Naganuma and Imura, 1979; Rabenstein and Fairhurst, 1975), and complexes with GSH have been identified in brain (Thomas and Smith, 1979), liver (Omata *et al.*, 1978), and bile (Refsvik and Norseth, 1975). Furthermore, the only therapeutic agents that are effective in reducing the MeHg body burden are those containing -SH groups. Thus, any evaluation of the membrane transport of MeHg must recognize the functional importance of this reaction. To date, mechanisms of membrane transport of MeHg have addressed only the transport of MeHg from blood to brain and from liver to bile. In both, transport of MeHg is closely linked to the transport of thiol-containing amino acids (Aschner and Clarkson, 1988, 1989; Ballatori and Clarkson,

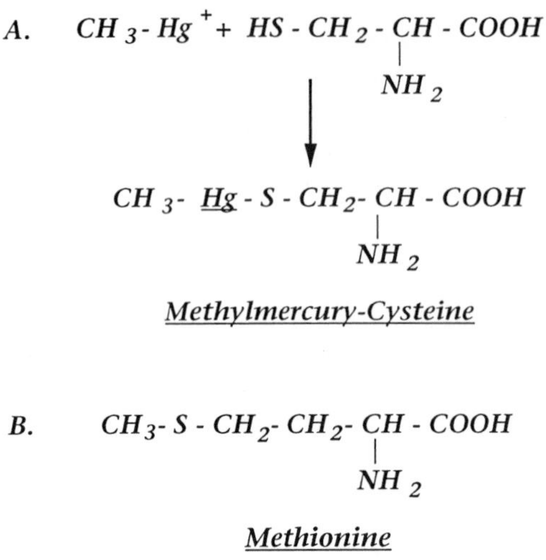

A. $CH_3\text{-}Hg^+ + HS\text{-}CH_2\text{-}CH\text{-}COOH$

$$\text{NH}_2$$

$$\downarrow$$

$CH_3\text{-}\underline{Hg}\text{-}S\text{-}CH_2\text{-}CH\text{-}COOH$

$$\text{NH}_2$$

<u>Methylmercury-Cysteine</u>

B. $CH_3\text{-}S\text{-}CH_2\text{-}CH_2\text{-}CH\text{-}COOH$

$$\text{NH}_2$$

<u>Methionine</u>

FIGURE 1. MeHg in the plasma complexes with L-cysteine to form a MeHg-cysteine adduct (A). A structural difference between this complex and methionine (B), a substrate for the neutral amino acid transport system L, includes the presence of the Hg^{2+} between the sulfur and methyl groups.

1985; Hirayama, 1980, 1985). It has also been shown that the initial rate of entry of intravenously injected MeHg into brains of mature rats is enhanced by coadministration of L-cysteine (Aschner and Clarkson, 1988; Hirayama, 1980, 1985).

Recognition of the seriousness of the environmental problem of Hg contamination intensified when it was discovered that in waterways inorganic mercuric ions can be methylated into the highly toxic and significantly more biologically mobile methyl- and dimethylmercury species. Two biochemical pathways of Hg^{2+} methylation have been identified, one anaerobic, the other aerobic. The former involves the methylation of inorganic Hg^{2+} by methylcobalamine compounds produced by methanogenic bacteria in a mildly reducing environment (Wood *et al.,* 1968). The aerobic pathway involves methylation of homocysteine-bound inorganic Hg^{2+} by those processes in the cell normally responsible for the formation of methionine (Jensen and Jernelov, 1969). In other words, the Hg-cysteine complex is methylated by "mistake." Aschner and Clarkson (1988, 1989) drew attention to the close structural similarity between MeHg-L-cysteine complexes and methionine, and postulated a cysteine-facilitated transport of MeHg across the blood–brain barrier. Structurally (Fig. 1), the MeHg-L-cysteine conjugate and methionine differ only by the presence or absence of the Hg atom between the -S- and CH_3 groups, and both possess linear bonds at an angle of 180° (Carty and Malone, 1979).

4.2. *In Vivo* Studies

In vivo studies were conducted in Long-Evans female rates to ascertain some aspects of the regulation of MeHg transport across the blood–brain barrier (Aschner and Clarkson, 1988). Fifteen seconds after intracarotid injection, brain ^{203}Hg concentration was significantly increased in animals coinjected with 0.05 mM [^{203}Hg]-MeHgCl plus 0.1 mM L-cysteine compared with control rats injected with [^{203}Hg]-MeHgCl alone (p < 0.05). This L-cysteine-enhanced ^{203}Hg brain uptake was abolished by coinjections of [^{203}Hg]-MeHgCl with 0.1 mM L-cysteine-L-methionine or 0.1 mM L-cysteine plus AT-125 (alpha S, 5S-alpha-amino-3-chloro-4,5-dihydro-5-isoxazol-acetic acid), an irreversible inhibitor of gamma-glutamyl transpeptidase. Coinjections of rats with [^{203}Hg]-MeHgCl and 0.1 mM D-cysteine did not result in an increase in the rate of ^{203}Hg uptake compared with controls. Furthermore, [^{203}Hg]-MeHg uptake at 15 sec after intracarotid injections in the rat was specific to the neutral amino-acid carrier, as ^{203}Hg uptake across the blood–brain barrier was not inhibited by coinjections of [^{203}Hg]-MeHgCl with aspartic acid, an acidic amino acid. More recently, Kerper *et al.* (1990) demonstrated a nonlinear concentration-dependent uptake of MeHg in rat brains following injections of MeHg-L-cysteine conjugates, exhibiting the characteristics of saturable transport. Furthermore, the transport of radiolabeled phenylalanine, a substrate for the neutral amino transport system L, was significantly inhibited by MeHg-L-cysteine, but not by MeHgCl. These results suggest the presence in brain capillaries of a transport system capable of selectively mediating MeHg uptake across the brain capillary endothelial cell membrane.

4.3. *In Vitro* Studies

To elucidate the relationship between MeHg transport and the neutral amino-acid transport carrier system L, regulatory aspects of MeHg transport across the bovine blood–brain barrier were also investigated in a highly pure fraction of isolated brain microvessels (Aschner and Clarkson, 1989). These capillaries are enzymatically active, displaying gamma-glutamyl-transpeptidase activity, and exhibiting Factor VIII staining, a widely used marker for endothelial cells in culture. The relationship between the neutral amino acid carrier System L and MeHg-L-cysteine uptake is further corroborated by the observation that incubations of [^{203}Hg]-MeHgCl with L-cysteine increase the initial rate of MeHg uptake compared to those cultures exposed to MeHg alone. This enhanced capillary uptake of ^{203}Hg is abolished by L-methionine or by L-cysteine plus AT-125. Exposure of bovine capillaries to [^{203}Hg]-MeHgCl conjugated to D-cysteine or L-cysteine at 0°C does not, however, result in an increase in the rate of ^{203}Hg uptake compared with controls.

5. ROLE OF ASTROCYTES IN HEAVY METAL TOXICITY

The prevailing thought that astrocytes function predominantly as passive metabolic or physical support for neurons has faded over the last 20 years. Today these stellar-shaped cells are credited with an expanded role, playing key functions in CNS development, homeostasis, and pathology. Although they are not the restrictive blood–brain barrier themselves, by virtue of their structural ensheathing of the endothelial cells they are of fundamental importance in the homeostatic control of the barrier. Furthermore, because the brain capillaries are almost completely surrounded by astrocytes, essential nutrients must traverse the astrocytes in order to reach the brain parenchyma (Goldstein and Betz, 1986).

Compelling evidence has accumulated to suggest that astrocytes may be involved in the etiology of heavy metal neurotoxicity. As early as 1966, Oyake suggested that in human autopsy brain tissue, MeHg may preferentially accumulate in astrocytes. This was confirmed by Garman *et al.* (1975), who demonstrated a dense labelling pattern of MeHg over astrocytes in areas of damaged cortex. The extent to which individual neurons are altered by MeHg accumulation in astrocytes is, however, unknown.

To better understand the relationship between the astrocyte and the mechanisms of MeHg's neurotoxicity, the uptake of MeHg by astrocytes in primary cultures was studied. Work by Aschner *et al.* (1990a) suggests that the uptake of [^{203}Hg]-MeHg when added to the media as the L-cysteine conjugate exhibits the kinetic criteria of a specific transport system. Saturation kinetics, substrate specificity and inhibition, and *trans* stimulation were demonstrated in the presence of this -SH-containing amino acid. Cysteine-mediated uptake of MeHg was inhibited by the coadministration of L-methionine, and 2-aminobicyclo-[2, 2, 1]-heptane-2-carboxylic acid (BCH), a specific substrate for the neutral amino acid transport system L (Christensen, 1984, 1985; Christensen *et al.*, 1969). 2-Methylaminoisobutyric acid (MeAIB) was ineffective in inhibiting the uptake of the MeHg-cysteine conjugate. Preloading of the astrocytes with glutamate was moderately effective in *trans*-stimulating the uptake of MeHg-cysteine conjugates, while in the absence of cysteine uptake of [^{203}Hg]-MeHg was unchanged. These results indicate the presence in astrocytes of a neutral amino-acid carried transport system L, capable of selectively mediating cysteine-MeHg uptake. Such a system has also been described by Speciale *et al.* (1989) for the uptake of L-kynurenine by a Na$^+$-independent transporter of neutral amino acids in primary astrocyte cultures. The substrate specificity and high affinity of this transport system resemble the properties of the system L neutral amino-acid transport across the blood–brain barrier in the rat (Aschner and Clarkson, 1988).

Additional studies indicate that the putative MeHg transport system in astrocytes can mediate MeHg transport in the net efflux direction (Aschner *et al.*, 1991). Metal exchange is not required for efflux, since efflux of [^{203}Hg]-MeHgCl occurs in MeHg-free buffer. The apparent stimulatory effects of extracellular L-cysteine-MeHg conjugates on the rate and amount of ^{203}Hg efflux are clearly shown to reflect displacement of [^{203}Hg]-MeHgCl from intracellular pools via a specific effect on the transport system itself. The simplest interpretation is that the efflux observed represents transport by the same neutral amino-acid system L that facilitates MeHg uptake (Aschner *et al.*, 1990a).

In accordance with the chemical affinity of MeHg to -SH containing ligands and the biphasic kinetic profile of MeHg efflux, several types of intracellular MeHg pools are postulated (Fig. 2). Although a finite amount of MeHg must exist as the chloride complex based on the Law of Mass Action, this amount must be very small in view of the 2×10^6-fold ratio between the thiol to chloride complex in eukaryotic cells (Hughes, 1957). Although MeHgCl can diffuse across lipid bilayers (Lackowicz and Anderson, 1980), it is unlikely that it can account for the rates of efflux. A second intracellular pool of MeHg can be assumed to contain intracellular complexes with low molecular weight -SH-containing compounds such as L-cysteine. Five to 10% of the total thiol content in eukaryotic cells is present in the form of small diffusible molecules, providing a mechanism for efflux of MeHg from the astrocytes in combination with one of these diffusible -SH-containing ligands. MeHg transport as the cysteine conjugate occurs primarily on the L system, with some possible contribution from neutral amino-acid transport systems A and ASC (Christensen, 1985; Shotwell *et al.*, 1983), as shown in Figure 2. Despite the apparent thermodynamic stability of the Hg-SH bonds, very rapid exchange of MeHg between -SH groups is known to occur (Rabenstein and Fairhurst, 1975). Hence, a third intracellular pool must represent irreversibly bound MeHg to high molecular weight -SH-containing ligands, shown as MeHg-SH-R' in Figure 2. Removal of MeHg from diffusible -SH-containing ligands into high molecular weight -SH-containing compounds is apparently a principal mechanism for concentrating MeHg within the astrocytes, since we have

NEURON   ASTROCYTE

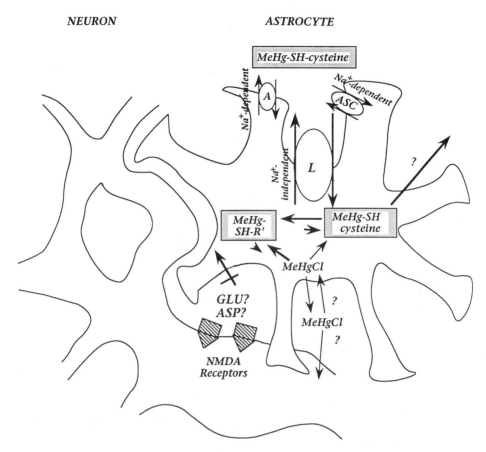

FIGURE 2. Schematic representation of the processes involved in MeHg uptake, efflux, and toxicity in astrocytes where MeHg can inhibit ion, glutamate, and aspartate uptake. See the text for explanation. The approximate relative rate constants of these reactions are indicated by the length of the arrows (not to scale).

found that the longer the preincubation time, the higher the fraction of MeHg that remains within the astrocytes (Aschner *et al.*, 1991).

MeHg has direct toxic effects on astrocyte functions, which can indirectly result in neuronal impairment, injury, and death (Aschner *et al.*, 1990b). MeHg (10^{-5} M) significantly inhibits the initial rate (5 min) of uptake of ^{86}RbCl, used as a tracer for K^+, and stimulates the release of intracellular ^{86}RbCl in a dose-dependent fashion. These observations support the hypothesis that the astrocyte plasma membrane is an important target for MeHg's toxic effect and specifically that small concentrations of this organometal can inhibit the ability of astrocytes to maintain a transmembrane K^+ gradient. This would be expected to compromise the ability of astrocytes to control extracellular K^+ and may also result in cellular swelling due to intracellular accumulation of NaCl (Kimelberg and Bourke, 1982). We therefore studied volume changes in cultured astrocytes in response to exposure to MeHg, using the uptake of [^{14}C]-3-O-methyl-D-glucose (Kletzien *et al.*, 1975). Exposure to MeHg (0–5×10^{-4} M) caused a marked concentration-dependent increase in cell volume (Aschner *et al.*, 1990b).

Another possible mechanism of neuronal damage is an "excitotoxic" injury (Figure 2) resulting from failure of glutamate uptake by the damaged astrocytes (Olney, 1979). MeHg (10^{-5} M) markedly inhibited the initial rate (1 min) of uptake of [^{3}H]-L-glutamate. This could be partly a secondary effect due to dissipation of ion gradients, since in these cells [^{3}H]-L-glutamate uptake is almost totally Na$^+$ dependent (Kimelberg *et al.,* 1989). An inhibitory effect of inorganic Hg ($HgCl_2$) on glutamate uptake by primary astrocyte cultures has also been demonstrated (Brookes, 1988).

An entirely different interpretation exists for the astrocytic uptake of MeHg. It is conceivable that the uptake of MeHg by astrocytes is a protective mechanism. MeHg compounds are known to be converted to inorganic Hg, with approximately 3–5% of total Hg being in its inorganic form (Friberg and Mottet, 1989). It has been postulated that the site of this conversion may be within the astrocytes (Rodier, personal communication). If specific membrane transport systems for MeHg or Hg^{2+} efflux are located at the perivascular surface of an astrocytic process or end foot (Peters *et al.*, 1976), closely apposed to capillaries, then astrocytic processes located beneath the pia matter and subependymal zone facing CSF could preferentially direct these compounds into the blood and CSF, respectively, for ultimate removal from the CNS. Alternatively, inorganic Hg or MeHg, after crossing the endothelial cells of the blood–brain barrier and then the astrocyte membranes, can become sequestered within the astrocytes as Hg^{2+} or MeHg-S-R$'$, where R$'$ is a thiol-containing macromolecule (see Fig. 2).

6. CLINICAL EFFECTS OF MeHg POISONING

The CNS is the principal target of adult MeHg exposure. Its earliest effects are quite nonspecific and involve complaints of paresthesia, blurred vision, and malaise. With progression of the disease, deafness, constriction of peripheral vision, ataxia, and dysarthria often occur (WHO, 1976).

There are two unique features to MeHg poisoning:

1. A characteristic of adult mammalian MeHg poisoning is its damage to the CNS. Degeneration of granular cells in the calcarine cortex and cerebellum are prominent, while other regions, such as the motor cortex, appear spared (Clarkson, 1983). This selective damage is a surprising finding in view of the chemical and physical properties of MeHg with its high affinity for -SH groups. When present in appropriate concentrations, MeHg will inhibit any enzyme, damage any membrane, and disturb any structural macromolecule with which it comes into contact. Not only is MeHg highly reactive, but it is also highly mobile within the body. Consistent with these properties, MeHg distributes in a uniform fashion throughout the body. While its affinity to -SH groups may be equated with its homogeneous distribution within the CNS, this fact presents "severe logistic problems" for explaining its toxicity (Rothstein, 1973), because almost all proteins contain -SH groups, rendering them potential targets for this metal. A variety of theories have been advanced to unravel the primary mechanism of MeHg poisoning and its predilection for CNS damage (Clarkson, 1983), but none can adequately explain the clinical findings in terms of the regional specificity of this metal.

2. A long latent period exists, which usually lasts several months or years. There is no adequate explanation for this phenomenon. A causal relation between environmental damage and late-onset neurological symptoms is strengthened, however, if compensatory

mechanisms are taken into account (Spencer *et al.*, 1986). Knowledge of regeneration in the CNS and more extensive understanding of such mechanisms in the periphery suggest several means of compensation for loss of neurons: (1) There exists a reserve of neurons in the brain, just as other organs are considerably larger than required for satisfactory functioning in early adult life. (2) Neurons can sprout and form extensive synaptic contacts with postsynaptic structures that have lost their normal innervations. (3) Presynaptic structures can increase the rate of synthesis of transmitter, a sensitive mechanism that is activated, in the case of dopamine, for example, by only 25% striatal depletion. (4) An increase in the number of receptors or a change in their conformation can increase the sensitivity of postsynaptic structures to incoming signals from damaged pathways (denervation supersensitivity). (5) The postsynaptic structure may improve its performance (for example, by hypertrophy, in the case of muscle surviving chronic partial denervation). In view of this capacity for compensation, thousands of neurons concerned with motor or intellectual function may be lost un-noticed; this capacity, however, is finite. As neurons continue to die, each surviving neuron acquires an expanded influence and responsibility, so its death has an impact far greater than the demise of its predecessors. It is also possible that surviving neurons are driven harder metabolically to compensate for their reduced numbers, exhausting their energy supplies; this process might hasten their own death.

7. BIOCHEMICAL EFFECTS OF MeHg POISONING

MeHg poisoning in Japan (Takeuchi, 1969) and Iraq (Bakir *et al.*, 1973) are among the best documented anthropogenic chemical poisoning disasters in history. Although the clinical effects of this compound were described by Edwards as early as 1866, little was known about its mechanisms of neurotoxicity. MeHg is damaging to the nervous system in many different ways, and a variety of mechanisms of injury have been demonstrated. Among these are disruption of the blood–brain barrier (Steinwall and Olsson, 1969), enzymatic interference (Salvaterra *et al.*, 1973; Webb, 1966), changes in electrical properties of axons (Shrivastav *et al.*, 1976), disruption of axonal transport (Abe *et al.*, 1975; Aschner *et al.*, 1986, 1987), homolytic cleavage of MeHg and the subsequent release of free radicals (Ganther *et al.*, 1975), the inhibition of acetylcholine transmission (Atchison, 1986, 1987), and the disruption of the neuronal cytoskeleton (Brown *et al.*, 1988). Some have been demonstrated only at very high doses, and others have been demonstrated only *in vitro*. Which one of these plays a causal role in the onset of symptoms of MeHg toxicity is still a matter of speculation.

Perhaps more firmly established are the biochemical alternations in protein synthesis with MeHg poisoning. Verity *et al.* (1977) and others (Cheung and Verity, 1983; Sarafian *et al.*, 1984) have demonstrated direct interaction between MeHg and the translational machinery in cerebellar cell preparations. While the peptide elongation process appears to be affected at high levels of MeHg, the first stage of synthesis associated with transfer RNAs and tRNA synthetase enzymes, and various translational and elongation factors, appears to be the most sensitive and proximate mechanism of organic mercurial impairment. It is worth noting that the base triplet adenine, uracil, and guanine (AUG) provides the sole initiation codon for protein synthesis and that the AUG codon represents methionine. Two types of tRNA can carry this amino acid. One is used for initiation, the other for recognizing AUG condons during elongation. The initiator tRNA carries a methionine residue that has been formylated on its amino group and is known as tRNA$_f^{Met}$. The other (nonformylated) methionine-carrying tRNA is known as tRNA$_m^{Met}$ and is responsible for recognizing codons in internal locations (Jagus *et al.*, 1981.). Accordingly, the MeHg-cysteine conjugate may exploit its molecular mimicry of methionine not only to gain entrance into the CNS, but also to exert its cytotoxic effects.

8. SUMMARY

It is striking to contemplate how much of today's research on MeHg is directed toward answering questions that were first raised almost a century ago. Much of what seemed mysterious then has become clear today. The old dogma that Hg can prolong life and secure immortality has long faded. In stride with the advances in our understanding of molecular and cellular events, the pathophysiology of MeHg has evolved to encompass transport and homeostatic processes within the CNS.

Aided by new advances in tissue-culture techniques, we can now begin to experimentally mimic the properties of the blood–brain barrier *in vitro* and to probe for the mechanisms that contribute to the etiology of MeHg neurotoxicity. Progress has been made in defining the physicochemical properties of MeHg as the MeHg-cysteine conjugate, providing a mechanism for blood–brain barrier transport. Competition studies have demonstrated the importance of sulfhydryl groups in the transport process. The role of astrocytes in MeHg neurotoxicity may provide some answers to long-asked questions about the long latency of clinically symptomatic MeHg neurotoxicity. Astrocytic demethylation of MeHg resulting in inorganic Hg accumulation may provide an explanation for this long latency. These and other mechanistic studies are essential to our understanding of the relative risks of acute and chronic low-dose exposure.

As MeHg is likely to continue to permeate the food chain and to remain a health hazard, a better understanding of its body distribution and cytotoxic mechanisms will undoubtedly continue to occupy a prominent position in our search for safe and acceptable levels of exposure to this environmental toxicant.

ACKNOWLEDGMENTS.   This chapter was supported in part by the National Institutes of Health NIEHS No. 5223 awarded to MA and NINDS No. 23750 awarded to HKK.

REFERENCES

Abe, T., Haga, T., and Murakawa, M., 1975, Blockage of axoplasmic transport and depolymerisation of reassembled microtubules by methylmercury, *Brain Res.* 86:504–508.

Aschner, M., and Clarkson, T.W., 1988, Uptake of methylmercury in the rat brain: Effects of amino acid, *Brain Res.* 462:31–39.

Aschner, M., and Clarkson, T.W., 1989, Methyl mercury uptake across bovine brain capillary endothelial cells in vitro: The role of amino acids, *Pharmacol. Toxicol.* 65:17–20.

Aschner, M., and Kimelberg, H.K., 1991, The use of astrocytes in culture as model systems for evaluating neurotoxic-induced-injury, *Neurotoxicology* 12:505–518.

Aschner, M., Rodier, P.M., and Finkelstein, J.N., 1986, Reduction of axonal transport in the rat optic system after direct application of methylmercury, *Brain Res.* 381:244–250.

Aschner, M., Rodier, P.M., and Finkelstein, J.N., 1987, Increased axonal transport in the rat optic system after systemic exposure to methylmercury: Differential effects in local vs. systemic exposure conditions, *Brain Res.* 401:132–141.

Aschner, M., Eberle, N.B., Goderie, S., and Kimelberg, H.K., 1990a, Methylmercury uptake in rat primary astrocyte cultures: The role of the neutral amino acid transport system, *Brain Res.* 524:221–228.

Aschner, M., Eberle, N.B., Miller, K., and Kimelberg, H.K., 1990b, Interactions of methylmercury with rat primary astrocyte cultures: Inhibition of rubidium and glutamate uptake and induction of swelling, *Brain Res.* 530:245–250.

Aschner, M., Eberle, N.B., and Kimelberg, H.K., 1991, Interactions of methylmercury with rat primary astrocyte cultures: Methylmercury efflux, *Brain Res.* 554:10–14.

Atchison, W.D., 1986, Extracellular calcium-dependent and -independent effects of methylmercury on spontaneous and potassium-evoked release of acetylcholine at the neuromuscular junction, *J. Pharmacol. Exp. Therap.* 237:672–680.

Atchison, W.D., 1987, Neurophysiological effects of mercurials, in: *The Toxicity of Methyl Mercury* (C.U. Eccles, and Z. Annau, eds.), Johns Hopkins University Press, Baltimore, pp. 189–219.

Bakir, F., Damluji, S.F., Amin-Zaki, L., Murthada, M., Khalidi, A., Al-Rawi, N.Y., Tikriti, S., Dhahrir, H.I., Clarkson, T.W., Smith, J.C., and Doherty, R.A., 1973, Methylmercury poisoning in Iraq, *Science* 181:230–242.

Ballatori, N., and Clarkson, T.W., 1985, Sulfobromophtalein inhibition of glutathione and methylmercury secretion into bile, *Am. J. Physiol.* 248:G238–G245.

Berlin, M., Jerksell, L.G., and Ubisch, H., 1966, Uptake and retention of mercury in the mouse brain. A comparison of exposure to mercury vapor and intravenous injection of mercuric salts, *Arch. Environ. Health* 12:33–42.

Bernard, C., 1878, *Leçons sur les Phénomènes de la Vie Communs aux Animaux et aux Végétaux,* Baillière, Paris.

Betz, A.L., and Goldstein, G.A., 1978, Polarity of the blood-brain barrier: Neutral amino acid transport into isolated brain capillaries, *Science* 202:225–227.

Brightman, M.W., and Reese, T.S., 1969, Junctions between intimately apposed cell membranes in the vertebral brain, *J. Cell Biol.* 40:648–677.

Brookes, N., 1988, Specificity and reversibility of the inhibition by $HgCl_2$ of glutamate transport in astrocyte cultures, *J. Neurochem.* 50:1117–1122.

Brown, D.L., Reuhl, K.R., Bormann, S., and Little, J.E., 1988, Effects of methyl mercury on the microtubule system of mouse lymphocytes, *Toxicol. Appl. Pharmacol.* 94:66–75.

Carty, A.J., and Malone, S.F., 1979, The chemistry of mercury in biological systems, in: *The Biogeochemistry of Mercury in the Environment* (J.O. Nrigau, ed.), Elsevier/North Holland Biomedical Press, Amsterdam, pp. 433–479.

Cheung, M., and Verity, M.A., 1983, Experimental methyl mercury neurotoxicity: Similar in vivo and in vitro perturbation of brain cell-free protein synthesis, *Exp. Mol. Pathol.* 38:230–242.

Christensen, H.N., 1984, Organic ion transport during seven decades: The amino acids, *Biochim. Biophys. Acta* 779:255–269.

Christensen, H.N., 1985, On the strategy of kinetic discrimination of amino acid transport systems, *J. Membr. Biol.* 84:97–103.

Christensen, H.N., Handlongten, M.E., Lam, I., Tager, H.S., and Zand, R.A., 1969, Bicyclic amino acid to improve discriminations among transport systems, *J. Biol. Chem.* 244:1510–1520.

Clarkson, T.W., 1983, Methylmercury toxicity to the mature and developing nervous system: Possible mechanisms, in: *Biological Aspects of Metals and Metal-Related Diseases* (B. Sarkar, ed.), Raven Press, New York, pp. 183–197.

Ehrlich, P., 1906, Das Sauerstoff-Bederfnis des Organismus, in: *Eine Farbenanalytische Studie* (P. Ehrlich, ed.), Herschenwald, Berlin, pp. 69–72.

Fedoroff, S., and Vernadakis, A., 1986, Astrocytes: Development, morphology, and regional specialization, in: *Astrocytes* (S. Fedoroff, and A. Vernadakis, eds.), Academic Press, London.

Friberg, L., and Mottet, N.K., 1989, Accumulation of methylmercury and inorganic mercury in the brain, *Biol. Trace Elem. Res.* 21:201–206.

Gage, J.C., 1961, The trace determination of phenyl and methyl mercury salts in biological material, *Analyst* 86:457–459.

Ganther, H.E., Goudie, C., Sunde, M.L., Kopecky, M.J., Wagner, P., Oh, S.-H., and Hoekstra, W.G., 1972, Selenium: Relation to decreased toxicity of methylmercury added to diets containing tuna, *Science* 175:1122–1124.

Garman, R.H., Weiss, B., and Evans, H.L., 1975, Alkylmercurial encephalopathy in the monkey, a histopathologic and autoradiographic study, *Acta Neuropathol.* 32:61–74.

Goldmann, E.E., 1913, Vitalfärbung am Zentralnervensystem, *Abh. Preuss. Akad. Wiss. Phys.-Math.* 1:1–60.

Goldstein, G.A., and Betz, A.L., 1986, The blood-brain barrier, *Sci. Am.* 255:74–83.

Hayes, A.D., and Rothstein, A., 1962, The metabolism of inhaled mercury vapor in the rat studies by isotope techniques, *J. Pharmacol. Exp. Ther.* 138:1–10.

Hirayama, K., 1980, Effects of amino acids on brain uptake of methyl mercury, *Toxicol. Appl. Pharmacol.* 55:318–323.

Hirayama, K., 1985, Effects of combined administration of thiol compounds and methylmercury chloride on mercury distribution in rats, *Biochem. Pharmacol.* 34:2032–2034.

Hughes, W.H., 1957, A physiochemical rationale for the biological activity of mercury and its compounds, *Ann. N.Y. Acad. Sci.* 65:454–460.

Inskip, M., and Piotrowski, J., 1985, Review of health effects of methylmercury, *J. Appl. Toxicol.* 5:113–133.

Jagus, R., Anderson, W.F., and Safer, B., 1981, The regulation and initiation of mammalian protein synthesis, *Prog. Nucleic Acids Res.* 25:127–185.

Jensen, S., and Jernelov, A., 1969, Biological methylation of mercury in aquatic organisms, *Nature* 223:753–754.

Kerper, L.E., Ballatori, N., and Clarkson, T.W., 1990, Methylmercury transport across the blood-brain barrier by molecular mimicry, *Toxicologist* 10:136.

Kimelberg, H.K., and Bourke, R.S., 1982, Anion transport in the nervous system, in: *Handbook of Neurochemistry* (A. Lajtha, ed.), Plenum Press, New York, pp. 31–67.

Kimelberg, H.K., and Norenberg, M.D., 1989, Astrocytes, *Sci. Am.* 260:66–76.

Kimelberg, H.K., Pang, S., and Treble, D.H., 1989, Excitatory amino acid-stimulated uptake of $^{22}Na^+$ in primary astrocyte cultures, *J. Neurosci.* 9:1141–1149.

Kletzien, R.F., Pariza, M.W., Becker, J.E., and Potter, V.R., 1975, A method using 3-o-methyl-D-glucose and phloretin for the determination of intracellular water space of cells in monolayer culture, *Anal. Biochem.* 68:537–544.

Koester, J., 1985, Cell biology of neurons, in: *Principles of Neural Sciences,* 2nd ed. (E.R. Kandel and J.H. Schwartz, eds.), Elsevier, New York, pp. 25–35.

Lackowicz, J.R., and Anderson, C.J., 1980, Permeability of lipid bilayers to methylmercury chloride: Quantification by fluorescence quenching of a carbazole-labelled phospholipid, *Chem.-Biol. Interact.* 30:309–323.

Magos, L., 1967, Mercury blood interaction and mercury uptake by brain, *Environ. Res.* 1:323–327.

Magos, L., Clarkson, T.W., and Greenwood, M.R., 1973, The depression of pulmonary retention of mercury vapor by ethanol; Identification of the site of action, *Toxicol. Appl. Pharmacol.* 26:180–183.

Magos, L., Webb, M., and Hudson, A.R., 1979, Complex formation between Se and MeHg, *Chem.-Biol. Interact.* 28:359–362.

Naganuma, A., and Imura, N., 1979, Methylmercury binds to a low molecular weight substance in rabbit and human erythrocytes, *Toxicol. Appl. Pharmacol.* 47:613–616.

National Academy of Sciences, An Assessment of Mercury in the Environment, National Academy of Sciences, Washington, DC (1978).

Norenberg, M.D., Hertz, L., and Schousboe, A., 1988, Preface, in: *The Biochemical Pathology of Astrocytes* (M.D. Norenberg, L. Hertz, and A. Schousboe, eds.), Alan R. Liss, New York, pp. xxiii–xxiv.

Oldendorf, W.H., 1970, Measurement of brain uptake of radiolabeled substances using a tritiated water internal standard, *Brain Res.* 24:372–376.

Olney, J.W., 1979, Excitotoxic amino acids and Huntington's disease, in: *Advances in Neurology* (T.N. Chase, N.S. Wexler, and A. Barbeau, eds.), Raven Press, New York, pp. 609–624.

Omata, S., Sakimura, K., Ishii, T., and Sugano, H., 1978, Chemical nature of a methylmercury complex with a low molecular weight in the liver cytosol of rats exposed to methylmercury chloride, *Biochem. Pharmacol.* 27:333–335.

Oyake, Y., Tanaka, M., Kubo, H., and Cichibu, H., 1966, Neuropathological studies on organic mercury poisoning with special reference to the staining and distribution of mercury granules, *Adv. Neurol. Sci.* 10:744–750.

Peters, A., Palay, S.L., and Webster, H.F., 1976, (eds.), The neuroglial cells, in: *The Fine Structure of the Nervous System: the Neurons and Supporting Cells,* W.B. Saunders, Philadelphia, pp. 231–263.

Phelps, C.H., 1972, The development of gliovascular relationships in the rat spinal cord. An electron microscopic study, *Z. Zellforsch.* 128:555–563.

Piotrowski, J.K., and Inskip, M.J., 1981, Health Effects of Methylmercury, MARC Report No. 24, Monitoring and Assessment Research Centre, Chelsea College, University of London.

Rabenstein, D.L., and Fairhurst, M.T., 1975, Nuclear magnetic resonance studies of the solution chemistry of metal complexes. XI. The binding of methylmercury by sulfhydryl-containing amino acids and by glutathione, *J. Am. Chem. Soc.* 97:2086–2092.

Rapoport, S.I., 1976, Permeability and osmotic properties of the blood-brain barrier, in: *Blood-Brain Barrier in Physiology and Medicine* (S.I. Rapoport, ed.), Raven Press, New York, pp. 87–127.

Refsvik, T., and Norseth, T., 1975, Methylmercuric compounds in rat bile, *Acta Pharmacol. Toxicol.* 52:22–29.

Rothstein, A., 1973, Mercaptans, the biological targets for mercurials, in: *Mercury, Mercurials and Mercaptans* (M.W. Miller, and T.W. Clarkson, eds.), Charles C. Thomas, Springfield, IL, pp. 68–92.

Rothstein, A., and Hayes, A.D., 1960, The metabolism of mercury in the rat studied by isotope techniques, *J. Pharmacol. Exp. Therap.* 130:166–167.

Salvaterra, P., Lown, B., Morganti, J., and Massaro, E.J., 1973, Alterations in neurochemical and behavioral parameters in the mouse induced by low doses of methylmercury, *Acta Pharmacol. Toxicol.* 33:177–190.

Sarafian, T.A., Cheung, M., and Verity, M.A., 1984, In vitro methyl mercury inhibition of protein synthesis in neonatal cerebellar perikarya, *Neuropathol. Appl. Neurobiol.* 10:85–100.

Shotwell, M.A., Kilberg, M.S., and Oxender, D.L., 1983, The regulation of neutral amino acid transport in mammalian cells, *Biochim. Biophys. Acta* 737:267–284.

Shrivastav, B.B., Brodwick, M.S., and Narahashi, T., 1976, Methylmercury effects on electrical properties of squid axon membranes, *Life Sci.* 18:11077–1082.

Speciale, C., Hares, K., Schwarcz, R., and Brookes, N., 1989, High affinity uptake of L-kynurenine by a Na$^+$-independent transporter of neutral amino acids in astrocytes, *J. Neurosci.* 9:2066–2072.

Spencer, P.S., Ludolph, A., Dwived, M.P., Dwijendra, N.R., Hugon, J., and Schamburg, H.H., 1986, Lathirism: Evidence for the role of the neuroexcitatory aminoacid BOAA, *Lancet* 2:1066–1067.

Steinwall, O., and Olsson, Y., 1969, Impairment of the blood-brain barrier in mercury poisoning, *Acta Neurol. Scand.* 45:351–361.

Stokes, P.M., and Wren, C.D., 1987, Bioaccumulation of mercury by aquatic biota in hydroelectric reservoirs: A review and consideration of mechanisms, in: *Lead, Mercury, and Arsenic in the Environment* (T.C. Hutchinson, and K.M. Meema, eds.), John Wiley, New York, pp. 255–278.

Takeuchi, T., Morikawa, N., Matsumoto, H., and Shiraishi, A., 1962, A pathological study of Minamata disease, *Acta Neuropathol.* 2:40–57.

Thomas, D.J., and Smith, C.J., 1979, Partial characterization of a low molecular weight methylmercury complex in rat cerebrum, *Toxicol. Appl. Pharmacol.* 47:547–556.

UN Food and Agricultural Organization, 1977, Food Balance Sheets, Details, Data Sources, FAO-ICS 1972–1974, FIPP United Nations Food and Agricultural Organization, Rome (quoted from reference #26).

USEPA, 1983, *Criteria Document for Mercury*, United States Environmental Protection Agency, ECAO CIN-025, Research Triangle Park, North Carolina.

Verity, M.A., Brown, W.J., Cheung, M., and Czer, G., 1977, Methyl mercury inhibition of synaptosome and brain slice protein synthesis: In vivo and in vitro studies, *J. Neurochem.* 29:673–679.

Webb, J.L., (ed.), 1966, Mercurials, in: *Enzyme and Metabolic Inhibitors*, Volume 2, Academic Press, New York, pp. 729–1070.

Wolff, J., 1963, Bitrage zur Ultrastruktur der Capillaren der normallen Grosshirnrinde, *Z. Zellforsch.* 60:409–431.

Wood, J.M., Kennedy, F.S., and Rosen, C.E., 1968, Synthesis of methylmercury compounds by extracts of methanogenic bacterium, *Nature* 220:173–174.

World Health Organization, 1976, *Environmental Health Criteria 1, Mercury,* WHP Publications, Geneva, Switzerland.

Chapter 2

The Neurotoxicity of Methylmercury in the Developing Nervous System

John R. O'Kusky

1. MERCURY AS A TOXIN

There is no known metabolic requirement for mercury (Hg). The presence of organic and inorganic compounds of Hg in mammalian tissues results from the uptake and accumulation of environmental pollutants. Compounds containing Hg can exist in a number of chemical forms, and the properties of these various species are largely responsible for determining the target organ (Shamoo, 1987). Inorganic compounds, which are transported by plasma proteins and have low lipid solubility, are deposited mainly in the liver and kidneys. Since metallic Hg is highly volatile, the inhalation of Hg vapor can result in damage to the respiratory tract and alveolar epithelial cells. Methylmercury (MeHg) and related alkylmercury compounds, which have high lipid solubility and can penetrate membrane barriers such as the blood–brain barrier and placenta, are highly neurotoxic.

Mercury can enter the environment through the erosion of natural geological deposits or through discharge from industrial sources (for reviews, see Goldwater, 1972; Nriagu, 1979). Levels in the Earth's crust have been estimated to range from approximately 0.05 to 0.08 ppm. The weathering of rock and soil releases Hg into aquatic and marine environments. Compounds of Hg in the crust degrade to the metallic form, which can evaporate into the atmosphere. Rainfall deposits up to 500 mg per acre annually. Additional Hg can enter the environment through discharge from industrial sources. Compounds of Hg are used in the manufacture of electrical equipment, mercury batteries, and

John R. O'Kusky • Department of Pathology, University of British Columbia, Vancouver, British Columbia, Canada V5Z 1M9.
The Vulnerable Brain and Environmental Risks, Volume 2: Toxins in Food, edited by Robert L. Isaacson and Karl F. Jensen. Plenum Press, New York, 1992.

paint, and in the electrolytic production of chlorine and alkali. Hg has been used in the extraction of gold by amalgamation and is present in tailing dumps and mine wastes. Compounds of Hg are potent fungicides and have been used in the pulp and paper industry, and in the fur and felt industry. MeHg was used extensively as a treatment for seed grain before being banned in 1970. The burning of fossil fuels, which can contain 20–300 ppm Hg, can release additional Hg into the atmosphere. Silver alloys amalgamated with Hg are used in dental fillings. Mercurial antiseptics, ointments, and diuretics have a long history in medicine, while compounds of Hg were used as the preferred treatment for syphilis.

The greatest threat to the general population is through the consumption of MeHg-contaminated fish and shellfish (Berglund *et al.*, 1971). Following discharge of inorganic compounds of Hg into aquatic and marine environments, methylation into the more neurotoxic organic compounds can occur through the action of methanogenic bacteria present in sediments. Of recent concern is evidence that acid rain can increase the rate of biological methylation and the accumulation of MeHg in fish (Jernelov, 1980). MeHg can account for 90% of the total Hg content in the flesh of edible fish, which can average up to 100–200 μg/kg in most marine and aquatic species. Higher concentrations are found in predatory species, such as swordfish (1150 μg/kg), tuna (350 μg/kg), and pike (250–600 μg/kg).

2. NEUROLOGICAL DISORDERS AND NEUROPATHOLOGY IN HUMANS

The toxicity of MeHg and related alkylmercury compounds in adults can produce severe and permanent damage to the CNS (for review, see Eccles and Annau, 1987). Epidemic poisonings have occurred in Japan and Iraq, resulting from the consumption of MeHg-contaminated fish (Berglund *et al.*, 1971; Harada, 1978; Tsubaki and Irukayama, 1977) and alkylmercury-treated seed grain (Bakir *et al.*, 1973; Rustam and Hamdi, 1974), respectively. Neurological disorders in adults most frequently included constriction of the visual field with reduced visual acuity, paresthesia of the extremities and perioral region, impaired two-point discrimination in the extremities, impaired vibration and joint sense, deafness to high tones, and ataxia. Neuropathology in these cases revealed characteristic lesions of the cerebellum and cerebral cortex (Harada, 1978; Takeuchi *et al.*, 1962). The cerebellum was severely atrophic, with granule-cell degeneration, proliferation of astrocytes, and thinning of the myelin. Atrophy in the cerebral cortex was most pronounced in the calcarine cortex (primary visual cortex) and in the precentral gyrus (primary somatosensory cortex).

The toxicity of MeHg in the human CNS during prenatal and early postnatal development has been associated with neurological disorders resembling cerebral palsy (Amin-Zaki *et al.*, 1974, 1979; Harada, 1978; Marsh *et al.*, 1980; Tsubaki and Irukayama, 1977). Neurological impairment in infants and children includes severe psychomotor retardation, progressive microcephaly, persistence of primitive reflexes, hyper-reflexia, hypersalivation, and incontinence. Additional motor signs include spasticity, hyperkinesia (particularly athetosis and chorea), ataxia, generalized tonic convulsions, and myoclonic jerking. Visual disturbances vary from constriction of the visual field to blindness. This syndrome is most likely to occur following intoxication during the third, trimester of gestation (Amin-Zaki *et al.*, 1979). Autopsies of infants and children exposed to MeHg in utero have revealed variable neuropathology (Choi *et al.*, 1978; Matsumoto *et al.*, 1965; Takeuchi, 1968). Many cases have demonstrated cerebral and cerebellar atrophy with widespread neuronal degeneration, cell loss, and gliosis. While there was a preferential localization of lesions in the calcarine and precentral cortices in adults, neurons throughout the cerebral hemispheres tend to be involved in the infants and children. During prenatal development earlier exposures to MeHg correlate with more widespread cortical lesions (Takeuchi, 1968). Hypoplasia of the corpus callosum, dysmyelination of the pyramidal tract, and hydrocephalus have also been reported. Disturbances in neuronal migration and cortical lamination within the cerebral and cerebellar cortices can occur in the absence of focal lesions (Choi *et al.*, 1978). Such differences in the nature and distribution of MeHg-induced histopathologies suggest that the particular stage of development at which peak exposure occurs will dictate the final clinical outcome.

During the epidemic poisonings in Japan and Iraq, it was found that mothers with mild paresthesia or no clinical symptoms gave birth to severely affected infants (Marsh, 1987). In other cases an infant appeared normal at birth, later expressing some neurological disorder as the CNS matured. In the Iraqi outbreak, the concentration of Hg in maternal hair during pregnancy varied from 0.4 to 640 μg/g (Bakir *et al.*, 1973). For offspring showing severe neurological effects, which were indistinguishable from cerebral palsy caused by hypoxia, peak maternal hair concentrations varied from 165 to 320 μg/g (Marsh *et al.*, 1980). No infant effects were observed at concentrations less than 18–20 μg/g. Abnormal muscle tone and deep tendon reflexes have been reported in Cree Indian children, following prenatal exposure to MeHg, where maternal hair concentrations of Hg were 14–24 μg/g (McKeown-Eyssen *et al.*, 1983). In a study of children in New Zealand, developmental abnormalities were correlated with maternal hair concentrations of Hg in the range of 6–20 μg/g (Kjellstrom *et al.*, 1986). A concentration of 6 μg/g can be achieved by the daily intake of approximately 3 oz of tuna (containing 0.3 ppm MeHg).

3. NEUROTOXICITY IN THE DEVELOPING CNS

Recent reviews of the developmental neurotoxicity of MeHg have stressed the importance of the developmental stage at which maximum exposure occurs (Burbacher *et al.*, 1990; Choi, 1989). The development of the mammalian CNS consists of a series of progressive and regressive events, which culminate in the consolidation of neuronal circuitry characteristic of the adult. Progressive events include neurulation, histogenesis of neurons and glia, migration of neurons, axon outgrowth and target finding, synaptogenesis, and myelination. Regressive events include naturally occurring neuron death, axon remodelling, and synapse elimination.

Clinical and experimental studies have demonstrated the transplacental transfer of MeHg and its accumulation in the CNS of the fetus (Amin-Zaki *et al.*, 1974; Null *et al.*, 1973). Concentrations of Hg in the brain of the fetus can be severalfold greater than those in the mother (King *et al.*, 1976; Null *et al.*, 1973). Additional intoxication results from the ingestion of MeHg-contaminated milk by the suckling infant. Neonatal tissues accumulate metals more rapidly than those of the adult, due to a higher rate of intestinal absorption and lower rates of both renal and biliary excretion (Ballatori and Clarkson, 1982; Kostial *et al.*, 1978). A prolonged retention of MeHg in the neonate has been demonstrated in experimental animals (Choi *et al.,* 1981b; Thomas *et al.,* 1982) and appears to occur in human infants (Amin-Zaki *et al.,* 1974, 1979).

The neurotoxicity of MeHg during embryonic and early fetal development is not generally associated with gross malformations of the brain resulting from neural-tube defects. In experimental animals, the embryotoxic effects have been shown to include gross organ defects, cleft palate, and growth retardation (Fuyuta *et al.,* 1978; Harris *et al.,* 1972; Khera, 1973). Telencephalic structures in the CNS can be reduced in size, with enlargement of the lateral ventricles (Inouye and Kajiwara, 1988), but neuronal architectonics are not grossly abnormal. The high rate of fetal resorption following MeHg intoxication during early development (Inouye and Kajiwara, 1988; Su and Okita, 1976) probably prevents viable offspring, which would exhibit gross malformations.

Histopathology of the cerebral cortex and cerebellum in humans (Choi *et al.,* 1978) and experimental animals (Inouye and Kajiwara, 1988; Khera, 1973) suggests that neuronal histogenesis and migration are grossly affected by MeHg. Following prenatal exposure to MeHg in experimental animals, decreased numbers of mitotic figures and mitotic arrest have been reported in the cerebral cortex, hippocampus, and cerebellum (Rodier *et al.,* 1984; Sager *et al.,* 1984). Human astrocytes in culture exhibit mitotic figures arrested in metaphase following exposure to MeHg (Choi *et al.,* 1981a), resulting from a lack of microtubules required for the formation of a mitotic spindle apparatus. MeHg can react with sulfhydryl groups to block the polymerization of tubulin monomers (Margolis and Wilson, 1981). In addition, MeHg can cause depolymerization of assembled tubules (Abe *et al.,* 1975). MeHg has been shown to alter cell-cycle kinetics during mitosis in cultured human fibroblasts (Vogel *et al.,* 1986).

MeHg can also affect neuronal migration. Human neurons in culture fail to migrate from explants (Choi *et al.,* 1981a). Following prenatal exposure to MeHg in mice, [^{3}H]thymidine-labeled neurons exhibited incomplete migration into the cerebral cortex (Choi, 1986; Peckham and Choi, 1988). Delayed migration of the external granule-cell layer in the cerebellum of mice has been reported following prenatal exposure to MeHg (Khera and Tabacova, 1973).

Relatively little is known concerning the effects of MeHg on axon outgrowth, target finding, and synaptogenesis. Effects of MeHg on regressive events have yet to be documented. Biochemical studies of the developing and adult brain at both clinical and subclinical stages of MeHg toxicity have documented alterations in cellular metabolism. These changes are likely to contribute to alterations in the development of normal axonal circuitry. Altered cellular metabolism in the CNS has been reported to involve changes in the synthesis of proteins and nucleic acids (Choi *et al.,* 1980; for review, see Thomas and Syversen, 1987) and of lipids (Grundt *et al.,* 1980). Disturbances in carbohydrate metabolism (Snell *et al.,* 1977), in mitochondrial respiration and oxygen consumption (Verity *et al.,* 1975; Von Burg *et al.,* 1979), and in the synthesis, release, and turnover rates of various neurotransmitters (for review, see Komulainen and Tuomisto, 1987) have been reported.

4. METHYLMERCURY-INDUCED MOVEMENT AND POSTURAL DISORDERS

4.1. The Animal Model

Experiments in the author's laboratory have investigated the pathogenesis of MeHg-induced movement and postural disorders in animals during early postnatal development.

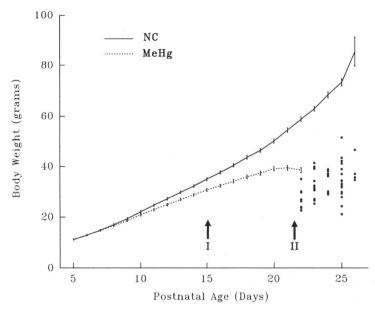

FIGURE 1. Postnatal changes in body weight for 55 matched pairs of MeHg-treated and normal control (NC) animals (vertical bars indicate ± standard error of the mean). Stages of toxicity are indicated by arrows: stage I (day 15), when MeHg rats continue to gain weight, although less rapidly than NC rats; and stage II (days 18–23), when a given MeHg rat exhibits a persistent loss of body weight for 12–24 hours. Neurological impairments begin to be observed on about day 23, and at this point individual data points for each of the MeHg-treated animals are shown in Figure 1. This marks the onset of the stage III toxicity.

These studies have employed an animal model in which Sprague-Dawley rat pups receive subcutaneous injections of 0.01 M methylmercuric chloride in physiological saline (5 mg Hg/kg/day or 6.26 mg CH_3HgCl/kg/day), beginning on postnatal day 5 and continuing until the onset of neurological impairment during the fourth week. Two subclinical stages of toxicity have been defined in this model, based on postnatal changes in body weight exhibited by MeHg-treated animals (Fig. 1). These animals exhibit the normal increase in body weight until days 10–12, at which time they continue to gain weight, although less rapidly than normal control (NC) animals. This is preclinical stage I. After attaining a maximum value between days 18 and 21, body weight gradually decreases (preclinical stage II), followed within 3–5 days by the onset of neurological impairment. The abnormal rate of growth displayed by MeHg animals requires the addition of weight-matched controls (WMC) to account for the possible effects of malnutrition during development. Given the relative immaturity of the central nervous system in rodents at birth, the dose schedule employed in this animal model would correspond to maximum exposure in humans during the third trimester of gestation.

Clinical signs of neurological impairment have been observed in MeHg animals between days 22 and 28. All animals displayed apparent spasticity, with mild to marked hypertonia of flexor muscles in all four limbs as judged by passive manipulation. This hypertonicity was symmetrical and more pronounced in the hindlimbs than in the forelimbs of most animals. Flexion deformities were noted in a number of postures (Fig. 2). When MeHg animals were held by the scruff, the forelimbs were flexed and abducted. When stimulated in this position by manipulation of the hindlimbs, extensor thrusts of the

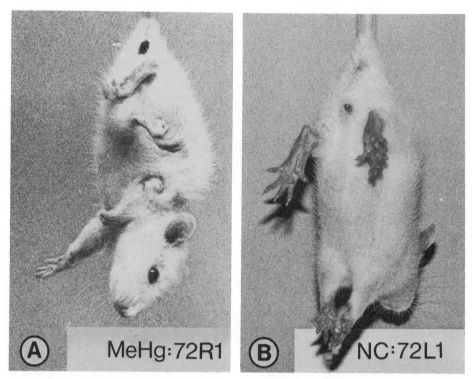

FIGURE 2. Flexion deformities in (A) a MeHg-treated rat as opposed to (B) a weight-matched control animal. When MeHg animals were suspended by the tail, extension of the limbs was weak and incomplete, with the hindlimbs excessively adducted in full flexion.

forelimbs were observed frequently, with abnormal rotation of the limbs and tight flexion of the digits. Hyper-reflexia was apparent in the auricular startle response, and hyper-salivation was noted in approximately 40% of MeHg animals. Some degree of visual impairment was observed in all MeHg animals. Unlike control animals, they failed to avoid a visual cliff and demonstrated difficulty in negotiating obstacles when placed in a novel environment. In approximately 30% of MeHg animals, myoclonic jerking of the hindlimbs was observed. In less than half of these animals, this localized jerking progressed into generalized motor seizures.

4.2. Histopathology in the Cerebral Cortex and Striatum

The most conspicuous lesions were largely limited to the cerebral cortex and striatum of MeHg-treated animals (O'Kusky, 1985; O'Kusky *et al.*, 1988b). Degenerating neurons

→

FIGURE 3. (A) Araldite-embedded section (0.5 μm, Toluidine blue) from the primary visual cortex of a MeHg-treated animal at subclinical stage II. Degenerating neurons, which were pyknotic with an accumulation of clear vacuoles in the cytoplasm, were found throughout layer IV. (B) Primary visual cortex in a MeHg-treated animal at stage III (30 μm, thionin). Note the almost complete loss of neurons from layer IV (indicated by the vertical bar). Calibration bars in micrometers.

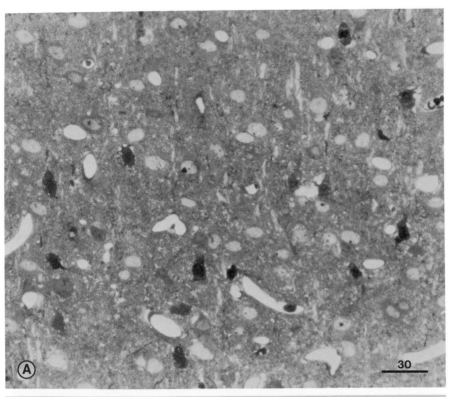

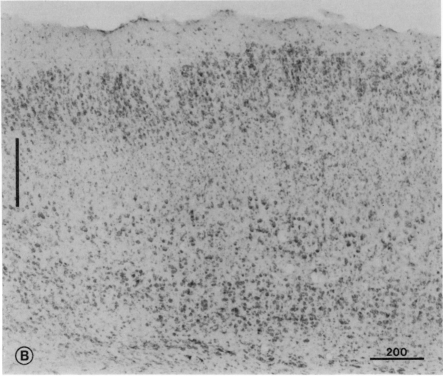

in the cerebral cortex were observed scattered throughout most cytoarchitectonic areas at subclinical stage II. They were most prominent in layer IV of the primary visual cortex (area 17, Fig. 3A), the somatosensory cortex (areas 1, 2, and 3), and the retrosplenial granular cortex (area 29). By the onset of neurological impairment (stage III), degenerating neurons were more numerous throughout the cerebral hemispheres. At this stage there was an almost complete loss of neurons from layer IV in the visual, somatosensory, and retrosplenial granular cortices (Fig. 3B). Degenerating neurons in these areas were concentrated mainly in the middle third of the cortex, extending from the lower boundary of layer III to the upper half of layer VI. On the basis of both morphological (O'Kusky, 1985) and biochemical (O'Kusky and McGeer, 1985, 1989; O'Kusky et al., 1988b) criteria, degenerating neurons in the cerebral cortex were found to consist largely of GABAergic interneurons. However, a specific subpopulation of GABAergic interneurons was spared in MeHg-induced lesions of the visual cortex (O'Kusky et al., 1988b). In these neurons GABA is colocalized with the neuropeptides somatostatin and neuropeptide Y.

Histopathology was observed in the striatum of MeHg-treated animals at subclinical stage II and at the onset of neurological impairment (O'Kusky et al., 1988b). At stage II a few degenerating neurons were observed scattered throughout the dorsolateral aspect of the caudate-putamen, while at stage III their numbers had increased markedly. Subsequent neurochemical studies (O'Kusky and McGeer, 1985, 1989; O'Kusky et al., 1988b) indicated that degenerating neurons comprised two distinct populations—somatostatin-immunoreactive interneurons and GABAergic neurons. In the caudate-putamen there was a 50–60% decrease in the tissue concentrations of somatostatin at stages II and III, while levels were normal in eight other regions of the CNS.

The functional implication of a relatively selective loss of GABAergic interneurons in the visual cortex is consistent with the abnormalities reported in clinical (Harada, 1978; Rustam and Hamdi, 1974) and experimental (Rice and Gilbert, 1982) studies of MeHg poisoning. The iontophoretic application of GABA antagonists has been shown to inhibit both orientation and directional specificity in cortical neurons (Sillito, 1975a, 1975b). Following impairment of GABAergic interneurons by MeHg, a loss of orientation specificity would account for decreased visual acuity. A loss of directional specificity in cortical neurons could contribute to the concentric narrowing of the visual field, since visual-field perimetry requires the detection of a moving stimulus in the periphery.

Abnormalities in GABAergic neurotransmission in the motor cortex and striatum have been implicated in several experimentally induced movement disorders. The application of GABA antagonists onto the motor cortex has been shown to produce dyskinesias affecting the distal musculature (Robin et al., 1980). Impairment of GABA synthesis or blockage of its postsynaptic action in the cortex has been shown to reduce convulsive thresholds (Wood, 1975). In the striatum, injections of GABA antagonists into the caudate-putamen increase motor activity, while injections of GABA or GABA agonists decrease activity (Wachtel and Anden, 1978). Injections of baclofen or diazepam into the caudate nucleus suppress experimentally induced dyskinesias (Neale et al., 1984). Similar injections of GABA have been shown to normalize spinal motoneuron disturbances (Jurna et al., 1978).

The cellular mechanism underlying a preferential degeneration of GABAergic neurons in MeHg-treated animals is not clear. Chronic hypoxia can reduce GABA levels in various brain regions (Arregui and Barer, 1980; Gibson et al., 1981). In this animal model, MeHg has been shown to inhibit the postnatal development of intracortical capillaries in the visual cortex (O'Kusky, 1989), reducing the length density of capillaries (L_v, total capillary length per unit volume) by 30–40% by stage II. The degeneration of GABAergic interneurons in the visual cortex may result, to some extent, from these vascular abnormalities.

Somatostatin-immunoreactive neurons in the caudate-putamen of the rat comprise a relatively sparse population of medium-sized aspiny interneurons. Although their function is largely unknown, there is evidence that they exert some influence on the extrapyramidal control of movement (Brown and Vale, 1975; Rezek et al., 1977). Abnormal tissue concentrations of somatostatin and altered morphology of somatostatin-immunoreactive neurons have been detected in patients with Parkinson's disease and Huntington's chorea (Dupont et al., 1982; Marshall and Landis, 1985; Nemeroff et al., 1983).

4.3. Postnatal Changes in Catecholamines and Indoleamines

Tissue concentrations of noradrenaline (NA), serotonin (5-HT), dopamine (DA), and selected metabolites were determined by high-pressure liquid chromatography in the CNS of MeHg-treated and control animals at the three stages of toxicity (O'Kusky et al., 1988a). In MeHg-treated animals, significant increases in levels of NA were detected in the spinal cord (42–51%) and striatum (98–116%) at subclinical stage II and at the onset of neurological impairment, when compared to either weight-matched control or normal control animals (Fig. 4). In the cerebral cortex of MeHg-treated animals, levels of NA were significantly lower than in weight-matched controls at stage I (30%), but they gradually increased to normal values by stage III.

Levels of 5-HT were significantly greater in MeHg-treated animals in the spinal cord (19–43%) and cerebral cortex (54–81%) at stages II and III (Fig. 4). Tissue concentrations of 5-hydroxyindoleacetic acid (5-HIAA), the major metabolite of 5-HT, were elevated in the spinal cord (98–152%), striatum (88–124%), and cerebral cortex (78–178%) at stages II and III. Furthermore, the ratio of 5-HIAA/5-HT, which is frequently used as an estimate of turnover for 5-HT, was significantly increased in all three regions (38–114%) at stages II and III.

In the striatum of MeHg-treated animals (Fig. 5) DA levels were significantly greater at the onset of neurological impairment (28–29%). Tissue concentrations of the DA metabolite, 3,4-dihydroxyphenylacetic acid (DOPAC), were reduced (20–35%) at stages II and III. Levels of homovanillic acid (HVA) were significantly reduced at stage II (20–24%), while an apparent reduction at stage III (17–18%) was only of borderline significance. The ratio of (DOPAC + HVA)/DA was significantly reduced in MeHg-treated animals (34–40%) at stages II and III, suggesting decreased turnover of DA.

An increased activity of serotonergic and noradrenergic neurons in the brainstem of MeHg-treated animals would be consistent with the motor signs displayed by these animals. The so-called 5-HT syndrome, which includes signs of hyperactivity, hyperreflexia, hypersalivation, hypertonicity of the hindlimbs, and myoclonic jerking, can be produced in adult animals by the administration of compounds that increase concentrations of 5-HT, increase its release from presynaptic terminals, or act as 5-HT agonists on the postsynaptic membrane (Gerson and Baldessarini, 1980). Both 5-HT and NA have been shown to facilitate directly the activity of motoneurons in the brainstem and spinal cord (Fung and Barnes, 1981; McCall and Aghajanian, 1979; White and Neuman, 1980). The activity of Renshaw cells in the spinal cord can be inhibited by the iontophoretic

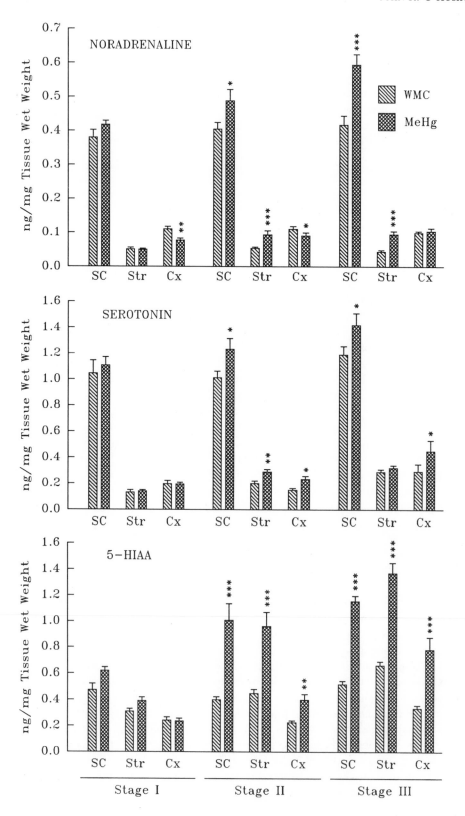

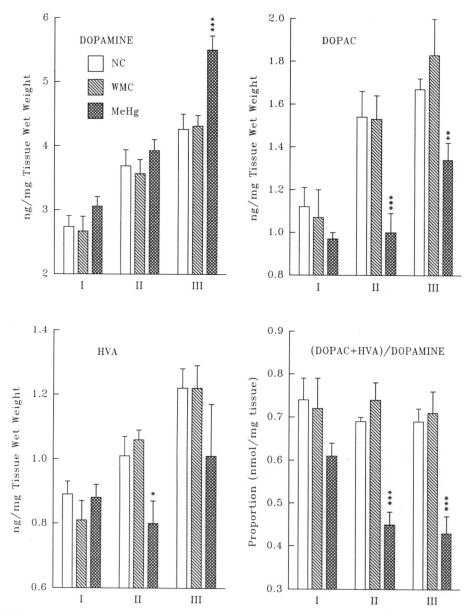

FIGURE 5. Tissue concentrations (mean ± standard error of the mean) of dopamine, DOPAC, and HVA in the striatum of MeHg-treated animals, weight-matched controls (WMC), and normal controls (NC) at the three stages of toxicity. Asterisks indicate the statistical significant of individual comparisons between MeHg and WMC animals (*p < 0.05, **p < 0.01, ***p < 0.001). Data from O'Kusky *et al.* (1988a).

←

FIGURE 4. Tissue concentrations (mean ± standard error of the mean) of noradrenaline, serotonin, and 5-HIAA in the spinal cord (SC), striatum (Str), and cerebral cortex (Cx) of MeHg-treated animals and weight-matched controls (WMC) at the three stages of toxicity. Asterisks associated with MeHg values indicate the statistical significance of individual comparisons between MeHg and WMC animals (**p < 0.05, **p < 0.01, ***p < 0.001). Data from O'Kusky *et al.* (1988a).

application of NA (Engberg and Ryall, 1966). Furthermore, hyperactivity of nor-adrenergic neurons or the hypertrophy of NA innervation in locus coeruleus terminal fields has been implicated in the pathogenesis of epileptiform seizures (Levitt and Noebels, 1981; Maurin *et al.*, 1982).

4.4. Cytochrome Oxidase Histopathology in the Brainstem

Cytochrome oxidase histochemistry was employed to investigate changes in the oxidative metabolic activity of neurons in the CNS of MeHg-treated animals during postnatal development (Dyck and O'Kusky, 1988). A population of intensely stained cytochrome oxidase-positive (ICO) neurons was first detected in the brainstem of MeHg-treated animals on postnatal day 16. These neurons were located in the magnocellular red nucleus and inter-rubral mesencephalon (Fig. 6). Morphometric analysis revealed a signif-icant increase in the number of ICO neurons from approximately 300 neurons on day 16 to 1300 neurons on day 18, followed by a gradual decrease to approximately 225 neurons on day 25. ICO neurons were not observed in either weight-matched control or normal control animals during postnatal development. The axonal projections of ICO neurons and the neurotransmitter(s) that they employ have yet to be determined.

Hemidecortication on postnatal day 10 did not alter the symmetrical distribution or total number of ICO neurons in the mesencephalon. However, hemicerebellectomy pro-

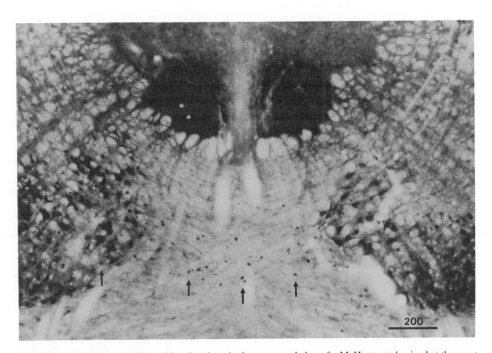

FIGURE 6. Cytochrome oxidase histochemistry in the mesencephalon of a MeHg-treated animal at the onset of neurological impairment. This frontal section is at the level of the red nucleus, with the oculomotor nucleus located on either side of the midline. Arrows indicate the distribution of ICO neurons in the magnocellular red nucleus and in the inter-rubral mesencephalon. Calibration bar in micrometers.

duced a significant decrease (36–37%) in the number of ICO neurons in the contralateral red nucleus and in the contralateral half of the interrubral mesencephalon. Thus, the increased oxidative metabolic activity of these neurons may result, at least in part, from abnormal activation by afferents from the cerebellum, particularly along excitatory interpositorubral axons. An increased firing rate by interpositorubral neurons could result from either a decreased inhibitory input from Purkinje cells or from an increased excitatory input from extracerebellar nuclei, such as the inferior olivary nucleus or pontine nuclei.

Although conspicuous lesions of the cerebellum were not detected by light microscopy in this animal model, the neurotoxicity of MeHg has been reported to produce characteristic histopathology in the cerebellum of humans and experimental animals. MeHg could produce a disinhibition of excitatory interpositorubral neurons following direct impairment of Purkinje neurons or following impairment of granule cells, which exert an excitatory influence on Purkinje neurons. In the present model, this impairment would involve pathophysiology in the absence of overt degenerative changes.

5. CONCLUSIONS

Despite the decreasing use of MeHg in industry, the general population is still at risk through the consumption of MeHg-contaminated fish and shellfish. The neurotoxicity of MeHg poses the greatest threat to the developing fetus and neonate. Doses of MeHg that are not toxic to the mother can produce permanent damage to the CNS of the offspring. Research in this laboratory indicates that certain neurotransmitter-specific neurons in the developing CNS are more susceptible to the neurotoxic effects of MeHg. GABAergic neurons in both the cerebral cortex and striatum, and somatostatin-immunoreactive interneurons in the striatum, degenerate preferentially at subclinical stages of toxicity. Furthermore, neurochemical changes that are consistent with increased activity in noradrenergic and serotonergic neurons have also been detected at these subclinical stages. Given the role of these neurons in the normal control of movement and posture, it is likely that they contribute to the pathogenesis of MeHg-induced neurological disorders. Further research is needed to document changes in cellular metabolism in these neurotransmitter-specific neurons, which precede neuronal degeneration and neurological impairment during development.

ACKNOWLEDGMENTS.   The research for this chapter was supported by grants from the United Cerebral Palsy Research and Educational Foundation, Inc. and from the British Columbia Health Care Research Foundation. The technical assistance of Richard H. Dyck in the preparation of photographs for Figure 2 is gratefully acknowledged.

REFERENCES

Abe, T., Haga, T., and Kurokawa, M., 1975, Blockage of axoplasmic transport and depolymerisation of reassembled microtubules by methyl mercury, *Brain Res.* 86:504–508.
Amin-Zaki, L., Elhassani, S., Majeed, M.A., Clarkson, T.W., Doherty, R.A., and Greenwood, M., 1974, Intrauterine methylmercury poisoning in Iraq, *Pediatrics* 54:587–595.
Amin-Zaki, L., Majeed, M.A., Elhassani, S.B., Clarkson, T.W., Greenwood, M.R., and Doherty, R.A., 1979, Prenatal methylmercury poisoning, *Am. J. Dis. Child.* 133:172–177.
Arregui, A., and Barer, G.R., 1980, Chronic hypoxia in rats: Alterations of striato-nigral angiotensin converting enzyme, GABA, and glutamic acid decarboxylase, *J. Neurochem.* 34:740–743.

Bakir, F., Damluji, S.F., Amin-Zaki, L., Murtadha, M., Khalidi, A., Al-Rawi, N.Y., Tikriti, S., Dhahir, H.I., Clarkson, T.W., Smith, J.C., and Doherty, R.A., 1973, Methylmercury poisoning in Iraq, *Science* 181:230–241.

Ballatori, N., and Clarkson, T.W., 1982, Developmental changes in the biliary excretion of methylmercury and glutathione, *Science* 216:61–63.

Berglund, F., Berlin, M., Birke, G., Von Euler, U., Fribert, L., Holmstedt, B., Jonsson, E., Ramel, C., Skerfving, S., Swensson, A., and Tejning, S., 1971, Methyl mercury in fish. A toxicological epidemiologic evaluation of risks, *Nord. Hyg. Tidskr.* Suppl. 4:1–364.

Brown, M., and Vale, W., 1975, Central nervous system effects of hypothalamic peptides, *Endocrinology* 96:1333–1336.

Burbacher, T.M., Rodier, P.M., and Weiss, B., 1990, Methylmercury developmental neurotoxicity: A comparison of effects in humans and animals, *Neurotoxicol. Teratol.* 12:191–202.

Choi, B.H., 1986, Methylmercury poisoning of the developing nervous system: I. Pattern of neuronal migration in the cerebral cortex, *Neurotoxicology* 7:591–600.

Choi, B.H., 1989, The effects of methylmercury on the developing brain, *Prog. Neurobiol.* 32:447–470.

Choi, B.H., Lapham, L.W., Amin-Zaki, L., and Saleem, T., 1978, Abnormal neuronal migration, deranged cerebral cortical organization, and diffuse white matter astrocytosis of human fetal brain: A major effect of methylmercury poisoning in utero, *J. Neuropathol. Exp. Neurol.* 37:719–733.

Choi, B.H., Cho, K.H., and Lapham, L.W., 1980, Effects of methylmercury on DNA synthesis of human fetal astrocytes: A radioautographic study, *Brain Res.* 202:238–242.

Choi, B.H., Cho, K.H., and Lapham, L.W., 1981a, Effects of methylmercury on human fetal neurons and astrocytes in vitro: A time-lapse cinematographic, phase and electron microscopic study, *Environ. Res.* 24:61–74.

Choi, B.H., Kudo, M., and Lapham, L.W., 1981b, A Golgi and electron microscopic study of cerebellum in methylmercury-poisoned neonatal mice, *Acta Neuropathol. (Berlin)* 54:233–237.

Dupont, E., Christensen, S.E., Hansen, A.P., Olivarius, B.F., and Orskov, H., 1982, Low cerebrospinal fluid somatostatin in Parkinson's disease: An irreversible abnormality, *Neurology* 32:312–314.

Dyck, R.H., and O'Kusky, J.R., 1988, Increased cytochrome oxidase activity of mesencephalic neurons in developing rats displaying methylmercury-induced movement and postural disorders, *Neurosci. Lett.* 89:271–276.

Eccles, C.U., and Annau, Z., (eds.), 1987, *The Toxicity of Methyl Mercury*, Johns Hopkins University Press, Baltimore.

Engberg, I., and Ryall, R.W., 1966, The inhibitory action of noradrenaline and other monoamines on spinal neurones, *J. Physiol. (London)* 185:298–322.

Fung, S.J., and Barnes, C.D., 1981, Evidence of facilitatory coerulospinal action in lumbar motoneurons of cats, *Brain Res.* 216:299–311.

Fuyuta, M., Fujimoto, T., and Hirada, S., 1978, Embryotoxic effects of methylmercury chloride administered to mice and rats during organogenesis, *Teratology* 18:362–366.

Gerson, S.C., and Baldessarini, R.J., 1980, Motor effects of serotonin in the central nervous system, *Life Sci.* 27:1435–1451.

Gibson, G.E., Peterson, C., and Sansone, J., 1981, Decreases in amino acid and acetylcholine metabolism during hypoxia, *J. Neurochem.* 37:192–201.

Goldwater, L.J., 1972, *Mercury. A History of Quicksilver*, York Press, Baltimore.

Grundt, I.K., Stensland, E., and Syversen, T.L.M., 1980, Changes in fatty acid composition of myelin cerebrosides after treatment of the developing rat with methylmercury chloride and diethylmercury, *J. Lipid Res.* 21:162–168.

Harada, M., 1978, Methyl mercury poisoning due to environmental contamination ("Minamata disease"), in: *Toxicity of Heavy Metals in the Environment* (F.W. Oehme, ed.), Marcel Dekker, New York, pp. 261–302.

Harris, S.B., Wilson, J.G., and Printz, R.H., 1972, Embryotoxicity of methylmercuric chloride in golden hamster, *Teratology* 6:139–142.

Inouye, M., and Kajiwara, Y., 1988, Developmental disturbances of the fetal brain in guinea-pigs caused by methylmercury, *Arch. Toxicol.* 62:15–21.

Jernelov, A., 1980, The effects of acidity on the uptake of mercury in fish, in: *Polluted Rain* (T.Y. Toribara, M.W. Miller, and P.E. Morrow, eds.), Plenum Press, New York, pp. 221–222.

Jurna, I., Brenner, M., and Drum, P., 1978, Abolition of spinal motor disturbance by injections of dopamine receptor agonist, atropine and GABA into the caudate nucleus, *Neuropharmacology* 17:35–44.

Khera, K.S., 1973, Teratogenic effects of methylmercury in the cat, *Teratology* 8:293–304.

Khera, K.S., and Tabacova, S.A., 1973, Effects of methylmercury on the progeny of mice and rats treated before or during gestation, *Food Cosmet. Toxicol.* 11:245–254.

King, R.B., Robkin, M.A., and Shepard, T.H., 1976, Distribution of ^{203}Hg in pregnant and fetal rats, *Teratology* 13:275–280.

Kjellstrom, T., Kennedy, P., Wallis, S., and Mantell, C., 1986, Physical and Mental Development of Children with Prenatal Exposure to Mercury from Fish. Stage 1: Preliminary Tests at Age 4, Solna, Sweden, National Swedish Environmental Protection Board, Report 3080.

Komulainen, H., and Tuomisto, J., 1987, The neurochemical effects of methylmercury in the brain, in: *The Toxicity of Methyl Mercury* (C.U. Eccles and Z. Annau, eds.), Johns Hopkins University Press, Baltimore, pp. 172–188.

Kostial, K., Kello, D., Jugo, S., Rabar, I., and Maljkovic, T., 1978, Influence of age on metal metabolism and toxicity, *Environ. Health Perspect.* 25:81–86.

Levitt, P., and Noebels, J.L., 1981, Mutant mouse tottering: Selective increase of locus coeruleus axons in a defined single locus mutation, *Proc. Natl. Acad. Sci. USA* 78:4630–4634.

Margolis, R.L., and Wilson, L., 1981, Microtubule treadmills: Possible molecular machinery, *Nature* 293:705–711.

Marsh, D.O., 1987, Dose-response relationships in humans: Methyl mercury epidemics in Japan and Iraq, in: *The Toxicity of Methyl Mercury* (C.U. Eccles, and Z. Annau, eds.), Johns Hopkins University Press, Baltimore, pp. 45–53.

Marsh, D.O., Myers, G.J., Clarkson, T.W., Amin-Zaki, L., Tikriti, S., and Majeed, M.A., 1980, Fetal methylmercury poisoning: Clinical and toxicological data on 29 cases, *Ann. Neurol.* 7:348–353.

Marshall, P.E., and Landis, D.M.D., 1985, Huntington's disease is accompanied by changes in the distribution of somatostatin-containing neuronal processes, *Brain Res.* 329:71–82.

Matsumoto, H., Koya, G., and Takeuchi, T., 1965, Fetal Minamata disease, *J. Neuropathol. Exp. Neurol.* 24:563–574.

Maurin, Y., Arbilla, S., Dedek, J., Lee, C.R., Baumann, N., and Langer, S.Z., 1982, Noradrenergic neurotransmission in the brain of a convulsive mutant mouse: Differences between the cerebral cortex and the brainstem, *Naunyn-Schmiedeberg's Arch. Pharmacol.* 320:26–33.

McCall, R.B., and Aghajanian, G.K., 1979, Serotonergic facilitation of facial motoneuron excitation, *Brain Res.* 169:11–27.

McKeown-Eyssen, G.E., Ruedy, J., and Neims, A., 1983, Methylmercury exposure in northern Quebec: II. Neurological findings in children, *Am. J. Epidemiol.* 118:470–479.

Neale, R., Gerhardt, S., and Liebman, J.M., 1984, Effects of dopamine agonists, catecholamine depletors, and cholinergic and GABAergic drugs on acute dyskinesias in squirrel monkeys, *Psychopharmacology* 82:20–26.

Nemeroff, C.B., Youngblood, W.W., Manberg, P.J., Prange, A.J., and Kizer, J.S., 1983, Regional brain concentrations of neuropeptides in Huntington's chorea and schizophrenia, *Science* 221:972–975.

Nriagu, J.O., (ed.), 1979, *The Biogeochemistry of Mercury in the Environment*, Elsevier/North Holland, Amsterdam.

Null, D.H., Gartside, R.S., and Wei, E., 1973, Methylmercury accumulation in brains of pregnant, non-pregnant and fetal rats, *Life Sci.* 12:65–72.

O'Kusky, J.R., 1985, Synaptic degeneration in rat visual cortex after neonatal administration of methylmercury, *Exp. Neurol.* 89:32–47.

O'Kusky, J.R., 1989, Methylmercury-induced movement and postural disorders in the developing rat: Inhibited development of intracortical capillary networks, *Neurosci. Abstr.* 15:685.

O'Kusky, J.R., and McGeer, E.G., 1985, Methylmercury poisoning of the developing nervous system in the rat: Decreased activity of glutamic acid decarboxylase in cerebral cortex and neostriatum, *Dev. Brain Res.* 21:299–306.

O'Kusky, J.R., and McGeer, E.G., 1989, Methylmercury-induced movement and postural disorders in developing rat: High-affinity uptake of choline, glutamate, and gamma-aminobutyric acid in the cerebral cortex and caudate-putamen, *J. Neurochem.* 53:999–1006.

O'Kusky, J.R., Boyes, B.E., and McGeer, E.G., 1988a, Methylmercury-induced movement and postural disorders in developing rat: Regional analysis of brain catecholamines and indoleamines, *Brain Res.* 439:138–146.

O'Kusky, J.R., Radke, J.M., and Vincent, S.R., 1988b, Methylmercury-induced movement and postural disorders in developing rat: Loss of somatostatin-immunoreactive interneurons in the striatum, *Dev. Brain Res.* 40:11–23.

Peckham, N.H., and Choi, B.H., 1988, Abnormal neuronal distribution within the cerebral cortex after prenatal methylmercury intoxication, *Acta Neuropathol.* 76:222–226.

Rezek, M., Havlicek, V., Leybin, L., Pinsky, C., Kroger, E.A., Hughes, K.R., and Friesen, H., 1977, Neostriatal administration of somatostatin: Differential effect of small and large doses on behavior and motor control, *Can. J. Physiol. Pharmacol.* 55:234–242.

Rice, D.C., and Gilbert, S.G., 1982, Early chronic low-level methylmercury poisoning in monkeys impairs spatial vision, *Science* 216:759–761.

Robin, M.M., Palfreyman, M.G., Zraika, M.M., and Schechter, P.J., 1980, Mapping of dyskinetic movements induced by local application of picrotoxin or (+)-gamma-acetylenic GABA on the rat motor cortex, *Eur. J. Pharmacol.* 65:411–415.

Rodier, P.M., Aschner, M., and Sager, P.R., 1984, Mitotic arrest in the developing CNS after prenatal exposure to methyl mercury, *Neurobehav. Toxicol. Teratol.* 6:379–386.

Rustam, H., and Hamdi, T., 1978, Methylmercury poisoning in Iraq, *Brain* 97:499–510.

Sager, P.R., Aschner, M., and Rodier, P.M., 1984, Persistent, differential alterations in developing cerebellar cortex of male and female mice after methylmercury exposure, *Dev. Brain Res.* 12:1–11.

Shamoo, A.E., 1987, Biological target sites of mercurials, in: *The Toxicity of Methyl Mercury* (C.U. Eccles, and Z. Annau, eds.), Johns Hopkins University Press, Baltimore, pp. 13–23.

Sillito, A.M., 1975a, The contribution of inhibitory mechanisms to the receptive field properties of neurones in the striate cortex of the cat, *J. Physiol. (London)* 250:305–329.

Sillito, A.M., 1975b, Inhibitory processes underlying the directional specificity of simple, complex and hypercomplex cells in the cat's visual cortex, *J. Physiol. (London)* 271:699–720.

Snell, K., Ashby, S.L., and Barton, S.J., 1977, Disturbances of perinatal carbohydrate metabolism in rats exposed to methylmercury in utero, *Toxicology* 8:277–283.

Su, M., and Okita, G.T., 1976, Behavioral effects on the progeny of mice treated with methylmercury, *Toxicol. Appl. Pharmacol.* 38:195–205.

Takeuchi, T., 1968, Pathology of Minamata disease, in: *Minamata Disease* (M. Kutsuma, ed.), Kumamoto University Press, Tokyo, pp. 141–228.

Takeuchi, T., Morikawa, N., Matsumoto, H., and Shiraishi, Y., 1962, A pathological study of Minamata disease in Japan, *Acta Neuropathol.* 2:40–57.

Thomas, D.J., Fisher, H.L., Hall, L.L., and Mushak, P., 1982, Effects of age and sex on retention of mercury by methyl mercury-treated rats, *Toxicol. Appl. Pharmacol.* 62:445–454.

Thomas, D.J., and Syversen, T.L.M., 1987, The alteration of protein synthesis by methyl mercury, in: *The Toxicity of Methyl Mercury* (C.U. Eccles, and Z. Annau, eds.), Johns Hopkins University Press, Baltimore, pp. 131–171.

Tsubaki, T., and Irukayama, K., 1977, *Minamata Disease: Methylmercury Poisoning in Minamata and Niigata, Japan,* Elsevier, Amsterdam.

Verity, M.A., Brown, W.J., and Cheung, M., 1975, Organic mercurial encephalopathy: In vivo and in vitro effects of methylmercury on synaptosomal respiration, *J. Neurochem.* 25:759–766.

Vogel, D.G., Rabinovitch, P.S., and Mottet, N.K., 1986, Methylmercury effects on cell cycle kinetics, *Cell Tissue Kinet.* 19:227–242.

Von Burg, R., Lijoi, A., and Smith, C., 1979, Oxygen consumption of rat tissue slices exposed to methylmercury in vitro, *Neurosci. Lett.* 14:309–314.

Wachtel, H., and Anden, N., 1978, Motor activity of rats following intracerebral injections of drugs influencing GABA mechanisms, *Naunyn-Schmiedeberg's Arch. Pharmacol.* 302:133–139.

White, S.R., and Neuman, R.S., 1980, Facilitation of spinal motoneurone excitability by 5-hydroxytryptamine and noradrenaline, *Brain Res.* 188:119–127.

Wood, J.D., 1975, The role of gamma-aminobutyric acid in the mechanism of seizures, in: *Progress in Neurobiology* (G.A. Kerkut and J.W. Phillis, eds.), Pergamon, Elmsford, New York, pp. 78–95.

Chapter 3

Intestinal Absorption of Aluminum

Relation to Neurotoxicity

Gijsbert B. van der Voet

1. INTRODUCTION

Aluminum is a ubiquitous metal in the natural and industrial environment and has been considered a harmless substance for a long time. It may occur in food and drinking water as a natural or added ingredient. Aluminum compounds are even used in orally administered antacids and phosphate-regulating drugs. Exposure—especially oral exposure—is almost unavoidable. However, aluminum is a proven neurotoxic only under rather artificial circumstances of oral and parenteral exposure. As yet, the neurotoxicity of aluminum in the population of patients with renal disorders undergoing dialysis procedures and/or receiving high oral doses of aluminum-containing phosphate-binding medication is the only proven type of aluminum neurotoxicity in humans. The relationship between oral aluminum intake and neurodegenerative disorders, such as Alzheimer's disease, has not been conclusively resolved. Research on intestinal absorption of aluminum may concentrate on the intraluminal speciation of aluminum compounds after ingestion and on the bioavailability of certain chemical species. This chapter will focus on the factors that determine systemic availability of aluminum from the intestine and may constitute a potential risk for neurotoxicity.

Gijsbert B. van der Voet • Toxicology Laboratory, University Hospital, Leiden, The Netherlands.
The Vulnerable Brain and Environmental Risks, Volume 2: Toxins in Food, edited by Robert L. Isaacson and Karl F. Jensen. Plenum Press, New York, 1992.

2. GENERAL ASPECTS

Aluminum is the third most abundant element in the crust of the Earth; the first and second are oxygen and silicon (Elinder and Sjögren, 1986). About 8% (w/w) of the Earth's crust consists of aluminum compounds. In nature aluminum does not occur in the free metallic chemical form but is mainly bound to oxygen and silicon as silicates. Aluminum is industrially obtained from bauxite, an impure water-containing aluminum oxide, which also contains a large amount of iron oxide. Pure metallic aluminum is produced by electrolysis of aluminum oxide. Large amounts of energy are required for the electrolytic reduction of aluminum oxide. Therefore, aluminum-processing chemical plants are usually located near relatively cheap power sources, e.g., at locations where hydroelectrically generated electricity is available.

Aluminum is used as packaging material, is processed into utensils, and is also used in the automobile and airplane industries. Aluminum sulphates are used as water purifying agents, and aluminum compounds are used as food additives (sodium-aluminum sulphate). Moreover, a number of aluminum compounds are used for medical purposes: aluminum hydroxide is used in antacids (acid-neutralizing agents recommended for the treatment of peptic ulcers and gastritis) and as phosphate binders for the regulation of phosphate levels in patients with kidney disorders.

Aluminum compounds may occur in food and drinking water, either as natural or added ingredients. Considering the abundance of aluminum in the Earth's crust, the natural presence of aluminum is not surprising. The most common sources of additional dietary aluminum are specific food additives, and aluminum from cookware and containers. As additives in baking powder, aluminum compounds have been traditionally used as leavening agents and antiadherence agents (sodium aluminum phosphate, sodium aluminum silicate) in the bakery industry. When acidic foods are cooked in aluminum vessels, there is a significant increase in aluminum concentration in the food.

3. EXPOSURE

There is a very large chance of being exposed to naturally occurring and industrially produced aluminum compounds. In fact, aluminum is everywhere: in solid and liquid food, in water, and in air. A relatively large amount of aluminum may enter the human body via inhalation of aluminum oxide-containing dust and by oral intake (2–6 mg/day for children and 6–14 mg/day for adults) (WHO Technical Report, 1989). However, no toxic effects have been observed or associated with aluminum exposure, as the systemic aluminum concentrations—the concentrations in the blood and tissues—are usually very low. This discrepancy is ascribed to the fact that aluminum compounds are hardly or not absorbed after inhalation or oral ingestion. Many organisms have evolved in the presence of considerable concentrations of aluminum. However, no essential need for aluminum as a dietary factor nor a physiological function of aluminum has yet been reported. Apparently organisms have either developed a tolerance for aluminum or an effective mechanism for exclusion of the metal. Toxicity, and especially neurotoxicity, occurs only under rather extreme circumstances of exposure, circumstances that seem to circumvent the exclusion mechanisms of the organism.

4. NEUROTOXICITY

In 1976 a neurologic disease was described among patients with renal deficiency on long-term hemodialysis (Alfrey *et al.*, 1976; Alfrey and Froment, 1990; Flendrig *et al.*, 1976). This disease, which became known as dialysis encephalopathy (DE), was characterized by speech disturbances (a mixture of dysarthria, speech dyspraxia, and dysphasia), twitching, myoclonic jerks, motor apraxia, and seizures. Psychiatric abnormalities occurred with visual and auditory hallucinations, leading to paranoid behavior of the patient. The EEG patterns were altered and dementia manifested itself gradually in the course of disease. Death within a year was common. After intensive research aluminum was found to be the cause of this disease. Aluminum accumulated diffusely in the grey cortex of the brain of the renal patients, leading to significantly increased levels, as shown after analysis of bulk brain tissue. Aluminum originated from the media used for dialysis of the patients. At this stage artificial parenteral exposure was considered as the ultimate cause of DE. Water purification procedures that lower the concentration of aluminum in dialysis media reduced the incidence of DE but did not eradicate the disease. It took several years to recognize that intestinal absorption of aluminum from orally administered phosphate binders, given in large amounts to these patients to reduce their phosphate levels, was a route of exposure, bearing a similar risk for toxicity as the dialysis medium. Due to the attention given to the aluminum-contaminated dialysis media as a cause for toxicity in renal patients, no attention was paid to the few investigators who had warned against the use of aluminum-containing oral medication (Berlyne *et al.*, 1970, 1972). The fact that as early as 1880 feeding aluminum-containing baking powder to dogs was claimed to result in increased aluminum in organs was also neglected (Smith, 1928). Apparently the traditional belief in the lack of absorption and toxicity of oral aluminum was hard to eradicate. Moreover, most case reports on aluminum toxicity described patients with both (1) reduced or absent renal function, (2) on hemodialysis procedures, and (3) on oral aluminum medication, all of which affect the development of toxicity. These factors, together with the lack of awareness of potential aluminum absorption, resulted in it taking quite some time to (1) discriminate between the relative contribution of oral medication and the dialysis media to the total aluminum body load and (2) notice that renal patients absorb more aluminum than healthy subjects. Intestinal absorption may be the main route of entry of aluminum into the body (De Wolff and Van der Voet, 1990). The implication of orally administered aluminum as a cause of DE (and aluminum osteotoxicity and anemia) has been gaining acceptance and recognition from clinicians. The DE-related neurotoxicity is relatively acute in nature, and extremely high dosages of oral aluminum that are significantly higher than normal dietary exposure are involved.

5. INTESTINAL ABSORPTION

5.1. Outline

Intestinal absorption may be defined as the appearance of aluminum in the (portal) blood after intraluminal exposure. Most studies attempt to correlate parameters of oral administration (dose, total dose, intraluminal concentration, exposure period) to elevated blood (usually peripheral) and tissue levels or to parameters of toxicity. Data on the intestinal absorption process are made available from case reports of adult and pediatric patients with renal deficiency. Oral aluminum-containing mediation given to control hyperphosphatemia and secondary hyperparathyroidism is the source of aluminum in most cases reported. A minority of reports deal with milk-based infant formula that has been contaminated with aluminum and orally administered to very young children. Data have also become available from controlled studies in healthy volunteers. The data from such human studies show that intestinal absorption depends on the aluminum compound (formulation), dose, and interaction with dietary factors. However, to what extent intestinal absorption is affected by the bioavailability of aluminum, exposure period, total dose, site of absorption, age of the absorbing organism, PTH levels, and calcium and phosphate metabolism is not sufficiently clarified by these human studies. Moreover, no molecular mechanism has been established. Therefore, *in vitro* and animal experiments are being performed to answer these questions.

An essential problem in almost all studies reported is the lack of knowledge of the aluminum species created. Various investigators have established the physiological situation experimentally and have detected active or passive absorption routes. The lack of knowledge of the actual species involved prevents comparison between most studies and hinders the extrapolation of data to the human situation.

Current research on the mechanism of intestinal absorption of aluminum concentrates on two working hypotheses: (1) Due to the absence of any physiological function, aluminum may use existing pathways for intestinal passage that are normally used by other essential substances, and (2) the chemical speciation of aluminum determines the actual availability of aluminum via a certain intestinal passage. The available information is discussed below in short sections that report data from *in vitro* and animal experiments. When possible, this information is used to interpret phenomena observed in humans.

5.2. Speciation

The aluminum compound absorbed is usually not the compound ingested. The chemical species (Martin, 1986) of aluminum found in the intestine is extremely variable. The type of aluminum compound ingested, acidity in the intestine, intraluminal aluminum concentration, and complexing factors (diet, drugs), determine the chemical form of aluminum. With aluminum chloride or aluminum sulphate at low pH (3–5), as established *in vitro* in aqueous solutions, the soluble (ionic) forms of aluminum prevail (Al^{3+}); at pH 5–8 insoluble aluminum hydroxide is formed gradually and soluble ionic structures disappear; above pH 8 soluble aluminate is formed (AlO_3^-). Moreover, numerous polymeric complexes exist between aluminum atoms and between aluminum and water. From this perspective it may not be strange to observe a pH effect of intestinal absorption; the pH value is essential to any speciation process. Using a perfusion technique utilizing rat small intestine (ileum plus jejunum) and aluminum chloride in a medium at pH 4.0 and 7.0, the intestinal absorption—measured as the appearance of aluminum in the portal and peripheral blood—at pH 4.0 was slightly increased above that detected in a pH 7.0 medium (Van der Voet and De Wolff, 1986). Apparently more aluminum is absorbed from ionic forms of intestinal aluminum than from (sub)colloidal aluminum hydroxide. In humans the upper duodenum and the lower stomach are suggested as absorption sites for aluminum, as they are the parts of the gastrointestinal tract where, due to their relatively high acidity, soluble aluminum is made available (Kaehny *et al.*, 1977).

Aluminum forms insoluble salts with phosphates; significant amounts of aluminum and phosphate are incompatible in solution at any pH. Traditionally it was thought that all intestinal aluminum was bound as insoluble aluminum phosphate in the intestine and excreted in the feces. Aluminum hydroxide is a common ingredient in preparations used for phosphate regulation in renal patients and in peptic ulcer therapy. Apart from the fact that often the exact molecular nature of the aluminum compound in the formulation is unclear, many different formulations are marketed, some in combination with calcium or magnesium compounds. Some formulations make more aluminum available for intestinal absorption than others. This is probably a matter of the quantity of a certain available species than of a completely different species. In a study performed by Kaehny et al. (1977), various formulations (aluminum hydroxide, aluminum carbonate, dihydroxy-aluminum aminoacetate, and aluminum phosphate) were administered orally to healthy human subjects. The aluminum plasma levels and excretion levels were significantly elevated after ingestion of the first three compounds, as compared to the aluminum phosphate group and the controls. The aluminum excretion after acetate ingestion was much higher than after ingestion of hydroxide, carbonate, and phosphate. The question arises as to which species is made available from these preparations for intestinal absorption. The aluminum hydroxide, as such, and the aluminum phosphates may not be available; therefore, it is likely that soluble ionic species or complexes are absorbed.

Complexing dietary compounds such as citrate have been shown to have a tremendous impact on intestinal absorption of aluminum. The *in vitro* species distribution of aluminum citrate suggests a neutral complex between aluminum and citrate at pH 2–5, while charged complexes occur above pH 5. The soluble neutral complex is claimed to be an effective means for aluminum to pass through membranes. Citrate increased the blood levels of aluminum in both portal and peripheral blood significantly when tested using a perfusion technique of rat small intestine with a combination of aluminum chloride and citrate at pH 4.0 (Van der Voet et al., 1989). Elevated aluminum levels were found in both the brain and bone of rats fed a diet containing aluminum citrate or citrate alone (Slanina et al., 1984, 1985). The citrate alone evidently chelates trace amounts aluminum in the diet. The aluminum blood level of humans taking aluminum hydroxide-containing medication rises substantially upon the intake of citrate. This process makes it unadvisable to combine aluminum-containing antacids with citrate-containing medication or diet (citrus fruit or juices). Although healthy individuals naturally exclude aluminum from their systems, solubilization of aluminum by citrate provides a means by which even healthy subjects may absorb aluminum.

Aluminum forms relatively strong complexes with fluoride ions. Ingesting small amounts of aluminum hydroxide decreases the absorption of fluoride from the intestine (Spencer et al., 1980).

5.3. Quantity

The intestinal absorption of aluminum as the chloride has been shown to be concentration dependent in a rat everted-gut sac prepared from a piece of jejunum and incubated at physiological pH (Feinroth et al., 1982). Both the intestinal uptake process of aluminum by the jejunal wall, as well as the passage process of aluminum through the intestinal wall, increased at increasing intestinal aluminum concentrations. A plateau—a sort of steady state—was reached for both these processes at rising intestinal aluminum concentrations, which may indicate saturation. Concentration dependence of both aluminum uptake and aluminum transport was confirmed *in vivo* in a perfusion system of rat jejunum and ileum at low pH (4.0); increasing the intraluminal aluminum concentration resulted in a rise in intestinal absorption, as shown by elevated blood levels of aluminum (Van der Voet and De Wolff, 1986).

The dose dependence of aluminum, which is a more indirect indicator than concentration dependence, is already known from earlier human and animal studies. The early animal studies of Berlyne *et al.* (1972) reported that the incidence of toxicity, as well as the plasma levels, correlated dose dependently with oral aluminum hydroxide. Studies in humans, especially in groups of pediatric patients, on oral aluminum hydroxide therapy mention significantly positive correlations between oral doses and the aluminum levels in plasma or serum (Andreoli *et al.*, 1984; Milliner *et al.*, 1987; Salusky *et al.*, 1985; Sedman *et al.*, 1984).

In kinetic terms, the intestinal absorption of aluminum, given as the chloride, may be a biphasic proces: A rather fast mucosal uptake of aluminum by the intestinal wall is followed by a gradual release of aluminum in the blood. Both the aluminum uptake and the release increase with time. These data are established in the rat with both everted-gut sac studies (pH 7.4) and the intestinal perfusion technique at pH 4.0 (Feinroth *et al.*, 1982; Van der Voet and De Wolff, 1984). A similar model was previously established for iron and calcium absorption (Manis and Schachter, 1962).

It should be noted that usually very low quantities of a given dose of aluminum are absorbed. In experimental studies with a rat everted-gut sac and a rat intestinal perfusion system, millimoles were administered intraluminally and only micromoles were detected in the blood (Feinroth *et al.*, 1982; Van der Voet and De Wolff, 1984). A bioavailability study (Gupta *et al.*, 1986) in rats that compared oral and intravenous doses of aluminum chloride calculated a significantly larger fraction absorbed (27%). Variation in the quantities absorbed is usually large. Wilhelm *et al.* (1990) reviewed the literature and found 0.06–27% absorption in animals and 0.001–24% in humans.

5.4. Absorption Routes

Due to aluminum speciation, various routes may exist for intestinal absorption. The kinetic processes of intestinal absorption for any substance involve energy-independent diffusion (passive and facilitated) processes and energy-dependent active transport. The physiological process may involve paracellular (along the enterocyte) and transcellular (through the enterocyte) routes of passage. The transcellular routes involve passage through the brush border membrane, cell, and basolateral membrane. Finally, the substance or its metabolites may then appear in the portal and peripheral blood. Passive diffusion through the tight junctions is usually characteristic for the paracellular routes. For each substance—sugars, organic acids, water, and metals—a route or a set of routes has been described. In view of the hypothesis that aluminum species share absorption routes with other substances, e.g., iron, calcium, sodium, citric acid, etc., knowledge of the absorption process for each of these substances is required to characterize the process for aluminum. The interactions may be determined by analogies in charge, mass, hydration, or complexation characteristics.

5.4.1. Calcium

5.4.1a. Duodenum. Adler and Berlyne (1985) studied aluminum absorption in *in vivo* perfused duodenal segments from vitamin D-deficient rats. Aluminum uptake could be resolved into saturable and nonsaturable components. Saturable absorption was significantly lower in the vitamin D-deficient group than in a vitamin D-replete control group. The presence of aluminum in the perfusion solutions reduced duodenal calcium absorption in the vitamin D-replete group but not in the vitamin D-deficient group. In a perfusion system of rat duodenum (Cochran *et al.*, 1990) using aluminum chloride at a physiological pH (8.5), further evidence was found for energy-dependent uptake of aluminum. The duodenal clearance was significantly reduced by the metabolic inhibitors NaCN, DNP, and vanadate, indicating the requirement for metabolic energy. Using verapamil, a slight but significant reduction in luminal clearance was observed, indicating calcium channels as a possible additional entry site.

5.4.1b. Jejunum. Feinroth *et al.* (1982) used a rat everted-gut sac (jejunum) system to study the intestinal absorption of aluminum chloride at physiological pH of the incubation medium. They observed a negative interaction between calcium and aluminum transport but no interaction between calcium and the mucosal uptake of aluminum. It was claimed that a part of the absorption process was energy dependent because removing intestinal glucose and reducing the incubation temperature reduced intestinal transport significantly. Dinitrophenol (DNP), an inhibitor of metabolic energy, reduced aluminum transport over the intestinal wall significantly but did not affect mucosal uptake of aluminum. Provan and Yokel found (1988a) that aluminum uptake by the rat jejunal slice was reduced by calcium channel blockers and a medium containing no added calcium. Conversely, aluminum uptake was increased by calcium channel activators and by the presence of calcium. Aluminum uptake was saturable and energy dependent. Aluminum uptake was increased by vanadate, an inhibitor of both the active calcium pump and Na/K-ATPase. These results suggest that aluminum interacts with the calcium-transporting system. Using the technique of perfusion of a segment of the rat upper jejunum, Provan and Yokel (1988b) noticed that aluminum uptake was decreased by the paracellular pathway blockers kinetin and 2,4,6-triaminopyrimidinium (TAP), by sodium removal with choline substitution, and by treatment with amiloride, an epithelial sodium transport blocker. They suggest that aluminum uptake occurs by an energy-independent, sodium-dependent, paracellular pathway-mediated process.

5.4.1c. Jejunum and Ileum. In an intestinal perfusion experiment with rat jejunum and ileum (Van der Voet and De Wolff, 1989), and aluminum chloride, given at pH 4.0, no effect of DNP was seen on mucosal uptake or on intestinal transport. A slight negative interaction was observed between calcium and aluminum in both mucosal uptake and in transport to the blood (Van der Voet *et al.*, 1991). Exogenous hyperparathyroidism, induced by injecting PTH in rats, leads to enhanced absorption of aluminum in the presence of calcium (Sips *et al.*, 1991). A negative interaction is reported between aluminum and sodium; an increase in aluminum uptake and appearance in the blood parallels sodium removal and choline substitution (Van der Voet and De Wolff, 1987a). Later Van der Voet *et al.* (1991) detected no interaction at all between aluminum and sodium using the same perfusion system.

5.4.1d. Gut.   In feeding experiments, exogeneous hyperparathyroidism induced by subcutaneous PTH treatment leads to enhanced absorption and redistribution of aluminum in
rats fed aluminum hydroxide (Drüeke *et al.*, 1985). Endogenous hyperparathyroidism,
induced by a low calcium diet and resulting in a low calcium level in plasma, leads to a
decrease in aluminum accumulation in liver and bone, while the intestinal absorption of
aluminum is also decreased (Drüeke *et al.*, 1985). Vitamin D supplementation of the diet,
together with oral aluminum hydroxide, seems to increase slightly aluminum retention by
the intestinal wall (Chan *et al.*, 1988; Drüeke *et al.*, 1985).

5.4.2. Iron

Iron absorption was reduced following oral administration of aluminum hydroxide to
young rats receiving isotopic iron chloride, indicating a negative relationship between
aluminum and iron absorption. Van der Voet and De Wolff (1987b) investigated the
interaction between di- and trivalent iron chloride on the intestinal absorption of aluminum chloride in rats via an intestinal perfusion technique. Neither the intraluminal disappearance, nor the appearance of aluminum in the blood were affected by the trivalent iron.
The divalent iron, however, enhanced the intraluminal disappearance and reduced the
appearance of aluminum in the blood. In humans iron has been shown to have a modulating influence on aluminum absorption; heavy iron loading was claimed to protect against
hyperabsorption of aluminum in uremics (Cannata *et al.*, 1984). Blaehr *et al.* (1986)
found that the presence of an iron-containing drug formulation facilitated aluminum
absorption.

5.4.3. Citrate

Citrate is able to increase significantly the intestinal absorption of aluminum. Rats
fed aluminum citrate, or even the citrate alone, showed an increased concentration of
aluminum in their blood, brains, and bones (Slanina *et al.*, 1984, 1985). Aluminum citrate
was gavaged with radiolabeled glucose in rats by Froment *et al.* (1989). Plasma aluminum
levels rose rapidly and peaked simultaneously with radioactive glucose. In *in vitro* duodenal and jejunal everted gut sacs from rats, incubation with aluminum citrate resulted in
increased tissue aluminum levels and enhanced passage of aluminum and citrate. They
suggest that aluminum as the citrate—probably as a neutral complex—is absorbed in the
proximal bowel via the paracellular pathway due to the opening of cellular tight junctions.
On the other hand, citrate-stimulated absorption aluminum was found to be decreased by
dinitrophenol (DNP), a metabolic energy inhibitor, in a rat intestinal perfusion system
(jejunum and ileum), indicating an energy-dependent, and probably transcellular, absorption route (Van der Voet *et al.*, 1989). In healthy human volunteers, citrate significantly
enhanced the intestinal absorption of aluminum from antacids (Slanina *et al.*, 1986a,
1986b). Renal patients treated with oral aluminum hydroxide and oral citrate solution to
treat metabolic acidosis developed serious hyperaluminemia in a very short period of time
(Hewitt *et al.*, 1988; Kirschbaum and Schoolwerth, 1989a) with concomitant signs of
neurotoxicity (Kirschbaum and Schoolwerth, 1989b).

5.4.4. Sites

The actual physiological sites for aluminum absorption are not known in great detail. From the studies with everted gut sacs from rat intestine and intestinal perfusion, it seems clear that various parts of the intestine (jejunum, ileum, duodenum) possess a potential for intestinal absorption of aluminum. In rats given aluminum citrate by oral gavage and radiolabeled glucose, aluminum absorption was significantly stimulated; aluminum and radiolabeled glucose appeared in the blood at the same time (Froment *et al.*, 1989). This indicated early proximal bowel absorption. Moreover, absorption sites for calcium and iron absorption are located in the early proximal bowel (Manis and Schachter, 1962). To date, in humans on aluminum hydroxide therapy, the upper duodenum and even the lower stomach have been suggested as absorption sites, since they are the parts of the gastrointestinal tract with the strongest acidity and the largest quantity of aluminum and they may be the sites of the interactions with calcium and iron.

5.5. Renal Function

In scientific terms, a renal condition does not mean elimination insufficiency alone but is a rather complex multivariate condition. Therefore it is not easy to discriminate between the separate factors affecting intestinal absorption. Ittel *et al.* (1987) administered aluminum intravenously to uremic rats and non-uremic controls. The uremic rats excreted significantly less aluminum during the first 24 hr following injection than the controls. A significant negative correlation between aluminum excretion in urine and serum creatinine was observed; at higher serum creatinine, i.e., with reduced renal function, less aluminum was excreted. This suggested that as renal impairment progressed, there was less capacity to excrete systemic aluminum. After oral administration of aluminum by gastric lavage, however, the overall urine excretion of aluminum was significantly elevated in uremic rats compared with controls. These observations suggest that measuring urinary aluminum underestimates aluminum absorption; as renal failure progresses, there is even further enhancement of intestinal absorption than reflected by renal excretion. This suggests that other endogenous factors inherent in a renal condition are likely to be affecting intestinal absorption beyond elimination insufficiency. The involvement of calcium metabolism is likely, especially calcium regulating factors such as parathyroid hormone and vitamin D. Many efforts are concentrating on unraveling the factors constituting the role of aluminum absorption in kidney disorders, bearing the patient in mind, rather than studying the mechanistic aspects of intestinal absorption itself. Humans with normal renal function have a sufficient capacity to eliminate aluminum and to prevent aluminum loading from dietary sources or even from antacids. Even absorption enhancement by citrate does not lead to aluminum loading in humans with intact renal function. In fact, citrate is shown to enhance aluminum elimination.

5.6. Age

Pediatric patients are claimed to be more sensitive to oral aluminum loading than adults. Most pediatric cases of intoxication reported deal with patients with renal disorders

(Santos *et al.*, 1986). On the other hand, a growing number of cases of intoxication in very young children using aluminum-contaminated milk from infant formula have been reported (Woollard *et al.*, 1990). The sensitivity of the pediatric patients is claimed to be greater than adults because (1) the greatest part of brain development occurs during the first year of life, (2) the immature blood–brain barrier and the poorly developed gastrointestinal tract should be more permeable to aluminum, and (3) the immature formation and function of the kidneys would also contribute to a higher aluminum body load in children. In spite of the reports, no difference can be made between age- and dose-dependent toxicity. Thus far, the risk of aluminum absorption and intoxication appears to be greatest in pediatric patients because of the high dose of aluminum-containing phosphate binders (per kilogram of body weight) required to control hyperphosphatemia. Adults usually consume less than 3 mg/kg day of elemental aluminum for phosphate binding. In contrast, pediatric patients with chronic renal failure have often required aluminum at doses of 100 mg/kg day or more to control hyperphosphatemia and secondary hyperparathyroidism.

6. ORAL ALUMINUM: A RISK FACTOR?

Oral aluminum is a risk factor for (neuro)toxicity in both adult and pediatric patients with reduced or absent renal function and on high-dose therapy. Oral citrate, and also parenteral citrate, combined with oral aluminum therapy, is also a risk factor in the development of aluminum (neuro)toxicity (Molitoris *et al.*, 1989). Research on intestinal absorption seems to concentrate on clarifying the issue in patients with renal disorders on high-dose therapy and on proposing alternative phosphate-regulating therapies. Therefore the experimental data show a large bias toward clinical modeling and thus overlook mechanistic aspects. It should be realized that the aluminum species is of great importance in any study of the site and mechanism of intestinal absorption. The so-called physiological conditions used by many investigators do not guarantee any similarity between the species involved. Therefore, differences between the outcomes of the studies may often have a methodological basis.

In recognizing aluminum as the cause of dialysis-related neurotoxicity, a role for aluminum was also suggested in the etiology of a number of neurodegenerative disorders (Alzheimer's disease [AD] and the amyotrophic lateral sclerosis/Parkinsonism-dementia (ALS/PD) complex of Guam) (Ganrot, 1986; Reed and Brody, 1975; Reed *et al.*, 1975; Yanagihara *et al.*, 1983). Aluminum levels after analysis of bulk brain tissue of AD patients were increased in some cases (Ganrot, 1986), and focal accumulations of aluminum were observed in the central core of senile plaques in AD and in the majority of the neurofibrillary tangle (NFT)-bearing neurons (Perl and Brody, 1980). Colocalization of aluminum and silicon, probably in the form of aluminosilicates (Candy *et al.*, 1986), in the central region of senile plaque cores has also been detected. Aluminum is apparently associated with the neuropathological hallmarks of AD—the senile plaques and the NFTs. As yet it is not clear whether aluminum plays a causal or only a secondary role in the etiology of AD. Epidemiologic studies, though inconclusive, have implicated oral exposure to aluminum from drinking water as a factor contributing to the increased incidence of dementia. In certain areas of England and Norway, increased levels of aluminum in drinking water have been associated with an increased incidence of AD (Martyn *et al.*, 1989; Vogt, 1988).

In both the ALS and PD cases in Guam, in some studies elevated aluminum levels in the spinal cord and brain were reported after an analysis of bulk tissue (Yoshimasu *et al.*,

1976, 1980), while focal accumulations of aluminum were detected in the NFT-containing neurons. Colocalization of aluminum with silicon and calcium has been detected (Garruto *et al.*, 1984, 1985, 1986). Epidemiological studies have correlated the high incidence of ALS and PD in the Guam population to environmental areas with high aluminum and low calcium in the soil, indirectly incriminating oral exposure to aluminum. Thus far, no conclusive evidence for a causal or other role for aluminum in ALS/PD has been found.

The development of dialysis-related neurotoxicity is relatively acute as compared to the more chronic nature of AD and ALS/PD. In DE, brain accumulation of aluminum is higher and more diffuse and not focal—in plaques and NFT-bearing cells—as in AD and ALS/PD. The epidemiological evidence in AD and ALS/PD, though inconclusive, implies that oral exposure to aluminum is a potential etiological factor. As yet hard evidence to incriminate chronic oral aluminum exposure in these disorders is insufficient. To date a role for oral aluminum in DE is proven. A role in AD and ALS/PD is merely implied. A role for aluminum in some other degenerative disorders is even more speculative.

The contribution of oral aluminum from food, drinking water, and food-preparing procedures (pots, pans, coffee percolators, etc.) to neurotoxicity is not known. Long lists of concentrations of aluminum in food components have recently become available (Sherlock, 1989). The actual analysis of aluminum levels in these materials has long been hampered by analytical problems. Therefore, the data should be considered with caution. However, correlations between dietary habits (e.g., consuming foodstuffs with a high aluminum level on a regular base or using aluminum pans for food storage for many years) and neurological or neuropsychological aberrations are not convincing. It may be speculated that the chronic aspect of aluminum intoxication is as yet insufficiently explored. Studies looking for correlations between subtle neuropsychological effects in humans and certain dietary habits (food patterns, use of certain cooking utensils) may be performed to clarify possible relationships. Even chronic experimental studies in animals (dogs, rabbits) may be performed giving oral aluminum for years. Lack of knowledge on the various neurological disorders and on the involvement of aluminum in these disorders and the common use of aluminum materials have created unnecessary public concern. Due to the recent nature of the aluminum issue, and because the relationship between dementia and aluminum exposure is not fully elucidated, regulations are not complete. As of this date, the FAO/WHO Expert Committee on Food Additives has evaluated all data available and has suggested a weekly acceptable intake of 7.0 mg aluminum per kilogram of body weight (WHO Technical Report, 1989).

More research into the mechanism of intestinal absorption on the molecular level is required to define all factors that make aluminum available to the nervous system. To clarify the absence or presence of any relation between intestinal absorption and neurodegenerative disorders, more epidemiological and occupational studies have to be performed and more chronic animal experiments have to be considered.

REFERENCES

Adler, A.J., and Berlyne, G.M., 1985, Duodenal aluminum absorption in the rat: Effect of vitamin D, *Gastrointest. Liver Physiol.* 12:G209–G213.

Alfrey, A.C., and Froment, D.C., 1990, Dialysis encephalopathy, in: *Aluminum and Renal Failure* (M.E. De Broe, and J.W. Coburn, eds.), Kluwer Academic Publishers, Dordrecht, pp. 249–257.

Alfrey, A.C., Legendre, G.R., and Kaehny, W.D., 1976, The dialysis encephalopathy syndrome. Possible aluminum intoxication, *N. Engl. J. Med.* 294:184–188.

Andreoli, S.P., Bergstein, J.M., and Sherrard, D.J., 1984, Aluminum intoxication from aluminum-containing phosphate binders in children with azotemia not undergoing hemodialysis, *N. Engl. J. Med.* 310:1079–1084.

Berlyne, G.M., Ben-Ari, J., Pest, D., Weinberger, J., Stern, M., Gilmore, G.R., and Levine, R., 1970, Hyperaluminaemia from aluminium resins in renal failure, *Lancet* 2:494–496.

Berlyne, G.M., Yagil, R., Ben Ari, J., Weinberger, G., Knopf, E., and Danovitch, G.M., 1972, Aluminium toxicity in rats, *Lancet* 1:564–567.

Blaehr, H., Madsen, S., and Rud Andersen, J., 1986, Effect of iron-loading on intestinal aluminium absorption in chronic renal insufficiency, in: *Aluminium and other Trace Elements in Renal Disease* (A. Taylor, ed.), Bailliere Tindall, London, pp. 71–75.

Candy, J.M., Oakly, A.E., Klinowski, J., Carpenter, T.A., Perry, R.H., Atack, J.R., Perry, E.K., Blessed, G., Fairbank, A., and Edwardson, J.A., 1986, Aluminosilicates and senile plaque formation in Alzheimer's disease, *Lancet* 1:354–357.

Cannata, J.B., Suarez, C., and Cruesta, V., 1984, Aluminium gastrointestinal absorption: Is it modulated by the iron-absorptive mechanism?, *Proc. EDTA-ERA* 21:354–359.

Chan, J.C.M., Jacob, M., Brown, S., Savory, J., and Wills, M.R., 1988, Aluminum metabolism in rats: Effects of vitamin D, dihydrotachysterol, 1,25-dihydroxyvitamin D and phosphate binders, *Nephron* 48:61–64.

Cochran, M., Goddard, G., and Ludwigson, N., 1990, Aluminum absorption by rat duodenum: Further evidence of energy-dependent uptake, *Toxicol. Lett.* 51:287–294.

De Wolff, F.A., and Van der Voet, G.B., 1990, Intestinal absorption of aluminum, in: *Aluminum and Renal Failure* (M.E. de Broe, and J.W. Coburn, eds.), Kluwer Academic Publishers, Dordrecht, pp. 41–56.

Drüeke, T., Lacour, B., Touam, M., Basile, C., and Bourdon, R., 1985, Oral aluminum administration to uremic, hyperparathyroid, or vitamin D-supplemented rats, *Nephron* 39:10–17.

Elinder, C-G., and Sjögren, B., 1986, Aluminum, in: *Handbook on the Toxicology of Metals*, Volume II (L. Friberg, G.F. Nordberg, and V.B. Vouk, eds.), Elsevier, Amsterdam, pp. 1–25.

Feinroth, M., Feinroth, M.V., and Berlyne, G.M., 1982, Aluminum absorption in the rat everted gut sac, *Miner. Electrolyte Metab.* 8:29–35.

Flendrig, J.A., Kruis, H., and Das, H.A., 1976, Aluminium and dialysis dementia, *Lancet* 1:1235.

Froment, D.PH., Molitoris, B.A., Buddington, B., Miller, N., and Alfrey, A.C., 1989, Site and mechanism of enhanced gastrointestinal absorption of aluminum by citrate, *Kidney Int.* 36:978–984.

Ganrot, P.O., 1986, Metabolism and possible health effects of aluminum, *Env. Health Perspect.* 65:363–441.

Garruto, R.M., Fukatsu, R., Yanagihara, R., Carleton Gajdusek, D., Hook, G., and Fiori, C.E., 1984, Imaging of calcium and aluminium in neurofibrillary tangle-bearing neurons in Parkinsonism-dementia of Guam, *Proc. Natl. Acad. Sci. USA* 81:1875–1879.

Garruto, R.M., Swyt, C., Fiori, C.E., Yanagihara, R., and Carleton Gajdusek, D., 1985, Intraneuronal deposition of calcium and aluminium in amyotrophic lateral sclerosis of Guam, *Lancet* 2:1353.

Garruto, R.M., Swyt, C., Yanagihara, R., Fiori, C.E., and Carleton Gajdusek, D., 1986, Intraneuronal co-localization of silicon with calcium and aluminium in amyotrophic lateral sclerosis and Parkinsonism with dementia of Guam, *N. Engl. J. Med.* 315:711–712.

Gupta, S.K., Waters, D.H., and Gwilt, P.R., 1986, Absorption and disposition of aluminum in the rat, *J. Pharm. Sci.* 75:586–589.

Hewitt, C.D., Poole, C.L., Westervelt, F.B., Savory, J., and Wills, M.R., 1988, Risks of simultaneous therapy with oral aluminium and citrate compounds, *Lancet* 2:849.

Ittel, T.H., Buddington, B., Miller, N.L., and Alfrey, A.C., 1987, Enhanced gastrointestinal absorption of aluminum in uremic rats, *Kidney Int.* 32:821–826.

Kaehny, W.D., Hegg, A.P., and Alfrey, A.C., 1977, Gastrointestinal absorption of aluminum from aluminum-containing antacids, *N. Engl. J. Med.* 296:1389–1390.

Kirschbaum, B.B., and Schoolwerth, A.C., 1989a, Hyperaluminaemia associated with oral citrate and aluminium hydroxide, *Human Toxicol.* 8:45–47.

Kirschbaum, B.B., and Schoolwerth, A.C., 1989b, Acute aluminum toxicity associated with oral citrate and aluminum-containing antacids, *Am. J. Med. Sci.* 297:9–11.

Manis, J.G., and Schachter, D., 1962, Active transport of iron by intestine: Features of a two step mechanism, *Am. J. Physiol.* 203:73–80.

Martin, R.B., 1986, The chemistry of aluminum as related to biology and medicine, *Clin. Chem.* 32:1797–1806.

Martyn, C.N., Barker, D.J.P., Osmond, C., Harris, E.C., Edwardson, J.A., and Lacey, R.F., 1989, Geographical relation between Alzheimer's disease and aluminium in drinking water, *Lancet* 1:59–62.

Milliner, D.S., Malekzadeh, M., Lieberman, E., and Coburn, J.W., 1987, Plasma aluminum levels in pediatric dialysis patients: Comparison of hemodialysis and continuous ambulatory peritoneal dialysis, *Mayo Clin. Proc.* 62:269–274.

Molitoris, B.A., Froment, D.H., Mackenzie, T.A., Huffer, W.H., and Alfrey, A.C., 1989, Citrate: A major factor in the toxicity of orally administered aluminum compounds, *Kidney Int.* 36:949–953.

Perl, D.P., and Brody, A.R., 1980, Alzheimer's disease: X-ray spectrometric evidence of aluminum accumulation in neurofibrillary tangle bearing neurons, *Science* 208:297–299.

Provan, S.D., and Yokel, R.A., 1988a, Influence of calcium on aluminum accumulation by the rat jejunal slice, *Res. Commun. Chem. Pathol. Pharmacol.* 59:79–92.

Provan, S.D., and Yokel, R.A., 1988b, Aluminum uptake by the *in situ* rat gut preparation, *J. Pharm. Exp. Ther.* 245:928–931.

Reed, D.M., and Brody, J.A., 1975, Amyotrophic lateral sclerosis and Parkinsonism-Dementia on Guam, 1945–1972. I. Descriptive epidemiology, *Am. J. Epidemiol.* 101:287–301.

Reed, D.M., Torres, J.M., and Brody, J.A., 1975, Amyotrophic lateral sclerosis and Parkinsonism-dementia on Guam, 1945–1972. II. Familial and genetic studies, *Am. J. Epidemiol.* 101:302–310.

Salusky, I.B., Coburn, J.W., Paunier, L., Sherrard, D.J., and Fine, F.N., 1984, Role of aluminum hydroxide in raising serum aluminum levels in children undergoing continuous ambulatory peritoneal dialysis, *J. Pediatr.* 105:717–720.

Santos, F., Massie, M.D., and Chan, J.C.M., 1986, Risk factors in aluminum toxicity in children with chronic renal failure, *Nephron* 42:189–195.

Sedman, A.B., Miller, N.L., Warady, B.A., Lum, G.M., and Alfrey, A.C., 1984, Aluminum loading in children with chronic renal failure, *Kidney Int.* 26:201–204.

Sherlock, J.C., 1989, Aluminium in foods and the diet, in: *Aluminium in Food and the Environment* (Proceedings of a Symposium organised by the Environment and Food Chemistry Groups of the Royal Society of Chemistry, London, 17th May 1988) (R. Massey and D. Taylor, eds.), The Royal Society of Chemistry, Cambridge, pp. 68–76.

Sips, A., Van der Voet, G.B., and De Wolff, F.A., 1992, Intestinal absorption of aluminium: Effect of calcium and PTH (submitted).

Slanina, P., Falkeborn, Y., Frech, W., and Cedergren, A., 1984, Aluminium concentrations in the brain and bone of rats fed citric acid, aluminium citrate or aluminium hydroxide, *Food Chem. Toxicol.* 22:391–397.

Slanina, P., Frech, W., Bernhardson, A., Cedergren, A., and Mattson, P., 1985, Influence of dietary factors on aluminium absorption and retention in the brain and bone of rats, *Acta Pharmacol. Toxicol.* 56:331–336.

Slanina, P., Frech, W., Ekström, L-G., Lööf, L., Slorach, S., and Cedergren, A., 1986a, Dietary citric acid enhances absorption of aluminium in antacids, *Clin. Chem.* 32:539–541.

Slanina, P., Frech, W., Ekström, L-G., Lööf, L., Slorach, S., and Cedergren, A., 1986b, Gastrointestinal absorption of aluminum-containing drugs-influence of dietary factors, *Trace Elem. Med.* 2:128–129.

Smith, E.E., 1928, *Aluminum Compounds in Food*, PB Hoeber Inc., New York.

Spencer, H., Kramer, L., Norris, C., and Wiatrowski, E., 1980, Effect of aluminum hydroxide on fluoride metabolism, *Clin. Pharmacol. Therap.* 28:529–535.

Van der Voet, G.B., and De Wolff, F.A., 1984, A method of studying the intestinal absorption of aluminium in the rat, *Arch. Toxicol.* 55:168–172.

Van der Voet, G.B., and De Wolff, F.A., 1986, Intestinal absorption of aluminium in rats: Effect of intraluminal pH and aluminum concentration, *J. Appl. Toxicol.* 6:37–41.

Van der Voet, G.B., and De Wolff, F.A., 1987a, Intestinal absorption of aluminum in rats: Effect of sodium, *Arch. Toxicol. Suppl.* 11:231–235.

Van der Voet, G.B., and De Wolff, F.A., 1987b, The effect of di- and trivalent iron on the intestinal absorption of aluminium in rats, *Toxicol. Appl. Pharmacol.* 90:190–197.

Van der Voet, G.B., Marani, E., Tio, S., and De Wolff, F.A., 1991, Aluminium neurotoxicity, *Progr. Histochem. Cytochem.* 23:235–242.

Van der Voet, G.B., Van Ginkel, M.F., and De Wolff, F.A., 1989, Intestinal absorption of aluminum in rats: Stimulation by citric acid and inhibition by dinitrophenol, *Toxicol. Appl. Pharmacol.* 99:90–97.

Van der Voet, G.B., Verwey, P.E., Sips, A., and De Wolff, F.A., 1992, Intestinal absorption of aluminium: Effects of sodium and calcium (submitted).

Vogt, T., 1986, Water Quality and Health: Study of a Possible Relation Between Aluminium in Drinking Water and Dementia. Sosiale og økonomiske studier 61, Central Bureau of Statistics, Oslo, Norway, pp. 1–99.

Wilhelm, M., Jäger, D.E., and Ohnesorge, F.K., 1990, Aluminium toxicokinetics, *Pharmacol. Toxicol.* 66:4–9.

Woollard, D.C., Pybus, J., and Woollard, G.A., 1990, Aluminum concentrations in infant formulae, *Food Chem.* 37:81–94.

WHO Technical Report, 1989, Evaluation of Certain Food Additives and Contaminants (Thirty-Third Report of the Joint FAO/WHO Expert Committee on Food Additives), WHO Technical Report Series. No. 776, p. 27.

Yanagihara, R.T., Garruto, R.M., and Gajdusek, D.C., 1983, Epidemiological surveillance of amyotrophic lateral sclerosis and Parkinsonism-dementia in the Commonwealth of the Northern Mariana islands, *Ann. Neurol.* 13:79–86.

Yoshimasu, F., Uebayashi, Y., Yase, Y., Iwata, S., and Sasajima, K., 1976, Studies on amyotrophic lateral sclerosis by neutron activation analysis, *Folia Psychiat. Neurol. J.* 30:49–55.

Yoshimasu, F., Yasui, M., Yase, Y., Iwata, S., Carleton Gajdusek, D., Gibbs, C.J., and Chen, K-M., 1980, Studies on amyotrophic lateral sclerosis by neutron activation analysis—2. Comparative study of analytical results on Guam PD, Japanese ALS and Alzheimer disease cases, *Folia Psychiat. Neurol. J.* 34:75–82.

Chapter 4

Aluminum Ingestion

A Risk Factor for Alzheimer's Disease?

D.R. McLachlan and *Joan Massiah*

". . . the inhabitants, in general, make use of well water, so impregnated with nitre, or alum or some other villainous mineral, that it is equally ungrateful to the taste and mischievous to the constitution"

Bath, April 28, 1771
Humphry Clinker

"The bread I eat in London is a deleterious paste, mixed up with chalk, alum and bone-ashes; insipid to the taste and destructive to the constitution."

London, June 8, 1771
Humphry Clinker

1. INTRODUCTION

Tobias Smollett, author of Humphry Clinker (Smollett, 1771), was greatly concerned about the bodily effects of the use of double salts of aluminum with ammonium and potassium to purify water and as an anticaking agent in flour. However, the use of aluminum salts for the treatment of wounds and the purification of water extended to at least Roman times (Pliny). The first systematic investigation of aluminum toxicity demonstrated that the "point of attack" in aluminum poisoning was the central nervous system (Siem, 1886). In the past 20 years, knowledge about aluminum neurotoxicity and a possible role in Alzheimer's disease (AD) has rapidly expanded. It is now appropriate to address the question of whether aluminum is a risk factor for Alzheimer's disease and

D.R. McLachlan and *Joan Massiah* • Centre for Research in Neurodegenerative Diseases, University of Toronto, Toronto, Ontario, Canada M5S 1A8.
The Vulnerable Brain and Environmental Risks, Volume 2: Toxins in Food, edited by Robert L. Isaacson and Karl F. Jensen. Plenum Press, New York, 1992.

whether a public health action to reduce human exposure to aluminum would reduce the incidence of Alzheimer's disease.

Alzheimer's disease is a slowly progressive fatal neurodegenerative disorder of unknown etiology. The incidence of AD increases with increasing age. It is estimated that the incidence doubles every 5 years over the age of 60 years. Since this is the age group that is most rapidly increasing in numbers, AD will become more prevalent in the near future. AD is also a chronic illness with a prolonged survival time and represents a major cost to health care delivery systems throughout the world.

The causes of Alzheimer's disease have not yet been discovered, but both genetic and environmental factors appear important. Through linkage analysis in selected families, there appears to be a mutation on chromosome 21 that contributes to the disorder (St. George-Hyslop, 1987). More recently, Goate et al. (1991) have reported two families with a point mutation in exon 17 of the amyloid precursor protein, a gene also found on chromosome 21. Amyloid is an insoluble fibrinous protein and a histopathological hallmark of AD. This mutation results in an amino acid substitution of valine to isoleucine in the transmembrane domain of the β-amyloid precursor protein at a site two amino acids from the amyloid peptide. However, it is unknown at present whether this point mutation actually causes AD or whether the mutation is closely linked to another, as yet undiscovered, gene responsible for AD on chromosome 21. In addition, linkage analysis by St. George-Hyslop et al. (1990) indicates that AD is not a single homogeneous disorder and that mutations on chromosomes other than 21 are highly probable. The much more common sporadic form of AD appears to result from unidentified environmental factors.

While several environmental agents have been considered as candidates, only aluminum, a proven neurotoxin, has been found in the tissues of Alzheimer individuals at postmortem. Since aluminum has a very small crystal ionic radius, 0.51 Å, and a high charge, +3, the time of dissociation from a biological ligand is about 500,000 times longer than for metal ions normally involved in biological complexes, such as sodium, potassium, and magnesium. This long relaxation time may contribute to the toxicity of aluminum.

It is generally considered that aluminum has no biological function. However, we speculate that aluminum, in trace amounts, may have a physiological function. Bulk analysis of mammalian neocortical gray matter reveals a remarkably uniform aluminum concentration in the range of 1.1–1.9 μg/g dry weight. Despite large exposure over a lifetime to aluminum, healthy brain gray matter concentration remains relatively constant (Crapper et al., 1976). Furthermore, within neocortical gray matter, approximately 95% of measured aluminum in bulk tissue can be accounted for by nuclear content (Crapper et al., 1980). Within the nucleus, aluminum is not equally distributed among all nuclear structures. One nuclear compartment is chromatin, which is composed of DNA and DNA binding proteins. In human and other mammalian neocortical gray matter nuclei, there is a 15- to 18-fold higher concentration of aluminum in condensed heterochromatin than in less condensed euchromatin and histone H1-depleted chromatin. Applied aluminum, injected intracerebrally, also results in a marked increase in aluminum concentration in the highly condensed heterochromatin in cerebral nuclei in cats, rabbits, and rats (Crapper et al., 1980). It is possible that low concentrations of intranuclear aluminum are carefully regulated and have an important biological role. In a postmitotic, postdifferentiated cell, such as a cerebral neuron, it is known that certain genes within the heterochromatized, highly condensed chromatin fraction are unlikely to be transcribed throughout the lifetime of the neuron. Heterochromatization involves a number of processes, including crosslinking of proteins and DNA. This process requires, in part, a metal ion-protein DNA electrostatic bond. The high bioavailability of aluminum, small ionic radius, high charge, and prolonged relaxation time make this ion well suited to interact in a protein-DNA interaction, which could suppress gene expression in a postdifferentiated cell for the lifetime of the organism. We postulate that aluminum may have a normal function in brain tissue through an effect upon protein folding and electrostatic crosslinks between DNA and certain proteins, thereby contributing to heterochromatization. This could assist in permanently removing from biological expression genes not required for the specialized function of neurons. If aluminum does indeed have a normal role in gene suppression, the concentration of this potentially toxic ion must be carefully regulated and maintained at a constant level throughout the lifetime of the organism by some as yet undiscovered regulatory mechanism. The data on bulk aluminum content in mammalian gray matter supports this hypothesis and suggests that sophisticated homeostatic mechanisms exist to regulate the amount of aluminum gaining access to the central nervous system. While the molecular mechanisms responsible for homeostasis of trivalent metal ions has not been elucidated, we postulate that this becomes defective in Alzheimer's disease (AD). Under these circumstances, environmental exposure to aluminum becomes a risk factor for the expression of the disease.

2. ALUMINUM AS A RISK FACTOR FOR ALZHEIMER'S DISEASE

Regardless of the exact molecular mechanism, what is the evidence in support of aluminum as a risk factor for AD? We submit that four independent lines of evidence support the hypothesis that aluminum is a risk factor for this common disorder. Briefly stated, the four independent arguments arise from the disciplines of toxicology, neurochemistry, epidemiology, and clinical therapeutics.

Toxicological studies employing estimates of the minimal lethal concentration of intracerebral aluminum at the time of death indicate that concentrations of 5–6 μg/g dry weight are lethal (Crapper and Tomko, 1975). This concentration is only four times greater than the naturally occurring concentration. We believe the importance of these toxicological studies is that approximately 23% of regions from Alzheimer-affected neocortical gray matter regions contain 5 μg/g dry weight or more of aluminum (Crapper *et al.*, 1976). Thus, the gap between naturally occurring concentrations of aluminum in healthy brain tissue (about 1.5 μg/g dry weight) gray matter and the concentration that is lethal to cats and rabbits is narrow. Rodents and some primates are more resistant to aluminum neurotoxicity than rabbits and cats. Indeed, the brain of healthy humans is able to tolerate bulk brain aluminum concentrations of 8 μg/g of aluminum or greater before developing neurological signs, as in patients on dialysis associated with renal failure. At brain concentrations in the range of 20–40 μg/g dry weight (Alfry, 1980), neurological deficits become marked. Subcellular fractionation and aluminum analysis from brains with dialysis dementia indicate that the nuclei do not contain elevated concentrations (Crapper *et al.*, 1980), whereas Alzheimer nuclei do contain elevated concentrations. When nuclear compartments are examined by employing light micrococcal nuclease digestion of chromatin to release fractions enriched in active genes, dinucleosomes released by this procedure reveal up to a 10-fold increase in aluminum content in Alzheimer-affected neocortex (Lukiw, unpublished data), but no increase in nucleosomes is seen in brains that have a history of dialysis dementia. Both of these studies indicate that aluminum gains access to compartments in Alzheimer's disease from which it is excluded in a number of other neurodegenerative diseases. While it is certain that the healthy human brain can tolerate aluminum concentrations approaching those of the aluminum-resistant animal, such as the rat, there is no certainty that the lower bulk concentrations found in Alzheimer's disease are not associated with neurotoxicity as found in aluminum-sensitive species, such as the cat and rabbit. While we submit that toxicological studies raise grave concerns about the possible neurotoxic effects of aluminum in Alzheimer's disease, they do not establish the precise risk of neurotoxicity.

3. ALUMINUM-INDUCED NEUROCHEMICAL BRAIN CHANGES

A second group of observations supporting the idea that aluminum is important in the pathogenesis of Alzheimer's disease come from the analysis of the many biochemical and neurochemical processes in brain tissue disturbed by elevated concentrations of aluminum. A partial list of aluminum toxic effects upon nuclear, cytoplasmic, cytoskeletal, membrane, and synaptic neurotransmitter functions has been reviewed elsewhere (McLachlan, 1989; McLachlan *et al.*, 1990). Which of the many neurotoxic effects of aluminum is central to the neurotoxic action in Alzheimer's disease has not been clearly established. There are several candidate toxic effects that should be considered. Particularly important is the observation that human neuroblastoma cells in culture treated with low doses of aluminum express epitopes that react with an antibody to an abnormally phosphorylated microtubule-associated protein, tau, which is also found in Alzheimer's disease (Guy *et al.*, 1991). Considerable evidence now indicates that one of the histopathological hallmarks of AD, neurofibrillary tangles, are composed of polymers of abnormally phosphorylated tau (Lee *et al.*, 1991). The antibody employed in the aluminum effect upon neuroblastoma cells reacted specifically with AD neurofibrillary tangles. In AD, the hyperphosphorylation of tau precedes the formation of tangles, and since aluminum in healthy neurons induces hyperphosphorylation of tau, aluminum may be involved in the process of Alzheimer-type neurofibrillary degeneration at an early stage, rather than as a terminal event of a dying neuron. Perl (1989), using a sensitive time-of-flight mass spectrometer, reported statistically significant elevations of aluminum restricted to neurofibrillary tangles AD. Perl prepared the tissue for analysis in the absence of tissue fixatives to exclude aluminum contamination. He also examined tissues with Alzheimer-type neurofibrillary degeneration from the island of Guam and the United States, and in all cases found increases in aluminum in neurofibrillary tangles, sometimes to very high concentrations, approaching 300 μg/g. The evidence suggests the possibility that aluminum accumulation may occur as an early event in the formation of Alzheimer neurofibrillary tangles, and local concentration may be very high. However, a direct cause-and-effect relationship has not been established, and aluminum does not produce paired helical filaments in laboratory models.

In vitro, aluminum at low concentrations stimulates adenylate cyclase, possibly as AlF_4^-, on the guanine nucleotide-binding regulatory component of the enzyme (Sternweis and Gilman, 1982). Chronic oral aluminum administration in rats results in significant increases in cyclic AMP levels (Johnson and Jope, 1987) and hyperphosphorylation of microtubule-associated protein-2 (MAP-2) and the 200-kDa neurofilament subunit (Johnson and Jope, 1988). In addition, there was a significant elevation in the basal and cyclic AMP-dependent phosphorylation of 11–12 other endogenous proteins (Johnson *et al.*, 1990). The activity of protein kinase C was also increased in the particulate fraction. These workers speculate that one important neurotoxic effect of aluminum may be mediated through chronic hyperphosphorylation and thus is consistent with the findings reported by Guy *et al.* (1991). Further work is required to define exactly how closely aluminum-induced hyperphosphorylation resembles what is found in AD.

The accumulation of aluminum within nuclear compartments in AD may also be of functional importance (Crapper *et al.*, 1980). AD is associated with a change in the structure of chromatin, characterized by a shift towards heterochromatization. This change in chromatin was not found in 10 other neurodegenerative diseases investigated (McLachlan *et al.*, 1989). The change in chromatin structure results in reduced transcription of certain neuron-specific genes, including the gene coding for low molecular weight protein of neurofilaments (Clark *et al.*, 1989; McLachlan *et al.*, 1988). The fraction containing repressed HNF-L genes released by micrococcal nuclease digestion contains dinucleosomes with a 10-fold increase in aluminum content (McLachlan *et al.*, 1989). Aluminum increases the affinity of binding of certain transcription repressor proteins to DNA and may contribute to gene repression (Lukiw *et al.*, 1987); however, some other event probably occurs first to allow the docking of repressor proteins to a particular DNA site. As a repressor of gene function, we visualize aluminum replacing magnesium at key DNA-protein binding sites. In this complex series of molecular events associated with gene repression, aluminum may play a pivotal role and cannot be overlooked as an important factor in the AD degenerative process.

4. EPIDEMIOLOGY: ALUMINUM INGESTION AND ALZHEIMER'S DISEASE

Six epidemiological studies have concluded that the higher the bioavailable aluminum in drinking water, the higher the incidence of AD in a geographic region (Flaten, 1990; Leventhal, 1986; Martyn *et al.*, 1989; Michel *et al.*, 1991; Still and Kelly, 1980; Vogt, 1986). A single epidemiological study suggests that exposure to aluminum-containing antiperspirants is also a risk factor for AD (Graves *et al.*, 1990). Each of the epidemiological studies can be criticized. Epidemiological studies establish association, but do not establish cause-and-effect relations. Ideal epidemiological studies would involve histopathological confirmation of the incidence of sporadic and familial AD in a geographic region, together with the aluminum species and organic aluminum ligands in drinking water, food, pharmaceuticals, dusts, and other sources. Factors influencing aluminum uptake, such as silicon and fluoride concentration, must also be measured. Such studies will be extremely costly to conduct and require several years of analysis before results become available. However, each of the epidemiological studies currently available conclude that aluminum is a risk factor for AD. The more rigorous the diagnostic criteria, and therefore, the diagnostic accuracy for AD, the greater the risk of an association between aluminum and AD. For instance, the lowest diagnostic accuracy is likely to be associated with the study conducted by Vogt (1986) in which death certificates were employed for the establishment of senile dementia. Here the risk was 1.48 times greater for high-aluminum compared to low-aluminum water ingestion. In contrast, the highest diagnostic accuracy is likely to be associated with the Michel *et al.* study in which the most appropriate clinical tests for AD appear to have been applied. The risk in this study was 4.53 times greater for populations exposed to 100 μg/l compared to populations exposed to 10 μg/l of aluminum in the drinking water.

A case control study involving 130 matched pairs of carefully diagnosed Alzheimer patients and controls concluded that lifetime exposure to aluminum through anti-perspirants was a risk factor for AD. There was a statistically significant trend for higher risk with increasing frequency of use, and the odds ratio for the highest tertile was 3.2. For each of the epidemiological studies relating aluminum in the drinking water to AD, the risk is relatively low, although statistically significant, compared to the association between smoking and carcinoma of the lung. Nevertheless, the fact that each of the six epidemiological studies concludes that a positive correlation exists between aluminum exposure and AD strongly supports the hypothesis that aluminum is an active factor in the pathogenesis of this disorder.

Aluminum exposure in the workplace and in the presence of renal failure appears to be a risk factor for altered cognitive function. Several new studies support this conclusion. The dialysis encephalopathy syndrome that is unaccompanied by any neuropathological changes is a well-recognized entity (Alfry et al., 1976). In dialysis encephalopathy there are markedly elevated serum aluminum concentrations, upwards of 200 μg/l, which occur in the presence of kidney failure. However, much lower concentrations are now recognized to be associated with impaired cognitive function. The performance of 27 long-term hemodialysis patients who had only a mildly raised serum aluminum concentration (mean, 59 μg/l; normal, <10 μg/l) was impaired on six tests of psychomotor function compared to matched controls (Altmann et al., 1989). An independent study revealed that signs of neurological dysfunction and impaired memory occurred in dialysis patients with a positive desferrioxamine challenge test (Sprague et al., 1988). These observations indicate that even moderate elevations in serum concentration are a risk for impaired cognitive function.

Interestingly, three recent studies (Kellet et al., 1986; Naylor et al., 1989; Van Rhijn et al., 1989) have demonstrated statistically significant elevated aluminum concentrations in the serum or whole blood in AD patients compared to carefully matched control patients. Since transferrin is the main serum transport protein for aluminum (Birchall and Chappell, 1987; Trapp, 1983), this raises the possibility that aluminum, even in low concentrations, may slowly gain access to aluminum-sensitive brain compartments, particularly in the presence of the antecedent events that may have initiated the AD disease process.

Rifat et al. (1990) reported consistent and significant differences in the performance of cognitive tests in miners exposed to aluminum dust in the air. The Mini-Mental State Examination, Ravens Colored Progressive Matrices Test, and Symbol Digit Modalities Tests were employed to measure general cognitive function in a group of miners exposed to finely ground alumina in the air. Alumina of particle size <2 μm was dispensed as a prophylaxis against silicosis to groups of Northern Ontario gold miners over the period 1944–1979. The alumina powder was dispensed in the miners' clothing change rooms for 10 min prior to each underground shift at a recommended concentration of 35 gm/m³. Applying current analytical techniques (Mitchell, personal communication), the powder was found to contain polymorphs of aluminum trihydroxide, bayerite, gibbsite, and norstrandite, and triangular plates of elemental aluminum, together with traces of iron. The annual alveolar burden of aluminum was estimated at 375 mg. Scores of 17 out of 30 for the MiniMental State Examination and scores of less than 2.5 standard deviations below the norm for individuals over the age of 65 years and with less than 12 years of formal education were used to assess the risk for cognitive impairment. Employing these criteria, the risk was 4.5 times greater for miners exposed to aluminum for more than 20 years, 3.1 for 10–20 years of exposure, and 2.4 for 1–10 years of exposure compared to miners with equal underground time who were not exposed to the aluminum dust.

The cognitive defects are likely to be due to aluminum rather than some unidentified confounding factor, since blood and urine concentrations of aluminum workers exposed to aluminum flake powders indicate that this element is retained and stored in several body compartments (Ljunggren et al., 1991). Clinical and histopathological examinations have not been completed on the miners exposed to aluminum dust, and no conclusion can be reached as to whether the cognitive deficits are more closely related to dialysis encephalopathy, a severe disorder in cortical function without a histopathological correlate, or whether the cognitive deficit is associated with an increased risk of Alzheimer's disease with the characteristic histopathology of this condition. Despite our incomplete understanding of aluminum-induced cognitive deficits, each of these studies indicate that aluminum exposure is a risk factor.

Which of the many neurotoxic effects of aluminum may account for the cognitive deficit is uncertain. Experimentally, cats (Crapper and Dalton 1973a, 1973b), rabbits (Pendlebury et al., 1988; Petit et al., 1980; Rabe et al., 1982; Solomon and Pendlebury, 1988; Yokel, 1983), and rats (Lipman et al., 1988) injected intracranially or fed orally with aluminum may demonstrate learning and memory disturbances prior to other neurological signs, although two of these species, the cat and rabbit, develop aluminum-induced 10-nm neurofibrillary tangles in some neurons. The rat is more resistant to these histopathological markers for aluminum neurotoxicity, but not to the toxic effects upon learning and memory. The formation of neurofibrillary tangles does not appear to be essential for the development of cognitive deficits. For example, hippocampal slices prepared from rabbits 5–7 days after intracranial aluminum injection demonstrated a reduced ability to develop long-term potentiation, a change thought to be analogous to the plastic changes associated with learning and memory phenomena (Farnell et al., 1985). Changes in long-term potentiation occurred in both the apical and basilar dendritic inputs to CA1 hippocampal neurons. By 10 days post aluminum injection, there was a very significant decline in long-term potentiation. These electrophysiological changes correspond in time to the observed onset of behavioral changes in performance of memory and learning tasks in the intact animal. Interestingly, increasing the in vitro calcium concentration in the bath from the control value of 2.4 mM to 4.8 mM restored long-term potentiation in hippocampal slices taken from the early and middle stages of the encephalopathy to near-control values. This suggests that the aluminum effect upon long-term potentiation operates upon the component of the molecular mechanisms responsible for plasticity through an effect mediated by calcium. The mechanism responsible for the calcium effect is largely unknown; however, the calcium conductance system is known to become active during membrane depolarization in the range of -20 to 0 mV. These high-voltage calcium conductance channels appear to be localized to the dendrites of hippocampal CA1 neurons and are completely blocked when intracellular ionic calcium is increased from the control concentration of 0.05 μM to 6.0 μM. It is to be emphasized that the CA1 hippocampal neurons involved in these studies of long-term potentiation do not show any morphological changes and, in particular, do not exhibit 10-nm neurofibrillary degeneration. Thus the neurofibrillary degeneration component of aluminum neurotoxicity is not an essential marker for the alteration in molecular events associated with altered learning-memory phenomena. We submit that this strengthens the concern about the finding of elevated concentrations of aluminum in the brain tissues of Alzheimer patients. Further, these observations weaken the argument that aluminum cannot be important in the disease, because aluminum induces neither of the hallmarks of Alzheimer's disease, paired helical filaments or amyloid formation, in experimental preparations.

5. ION-SPECIFIC CHELATION AND CLINICAL COURSE OF ALZHEIMER'S DISEASE

A fourth independent line of evidence has tested the hypothesis that if aluminum is an important pathological factor in AD, removal of aluminum by ion-specific chelating agents should alter the progression of the disease. We have recently reported that desferrioxamine, 125 mg every 12 hours, 5 days per week for a 2-year period, results in a slowing, but not complete arrest, of the cognitive deficits associated with AD (McLachlan *et al.*, 1991). In a phase II drug trial paradigm, 48 people living at home with probable AD were assigned randomly into three groups: a desferrioxamine-treated group, oral lecithin, and no treatment. Homeopathic doses of lecithin, 500 mg b.i.d., were employed as a placebo.

The results of this pilot experiment indicate that all groups deteriorated, but there was no statistical difference in the average rate of decline over a 2-year interval between the lecithin and the no-treatment groups. However, when the data from these latter two groups was taken together and compared to the desferrioxamine-treated group, there was a statistically significant difference in the rate of deterioration and end-point scores between the treated and no-treatment groups. The average 2-year decline was 25% of the maximum score in the desferrioxamine-treated group compared to the average decline of 57% for the no-treatment group. While the results of this initial study are encouraging, a double-blind, placebo-controlled multicentered trial must now be conducted to confirm these results. However, based on the currently available evidence, the trivalent metal ion binding agent, desferrioxamine, appears to slow the progression of the dementia of Alzheimer's disease. These results further support the hypothesis that aluminum is a significant toxic environmental factor in the pathogenesis of the disease.

No single experiment or observation establishes a cause-and-effect relation between aluminum and altered cognitive function in AD. However, the sum of the evidence concerning aluminum neurotoxicity strengthens the position that ingestion of high amounts of aluminum, in certain forms, is both a risk factor for AD and a contributor to the progression of the disease. Furthermore, we conclude that while a complete and totally convincing argument cannot be made at this time, sufficient evidence is now available that a concerned person may wish to limit aluminum ingestion. Since information on aluminum content in food, cosmetics, pharmaceuticals, and water is not generally available, we recommend that a survey of all products to which humans are exposed be conducted. Such a survey should be undertaken by laboratories employing internationally recognized analytical techniques and internationally accepted analytical standards. The results of such a survey should then be made available to the public for political discussion. A decision will have to be made on whether legislation is required to limit aluminum exposure or whether the free market itself will regulate exposure.

The end goal is to limit aluminum ingestion. There are now several areas in which the presence of elevated aluminum is known. Complex studies are required to bring about necessary change at some levels; simple adjustments in life-style can significantly reduce aluminum consumption at the personal level.

There are many sources of aluminum in the present-day environment other than naturally occurring aluminum. Naturally occurring water at neutral acidity is generally low in aluminum content. However, aluminum is often employed in processing water for large communities (Miller *et al.*, 1984). From evidence produced in epidemiological studies, it would seem reasonable to limit potable water to 50 μg/l for the present, with a long-term goal of 10 μg/l. Filtered municipal water resulting in low aluminum content (<10 μg/l) is perhaps preferable to commercial bottled water with very low aluminum content, because many municipalities carefully monitor water for bacteria and many other toxic substances. Unfortunately, after processing, secondary water-pumping equipment in tall buildings may add aluminum to the water supply, despite the careful regulation of aluminum content of source water.

The concern over aluminum migrating into water from kettles has abated, since most kettles are now stainless steel or lined with Teflon (Greger, 1985). Nevertheless, boiled unused water should be discarded.

The outer skin of many root vegetables may be naturally high in aluminum; they should be carefully cleaned or peeled. Tomatoes (Greger *et al.*, 1985) and rhubarb (Coriat *et al.*, 1986) cooked in aluminum pots take up considerable amounts of aluminum. The leaves of herbs contain less aluminum than the stems.

At present, the chemical nature of food additives and coloring agents is not made public. These additives, such as aluminum salts used in pickling, are an important source of dietary aluminum. Other foods with aluminum-containing additives are baked goods with chemical leavening agents, processed cheeses, cocoa, and some nondairy creamers (Greger, 1985). Partially prepared foods and mixes are frequently held in that state through the inclusion of additives. Aluminum is also added to certain table salts and baking powders as an anticaking agent.

Tea, including herbal types, is reported to be high in aluminum content (Flaten and Odegård, 1988) and may represent a significant bioavailable source. Certain decaffeination processes for coffee add aluminum. Acidic cola drinks may remove aluminum from glass bottles, but not from Teflon-lined aluminum cans.

A number of infant formulas contain high amounts of aluminum. At present, neither the bioavailability nor the absorption of aluminum by infants is completely documented. However, Bishop *et al.* (1989) draw attention to the fact that both bone and brain growth in early infancy may be impaired by aluminum deposit derived from infant formulas.

Food may take up aluminum from aluminum containers, foil wrap, foil containers, and cooking pots. Evidence of this migration may be seen when tiny holes appear in the foil wrap used to store frozen foods.

Many deodorant products, including some toilet soaps and toothpastes, contain aluminum that may be absorbed. Antiperspirants, for the most part, are high in aluminum content. One epidemiological study suggests that aluminum-containing antiperspirants is a risk for AD (Graves *et al.*, 1990). In a trade magazine, Fox (1991) reported a formula for an unnamed antiperspirant that contained 26.7% zirconium aluminum glycine hydroxy chloride.

Most facial makeup has aluminum in it. Bright-red lipsticks, in particular, tend to contain large amounts. Aluminum is often part of the composition of creams and lotions. Though the skin is a good barrier, the aluminum in these products may be absorbed in small amounts. More importantly, some are inhaled, as are aerosol contaminants. Olfactory nerve retrograde transport of aluminum compounds has been demonstrated by Perl and Good (1987).

Nonprescription drugs, such as antacids, buffered aspirin, and antidiarrheal compounds, usually contain aluminum. Frequent and long-term use of these aids can result in raised levels of aluminum in the body. This can be especially damaging to premature infants under certain circumstances (Puntis *et al.*, 1989).

Intravenous fluids frequently contain fairly high concentrations of aluminum. Individuals at risk here are those with poor renal function and premature infants. Small children on intravenous sera with rapidly developing skeletal and nervous systems may be susceptible to neurological damage (Sedman *et al.*, 1985) with long-range effects. The potential neurotoxicity of aluminum absorbed from alum-precipitated allergenic extracts and toxoids requires investigation.

The cost of reducing human exposure to aluminum will be high, but the data seem to justify such an expenditure. Manufacturers and food processors should be encouraged to develop more sensitive measurements of potentially neurotoxic additives, such as aluminum, and acceptable levels of aluminum in products must be established. Alternatives to the use of aluminum in widely used products should be found.

ACKNOWLEDGMENTS.   Supported by the Ontario Mental Health Foundation, Health and Welfare Canada, Medical Research Council of Canada, and the Scottish Rite Charitable Foundation.

REFERENCES

Alfry, A.C., 1980, Aluminum metabolism in uremia, *Neurotoxicology* 1:43–53.

Alfry, A.C., LeGendre, G.R., and Kaehny, W.D., 1976, The dialysis encephalopathy syndrome. Possible aluminum intoxication, *N. Engl. J. Med.* 294:184–188.

Altmann, P., Dhanesha, U., Hamon, C., Cunningham, J., Blair, J., and Marsh, F., 1989, Disturbance of cerebral function by aluminum in haemodialysis patients without overt aluminum toxicity, *Lancet* 1:7–11.

Birchall, J.D., and Chappell, J.S., 1988, Aluminum, chemical physiology, and Alzheimer's disease, *Lancet* 1:1008–1010.

Bishop, N., McGraw, M., and Ward, N., 1989, Aluminum in infant formulas, *Lancet* 1:490.

Clark, A.W., Krekoski, C.A., Parhad, I.M., Liston, D., Julien, J-P., and Hoar, D.I., 1989, Altered expression of genes for amyloid and cytoskeletal proteins in Alzheimer cortex, *Ann. Neurol.* 25(4):331–339.

Coriat, A.M., and Gillard, R.D., 1986, Beware the cups that cheer, *Nature* 321:570 (letter).

Crapper, D.R., and Dalton, A.J., 1973a, Alterations in short term retention, conditioned avoidance response acquisition and motivation following aluminum induced neurofibrillary degeneration, *Physiol. Behav.* 10:925–933.

Crapper, D.R., and Dalton, A.J., 1973b, Aluminum induced neurofibrillary degeneration, brain electrical activity and alterations in acquisition and retention, *Physiol. Behav.* 10:935–945.

Crapper, D.R., and Tomko, G., 1975, Neuronal correlates of an encephalopathy associated with aluminum neurofibrillary degeneration, *Brain Res.* 97:253–264.

Crapper, D.R., Krishnan, S.S., and Quittkat, S., 1976, Aluminum, neurofibrillary degeneration and Alzheimer disease, *Brain* 99:67–79.

Crapper, D.R., Quittkat, S., Krishnan, S.S., Dalton, A.J., and De Boni, U., 1980, Intranuclear aluminum content in Alzheimer's disease, dialysis encephalopathy, *Acta Neuropathol. (Berlin)* 50:19–24.

Farnell, B.J., Crapper McLachlan, D.R., Baimbridge, K., De Boni, U., Wong, L., and Wood, P.L., 1985, Calcium metabolism and aluminum encephalopathy, *Exp. Neurol.* 88:68–83.

Flaten, T.P., 1990, Geographical associations between aluminum in drinking water and registered death rates with dementia (including Alzheimer's disease, Parkinson's disease and amyotrophic lateral sclerosis) in Norway, *Environ. Geochem. Health* 12:152–167.

Flaten, T.P., and Odegård, M., 1988, Tea, aluminum and Alzheimer's disease, *Food Chem. Toxicol.* 26(11–12):959–960.

Fox, C., 1991, Technically speaking, *Cosmet. Toiletries* 106(3):26.

Goate, A., Chartier-Harlin, M-C., Mullan, M., Brown, J., Crawford, F., Fidani, L., Giuffra, L., Haynes, A., Irving, N., James, L., Mant, R., Newton, P., Rooke, K., Roques, P., Talbot, C., Williamson, R., Rossor, M., Owen, M., and Hardy, J., 1991, Segregation of a missense mutation in the amyloid precursor protein gene with familial Alzheimer's disease, *Nature* 349:704–706.

Graves, A.B., White, E., Koepsell, T.D., Reifler, B.V., van Belle, G., and Larson, E.B., 1990, The association between aluminum-containing products and Alzheimer's disease, *J. Clin. Epidemiol.* 43(1):35–44.

Greger, J.L., 1985, Aluminum content of the American diet, *Food Tech.* 39(5):73–80.

Greger, J.L., Goetz, W., and Sullivan, D., 1985, Aluminum levels in foods cooked and stored in aluminum pans, trays and foil, *J. Food Protect.* 48(9):772–777.

Guy, S.P., Jones, D., Mann, D.M.A., and Itzhaki, R.F., 1991, Human neuroblastoma cells treated with aluminium express an epitope associated with Alzheimer's disease neurofibrillary tangles, *Neurosci. Lett.* 121:166–168.

Johnson, G.V.M., and Jope, R.S., 1987, Aluminum alters cyclic AMP and cyclic GMP levels but not presynaptic cholinergic markers in rat brain *in vivo*, *Brain Res.* 403:1–6.

Johnson, G.V.M., and Jope, R.S., 1988, Phosphorylation of rat brain cytoskeletal proteins is increased after orally administered aluminum, *Brain Res.* 456:95–103.

Johnson, G.V.W., Gogdill, K.W., and Jope, R.S., 1990, Oral aluminum alters *in vitro* protein phosphorylation and kinase activities in rat brain, *Neurobiol. Aging* 11:206–216.

Kellet, J.M., Taylor, A., and Oram, J.J., 1986, Aluminosilicates and Alzheimer's disease, *Lancet* 1:682.

Lee, V.M.Y., Balin, B.J., Otvos, L., and Trojanowski, J.Q., 1991, A68: A major subunit of paired helical filaments and derivatized forms of normal tau, *Science* 252:675–678.

Leventhal, G.H., 1986, Alzheimer's Disease and Environmental Aluminum in Maryville and Morristown, Tennessee, PhD Thesis, University of Tennessee.

Lipman, J.J., Colowick, S.P., Lawrence, P.L., and Abumrad, N.N., 1988, Aluminum induced encephalopathy in the rat, *Life Sci.* 42:863–875.

Ljunggren, K.G., Lidums, V., and Sjögren, B., 1991, Blood and urine concentrations of aluminum among workers exposed to aluminum flake powders. *Br. J. Ind. Med.* 48:106–109.

Lukiw, W.J., Kruck, T.P.A., and McLachlan, D.R., 1987, Alterations in human linker histone-DNA binding in the presence of aluminum salts *in vitro* and in Alzheimer's disease, *Neurotoxicology* 8(2):291–302.

Martyn, C.N., Barker, D.J.P., Osmond, C., Harris, E.C., Edwardson, J.A., and Lacey, R.F., 1989, Geographical relation between Alzheimer's disease and aluminum in drinking water, *Lancet* 1:59–62.

McLachlan, D.R., Crapper, Lukiw, W.J., Wong. L., Bergeron, C., and Bech-Hansen, N.T., 1988, Selective messenger RNA reduction in Alzheimer's disease, *Mol. Brain Res.* 3:255–262.

McLachlan, D.R.C., 1989, Aluminum neurotoxicity: Criteria for assigning a role in Alzheimer's disease, in: *Environmental Chemistry and Toxicology of Aluminum* (T.E. Lewis, ed.), Lewis Publishers, South Main, MI, pp. 299–317.

McLachlan, D.R.C., Lukiw, W.J., and Kruck, T.P.A., 1989, New evidence for an active role of aluminum in Alzheimer's disease, *Can. J. Neurol. Sci.* 16:490–497.

McLachlan, D.R.C., Lukiw, W.J., and Kruck, T.P.A., 1990, Aluminum altered transcription and the pathogenesis of Alzheimer's disease, *Environ. Geochem. Health* 12:103–114.

McLachlan, D.R.C., Dalton, A.J., Kruck, T.P.A., Bell, M.Y., Smith, W.L., Kalow, W., and Andrews, D.F., 1991, Intramuscular desferrioxamine and Alzheimer's disease, *Lancet* 337:1304–1308.

Michel, P., Commenges, D., Dartigues, J.F., Gagnon, M., Barberger-Gateau, P., Letenneur, L., and the Paquid Research Group, 1990, Study of the relationship between aluminum in drinking water and risk of Alzheimer's disease, in: *Alzheimer's Disease: Basic Mechanisms, Diagnosis and Therapeutics* (K. Iqbal, D.R.C. McLachlan, B. Winblad, and H.M. Wisniewski, eds.), John Wiley, Chichester, pp. 387–392.

Miller, R.G., Kopfler, F.C., Kelty, K.C., Stober, J.A., and Ulmer, N.S., 1984, The occurrence of aluminum in drinking water, *J. Am. Waterworks Assoc.* 76(1):84–91.

Naylor, G.J., Smith, A.H.W., McHarg, A., Walker, P.J., Shepherd, B., Ward, N.I., and Harper, M., 1989, Raised serum aluminum concentration in Alzheimer's disease, *Trace Elements Med.* 6(3):93095.

Pendlebury, W.W., Perl, D.P., Schwentker, A., Pingree, T.M., and Solomon, P.R., 1988, Aluminum-induced neurofibrillary degeneration disrupts acquisition of the rabbit's classically conditioned nictitating membrane response, *Behav. Neurosci.* 102(5):615–620.

Perl, D.P., 1989, Aluminum and Alzheimer neurofibrillary degeneration. Abstract. Aluminum and Health International Symposium, Orlando, FL.

Perl, D.P., and Good, P.F., 1987, Uptake of aluminum into central nervous system along nasal-olfactory pathways, *Lancet* 1:1028.

Petit, T.L., Biederrman, G.B., and McMullen, P.A., 1980, Neurofibrillary degeneration, dying back and learning-memory deficits after aluminum administration, implications for brain aging, *Exp. Neurol.* 67:152–162.

Pliny, C.S., 1950, in: *De Re Metallica*, by G. Agricola, Translated by M.C. and L.H. Hoover. Dover Publications, New York, pp. 566–567 (footnotes).

Puntis, J.W., Ballantine, N.E., and Durbin, G.M., 1989, Raised plasma aluminum in an infant on antacid, *Lancet* 2:923 (letter).

Rabe, A., Lee, M.H., Shek, J., and Wisniewski, H.M., 1982, Learning deficit in immature rabbits with aluminum-induced neurofibrillary changes, *Exp. Neurol.* 76:441–446.

Rifat, S., Eastwood, M.R., McLachlan, D.R.C., and Corey, P.N., 1990, Evidence regarding the effect of prolonged aluminum exposure on cognitive function, *Lancet* 336:1162–1165.

St. George-Hyslop, P.H., Haines, J.L., Farrer, L.A., Polinsky, R., Van Broeckhoven, C., Goate, A., Crapper McLachlan, D.R., Orr, H., Bruni, A.C., Sorbi, S., Rainero, I., Foncin, J-F., Pollen, D., Cantu, J-M., Tupler, R., Voskresenskay, N., Mayeux, R., Growdon, J., Fried, V.A., Myers, R.H., Nee, L., Backhovens, H., Martin, J-J., Rossor, M., Owen, M.F., Mullan, M., Percy, M.E., Karlinsky, H., Rich, S., Heston, L., Montesi, M., Mortilla, M., Nacmias, N., Gusella, J.F., Hardy, J.A., and other members of the FAD Collaborative Study group, 1990, Genetic linkage studies suggest that Alzheimer's disease is not a single homogeneous disorder, *Nature* 347:194–197.

Sedman, A.B., Klein, G.L., Russel, J.M., Merritt, R.J., Miller, N.L., Weber, K.O., Gill, W.L., Anand, H., and Alfrey, A.C., 1985, Evidence of aluminum loading in infants receiving intravenous therapy. *New Eng. J. Med.* 312:1337–43.

Siem, C.M. (1886), quoted in Doellken (1897), Über die Wirkung des aluminum mit besonderer Berücksichtiqung der durch das aluminum verursachten Lasionen im Zentralnervensystem. *Naunyn-Schmiedebergs Archiv. Exp. Path. Pharm.* 40:58–120.

Smollett, T., *Humphry Clinker,* first printed 1771, reprinted 1985, Penguin, London, pp. 76 and 152.

Solomon, P.R., Pingree, T.M., Baldwin, D., Koota, D., Perl, D.P., and Pendlebury, W.W., 1988, Disrupted retention of the classically conditioned nictitating membrane response in rabbits with aluminum-induced neurofibrillary degeneration, *Neurotoxicology* 9(2):209–222.

Sprague, S.M., Corwin, H.L., Tanner, C.M., Wilson, R.S., Green, B.J., and Goetz, C.G., 1988, Relationship of aluminum to neurocognitive dysfunction in chronic dialysis patients, *Arch. Intern. Med.* 148.

Sternweis, P.C., and Gilman, A.G., 1982, Aluminum: A requirement for activation of the regulatory component of adenylate cyclase by fluoride, *Proc. Natl. Acad. Sci. USA* 79:4888–4891.

Still, C.N., and Kelly, P., 1980, On the incidence of primary degenerative dementia vs. water fluoride content in South Carolina, *Neurotoxicology* 4:125–131.

Trapp, G.A., 1983, Plasma aluminum is bound to transferrin, *Life Sci.* 33:311–316.

Van Rhijn, A., Corrigan, F.M., and Ward, N.I., 1989, Serum aluminum in senile dementia of Alzheimer's type and in multi-infarct dementia, *Trace Elem. Med.* 6(1):24–26.

Vogt, T., 1986, Water quality and health—study of a possible relationship between aluminum in drinking water and dementia (Sosiale og okonomiske studier 61, English abstract), Oslo: Central Bureau of Statistics of Norway.

Yokel, R.A., 1983, Repeated systemic aluminum exposure effects on classical conditioning of the rabbit, *Neurobehav. Toxicol. Teratol.* 5:41–46.

Chapter 5

The Concept of Direct and Indirect Neurotoxicity and the Concept of Toxic Metal/Essential Element Interactions as a Common Biomechanism Underlying Metal Toxicity

Louis W. Chang

1. INTRODUCTION

The toxicities of many metals have been well defined. Many of these metals, such as mercury, lead, cadmium, manganese, aluminum, and alkyltin, have demonstrated a special target affinity towards the nervous system.

In the past decade, numerous studies have been performed to explore the effects and toxic mechanisms of these toxic metals. Excellent reviews are also available on these subjects: mercury (Chang, 1979, 1980, 1982, 1985, 1987a, 1987c), lead (Minnema, 1989; Silbergeld and Hruska, 1980; Winder and Lewis, 1985), cadmium (Chang *et al.*,

Louis W. Chang • Departments of Pathology, Pharmacology, and Toxicology, University of Arkansas for Medical Sciences, Little Rock, Arkansas 72205.

The Vulnerable Brain and Environmental Risks, Volume 2: Toxins in Food, edited by Robert L. Isaacson and Karl F. Jensen. Plenum Press, New York, 1992.

1981), aluminum (McLachlan and Farnell, 1985; Petit, 1989), and alkyltin (Chang, 1986, 1987a, 1987b, 1990). The prime objectives of the present chapter are therefore not to simply "re-review" these subjects, but to present to the readers two seldom discussed, yet challenging, concepts: (1) direct vs. indirect neurotoxicity and (2) the interaction of metals with essential nutritional elements as a common biomechanism underlying metal-induced toxicities.

2. DIRECT NEUROTOXICITY

The term *direct neurotoxicity* is to be defined as the neurotoxic phenomenon in which there is a direct correlation between the toxicant or its metabolite distributions and the loci and extent of toxic changes in the nervous system. This concept follows the general basic principle of a dose response relationship, at least at the tissue level, of toxicology. Thus, the tissue that accumulates a higher amount (dose) of the toxic compound will show a more severe toxic lesion (response) than those that accumulate lesser amounts of the compound or substance. This basic concept can be best illustrated with methylmercury intoxication.

2.1. Mercury Intoxication

Mercury is one of the oldest known toxic metals to humans. Among all mercury compounds, organomercurials, particularly methylmercury (alkylmercury), have the most potent toxic impact on the nervous system.

Since the outbreak of Minamata disease (methylmercury poisoning) in Japan in the early 1950s (Takeuchi *et al.*, 1959, 1962a, 1962b), mercury, particularly methylmercury, has been recognized as an extremely hazardous environmental pollutant (Bache *et al.*, 1971; Katsuki *et al.*, 1957; Okinaka *et al.*, 1964; Tokuomi, 1961; Tokuomi *et al.*, 1966).

The primary clinical signs for methylmercury toxicity are ataxia, constriction of the visual field, and sensory disturbance. Pathological lesions in the cerebellar cortex, visual cortex, and dorsal root ganglia correlate well with the neurological problems of the patients. Distributional studies also indicated a *direct* correlation of the target areas of mercury accumulation (cerebellum, visual cortex, and spinal ganglia) with the major loci of lesion development.

Despite the large variations in experimental designs (different species employed, chronicity in toxicity, etc.), the basic neurotoxocity and pathological pattern induced by methylmercury in the nervous system is comparable with that observed in human cases.

In methylmercury poisoning, there is a histologically characteristic disappearance of granule cells that takes place under the Purkinje cell layer (Morikawa, 1961), particularly affecting those cells at the depth of the sulci.

The sensory neurons of the dorsal spinal ganglia are also extremely sensitive to the toxicity of mercury (Chang and Hartmann, 1972a, 1972b). These observations have been confirmed by Herman *et al.* (1973).

2.2. Pathogenetic Mechanism of Organic Mercury-Induced Neuropathology

Since the blood–brain barrier constitutes the immediate "gateway" between the blood vessels and the nervous system, it is important to consider the influence of chronic mercury poisoning on this system. By means of light and electron microscopy, Chang and coworkers have demonstrated that when mercury ions are absorbed into the bloodstream, even in minute amounts (1.0 ppm), they are capable of impairing the blood–brain system within hours, leading to an increased permeability of normally barred plasma solutes (Chang and Hartmann, 1972d; Ware *et al.*, 1974).

The blood–brain barrier is considered to be a complex of multiple systems regulating the exchange of metabolic material between the brain and blood (Broman, 1967; Lajtha, 1962; Steinwall, 1961, 1969; Tower, 1962). Therefore, the blood–brain barrier acts as an active site for the regulation of the uptake of biological metabolites from the blood to the nervous system (Broman and Steinwall, 1967; Lejtha, 1962). It is conceivable, therefore, that the impairment of the blood–brain barrier, together with the possible inhibition of certain associated enzymes by mercury, will affect the normal metabolism of the nervous system.

By means of electron microscopic histochemical methods, Chang and coworkers further demonstrated mercury binding on the membranous organelles within the cell, such as the mitochondria and endoplasmic reticulum (Chang and Hartmann, 1972c). Biochemical investigations confirmed a definitive reduction in mitochondrial function (Verity *et al.*, 1975) and a disturbance in the glycolytic enzyme system (Paterson and Usher, 1971; Salvaterra *et al.*, 1973), as well as in protein synthesis (Cavanagh and Chen, 1971; Steinwall, 1969; Yoshino *et al.*, 1966) in the nervous system following mercury intoxication. Such biochemical alterations may have a direct bearing on the selective binding of mercury to the mitochondria and endoplasmic reticulum.

Therefore, the toxic relationships between mercury and the nervous system may be conceived as a "direct" one: Mercury crosses the blood–brain barrier directly, inducing a blood–brain barrier dysfunction; mercury selectively accumulates in higher quantities in the cerebellum, visual cortex, and spinal dorsal root ganglia, inducing more extensive pathological and neurological changes in these target areas of the nervous system; intracellularly, mercury selectively deposits (binds) on membranous organelles, such as mitochondria, endoplasmic reticulum, and the Golgi complex, inducing noticable disruptions in mitochondrial functions and protein synthesis.

The precise molecular toxic mechanisms of mercury neurotoxicity, obviously, are much more complex than this. Further discussions on some of these concepts will be presented in a later section of this chapter. The concept of "direct" neurotoxicity, however, is clear. The overall biomechanism of mercury is illustrated in Figure 1.

3. INDIRECT NEUROTOXICITY

As opposed to direct neurotoxicity, *indirect neurotoxicity* may be defined as the neurotoxic phenomenon in which there is a lack of correlation between the foci of lesion development in the nervous system and the quantitative distribution of the toxicant in the nervous system; that is, the distributional pattern of the toxicant in the nervous system does not necessarily match with the pathological pattern resulting from intoxication.

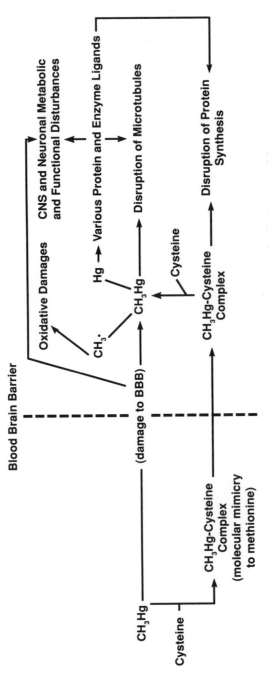

FIGURE 1. Schematic representation of proposed mechanisms of methylmercury toxicity.

This type of indirect neurotoxicity may be best exemplified by alkyltin, particularly trimethyltin (TMT), neurotoxicity in the central nervous system (CNS).

3.1. Trimethyltin Neurotoxicity

Although inorganic tin compounds are not known to be particularly neurotoxic, recent investigations have demonstrated that organotin compounds, such as trimethyltin (TMT) and triethyltin (TET), are potent neurotoxicants, producing rapid and extensive damage to the central nervous system. While TET is known to be primarily myelinotoxic in the central nervous system (Watanabe, 1977, 1980), TMT is found to be extremely neuronotoxic (Bouldin et al., 1981; Brown et al., 1979; Chang, 1984b; Chang et al., 1982a, 1982b, 1982c, 1983a, 1983b; Chang and Dyer, 1983a, 1983b).

Mice were found to be extremely sensitive to TMT poisoning. Severe whole-body tremors and neuronal degeneration, particularly in the limbic system and brainstem, were observed within 48 hr after a single injection of 3.0 mg TMT/kg body weight (Chang et al., 1982a, 1982b, 1982c, 1983a, 1983b). Degenerative changes in many brainstem neurons were particularly prominent, with extensive chromatolytic and vacuolar changes characterizing the pathological alterations in these nerve cells. In the brainstem, the mesencephalic trigeminal nuclei, locus ceruleus nuclei, and the raphe nuclei were most severely affected. However, scattered neuronal degeneration was also present in other parts of the brainstem. Similar degenerative changes in the larger spinal motoneurons have also been reported (Chang et al., 1984b). Extensive degeneration of the fascia dentata was also observed in mice treated with TMT with little damage to the Ammon's horn of the hippocampus.

The overall pathological effects of TMT on rats were much milder than those on mice. Examination of the hippocampus from animals treated with 6.0 mg/kg TMT revealed extensive neuronal loss in the Ammon's horn. However, involvement of fascia dentata was much less than that observed in mice (Chang et al., 1983b). An inverse relationship on lesion developments between the dentate granule cells and the Ammon's horn neurons in rats was also noted (Chang and Dyer, 1985a).

Although brainstem lesions also occurred in rats, these lesions were confined to chromatolytic changes without the extensive vacuolar degeneration as those observed in mice. However, extensive pathological lesions in the olfactory tubercle and in the pyriform/entorhinal cortices were also observed (Chang and Dyer, 1983a).

Despite the extensive study of TMT neurotoxicity in adult animals, comprehensive studies on the impact of TMT on the developing nervous system are relatively few (Chang, 1984a, 1984b; Reuhl et al., 1982). Among these studies, the most significant observations were perhaps those made by Chang and coworkers (Chang, 1984a, 1984b). These investigators injected TMT (6.0 mg TMT/kg body weight) into neonatal rat pups at various neonatal ages. Selective populations of neurons in the hippocampal Ammon's horn were destroyed. Since these pathological patterns were well correlated with the developmental and functional maturity of these hippocampal neurons, these investigators suggested that the production of lesions in the Ammon's horn neurons of the hippocampus, particularly those in subfield CA_3, required functionally mature and intact granule cells of the fascia dentata and their fibers (mossy fibers). The concept of "functional toxicity" was first introduced by these investigators to indicate that damage to some neurons may be the result of adverse alterations of the functional state (e.g., hyperexcita-

TABLE 1.   TMT Effects on Brain Glutamate Metabolism and System

↓ Glutamate uptake	Naalsund et al., 1985; Patel et al., 1990
↓ Glutamate synthesis	Patel et al., 1990
↓ GABA synthesis	Doctor et al., 1982; Dehaven et al., 1984; Mailman et al., 1985
↑ Glutamate release	Patel et al., 1990
↑ Brain tissue glutamine and serum ammonia	Wilson et al., 1986; Hikal et al., 1988
↑ Damage to GABAergic neurons (dentate basket cells)	Chang and Dyer, 1985

tion or hyperstimulation) of these nerve cells under the influence of a toxic chemical (Chang, 1984a, 1984c).

Although there is a lack of specific loci of tin deposit in the brain, the most distinct neuropathology for TMT in rat is located in the hippocampal formation (Doctor et al., 1982b). Based on the biochemical data, the different patterns of pathological lesion development in mice and rats, as well as those in adult versus neonatal animals, Chang (1986, 1990) proposed that neuronal "hyperexcitation" in the limbic system was the mechanism for TMT toxicity in the hippocampal formation (Chang and Dyer, 1984, 1985a).

A disturbance of brain glutamate metabolism and the GABAergic system by TMT had been reported by various laboratories (Table 1). The reduction in glutamate uptake and synthesis will deplete neuronal glutamate, which, together with a reduction in brain taurine, probably produces the tremor seen in animals. A reduced GABA synthesis was also reported. This reduction of GABA synthesis in the GABAergic neurons (inhibitory), together with an increased neuronal release of glutamate under the influence of TMT, will promote the situation of "hyperexcitation." The fact that TMT's toxic impact on the hippocampus can either be promoted or alleviated by manipulating the levels of corticosterone (Chang et al., 1989), a known inhibitor of hippocampal activity (McEwen et al., 1975; Pfaff et al., 1971), further supports the hyperexcitation hypothesis (Chang, 1986, 1990) (Table 2).

Chang further suggested that this "chain" of hyperexcitation activity propagated

TABLE 2.   Hippocampal Corticosterone

Binding
    $CA_{1,2} > CA_3 >$ dentate fascia granule neurons
        (McEwen et al., 1975)
Function
    Inhibition and modulation of neuronal firing rate in the
        hippocampus   (Pfaff et al., 1971)
General vulnerability to TMT toxicity
    d.f. granule neurons $> CA_3 > CA_{1,2}$
        (Chang, 1986)
Effect of adrenalectomy on TMT toxicity
    Adrenalectomized animals show greater lesions than intact
        animals   (Chang et al., 1989)
    Corticosterone supplementation blocks TMT-induced lesion
        development   (Chang et al., 1989)

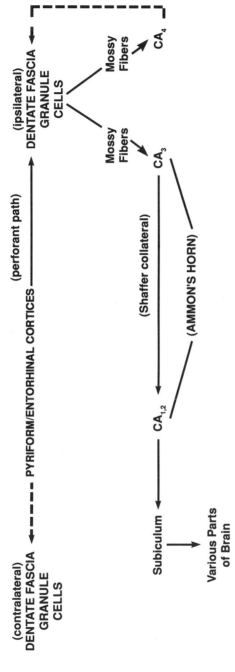

FIGURE 2. Proposed neural pathways involved in the toxic effects of TMT-induced lesion development.

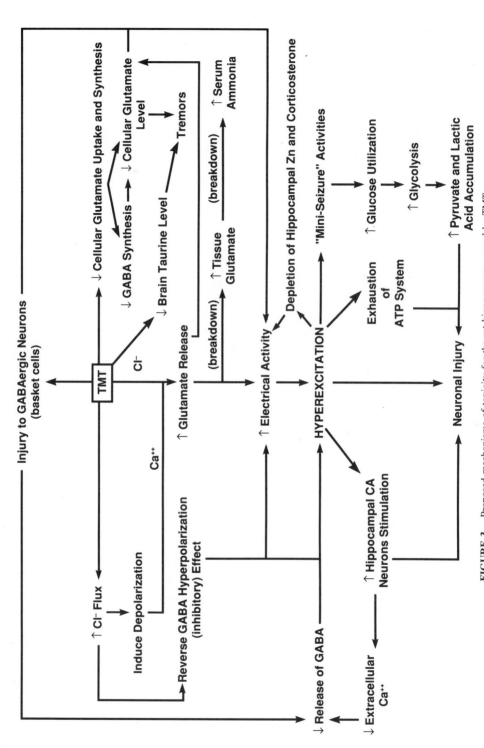

FIGURE 3. Proposed mechanisms of toxicity for the rat hippocampus caused by TMT.

along the limbic circuitry pathway: entorhinal cortex → dentate fascia granule → hippo-campal CA_3 neurons → hippocampal CA_1 and CA_2 neurons (Fig. 2). Investigation by Chang and his coworkers tested this hypothesis by the elimination of cell populations along this "pathway" and demonstrated that elimination of any given group (e.g., dentate granule cells) will spare the neuronal groups (e.g., hippocampal neurons) at the lower end of the circuitry from injury stemming from TMT exposure (Fig. 2). Thus, severe loss of dentate granule cells in mice or rats reduced damages to the hippocampal Ammon's horn neurons (Chang et al., 1983b). Furthermore, early destruction of the pyriform/entorhinal cortices would yield little lesion development in the dentate fascia and in the Ammon's horn (Chang, 1990).

The overall hypothesis on the biomechanism for TMT toxicity in the hippocampus is presented in Figure 3. This working hypothesis indicates that the occurrence of specific foci of lesion development (hippocampus) without specific loci of TMT accumulation is an example of "indirect" neurotoxicity; that is, the injury of the neurons in question (hippocampal) is not a direct toxic impact on these nerve cells by TMT. The lack of lesion development by TMT in early neonatal life of these animals further supports the idea that injuries to these nerve cells (e.g., hippocampal neurons) are "secondary" to toxic-induced functional changes in afferent neurons (e.g., entorhinal and dentate granule cells) at distant sites of the limbic system, rather than by direct toxic effects on the degenerating nerve cells in the Ammon's horn.

4. COMBINED DIRECT AND INDIRECT NEUROTOXICITIES

Following the general concepts on direct and indirect neurotoxicities presented, a "combined" direct and indirect neurotoxic phenomenon, when it occurs, represents the situation in which the toxicopathological consequences of the intoxication are partially the result of a direct impact of the toxicant on the nerve cells involved and partially the result of secondary alterations of structures or functions of the nervous system at distant sites from the primary target neurons of involvement. This phenomenon can be demonstrated with lead neurotoxicity.

5. LEAD NEUROTOXICITY

Lead neurotoxicity, particularly that of inorganic lead, has received ample attention in the past two decades. Numerous investigations were performed to elucidate the tox-icologic mechanisms of lead. Two excellent reviews were recently published on this subject by Winder and Lewis (1985) and by Minnema (1989). In the present chapter, the complex issue of lead toxicity will be greatly simplified so that the basic concept of "combined direct and indirect" neurotoxicity may be illustrated.

Unlike methylmercury, which produces very well-defined loci of toxicity (cerebellar granule cells, visual cortical neurons, dorsal root ganglia) that are highly correlated with mer-cury accumulation, lead produces a much more diffused toxic "encephalopathy," with an isolated pattern of edematous and neuronal necrosis in the brain (Winder and Lewis, 1985). Hemorrhagic episodes may also occur in acute exposures and in very young (neonates) animals. All these pathological observations strongly suggest generalized vascular alter-ations in the brain, leading to hemorrhage and cerebral edema, as a result of lead toxicity.

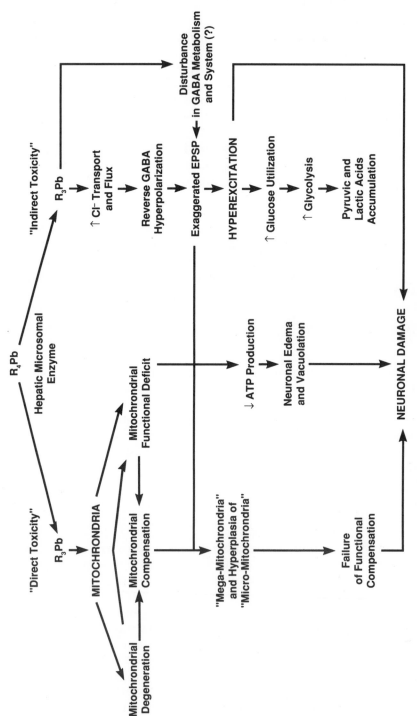

FIGURE 4.   Proposed neurotoxic mechanisms of tetraalkylead.

One possible explanation of lead's ability to cross the blood–brain barrier is that it has a very similar ionic radius and charge to calcium ion. Thus lead may cross the blood–brain barrier readily via the calcium carriers and channels.

The effects of lead on the blood–brain barrier and cerebral vasculatures (Goldstein, 1991; Jacobs, 1980) are well established. Damage to the cerebral vasculature system will lead to blood–brain barrier dysfunction, petechial hemorrhage, cerebral edematous changes, and "secondary" neuronal and myelin changes and degeneration.

On the other hand, lead has been demonstrated to have a definitive and direct effect on the calcium metabolism. Indeed, among all biomolecular mechanisms proposed for lead neurotoxicity, the disturbance of calcium metabolism is perhaps the most important and has the most "direct" relationship to cell injuries (both endothelial cell and neuronal injuries) and neurodysfunctions induced by lead.

As stated earlier, lead may mimic calcium in the biological system. This mimicry will allow lead, like calcium, to concentrate in mitochondria within the cells. Therefore, mitochondria become one of the targets for lead neurotoxicity, leading to a disturbance in the energy (ATP) production and respiratory (oxidation) function of the cells. By the same token, when lead mimics calcium in the synaptic sites, it will disrupt the synaptic transmission, particularly those related to the release of acetylcholine (Cooper *et al.*, 1984). Therefore, certain changes in the nervous system may be "directly" correlated with the accumulation and actions of lead in the mitochondria or at the synaptic terminals.

This combined phenomenon is also observed with alkyl lead poisoning, where many of the central nervous system changes (limbic system, particularly the hippocampus) resemble those in trimethyltin intoxication; thus, hyperexcitory neurotoxicity (an "indirect" neurotoxicity) is suspected. However, in the dorsal root ganglia neurons, nerve cells in the peripheral nervous system, mitochondrial degeneration, and compensatory changes in these nerve cells are also observed (a "direct neurotoxicity") (Chang *et al.*, 1984a, 1987). Similar mitochondrial changes could also be demonstrated in the CNS neurons. A scheme of biomechanism for alkyl lead neurotoxicity is presented in Figure 4 to illustrate this concept of combined direct and indirect neurotoxicity.

6. TOXIC METAL AND ESSENTIAL NUTRITIONAL ELEMENT INTERACTIONS

The term *interaction* for metals was defined by the Task Group on Metal Interaction (1978) as "a process by which metals in their various forms change the critical concentration or a critical effect of a metal under consideration." In addition, the term *interaction* may also be used to describe "any influence of metals and other substances and factors on the metabolism and toxicity of the metal under consideration."

Current evidence indicates that among 90 naturally occurring elements and metals, approximately one fourth of them are essential to life. The exposure to non-essential, perhaps "toxic," metals, such as lead, mercury, cadmium, and arsenic, may induce metal/metal or metal/element interactions between the essential elements or metals and the nonessential ("toxic") metals. These interactions may produce an alteration in the otherwise well-balanced microenvironment within the biological system. Such a disturbance of the normal balance and metabolism of the essential metals and elements in the biological system may become the basis, or set the "stage" for, some of the subsequent "toxicities" observed.

While there are over 20 essential elements, and each has possible interactions with various "toxic" metals, the present chapter will select three major examples—calcium, zinc, and selenium—for the illustration of their influences on various metal toxicities. Furthermore, because a majority of these examples were obtained from situations other than "neurotoxicity," for the sake of comprehensive presentation, other toxic conditions and metabolisms of the metals and elements of concern, in addition to neurotoxicity, will also be included in the present discussion.

6.1. Interactions of Calcium with Lead and Cadmium

As early as the 1970s, Mahaffey-Six and Goyer (1970) had demonstrated that a calcium-deficient diet will potentiate tissue lead deposit, as well as biochemical and pathological changes associated with lead toxicity. Similar observations were later reported by Quarterman and Morrison (1975). Other investigators further demonstrated a reduced gastrointestinal absorption of lead in the presence of a high calcium-containing diet (Barltrop and Khoo, 1976; Meredith et al., 1977).

Numerous investigators have demonstrated repeatedly that calcium can influence lead metabolism and vice versa (Barton et al., 1978; Hsu et al., 1975; Meredith et al., 1977; Quarterman and Morrison, 1975). Retention of lead decreased as the dietary calcium was increased. In addition, there was also greater elimination of lead that was previously incorporated into the body when animals were given high dietary calcium. In fact, Lederer and Bing, as early as in 1940, suggested that increased amounts of calcium in the diet would diminish the lead stored in the body. Although phosphate frequently accompanied its metabolism, the amount of phosphate alone had no effect on the biologically stored lead. These observations were later confirmed by Morrison and co-workers (1977), who indicated that the dietary content of calcium, phosphorus, and sulfur had a great influence on the absorption, retention, and elimination of lead.

Similar to the lead situation, a reduction of cadmium absorption was also observed with increasing dietary levels of cadmium. This phenomenon may be related to a toxic effect of cadmium on the intestinal mucosa (Hamilton and Smith, 1977; Richardson and Fox, 1974; Richardson et al., 1974). Indeed, development of a negative calcium balance in rats during chronic oral cadmium exposure has been reported (Kobayashi, 1974). On the other hand, animals fed a calcium-deficient diet also showed an increase in cadmium absorption (Larsson and Piscator, 1971; North et al., 1984; Washko and Cousins, 1975).

Both the suppression of calcium uptake by cadmium or an elevated uptake of cadmium due to low dietary calcium will lead to the consequence of increased cellular injury and dysfunction ("toxicity"). Thus the awareness of the interaction between cadmium and calcium should be seriously taken into account when cadmium exposure and cadmium toxicity are being considered.

6.2. Interactions of Zinc and Copper with Lead and Cadmium

It has been reported that zinc-treated animals, although showing an increased renal lead concentration, exhibited a decrease in brain lead content (Willoughby et al., 1972a, 1972b). The elevated lead in the kidneys may be interpreted as an increase in renal excretion of the metal. Cerklewski and Forbes (1976) further indicated that as dietary zinc increased, the severity of lead toxicity decreased. Such reduction of lead toxicity might be the result of a reduction in lead absorption at the level of the gastrointestinal tract and an increase in lead elimination.

With zinc supplementation, both *in vivo* and *in vitro*, the inhibition of a zinc-dependent enzyme, γ-aminolevulinic acid dehydratase, by lead could be reversed (Abdulla *et al.*, 1979). Together with iron, dietary copper was also found to greatly reduce the toxic effects of lead on the hematopoietic system (Davis and Campbell, 1977; Petering, 1980). These examples suggest that lead may be "competing" or "displacing" the essential metals, such as zinc, iron, and copper, inducing "deficiency syndromes" of those essential elements: a reduction of heme synthesis, anemia, and neurodysfunction. Supplementation of these essential nutrients (zinc, iron, and copper) would reduce such toxic syndromes.

Zinc and copper are also found to alter the deposition of lead in various regions of the central nervous system. Rehman and Chandra (1984) reported a reduction of lead deposits in the brain by copper supplementation. With lead administration, there was an increase of copper and a reduction of zinc in the hippocampus, cerebral cortex, and cerebellum; a reversed pattern (decreased copper and increased zinc contents) was found in the amygdala and hypothalamus (Rehman and Chandra, 1984).

It is also of interest that when lead was administered together with copper, there was a greater increase of copper in the brain, particularly in the areas of hippocampus, cerebellum, and brainstem, than if copper was administered alone (Rehman and Chandra, 1984). The significance of enhancement of copper uptake by brain in the presence of lead is still unknown. When zinc was given together with lead, certain parts of the brain (hypothalamus and amygdala) showed a higher zinc concentration, while other parts of the brain (cerebellum) displayed a lower zinc concentration compared to those animals receiving zinc injections alone (Rehman and Chandra, 1984). These observations suggest that the zinc/lead interaction is very complex and may vary from region to region of the nervous system. The basic function of the nerve cells in each region and their basic need for the mineral elements involved will probably be influential in the outcome of this interaction.

Another study by Hasan and Seth (1981) also showed that zinc, when administered with lead, reduced the amount of lead deposited in the brain by about 25% when compared to the brains of animals exposed to similar doses of lead alone. Likewise, the copper content was also lower than that animals injected with lead alone. Thus, while zinc may offer some "protection" of the brain from lead toxicity by a reduction of lead accumulation in the brain, care must be taken with the seemingly suggestive "antagonistic" action of zinc with copper, which also plays a vital role for brain metabolism and function.

Zinc and cadmium share many similar physical and chemical properties and therefore are likely to compete with each other for various reactive sites in the biological system. The administration of cadmium is known to deplete zinc content in the biological tissues (Parizek, 1957; Webb, 1972). In fact, some of the clinical signs of chronic cadmium poisoning resemble those of the zinc deficiency syndrome (Bunn and Matrone, 1966; Hill *et al.*, 1963; Petering *et al.*, 1971; Powell *et al.*, 1964), and many of the signs and symptoms of cadmium poisoning can be prevented or reversed by dietary zinc supplementation. Thus, cadmium has been referred to as an *antimetabolite* of zinc by Cotzias and Papvasiliou (1964). The protective effect of zinc against cadmium toxicity may be related, at least in part, to the reduction of the activities of several zinc-dependent enzymes by cadmium (Vallee and Ulmer, 1972). Such enzymatic disruption would contribute cellular dysfunctions similar to those observed in zinc deficiency. In other words, supplementation of zinc simply represents a remedy in the reduction of the *cadmium-induced zinc depletion syndrome*.

Similarly, cadmium has an antagonistic action with copper. Thus, in the condition of low or marginal copper intake, exposure to cadmium would induce the onset of *copper deficiency syndrome,* which represents one of the earliest clinical manifestations of cadmium toxicosis (Bremner and Campbell, 1977; Davies and Campbell, 1977).

Since copper and zinc are two of the most important mineral elements for the metabolic and functional integrity of the nervous system, depletion of copper would certainly induce adverse effects on the nervous system. Indeed, it has been reported that animals fed on cadmium-contaminated grass displayed signs of copper and zinc deficiencies, and their offsprings had high incidences of demyelinating disease (Grun *et al.,* 1977).

In sum, lead and cadmium exert their toxicities, at least in part, as antinutritional metabolites for essential elements such as zinc and copper, inducing toxic syndromes similar to nutritional deficiency of these elements. Supplementation of zinc and copper, therefore, is effective in reducing or reversing some of the toxic effects of lead.

6.3. Interactions of Selenium with Cadmium and Mercury

Selenium is an essential nutritional element and plays an important role in the glutathione regulation (Rotruck *et al.,* 1973) and has antioxidation function in the biological systems (Oh *et al.,* 1974). Although selenium is toxic at high dose levels, at dietary levels, selenium has been shown to reduce the toxicities of various heavy metals, noticeably cadmium and mercury (Flora *et al.,* 1982; Kar *et al.,* 1969; Holmberg and Ferm, 1969; Parizek *et al.,* 1968, 1971, 1974; Tiobias *et al.,* 1946).

Unlike zinc and calcium, which reduce the toxicities of lead or cadmium with a significant reduction of intestinal absorption and tissue accumulation of the metal involved, selenium exerts its protective effects against cadmium or mercury toxicity without actually reducing tissue concentrations of cadmium or mercury (Fox, 1974; Whanger *et al.,* 1980). In other words, in the presence of selenium, tissues would be protected against toxic injuries despite the concentrations of the metal, cadmium or mercury, remaining significantly elevated.

Although prevention of testicular injury is the most significant interaction of selenium with cadmium (Gunn *et al.,* 1966; Kar *et al.,* 1960; Mason and Young, 1967; Parizek *et al.,* 1971, 1974; Whanger *et al.,* 1980), reduction of cadmium-induced mortality, teratogenicity, and renal toxicity by selenium have also been reported (Flora, 1982; Holmbey and Fern, 1969; Parizek *et al.,* 1971).

The basic mechanism of selenium's protection against cadmium toxicity is believed to be largely the ability of selenium (as selenide) to form large, high molecular weight selenoproteins, with a molecular weight between 115,000 and 150,000 Da (Chen *et al.,* 1974b, 1975b; Chen and Ganther, 1975). These large selenoproteins will divert the binding of cadmium in tissues and plasma from otherwise "sensitive" sites of cells and tissues. This is because selenoproteins are very thiol rich and have a high affinity towards metals such as cadmium and mercury.

Similarly, selenium is found to protect against both inorganic and organic mercury toxicity without a reduction of mercury levels in the tissues (Chang *et al.,* 1977; Groth *et al.,* 1973; Iwata *et al.,* 1973; Johnson and Pond, 1974; Ohi *et al.,* 1975, 1976; Potter and Matrone, 1974; Skerfring, 1978; Stoewsand *et al.,* 1977; Welsh and Soares, 1976).

For inorganic mercury, the selenium/mercury interaction probably is similar to the selenium/cadmium interaction; that is, the binding of mercury in the tissues is diverted from a low molecular weight protein (about 10,000) to a much larger selenium-containing protein (MW 150,000) (Chen *et al.*, 1974a).

Further studies revealed that although in most tissues the mercury/selenium ratio is usually close to 1:1 (Kosta *et al.*, 1975), a much smaller molar quantity of selenium is capable of protecting a much larger molar quantity of mercury against neurotoxicity (Ganther and Sunde, 1974). In view of these studies, Chang and coworkers proposed that small amounts of selenium may form a large complex of selenoprotein, which in turn may bind to ("arrest") a large molar quantity of mercury in the nervous system (Chang *et al.*, 1977).

Chang and coworkers (Chang *et al.*, 1976, 1977; Chang, 1983) further showed that selenium protected against methylmercury neurotoxicity, both in terms of morphological integrity and in terms of biochemical parameters (protein synthesis). Biochemical analysis by Chen and co-workers (1975a), however, indicated that selenium did not divert methylmercury binding, as it did with inorganic mercury. Thus, the protective interaction of selenium with methylmercury is probably different from that with inorganic mercury.

Indeed, one of the possible mechanisms of methylmercury neurotoxicity is the formation of methyl free radicals as a result of homolytic cleavage of the carbon-mercury bond. Methyl free radicals can initiate lipid peroxidation, which is highly injurious to cells (Clarkson, 1987; Ganther, 1978). Glutathione peroxidase was found to be a selenoenzyme (Rotruck *et al.*, 1973) that is important in antioxidative functions in the cells. The interaction of selenium and methylmercury, therefore, may be via the antioxidative path of the glutathione system (Chang and Suber, 1982). Indeed, other antioxidants, such as N, N'-diphenyl-p-phenylenediamide (DPPD) (Whanger, 1981), vitamin E (Chang *et al.*, 1978; Ganther, 1978), and ascorbic acid (Whanger, 1985), have also displayed a potential for reducing the toxicity of methylmercury. However, it must be emphasized that while antioxidation may serve as the general basis for protection against methylmercury toxicity by antioxidants, the precise mechanism for such an interaction may be different for each antioxidant.

Reductions in the glutathione concentration and enzyme activities in the glutathione system were also found in animals exposed to mercury (Chung *et al.*, 1982). Supplementation of selenium would therefore help to overcome the reduction of this important cellular function and therefore reduce cellular damage.

In sum, selenium interacts with both cadmium and mercury in the reduction of toxicities of these metals without reducing the uptake or tissue accumulation of these metals. For the inorganic metal salts, selenium protection is exerted probably via diversion of metal ion binding to high molecular weight selenoproteins away from sensitive sites of the cells. For an organic metal compound (methylmercury), selenium interaction may be established through antioxidation activities via the glutathione peroxidase system. Regardless of the "mechanisms" of these interactions, the basic phenomena of nutritional elements/toxic metal interactions are well established and demonstrated.

7. MOLECULAR MIMICRY OF ESSENTIAL METABOLITES BY TOXIC METALS AS AN UNDERLYING MECHANISM FOR TOXICITY

Another important and interesting possibility for metals to exert their "toxicities" is for those metals to form compounds "mimicking" essential metabolites, therefore disrupting normal metabolism and functions of the cells.

One of the earliest and perhaps most important "toxicities" of methylmercury in the nervous system is a significant suppression in neuronal protein synthesis (Cavanagh and Chen, 1971; Yoshino *et al.*, 1966). While one may speculate about the possible disruption of amino acid uptake (Cavanagh and Chen, 1971) or disintegration of polyribosomes and rough endoplasmic reticulum (Nissl substance) in nerve cells (Chang and Hartmann, 1972a; Chang *et al.*, 1972a, 1972), an interesting molecular mechanism for such an event remains that methylmercury may form a complex that can "block" protein synthesis. It has been suggested that methylmercury, having a high affinity towards thiol or sulfhydryl (-SH) groups, will form complexes with -SH-rich compounds, including the amino acid cysteine. The structure of methylmercury-cysteine complex resembles that of the amino acid methionine, which is important in the initiation of polypeptide chains in the process of protein synthesis (Clarkson, 1987). The mimicry of the methylmercury-cysteine complex with methionine (Fig. 5A) may compete for the polypeptide chain formation and disrupt the process of protein synthesis (Fig. 1).

Other examples of "mimicry" of essential metabolites by heavy metals also exist. Arsenic, when present in the biological system, usually exists as arsenate. This is an oxyanion with a structure similar to that of the phosphate oxyanion (Fig. 5B). This mimicry of arsenic with phosphate would establish the "arsenolysis reaction," in which

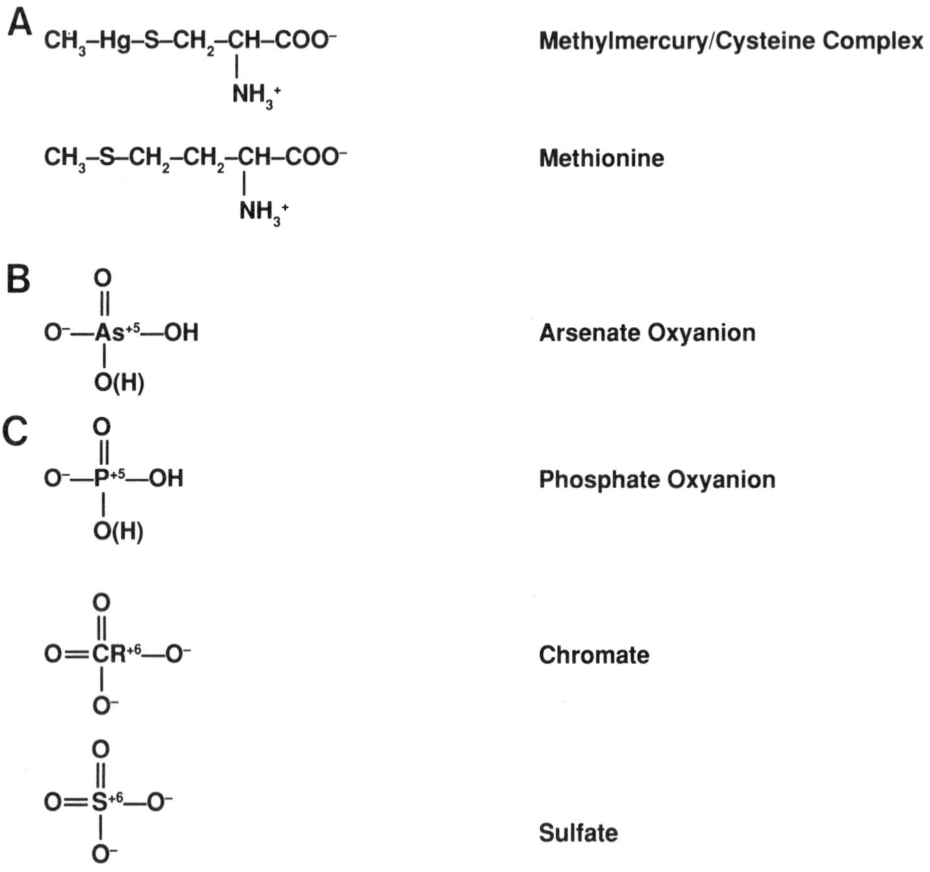

A $CH_3-Hg-S-CH_2-CH-COO^-$ **Methylmercury/Cysteine Complex**
  |
  NH_3^+

  $CH_3-S-CH_2-CH_2-CH-COO^-$ **Methionine**
  |
  NH_3^+

B O-As^{+5}-OH **Arsenate Oxyanion**

C O-P^{+5}-OH **Phosphate Oxyanion**

O=CR^{+6}-O^- **Chromate**

O=S^{+6}-O^- **Sulfate**

FIGURE 5. Examples of the mimicry of amino acids by various metal complexes.

arsenic replaces phosphate in the process of ATP synthesis. This uncoupling of ATP synthesis becomes the basis of arsenic toxicity.

Similar phenomenon may be observed with chromium. Trivalent chromium ion (Cr^{3+}), although highly reactive with enzymes and macromolecules (e.g., nucleic acids), is relatively inert toward intact cells. Hexavalent chromium ion (Cr^{6+}), on the other hand, is highly toxic to intact cells, but by itself is relatively unreactive with macromolecules and enzymes *in vitro*. This seemingly paradoxical phenomenon may be explained by the fact that the hexavalent chromium, *in vivo*, forms an oxyanion similar to the structure of that of sulfate oxyanions (Fig. 5C). The chromium oxyanion can be transported into cells via the same channels and carriers as sulfates (Jennette, 1981). Once inside the cell, the hexavalent chromium may then be released from the oxyanion complex and be reduced to the trivalent form, which is highly reactive with macromolecules (e.g., DNA) for the induction of toxicity and even carcinogenesis.

8. CONCLUDING REMARKS

Metal toxicity, either in the nervous system or in other systems, is complex. In the nervous system, depending on the metal involved, the toxic impact may be "direct," showing a positive correlation of metal distribution and accumulation with the distribution and foci of lesion development in the nervous system. The toxic impacts, many times, may be "indirect," in which no correlation of metal distribution and the loci of lesion developments can be established. Investigators, therefore, should not simply focus or single out the nerve cells in areas of "degeneration" in search for toxic mechanisms. Indeed, the degeneration observed in any given area of the brain may simply be secondary to alterations of the nervous system at some distant sites from the lesion (for example, vasculature changes due to lead intoxication or neural circuitry activity changes due to trimethyltin intoxication). Neurotoxicology, therefore, should not be based simply on the understanding of the principles of toxicology alone, but should also be tied closely to the principles of neuroscience and the understanding of neural functions.

By the same token, the study of metal toxicology, either in the nervous system or in other systemic organs, should encompass not only the "toxicology" of the metal involved, but must also include the basic nutritional concepts of other essential nutritional metals and elements that may interact with the metal of concern. The considerations of metal/metal and metal/element interactions should be borne in mind when the "toxicity" of any given metal is considered. As illustrated in this chapter, many of the "toxicities" of metals may be, at least in part, attributed to disturbances of normal essential element metabolism and the balanced "microenvironments" within the cells. Frequently, supplementation of nutritional elements would "relieve" or reduce the "toxic" syndromes observed. Thus, the vulnerability of the brain towards toxins/toxicants and nutritional elements may not always be separate phenomena. In metal toxicity, these two entities are frequently interrelated and inseparable.

REFERENCES

Abdulla, M., Svensson, S., and Haeger-Aronsen, B., 1979, Antagonistic effects of zinc and aluminum on lead inhibition of γ-aminolevulinic acid dehydratase, *Arch. Environ. Health* 34:464.

Bache, C.A., Gutenamann, W.H., and Lick, D.J., 1971, Residues of total mercury and methyl mercuric salts in lake trout as a function of age, *Science* 172:951.

Barltrop, D., and Khoo, H.E., 1976, The influence of dietary minerals and fat on the absorption of lead, *Sci. Total Environ.* 6:265.

Barton, T.C., Conrad, M.E., Harrison, L., and Nuby, S., 1978, Effects of calcium on the absorption and retention of lead, *J. Lab. Clin. Med.* 91:366.

Bouldin, T.W., Goines, N.D., Bagnell, C.R., and Krigman, M.R., 1981, Pathogenesis of trimethyltin neuronal toxicity, *Am. J. Pathol.* 104:237.

Bremner, I., and Campbell, J.K., 1980, The influence of dietary copper intake on the toxicity of cadmium, *Ann. N.Y. Acad. Sci.* 355:319.

Broman, T., 1967, On vascular aspects of the blood-brain barrier, in: *Pathology of the Nervous System,* Vol. 1 (J. Minckler, ed.), Blakiston, New York, chap. 33.

Broman, T., and Steinwall, O., 1967, Blood-brain barrier, in: *Pathology of the Nervous System,* Vol. 1 (J. Minckler, ed.), Blakiston, New York, chap. 2.

Brown, A.W., Aldridge, W.N., Street, B.W., and Verschoyle, R.D., 1979, The behavioral and neuropathologic sequelae of intoxication by trimethyltin compounds in the rat, *Am. J. Pathol.* 97:59.

Bunn, C.R., and Matrone, G., 1966, In vivo interactions of cadmium, copper, zinc and iron in the mouse and rat, *J. Nutr.,* 90:395.

Cavanagh, J.B., and Chen, F.C.K., 1971, Amino acid incorporation in protein during the "silent phase" before organo-mercury and p-bromophenylacetylurea neuropathology in the rat, *Acta Neuropathol.* 19:216.

Cerklewski, F.L., and Forbes, R.M., 1976, Influence of dietery zinc on lead toxicity in the rat, *J. Nutr.* 106:689.

Chang, L.W., 1979, Pathological effects of mercury poisoning, in: *Biogeochemistry of Mercury* (J.O. Nriagu, ed.), Elsevier, New York, pp. 519–580.

Chang, L.W., 1980, Neurotoxic effects of mercury, in: *Experimental and Clinical Neurotoxicology* (P.S. Spencer, and H.H. Schaumberg, eds.), Williams and Wilkins, Baltimore, pp. 508–526.

Chang, L.W., 1982, Pathogenetic mechanisms of the neurotoxicity of methylmercury, in: *Mechanisms of Neurotoxic Substances* (K.N. Prasad, and A. Vernadakis, eds.), Raven Press, New York, pp. 51–66.

Chang, L.W., 1983, Protective effects of selenium against methylmercury neurotoxicity: A morphological and biochemical study, *Exp. Pathol.* 23:143.

Chang, L.W., 1984a, Trimethyltin-induced hippocampal lesions at various neonatal ages, *Bull. Environ. Contam. Toxicol.* 33:295.

Chang, L.W., 1984b, Hippocampal lesions induced by TMT in the neonatal rat brain, *Neurotoxicology* 5:205.

Chang, L.W., 1985, Neuropathological effects of toxic metal ions, in: *Metal Ions in Neurology and Psychiatry,* Alan R. Liss Series in Neurology and Neurobiology (S. Gabay, J. Harris, and B.T. Ho, eds.), Alan R. Liss, New York, pp. 207–230.

Chang, L.W., 1986, Neuropathology of trimethyltin: A proposed pathogenetic mechanism, *Fundam. Appl. Toxicol.* 6:217.

Chang, L.W., 1987a, Central nervous system changes: Selective and non-selective effects, in: *Structural and Functional Effects of Neurotoxicants: Organometals* (H.A. Tilson and S.B. Sparber, eds.), John Wiley, New York, pp. 82–116.

Chang, L.W., 1987b, A proposed pathogenic mechanism on trimethyltin-induced lesions in the hippocampus of adult and neonatal rats, in: *Biological Trace Element Research* (J. Pounds, ed.), Humana Press, New York, pp. 77–88.

Chang, L.W., 1987c, Experimental neuropathology of organic mercurials, in: *The Toxicity of Methylmercury* (Z. Annau and C. Eccles, eds.), The Johns Hopkins University Press, Baltimore, pp. 54–72.

Chang, L.W., 1990, Neurotoxicity of trimethyltin in hippocampus: A hyperexcitatory toxicity, *Korean J. Toxicol.* 6(2):191.

Chang, L.W., and Dyer, R.S., A time-course study of trimethyltin-induced neuropathology in rats, *Neurobehav. Toxicol. Teratol.* 5:443.

Chang, L.W., and Dyer, R.S., Effects of trimethyltin on sensory neurons, *Neurobehav. Toxicol. Teratol.* 5:673.

Chang, L.W., and Dyer, R.S., 1984, Trimethyltin-induced zinc depletion in rat hippocampus, in: *Neurobiology of Zinc,* Vol. II, Alan R. Liss Series in Neurology and Neurobiology (Frederickson, C., and Howell, G., eds.), Alan R. Liss, New York, pp. 175–190.

Chang, L.W., and Dyer, R.S., 1985a, Septotemporal gradients of trimethyltin-induced hippocampal lesions, *Neurobehav. Toxicol. Teratol.* 7:43.

Chang, L.W., and Dyer, R.S., 1985b, Early effects of trimethyltin in the dentate gyrus basket cells: A morphological study, *J. Toxicol. Environ. Health* 16:641.

Chang, L.W., and Hartmann, H.A., 1972a, Ultrastructural studies of the nervous system after mercury intoxication, I. Pathological changes in the nerve cell bodies, *Acta Neuropathol.* 20:122.

Chang, L.W., and Hartmann, H.A., 1972b, Ultrastructural studies of the nervous system after mercury intoxication, II. Pathological changes in the nerve fibers, *Acta Neuropathol.* 20:316.

Chang, L.W., and Hartmann, H.A., 1972c, Electron microscopic histochemical study on the localization and distribution of mercury in the nervous system after mercury intoxication, *Exp. Neurol.* 35:122.

Chang, L.W., and Hartmann, H.A., 1972d, Blood-brain barrier dysfunction in experimental mercury intoxication, *Acta Neuropathol.* 21:179.

Chang, L.W., and Suber, R., 1982, Protective effects of selenium or methylmercury toxicity: A possible mechanism, *Bull. Environ. Contamin. Toxicol.* 29:285.

Chang, L.W., Desnoyers, P.A., and Hartmann, H.A., 1972a, Quantitative cytochemical studies of RNA in experimental mercury poisoning, I. Changes in RNA content, *J. Nueropathol. Exp. Neurol.* 31:389.

Chang, L.W., Martin, A.H., and Hartmann, H.A., 1972b, Quantitative autoradiographic study of the RNA synthesis in the neurons after mercury intoxication, *Exp. Neurol.* 37:62.

Chang, L.W., Ganther, H.E., Dudley, A.W. Jr., and Sunde, M.L., 1976, Modification of neuropathology of methylmercury by dietary selenium, *Food Res. Inst. Annual Report,* Univ. of Wisconsin-Madison, pp. 382–383.

Chang, L.W., Dudley, A.W., Dudley, M.A., Ganther, H.E., and Sunde, M.L., 1977, Modification of neurotoxic effects of methylmercury by selenium, in: *Neurotoxicology* (L. Roizin, H. Shiraki, and N. Gircevic, eds.), Raven Press, New York, pp. 137–145.

Chang, L.W., Gilbert, M.M., and Sprecher, T.A., 1978, Modification of the neurotoxic effects of methylmercury by vitamin E, *Environ. Res.* 17:356.

Chang, L.W., Reuhl, K.R., and Wade, P.R., 1981, Pathological effects of cadmium, in: *Biogeochemistry of Cadmium. II. Health Effects* (J.O. Nriagu, ed.), Elsevier, New York, pp. 783–840.

Chang, L.W., Tiemeyer, T.M., Wenger, G.R., McMillan, D.E., and Reuhl, K.R., 1982a, Neuropathology of trimethyltin intoxication, I. Light microscopic study, *Environ. Res.* 29:435.

Chang, L.W., Tiemeyer, T.M., Wenger, G.R., McMillan, D.E., and Reuhl, K.R., 1982b, Neuropathology of trimethyltin intoxication, II. Electron microscopic study of the hippocampus, *Environ. Res.* 29:445.

Chang, L.W., Tiemeyer, T.M., Wenger, G.R., and McMillan, D.E., 1982c, Neuropathology of mouse hippocampus in acute trimethyltin intoxication, *Neurobehav. Toxicol. Teratol.* 4:149.

Chang, L.W., Tiemeyer, T.M., Wenger, G.R., and McMillan, D.E., 1983a, Neuropathology of trimethyltin intoxication, III. Changes in the brain stem neurons, *Environ. Res.* 30:399.

Chang, L.W., Wenger, G.R., McMillan, D.E., and Dyer, R.S., 1983b, Species and strain comparison of acute neurotoxic effects of trimethyltin in mice and rats, *Neurobehav. Toxicol. Teratol.* 5:377.

Chang, L.W., Tilson, H.A., and Walsh, T.J., 1984a, Neuropathological changes induced by triethyl and trimethyl led compounds, *Toxicologist* 4:164.

Chang, L.W., Wenger, G.R., and McMillan, D.E., 1984b, Neuropathology of trimethyltin intoxication, IV. Changes in the spinal cord, *Environ. Res.* 34:123.

Chang, L.W., Hough, A.J., Bivens, F., and Cockerill, D., 1989, Effects of adrenalectomy and corticosterone on hippocampal lesions induced by trimethyltin, *Biomed. Environ. Sci. Res.* 2:54.

Chen, R.W., and Ganther, H.E., 1975, Some properties of a unique cadmium-binding moiety in the soluble fraction of rat testes, *Environ. Physiol. Biochem.* 5:235.

Chen, R.W., Whanger, P.D., and Fang, S.C., 1974a, Diversion of mercury binding in rat tissues by selenium: A possible mechanism of protection, *Pharm. Res. Comm.* 6:571.

Chen, R.W., Wagner, P.A., Hoekstra, W.G., and Ganther, H.E., 1974b, Affinity labelling studies with [109]cadmium in cadmium-induced testicular injury in rats, *J. Reprod. Fertil.,* 38:293.

Chen, R.W., Lacy, V.L., and Whanger, P.D., 1975a, Effect of selenium on methylmercury binding to subcellular and soluble proteins in rat tissues, *Res. Commun. Chem. Pathol. Pharm.* 12:297.

Chen, R.W., Whanger, P.D., and Weswig, P.H., 1975b, Selenium-induced redistribution of cadmium-binding to tissue proteins: A possible mechanism of protection against cadmium toxicity, *Bioinorg. Chem.* 4:125.

Chung, A.S., Maines, M.D., and Reynolds, W.A., 1982, Inhibition of the enzymes of glutathione metabolism by mercuric chloride in the rat kidney: Reversal by selenium, *Bioch. Pharmacol.* 31:3093.

Clarkson, T.W., 1987, Metal toxicity in the central nervous system, *Environ. Health Perspect.* 75:59.

Cooper, G.P., Suszkiw, T.B., and Manalis, R.S., 1984, Heavy metals: Effects on synaptic transmission, *Neurotoxicology* 5(3):247.

Cotzias, G.C., and Papavasiliou, P.S., 1964, Specificity of zinc pathway through the body: Homeostatic considerations, *Am. J. Physiol.* 206:787.

Davies, N.T., and Campbell, J.K., 1977, The effect of cadmium on intestinal copper absorption and binding in the rat, *Life Sci.* 20:955.

De Haven, D.L., Walsh, T.J., and Mailman, R.B., 1984, Effects of TMT on dopaminergic and serotonergic functions in the CNS, *Toxicol. Appl. Pharmacol.* 74:182.

Doctor, S.V., Costa, L.G., Kendall, D.A., and Murphy, S.D., 1982a, Trimethyltin inhibits uptake of neurotransmitters into mouse forebrain synaptocomes, *Toxicology* 25:213.

Doctor, S.V., Costa, L.G., Kendall, D.A., and Murphy, S.D., 1982b, Trimethyltin in various tissues of the male mouse, *Toxicol. Lett.* 17:43.

Donaldson, J., and Barbeau, A., 1985, Manganese neurotoxicity: Possible clues to the etiology of human brain disorders, in: *Metal Ions in Neurology and Psychiatry* (S. Gabay, T. Harris, and B.T. Ho, eds.), Alan R. Liss, New York, pp. 259–285.

Flora, S.J., Behari, J.R., Ashquin, M., and Tandon, S.K., 1982, Time-dependent protective effect of selenium against cadmium-induced nephrotoxicity and hepatotoxicity, *Chem. Biol. Interact.* 42:345.

Fox, M.R.S., 1974, Effect of essential minerals on cadmium toxicity, *J. Food Sci.* 39:321.

Ganther, H.E., 1978, Modification of methylmercury toxicity and metabolism by selenium and vitamin E: Possible mechanisms, *Environ. Health Persp.* 25:71.

Ganther, H.E., and Sunde, M.L., 1974, Effects of tuna fish and selenium on the toxicity of methylmercury: A progress report, *Science* 39:1.

Goldstein, G.W., 1992, Blood-brain barrier as target for lead toxicity, *Neurotoxicology* (in press).

Groth, D.H., Vignati, L., Lowry, L., Mackay, G., and Stokinger, H.E., 1973, Mutual antagonistic and synergistic effects of inorganic selenium and mercury salts in chronic experiments, in: *Trace Substances in Environ. Health* (D.D. Hemphill, ed.), Univ. of Missouri Press, Columbia, MO, pp. 187–189.

Grun, M., Anke, M., and Partschefeld, M., 1977, Cadmium toxicity, in: *Kadmium-Symposium*, Friedrich-Schillr-Universitat, Jena, German Democratic Republic, 1977.

Gunn, S.A., Gould, T.C., and Anderson, W.A.D., 1966, Protective effect of thiol compounds against cadmium-induced vascular damage to testis, *Proc. Soc. Exp. Biol. Med.* 122:1036.

Hamilton, D.L., and Smith, M.W., 1977, Cadmium inhibits calcium absorption in rat intestine, *J. Physiol.* 265(1):54.

Hasan, M.Z., and Seth, T.D., 1981, Effects of lead and zinc administration on liver, kidney, and brain levels of copper, lead, manganese, and zinc and on erythrocyte ALA-D activity in rats, *Toxicol. Lett.* 7:353.

Herman, S.P., Klein, R., Talley, F.A., and Krigman, M.R., 1973, An ultrastructural study of methylmercury-induced primary sensory neuropathy in rats, *Lab. Invest.* 28:104.

Hikal, A.H., Light, G.W., Shikker, W., Scarlet, A., and Ali, A.F., 1988, Determination of amino acid in different regions of rat brain application to acute effects of TMT, *Life Sci.* 42:2029.

Hill, C.H., Matrone, G., Payne, W.L., and Barber, C.W., 1963, In vivo interactions of cadmium with copper, zinc and iron, *J. Nutr.* 80:227.

Holmberg, R.E. Jr., and Ferm, V.H., 1969, Interrelationships of selenium, cadmium, and arsenic in mammalian teratogenesis, *Arch. Environ. Health* 18:873.

Hsu, F.S., Krook, L., Pond, W.G., and Duncan, J.R., 1975, Interaction of dietary calcium with toxic levels of lead and zinc in pigs, *J. Nutr.* 105:112.

Iwata, H., Okamoto, H., and Ohsawa, Y., 1973, Effect of selenium on methylmercury poisoning, *Res. Commun. Chem. Pathol. Pharm.* 5:673.

Jacobs, J.M., 1980, Vascular permeability and neural injury, in: *Experimental and Clinical Neurotoxicology* (P.S. Spencer and H.H. Schaumburg, eds.), Williams and Wilkins, Baltimore, pp. 102–117.

Jennette, K.W., 1981, Role of metals in carcinogenesis: Biochemistry and metabolism, *Environ. Health Perspect.* 40:233.

Johnson, S.L., and Pond, W.G., 1974, Inorganic vs. organic Hg toxicity in growing rats: Protection by dietary Se but not Zn, *Nutr. Rep. Intl.* 9:135.

Kar, A.B., Das, R.P., and Mukerji, B., 1960, Prevention of cadmium-induced changes in the gonads of rats by zinc and selenium. A study in antagonism between metals in the biological system, *Proc. Natl. Inst. Sci. India* 26:40.

Katsuki, S., Hirai, S., and Terao, T., 1957, On the disease of central nervous system in Minamata District with unknown etiology, with special references to the clinical observation, *Kumamoto Igakkai Zasshi* 31 (Suppl 23):110.

Kobayashi, J., 1974, Effects of cadmium on calcium metabolism of rats, in: *Trace Substances in Environmental Health VII* (D.D. Hemphill, ed.), Univ. of Missouri, Columbia, MO, pp. 263–280.

Kosta, L., Byrne, A.R., and Zelenko, V., 1975, Correlation between selenium and mercury in man following exposure to inorganic mercury, *Nature* 254:238.

Lajtha, A., 1962, The brain barrier system, in: *Neurochemistry*, 2nd ed. (K.A.C. Elliott, I.H. Page, and J.H. Quastel, eds.), Charles C. Thomas, Springfield, IL, pp. 229–430.

Larsson, S.E., and Piscator, M., 1971, Effect of cadmium on skeletal tissue in normal and calcium-deficient rats, *Isr. J. Med. Sci.*, 7:495.

Lederer, L.B., and Bing, F.C., 1940, Effect of calcium and phosphorus on retention of lead by growing organisms, *JAMA* 114:2457.

Mahaffey-Six, K., and Goyer, R.A., 1970, Experimental enhancement of lead toxicity by low dietary calcium, *J. Lab. Clin. Med.* 76:933.

Mailman, R.B., Krigman, M.R., Frye, G.D., and Hannin, Z., 1983, Effects of postnasal trimethyltin or triethyltin treatment of CNS catecholamines, GABA, and acetyl choline systems in the rat, *J. Neurochem.* 40:1423.

Mason, K.E., and Young, J.O., 1967, Effectiveness of selenium and zinc in protecting against cadmium-induced injury of the rat testis, in: *Symposium: Selenium in Biomedicine* (O.H. Muth, J.E. Oldfield, and P.H. Weswig, eds.), AVI Westport, CT, pp. 383–394.

McEwen, B.S., Gerlach, J.L., and Micco, D.J., 1975, Putative glucocorticoid receptors in hippocampus and other regions of the rat brain, in: *The Hippocampus*, Vol. 1 (R.L. Isaacson, and K.H. Pribram, eds.), pp. 285–322.

McLachlan, D.R.C., and Farnell, B.J., 1985, Aluminum and neuronal degeneration, in: *Metal Ions in Neurology and Psychiatry* (S. Gabay, J. Harris, and B.T. Ho, eds.), Alan R. Liss, New York, pp. 69–87.

Meredith, P.A., Moore, M.R., and Goldberg, A., 1977, The effects of calcium on lead absorption in rats, *Biochem. J.* 166:531.

Minnema, D.J., 1989, Neurochemical alterations in lead intoxication—an overview, in: *Comments on Toxicology* Vol. 3(3), (L.W. Chang, ed.), Gordon and Breach, London, pp. 207–224.

Morikawa, N., 1961, Pathological studies on organic mercury poisoning, *Kumamoto Med. J.* 14:71.

Morrison, J.N., Quarterman, J., and Humphries, W.R., 1977, The effects of dietary calcium and phosphate on lead poisoning in rats, *J. Comp. Pathol.* 87:417.

Naalsund, L.V., Suen, C.N., and Fonnum, F., 1985, Changes in neurobiological parameters in the hippocampus after exposure to TMT, *Neurotoxicology* 6:145.

Nath, R., Prasad, R., Palinal, V.K., and Chopra, R.K., 1984, Molecular basis of cadmium toxicity, *Prog. Food Nutr. Sci.* 8:109.

Oh, S.H., Ganther, H.E., and Hoekstra, W.G., 1974, Selenium as a component of glutathione peroxidase isolated from bovine erythrocytes, *Biochemistry* 13:1925.

Ohi, G., Nishigaki, S., Seki, H., Tamura, Y., Maki, T., Maeda, H., Ochiai, S., Yamada, H., Shimamura, Y., and Yagyu, H.,

1975, Interaction of dietary methylmercury and selenium on accumulation and retention of these substances in rat organs, *Toxicol. Appl. Pharmacol.* 32:527.

Ohi, G., Nishigaki, S., Seki, H., Tamura, Y., Maki, T., Konno, H., Ochiai, S., Yamada, H., Shimamura, Y., Mizoguchi, I., and Yagyu, H., 1976, Efficacy of selenium in tuna and selenite in modifying methylmercury intoxication, *Environ. Res.* 12:49.

Okinaka, S., Yoshikawa, M., Mozai, T., Mizune, Y., Tereio, T., Wataushe, H., Ogiharo, K., Hirai, S., Yoshino, Y., Inose, T., Azar, S., and Tsuda, M., 1964, Encephalomyalopathy due to an organic mercury compound, *Neurology* 4:68.

Parizek, J., 1957, The destructive effect of cadmium ion on testicular tissue and its prevention by zinc, *J. Endocrinol.* 15:56.

Parizek, J., Ostadalova, I., Benes, I., and Babicky, A., 1968, Pregnancy and trace elements: The protective effect of compounds of an essential trace element—selenium—against the peculiar toxic effects of cadmium during pregnancy, *J. Reprod. Fertil.* 16:507.

Parizek, J., Ostadalova, I., Kalouskova, J., Babicky, A., and Benes, J., 1971, The detoxifying effects of selenium interrelations between compounds of selenium and certain metals, in: *Newer Trace Elements in Nutrition* (W. Mertz, and W.E. Cornatzer, eds.), Marcel Dekker, New York, pp. 85–98.

Parizek, J., Kalouskova, J., Babicky, A., Benes, J., and Pavlik, L., 1974, Interaction of selenium with mercury, cadmium and other toxic metals, in: *Trace Elements Metabolism in Animals,* Vol. 2 (W.G. Hoekstra, J.W. Suttie, H.E. Ganther, and W. Mertz, eds.), University Park Press, Baltimore, MD, pp. 119–125.

Patel, M., Ardelt, B.K., Yim, G.K.W., and Isom, G.E., 1990, Interaction of trimethyltin with hippocampal glutamate, *Neurotoxicology* 11:601.

Paterson, R.A., and Usher, D.R., 1971, Acute toxicity of methylmercury on glycolytic intermediates and adenine nucleotides of rat brain, *Life Sci.* 10:121.

Petering, H.G., 1980, The influence of dietary zinc and copper on the biologic effects of orally ingested lead in the rat, *Ann. N.Y. Acad. Sci.* 355:298.

Petering, H.G., Johnson, M.A., and Stemmer, K.L., 1971, Studies on zinc metabolism in the rat, I. Dose-response effects of cadmium, *Arch Envir. Hlth.* 23:93.

Petit, T.L., 1989, Issues in aluminum neurotoxicity, in: *Comments on Toxicology* Vol. 3(3) (L.W. Chang, ed.), Gordon and Breach, London, pp. 225–238.

Pfaff, D.W., Silva, M.T.A., and Weiss, T.M., 1971, Telemetered recording of hormone effects on hippocampal neurons, *Science* 172:384.

Potter, S., and Matrone, G., 1974, Effect of selenite on the toxicity of dietary methylmercury and mercuric chloride in the rat, *J. Nutr.* 104:638.

Powell, G.W., Miller, W.J., Morton, J.D., and Clifton, C.M., 1964, Influence of dietary cadmium level and supplemental zinc on cadmium toxicity in the bovine, *J. Nutr.* 84:205.

Quarterman, J., and Morrison, J.N., 1975, The effects of dietary calcium and phosphorus on the retention and excretion of lead in rats, *Br. J. Nutr.* 34:351.

Rehman, S., and Chandra, O., 1984, Regional interrelationships of zinc, copper, and lead in the brain following lead intoxication, *Bull. Environ. Contam. Toxicol.* 32:157.

Reuhl, K.R., Mackenzie, B., and Chang, L.W., 1982, Neuropathological lesions in mice following neonatal exposure to trimethyltin, *Toxicologist* 2:22.

Richardson, M.E., and Fox, M.R.S., 1974, Dietary cadmium and enteropathy in Japanese quail. Histochemical and ultrastructural studies, *Lab. Invest.* 31:722.

Richardson, M.E., Fox, M.R.S., and Fry, B.E. Jr., 1974, Pathological changes produced in Japanese quail by ingestion of cadmium, *J. Nutr.* 104:323.

Rotruck, J.T., Pope, A.L., Ganther, H.E., Swanson, A.B., Hafeman, D.G., and Hoekstra, W.G., 1973, Selenium: Biochemical role as a component of glutathione peroxidase, *Science* 179:588.

Salvaterra, P., Lown, B., Morganti, J., and Massaro, E.J., 1973, Alterations in neurochemical and behavioral parameters in the mouse induced by low doses of methylmercury, *Acta Pharmacol. Toxicol.* 33:177.

Silbergeld, E.K., and Hruska, R.E., 1980, Neurochemical investigations of low level lead exposure, in: *Low Level Lead Exposure—The Clinical Implications of Current Research* (H.L. Needleman, ed.), Raven Press, New York, pp. 135–156.

Skerfring, S., 1978, Interaction between selenium and methylmercury, *Environ. Health Perspect.* 25:57.

Steinwall, O., 1961, Transport mechanisms in certain blood-brain barrier phenomena—a hypothesis, *Acta Psychiatr. Neurol. Scand.* 36 (Suppl 150):314.

Steinwall, O., 1969, Brain uptake of Se[75]: Selenomethionine after damage to blood-brain barrier by mercuric ions, *Acta. Neurol. Scand.* 45:362.

Steinwall, O., and Synder, H., Brain uptake of C[14]-cyclo-leucine after damage to blood-brain barrier by mercuric ions, *Acta Neurol. Scand.* 45:369.

Stoewsand, G.L., Anderson, J.L., Gutenmann, W.H., and Lisk, D.J., 1977, Form of dietary selenium on mercury and selenium tissue retention and egg production in Japanese quail, *Nutr. Rep. Intl.* 15:81.

Takeuchi, T., Kambara, T., Morikawa, N., Matsumoto, H., Shiraishi, Y., and Ito, H., 1959, Pathologic observations of the Minamata disease, *Acta Pathol. Jpn.* 9:768.

Takeuchi, T., Matsumoto, H., Shiraishi, T., Koya, G., Saski, M., Hirata, Y., Fukinoto, K., Miyazaki, T., and Ogi, J., 1962a, An experimental pathological study on the etiology of Minamata's disease, especially the role of methyl mercuric sulfide, *Kumamoto Med. J.* 16:713.

Takeuchi, T., Morikawa, N., Matsumoto, H., and Shiraishi, Y., 1962b, A pathological study of Minamata disease in Japan, *Acta Neuropathol.* 2:40.

Task Group on Metal Interaction, 1978, Factors influencing metabolism and toxicity of metals: A consensus report, *Environ. Health Perspect.* 25:3.

Tobias, J.M., Lushbaugh, C.C., Path, H.M., Postel, S., Swift, M.N., and Gerard, R.W., 1946, The pathology and therapy with 2,3-dimercaptopropanol (BAL) of experimental Cd poisoning, *J. Pharmacol. Exp. Ther.* 87:102.

Tokuomi, H., 1961, Minamata disease: An unusual neurological disorder occurring in Minamata, Japan, *Kumamoto Med. J.* 14:47.

Tokuomi, H., Hirata, Y., and Miyazaki, T., 1966, Studies on Minamata disease, V. On the etiology of this disease, clinical and experimental studies, *Kumamoto Igakkai Zasshi* 34 (Suppl 3):78.

Tower, D.B., 1962, Molecular transport across neural and non-neural membranes, in: *Properties of Membranes and Diseases of the Nervous System,* Springer, New York.

Vallee, B.L., and Ulmer, D.D., 1972, Biochemical effects of mercury, cadmium, and lead, *Ann. Rev. Biochem.* 41:91.

Verity, M.A., Brown, W.J., and Cheung, M., 1975, Organic mercurial encephalopathy: In vivo and in vitro effects of methyl mercury on synaptosomal respiration, *J. Neurochem.* 25:759.

Ware, R.A., Chang, L.W., and Burkholder, P.M., 1974, An ultrastructural study on the blood-brain barrier dysfunction following mercury intoxication, *Acta Neuropathol.* (Berlin) 30:211.

Washko, P.W., and Cousins, R.J., 1975, Effect of low dietary calcium on chronic cadmium toxicity in rats, *Nutr. Rep. Intl.* 11:113.

Watanabe, I., 1977, Effect of triethyltin on the developing brain of the mouse, in: *Neurotoxicology* (L. Roizin, H. Shiraki, and N. Grcevic, eds.), Raven Press, New York, pp. 317–326.

Watanabe, I., 1980, Organotins, in: *Experimental and Clinical Neurotoxicology* (P.S. Spencer, and H.H. Schaumburg, eds.), Williams and Wilkins, Baltimore, pp. 545–557.

Webb, M., 1972, Protection by zinc against cadmium toxicity, *Biochem. Pharmacol.* 21:2767.

Welsh, S.O., and Soares, J.H., 1976, The protective effect of vitamin E and selenium against methylmercury toxicity in the Japanese quail, *Nutr. Rep. Intl.* 13:43.

Whanger, P.D., 1985, Metabolic interactions of selenium with cadmium, mercury, and silver, in: *Advances in Nutritional Research,* Vol. 7 (H.H. Draper, ed.), Plenum Press, New York, pp. 221–250.

Whanger, P.D., Ridlington, J.W., and Holcomb, C.L., 1980, Interactions of zinc and selenium on the binding of cadmium to rat tissue proteins, *Ann. N.Y. Acad. Sci.* 355:333.

Winder, C., and Lewis, P.D., 1985, The experimental neurotoxicity of lead: Neuropathological and neurochemical aspects, in: *Metal Ions in Neurology and Psychiatry* (S. Gabay, J. Harris, and B.T. Ho, eds.), Alan R. Liss, New York, pp. 231–245.

Willoughby, R.A., MacDonald, E., McSherry, B.J., and Brown, G., 1972a, Lead poisoning and the interaction between lead and zinc poisoning in the foal, *Can. J. Comp. Med.* 36:348.

Willoughby, R.A., Thirapatsakun, T., and McSherry, B.J., 1972b, Influence of rations low in calcium and phosphorus on blood and tissue lead concentrations in the horse, *Am. J. Vet. Res.* 33:1165.

Wilson, W.E., Hudson, B.M., Kanamatsu, D., Kanamatsu, D., Walsh, T., Tilson, H., and Hong, J., 1986, TMT-induced alterations in brain amino acid, amines and amine metabolites: Relationship to hyperammoniemia, *Neurotoxicology* 7:63.

Yoshino, Y., Mozai, T., and Nakao, K., 1966, Biochemical changes in the brain of rats poisoned with an alkyl mercuric compound with special reference to the inhibition of protein synthesis in brain cortex slide, *J. Neurochem.* 13:1223.

Chapter 6

Neurotoxic Metals and Neuronal Signalling Processes

Daniel Minnema

1. INTRODUCTION

Many of the metals are recognized neurotoxicants. The circumstances of human exposure to these metals varies. In the case of the chemotherapeutic agent cisplatin, exposure is the deliberate result of this drug's use in cancer treatment. Exposure to neurotoxic concentrations of the essential element manganese is associated almost exclusively with manganese ore mining and steel mill operations. Although human neurotoxicity resulting from exposure to organic tin compounds has been associated mainly with industrial settings, the increasing use of these compounds (as heat stabilizers for PVC products, catalysts for polyurethane foam and silicone rubber elastomers, biocides, and anthelmintics) increases the risk of the general population to alkyltin exposure. Similarly, exposure to cadmium, which is used for coating and plating, batteries, paint pigments, plastic stabilizers, and metal alloys, is mainly an industrial problem at present, although the amount of cadmium in the general environment is increasing. Methylmercury contamination, largely from the wood-pulp industry, chlorine alkali plants, and the bacterial conversion of other mercury compounds released into the environment, continues to be a significant environmental problem, as illustrated by the bioaccumulation of methylmercury in many different fish populations. Since elemental mercury vapor is a known neurotoxicant, there recently has been some concern, based on anecdotal evidence, that the release of Hg° from amalgam dental fillings may induce neurological illnesses. Aluminum, which is used extensively (cooking utensils, antacids, antiperspirants), has been implicated in Alzheimer's disease. The use of inorganic lead in a variety of materials, particularly paints, has made this metal prevalent in the general environment. The persistence of inorganic lead in the environ-

Daniel Minnema • Hazleton Washington, Vienna, Virginia 22182.
The Vulnerable Brain and Environmental Risks, Volume 2: Toxins in Food, edited by Robert L. Isaacson and Karl F. Jensen. Plenum Press, New York, 1992.

ment, combined with the evidence that childhood exposure to relatively low lead levels produce cognitive deficits, continues to create concern about exposure to this metal. The removal of organic lead from gasoline has eliminated a major source of potential organic lead exposure, although organic lead is still used in aviation fuels.

While all the aforementioned metals are recognized neurotoxicants, current social concern is with the possibility that chronic exposure to relatively low concentrations of these metals may be associated with subtle nervous system dysfunction. For example, children chronically exposed to relatively low levels of lead, levels that were previously believed to be safe, are now recognized to be at increased risk for diminished cognitive function. It is not clear if this lead-induced developmental insult persists into adulthood. Similarly, chronic exposure of the mature nervous system to certain metals may have an impact later in life, as suggested by the possible role of aluminum in Alzheimer's disease. Concern for possible long-term nervous system damage following chronic, low-level metal exposure is the driving force behind the research examining the effects of these metals on neuronal signalling processes. This chapter will describe "normal" signalling and signal transduction processes, the roles such processes serve in neuronal function, and the potential interaction of neurotoxic metals with certain neuronal signalling and signal transduction processes. Since the consequences of altered neuronal signalling processes are not well characterized, particularly with respect to metal exposure, the section of the chapter that deals with this topic is speculative, describing possible outcomes that may represent important endpoints in metal neurotoxicity.

2. OVERVIEW OF THE NEURONAL SIGNALLING PROCESS

In the context of this review, neuronal signalling refers to those processes by which neurons interact with other neurons, as well as with non-neuronal tissue. More specifically, neuronal signalling includes those processes by which the nerve transmits and receives extracellular information, and the mechanisms by which such signals are transduced to produce cellular responses. Essentially all aspects of neuronal regulation are affected by the neuronal milieu, which consists mainly of various ions, input from other neurons, and a variety of growth/hormonal factors. To a large extent, neurons interact with their extracellular milieu through membrane and intracellular receptors and membrane ion channels. Due to their excitable nature, neurons are particularly sensitive to changes in intra- and extracellular ion concentrations. Intraneuronal ion concentrations are tightly regulated by a relatively impermeable membrane, various ion pumps, intracellular ion binding sites, and a variety of specific ion channels. In some cases, these membrane ion channels are voltage sensitive, others are directly associated with membrane receptors, whereas others are operationally linked with, or controlled by, a cascade of intracellular signals (i.e., second messengers). In addition to modulating certain ion channels, membrane receptors are also linked to a variety of intraneuronal processes that play roles in neuronal growth, differentiation, plasticity, and survival. There are also intraneuronal receptor proteins that interact with both steroidal and non-steroidal hormones to influence gene transcription.

A major aspect of neuronal signalling involves synaptic transmission. Usually the response of a nerve to a neurotransmitter and/or neuromodulatory substance is a change in the net activity (i.e., firing rate or rate of membrane depolarizations) of that nerve. Chronic short-term changes in neuronal activity can have an impact on both short- and long-term aspects of neuronal function. Short-term changes in synaptic plasticity, as defined by the potentiation, augmentation, and/or depression of postsynaptic potentials (Zucker, 1989), may be important in the progression to long-term neuronal plasticity. From a biochemical point of view, some short-term changes in synaptic plasticity may involve a shutdown of membrane K^+ channels by protein kinase C (PK_C) (Alkon and Nelson, 1990). Long-term changes in neuronal activity are usually dependent on increases/decreases in the synthesis of new proteins (Nelson and Alkon, 1990). Although the consequences of altered neuronal signalling processes are not fully recognized, the interaction of neurotoxic metals with various aspects of such processes could potentially affect a number of neuronal functions, ranging from subtle short-term changes in neuronal activity to neuronal death. Neurons appear to be sensitive to certain signals during their development, specifically those signals that induce neuronal differentiation, growth, migration, and synaptogenesis. The interaction of metals with these developmental signals may result in a nervous system dysfunction that persists long after neuronal maturation.

3. CONSEQUENCES OF ALTERED NEURONAL SIGNALS

Despite the great potential for involvement, there are few instances in which a disease is known to be linked to altered neuronal signalling processes (Snyder and Narahashi, 1990). Some environmental toxicants are clearly capable of inducing their toxicity by interacting with signalling processes; for example, the inhibition of $GABA_A$ receptor-mediated Cl^- movement by cyclodiene organochloride insecticides (Gant et al., 1987). However, at present, no clear relationship has been ascribed between the neurotoxicity induced by the neurotoxic metals and their interaction with neuronal signalling processes. Part of the difficulty in describing such a relationship is the differential toxicological profiles that result from different conditions of metal exposure. The neurological symptoms resulting from acute exposure to relatively high concentrations of certain metals are fairly well characterized; however, the more subtle nature of the neurotoxic effects resulting from chronic exposure to relatively low concentrations of these metals makes it more difficult to describe the precise nature of the insult, particularly when the developing nervous system is the target. Various processes unique to the developing nervous system, specifically neuronal differentiation, growth, migration, survival, and synaptogenesis, may represent selective targets of metal-induced insult. Thus it is necessary to differentiate between the neurotoxicity of the metals on the mature vs. the developing nervous system.

3.1. Neurotoxicity in the Mature Nervous System

In the adult mammal, there is essentially no turnover of neurons in the brain. To compensate for this lack of regenerative capabilities, the nervous system is redundant and adaptive (Lynch, 1986). Such adaptive processes can be described at the functional level (behavioral), the morphological level (dendritic sprouting), and the neurochemical level (synaptic plasticity). However, these adaptive capabilities are finite. At some point in the organism's life span, toxicant-induced neuronal death, combined with "normal" neuronal attrition, could lead to loss of nervous system function. In addition, altered neurotransmission can induce neuronal degeneration, as demonstrated by the ability of excessive stimulation of excitatory amino acid (glutamate, aspartate) receptors to induce cell death (Olney, 1990; Chapter 15). Altered neurotransmission can also result in the inability of various target organs to compensate for the altered signal, as occurs following exposure to acetylcholinesterase inhibitors. Long-term changes in other aspects of neurotransmission may lead to more subtle effects, as reflected by neuronal plasticity. Neuronal plasticity can involve the up/downregulation of those processes directly involved in neurotransmission (e.g., receptors). Whether the plasticity of particular neuronal systems can be considered a consequence of toxicant exposure is not clear at the present time, since compensation/adaption is a normal physiological response. Metal-induced toxic changes involve the regulation and/or activity of neuronal systems that compromise an individual's capacity to respond appropriately to the immediate environment. For example, the upregulation of dopamine receptors resulting from long-term dopamine antagonist therapy can result in tardive dyskinesia.

3.2. Neurotoxicity in the Developing Nervous System

The developing nervous system is known to be more susceptible to metal-induced insults than the adult nervous system. This developmental susceptibility may result from a number of factors, such as a propensity for increased metal absorption, and/or an immature blood–brain barrier, which exhibits increased permeability to a number of substances. In addition, increased vulnerability may reflect the interaction of metals with those signalling processes associated with various trophic and adhesion proteins. These proteins regulate a number of interrelating neuronal developmental processes, including cell division, differentiation, growth, functional maintenance (including survival), and neuronal architecture (i.e., neuronal migration, outgrowth and branching of dendritic processes, target recognition, and synaptogenesis). The interaction of metals with the signalling processes that regulate these aspects of neuronal development could affect the rate of nervous system maturation and/or compromise the organization (and thus the function) of the nervous system at maturity.

3.2.1. Toxicity in Neuronal Precursor Cells

The toxicity of some metals may involve effects on neuronal-precursor cells that are actively proliferating. Toxicity may be expressed as either an alteration in the rate of cell division and/or cell survival. An obvious concern with proliferating cells is that toxicant exposure will affect the progress of cells through the cell cycle (i.e., an altered rate of proliferation), as observed with prenatal ethanol exposure (Miller, 1986). Recent observations with other cell types indicate that some signal (or removal of a signal) can trigger a cascade of events during the cell cycle that causes the cell to commit to death during the G_1 phase of the cell cycle. This process is referred to as signalled cell death, also called *apoptosis* (Hooper, 1990). Although there has been little research examining signal-induced death in proliferating neuronal precursor cells, it is reasonable to suppose that such a process can occur. Signalled cell death is differentiated from necrotic (injury-induced) cell death in that the former can be markedly delayed or prevented by pretreatment with agents that inhibit mRNA or protein synthesis. The possibility that neurotoxic metals could induce programmed death in neuronal precursor cells is suggested by the observation that tributyltin and Ca^{2+} ionophores induce apoptosis in thymocytes (Aw *et al.*, 1990; McConkey *et al.*, 1989).

3.2.2. Neuronal Differentiation

Neuronal differentiation is characterized morphologically by the outgrowth of neurite processes and neurochemically by the appearance of membrane Na^+ channels. Although the developmental importance of this neuronal process has been recognized by neurotoxicologists (Fujita *et al.*, 1989), there has been limited toxicological research on this phenomenon. The prototype system for examining neuronal differentiation has been the PC12 rat pheochromocytoma cell line, in which the role of the trophic factor, nerve growth factor (NGF), has been well characterized. NGF has been identified as a major factor for promoting differentiation in sympathetic and neural crest-derived sensory neurons. NGF-induced neuronal differentiation is mediated by specific membrane receptors, specifically the *trk* protooncogene-encoded high-affinity NGF receptor (Fujita *et al.*, 1989; Klein *et al.*, 1991). In the CNS, other trophic factors, such as brain-derived neurotrophic factor (BDNF) and neurotrophin 3 (NT-3), may stimulate the differentiation (and survival) of specific populations of neurons (Knusel *et al.*, 1991). Neurons also respond to growth factors that are not normally associated with neuronal tissue, such as epidermal growth factor, fibroblast growth factor, and insulin-like growth factor. The significance of such responses is not fully understood at present. Differentiation induced by NGF occurs in a cell-cycle specific manner (Ridkin *et al.*, 1989). The cells must be in a compartment of G_1 (called G_D for differentiation; Scott *et al.*, 1982) before they can differentiate. Thus, toxicant exposure that affects the signalling processes involved in differentiation would have the greatest impact on those cells that were in the appropriate phase of the cell cycle during exposure. Alterations in differentiation could result in incomplete or altered development of critical neuronal pathways, a loss of a specific population of cells, or a population of growing, incompletely differentiated nerve cells. A variety of neuroblastoma cell lines (which have been suggested to be incompletely differentiated nerve cells) exhibit defects in their NGF receptors, suggesting that NGF is, in part, responsible for the complete differentiation of these cells under normal (intact NGF-3 receptor) circumstances (Azar *et al.*, 1990). Trophic factors are likely to be involved in the neurite outgrowth and growth-cone motility that occurs shortly after differentiation. Additionally, trophic factors are involved in neuronal survival, as discussed below.

3.2.3. Signalled Neuronal Death

Current evidence indicates that signalled neuronal death occurs in the early stages of neuronal growth following differentiation (Johnson *et al.*, 1989). It is estimated that during the development of the mammalian nervous system approximately 50% of the newly differentiated, non-proliferating nerves die (Oppenheim, 1985). The survival of the remaining neurons appears to be dependent on several factors, including trophic factors from target tissues and the activity of impinging nerves. There is ample evidence that, during development, NGF is synthesized and secreted in minute quantities by target tissue that will eventually be innervated by sympathetic and sensory neurons. Although specific neuronal membrane receptors for NGF have been characterized, it is not known which of these NGF receptors are involved in neuronal survival. The appearance of the internalized NGF/receptor complex in the soma (following retrograde transport down the axon) may be important for sympathetic neuron survival. Additionally, trophic factors secreted by target tissues may actually stimulate the production of neurons, as suggested by a recent study in which the presence of male genitalia controls neurogenesis in the leech (Baptista *et al.*, 1990).

Neuronal death caused by NGF deprivation is dependent on mRNA and protein synthesis, as the death of NGF-deprived sympathetic neurons could be prevented in the presence of inhibitors of protein and/or RNA synthesis (Johnson *et al.*, 1989). However, unlike the signalled programmed death processes described in other cell types (Hooper, 1990), programmed death in sympathetic neurons is not associated with DNA fragmentation. Indeed, very few of the sympathetic neurons that die following NGF deprivation exhibit the morphological changes that characterize apoptosis. As sympathetic nerves reach "maturity," at which time they have grown and innervated their target tissues, these nerves are no longer dependent on the presence of NGF for their survival. This change in NGF dependence indicates that some yet-unidentified change in the signalled death cascade is altered as nerves reach maturity. This alteration may involve intracellular $[Ca^{2+}]_i$ (Koike *et al.*, 1989). Immature, acutely NGF-dependent neurons have low $[Ca^{2+}]_i$. It has been proposed that, in order to survive, the trophic factor "substitutes" or "protects" the neuron from the signalled death process that would normally ensue in trophic-factor-deprived neurons. Treatments that increase $[Ca^{2+}]_i$ (e.g., membrane depolarization) also increase sympathetic neuron survival following NGF deprivation. In accordance with this hypothesis, the decrease in NGF dependence of sympathetic neurons is associated with an increase in $[Ca^{2+}]_i$. Such an increase in $[Ca^{2+}]_i$ would be expected as growing neurons receive more afferent/excitatory input, emphasizing the potential for those metals that affect transmitter release to have an impact on neuronal survival. However, excessive $[Ca^{2+}]_i$ is potentially toxic to the neuron, and only at some optimum intermediate $[Ca^{2+}]_i$ is neuronal survival independent of trophic factor. Thus, the ability of many of the neurotoxic metals to affect intraneuronal Ca^{2+} homeostasis indicates that such metals could potentially affect neuronal survival during specific stages of neuronal development.

3.2.4. Neuronal Architecture and Synaptogenesis

The neurotoxic metals may interact with the factors that regulate neuronal architecture and synapse formation. In addition to trophic factors, neural-cell adhesion molecules (NCAMs) play a major role in neurodevelopmental processes (Rutishauser *et al.*, 1988). During development, the membrane-associated NCAMs of one cell interact with other NCAMs of an apposing cell. The degree of this affinity between NCAM proteins is dependent on the extent of NCAM polysialylation, which is greater in the developing (perinatal or embryonic) form of NCAMs vs. the adult form. NCAMs, through neuron-neuron, neuron-astrocyte, and astrocyte-astrocyte interactions, determine, in part, neuronal architecture by regulating growth-cone development, fiber outgrowth, migration, branching, and synapse formation. A number of different adhesion molecules have been identified that are categorized as either immunoglobulins (which includes NCAMs), integrins, and the Ca^{2+}-dependent adhesion molecules (cadherins). The precise roles of these molecules during neuronal development and their interactions with trophic factors (e.g., NGF) remain to be resolved. Additionally, synaptic transmission itself may play an important role during neuronal migration and synaptic development. For example, neurotransmission has been shown to regulate neuronal growth cones that are involved in neurite elongation, directional pathfinding, and target recognition (McCobb and Kater, 1988). This regulation may be the result of depolarization-induced changes in $[Ca^{2+}]_i$, since moderate elevations in $[Ca^{2+}]_i$ produce dendritic pruning, whereas higher elevations in $[Ca^{2+}]_i$ result in neuronal death (Kater et al., 1989). It is reasonable to speculate that metal-induced changes in either synaptic transmission or intracellular Ca^{2+} regulation during development may result in altered neuronal organization and/or altered basal activity of a population of neurons.

4. NEURONAL SIGNALLING PROCESSES: POTENTIAL SITES OF METAL ACTION

As characterized in Figure 1, the neurotoxic metals could potentially affect signalling at several levels. (1) Metals could affect the resting membrane potential and/or the rate of electrical conduction of the nerve by interacting with myelin (glial cells), membrane ion channels, membrane Na,K-ATPases, and/or the membrane directly (e.g., permeability). (2) Metals could affect the synthesis, storage, and/or release (secretion) of chemical signals that can influence a number of neuronal functions. The release of such chemicals can be directly from neurons (i.e.g, neurotransmitters, neuromodulators), from neuronal support cells (Schwann cells, neuroglia), from target tissue (i.e., muscle), or from certain endocrine organs. (3) Metals could affect the amount of chemical signal reaching the neuronal receptor site subsequent to release (e.g., inhibition of transmitter uptake). (4) Metals could interact with membrane and/or intracellular receptor proteins, thus altering the affinity of the receptor for the ligand and/or altering the conformation of the receptor-ligand complex to reduce its activity. (5) Metals could interact with receptor transduction processes to alter the expression of second messengers, specifically Ca^{2+}, cAMP, cGMP, inositol 1,4,5-trisphosphate (IP_3), and 1,2-diacylglycerol (1,2-DAG). Possible sites at which metals could affect the expression of second messengers include membrane Ca^{2+} channels, G-proteins, adenylate cyclase, guanylate cyclase, and phospholipase C. (6) Along the same line, metals could interact with intracellular organelles, specifically mitochondria and endoplasmic reticulum, to alter their ability to regulate Ca^{2+} fluxes, thereby altering $[Ca^{2+}]_i$. (7) Metals could interact with a number of proteins that are normally regulated by signalled processes, specifically protein kinases, Ca^{2+}-activated enzymes/cofactors, and DNA-binding proteins (including third messenger systems). (8) Metals could interact with nucleic acids (i.e., DNA, RNA), the nuclear membrane/matrix, and/or various promotor factors to alter transcription accuracy and/or rate. (9) The metals could indirectly exert their influence on these aforementioned processes by interacting with various metabolic processes involved in energy production, such as oxidative phosphorylation and/or ATP production.

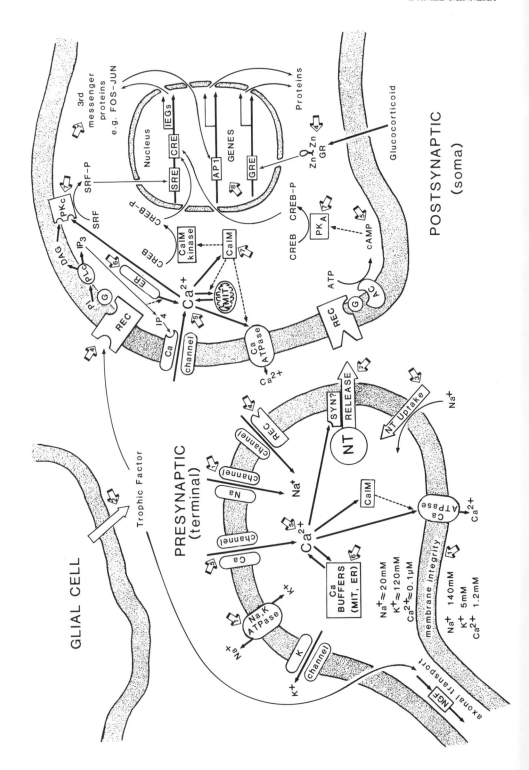

4.1. Membrane Depolarization

Neuronal activity is often defined in electrical terms as the rate of membrane depolarization. Propagation of the action potential down the axon is the major means by which neuronal signals are transmitted from one end of the nerve to the other, ultimately inducing the release of transmitter from the nerve terminal. Some chemical signals, including growth factors, can utilize anterograde and retrograde transport processes to traverse the axon. Basically, depolarization of the neuronal membrane involves membrane permeability, Na,K-ATPase activity, and the opening and closing of membrane Na^+ and K^+ channels. Myelin, provided by Schwann cells and oligodendrocytes, also plays a major role in the conduction velocity of the action potential down the axon. Many of the metals, including triethyllead, methylmercury, and mercury, increase the permeability of the neuronal membrane. Such metal-induced increases in membrane permeability may not be the result of generalized decreases in membrane integrity, but rather manifestations of metal interaction with specific membrane channel proteins. Insult to the axonal myelin sheath can produce alterations in conduction velocity, as illustrated by the interference with oxidative phosphorylation by triethyltin following its accumulation into myelin. Several of the metals are also potent inhibitors of Na^+,K^+-ATPase activity (e.g., Hg^{2+}, Cd^{2+}) and therefore can produce a gradual depolarization of the neuronal membrane.

4.2. Neurotransmitter/Neuromodulator Release

The major means by which the activity of one neuron influences the activity of another neuron (or target tissue) is by chemical transmission. Classically, the release of transmitter from the presynaptic terminal is dependent on the activity of that neuron. Neuromodulators (often small peptides), which do not act as classical "point-to-point" neurotransmitters, but rather as pre- or postsynaptic modulators of neurotransmission, are often released from the presynaptic terminal along with neurotransmitter. Neuromodulator release is likely to be subject to most of the same influences as neurotransmitter release. A number of factors can affect transmitter release from the nerve terminal, including the amount and storage of transmitter, the permeability of the presynaptic membrane, membrane enzymatic activity, activity of presynaptic receptors, and intraterminal Ca^{2+} homeostasis.

Under normal conditions, the depolarization-evoked release of transmitter from the presynaptic terminal is dependent on $[Ca^{2+}]_i$, which is largely controlled by membrane

← _____

FIGURE 1. Possible sites at which neurotoxic metals can interact with neuronal signalling processes. This figure illustrates several major pre- and postsynaptic processes that are involved in signalling and signal transduction. The shaded arrows with the enclosed numbers indicate possible sites of metal action, as described in the text. The following abbreviations are used: Na = sodium; K = potassium; Ca = calcium; REC = receptor; PL_C = phospholipase C; PK_A = protein kinase A; PK_C = protein kinase C; CalM = calmodulin; MIT = mitochondria; ER = endoplasmic reticulum; NGF = nerve growth factor; G = guanine nucleotide binding protein (G-protein); PI = phosphatidylinositol 4,5-bisphosphate; IP_3 = inositol 1,4,5-trisphosphate; IP_4 = inositol 1,3,4,5-tetraphosphate; DAG = 1,2-diacylglycerol; SRF = serum-responsive factor; SRF-P = phosphorylated SRF; SRE = serum-responsive element; CREB = calcium-responsive element binding protein; CREB-P = phosphorylated CREB; CRE = calcium-responsive element; GR = glucocorticoid receptor (a Zn-twist protein); GRE = glucocorticoid-responsive element; IEGs = immediate early genes; ATP = adenosine triphosphate; cAMP = cyclic adenosine monophosphate; SYN = synaptophysin; NT = neurotransmitter.

voltage-dependent Ca^{2+} channels (Augustine *et al.*, 1987; Reichardt and Kelly, 1983). Normally, a relatively Ca^{2+}-impermeable membrane aids in maintaining $[Ca^{2+}]_i$ at ~0.1 μM relative to $[Ca^{2+}]_e$, which is ~1200 μM. When the action potential arrives at the nerve terminal, specific voltage-dependent Ca^{2+} channels open, allowing $[Ca^{2+}]_e$ to move down its concentration gradient into the terminal and increasing $[Ca^{2+}]_i$ up to 5–10 μM (Nicholls, 1986; Snelling and Nicholls, 1985). This increase in $[Ca^{2+}]_i$ triggers the release of transmitter from the presynaptic terminal. Although the precise interaction between $[Ca^{2+}]_i$ and transmitter release has not been established, it is believed that the protein synaptophysin is involved (Thomas *et al.*, 1988). $[Ca^{2+}]_i$ is also regulated by intraterminal mitochondria and endoplasmic reticulum, which can bind and release Ca^{2+}. A membrane calmodulin-dependent Ca^{2+}-ATPase pump removes Ca^{2+} from the nerve terminal.

Many of the neurotoxic metals are believed to interact with specific Ca^{2+}-mediated processes and therefore could alter transmitter release. Ca^{2+} is involved in membrane stability (Rubin, 1981). A metal-induced increase in membrane permeability could affect transmitter release by altering (i.e., gradually depolarizing) the resting membrane potential, increasing the influx of Ca^{2+}, and/or permitting transmitter to "leak" out of the terminal. Some metals can interact directly at membrane Ca^{2+} channels. For example, Pb^{2+} and Cd^{2+} can attenuate depolarization-evoked transmitter release by inhibiting the influx of Ca^{2+} through voltage-dependent membrane Ca^{2+} channels. Some of the metals (e.g., Pb^{2+}) may be affecting intraterminal Ca^{2+} homeostasis by interacting with intra-terminal Ca^{2+}-buffering processes and/or enzymes. Such interactions may reflect the metal's ability to mimic or antagonize directly the actions of Ca^{2+}.

Some metals can also alter neurotransmitter release by interacting with specific membrane proteins (e.g., Hg^{2+}'s interaction with SH groups). Such interactions could alter a number of membrane processes, including membrane permeability and/or integrity, specific ion channels, membrane ion pumps, receptors, and neurotransmitter carriers (uptake mechanisms). For example, interactions of neurotoxic metals with the membrane Ca^{2+}-ATPase pump could alter the activity of that pump, resulting in an alteration in $[Ca^{2+}]_i$. Inhibition of membrane Na^+, K^+-ATPase can increase transmitter release (Baker and Crawford, 1975; Sweadner, 1985). It is believed that the increase in $[Na^+]_i$ that accompanies Na,K-ATPase inhibition induces the efflux of Ca^{2+} from intraterminal mitochondria, thus increasing $[Ca^{2+}]_i$. Activation of presynaptic receptors for neuro-transmitters and/or neuromodulators (see below) usually results in an altered neuronal firing rate, mainly by affecting the membrane conductance of specific ions, which, in turn, alters the resting potential of the presynaptic membrane. In addition, presynaptic receptors may regulate the synthesis and/or storage of transmitter, which, in turn, influences the amount of transmitter released with every depolarization. These presynaptic receptors may also influence transmitter reuptake, thus altering the amount of transmitter in the synaptic cleft.

4.3. Inactivation of Released Transmitter

The signal provided to the receptor by the neurotransmitter is obviously dependent on the amount of transmitter available to interact with the receptor. The amount of transmitter in the synaptic cleft is determined by the balance of transmitter release and removal.

Transmitter is removed either by metabolism and/or by presynaptic high-affinity transmitter uptake mechanisms. Metals could interact directly with membrane transmitter carriers (e.g., binding to protein SH groups), or metals may interfere with the movement of Na^+ to affect Na^+-dependent carrier systems. For example, GABA uptake carriers have been reported to be particularly sensitive to triethyllead.

4.4. Neuronal Membrane Receptors

Many different receptors are associated with the neuronal membrane, the characteristics of which are determined by the location and function of the neuron. In addition to neurotransmitter/neuromodulator receptors, there exist membrane receptors for other signals, including trophic factors. In some cases the receptor protein complex contains an ion channel (e.g., Cl^- channel in $GABA_A$ receptor complex), thus allowing for ligand-mediated regulation of ion movement through the channel. Many receptor complexes have several ligand-specific binding sites such that binding of one ligand to one site will influence the binding of another ligand to another site. For example, neuromodulators can alter the affinity of a receptor for a neurotransmitter by binding at a site on the neurotransmitter receptor protein.

The effectiveness of a chemical signal (ligand) in influencing a particular neuron is regulated, in part, by the affinity of the receptor for the ligand and the number of receptors for a specific ligand. The affinity of the receptor can be regulated, in some cases, by the phosphorylation of specific domains of the receptor protein. Some metals may affect the affinity of membrane receptors for their ligand, either by direct interactions with the receptor or ligand proteins, or by interactions with those processes involved in protein phosphorylation. In some situations, particularly following exposure to specific pharmacological agents, it is postulated that neuromodulator processes may influence receptor number. Downregulation of receptors (e.g., decrease in receptor number) can occur by endocytosis, in which the receptor is internalized and either stored or destroyed. Although lacking experimental evidence, decreased numbers of receptors may also be mediated by decreased transcription, increased mRNA degradation, and/or decreased receptor protein stability. Upregulation of receptor number can involve an increase in the expression of the receptor gene (i.e., increased transcription, increased mRNA stability, increased protein stability, and/or decreased protein degradation). Increased transcription of the receptor gene may reflect the activity of third messenger systems, as described in Section 4.6.

4.5. Second Messengers

In many cases membrane receptor activation is linked to the activation of membrane-associated G-proteins, and the subsequent increase in the intraneuronal concentration of second messengers (e.g., cAMP, cGMP, Ca^{2+}, IP_3, and/or 1,2-DAG). This transduction process allows for signal amplification, as well as a number of sites for signal regulation. Second messengers, in turn, can interact with a number of intracellular and/or membrane proteins to modulate neuronal function. Some metals may interact with specific G-proteins, potentially altering the yield of second messenger resulting from receptor-ligand interaction. One major means by which second messengers (i.e., cAMP, Ca^{2+}, 1,2-

DAG) control neuronal function is by the activation of protein kinases (e.g., protein kinase C, CalM kinase I and II, protein kinase A). The relative amounts and types of kinases appear to be specific for certain populations of neurons, thus dictating the response neurons make to certain signals (Kennedy, 1989). The second messenger IP_3 regulates $[Ca^{2+}]_i$ by increasing Ca^{2+} efflux from endoplasmic reticulum and (following metabolism to IP_4) by increasing Ca^{2+} influx through membrane Ca^{2+} channels, illustrating the interaction between Ca^{2+} and IP_3 (Berridge and Irvine, 1989). The Ca^{2+} and cAMP messenger systems can interact in a cooperative, hierarchical, antagonistic, sequential, or redundant fashion to mediate neuronal responses (Rasmussen et al., 1989). The complexity of $[Ca^{2+}]_i$ as a second messenger is demonstrated by sustained neuronal response in which $[Ca^{2+}]_i$ returns to basal levels following a transient increase, but a net increase in neuronal Ca^{2+} influx and efflux (i.e., Ca^{2+} cycling) persists (Rasmussen et al., 1989). These investigators suggest that this sustained increase in Ca^{2+} cycling results in an increase in $[Ca^{2+}]$ in a subdomain of the plasma membrane, thus regulating Ca^{2+}-sensitive, plasma membrane-associated transducers (e.g., protein kinase C, Ca-ATPase pump). In light of Ca^{2+}'s role as a second messenger, the ability of certain metals to interact with Ca^{2+}-mediated processes can impact on a variety of neuronal functions. For example, two major Ca^{2+}-activated proteins, calmodulin (activated by $\uparrow [Ca^{2+}]_i$) and protein kinase C (activated by 1,2-DAG and $\uparrow [Ca^{2+}]_i$), have been proposed as sites of action for several neurotoxic metals.

4.6. Third Messengers

It is currently believed that the signal-induced long-term changes in neuronal function (i.e., neuronal plasticity) initially involve the expression of a certain set of genes known as immediate early genes (IEGs) (Curran and Morgan, 1990). The mRNAs and proteins resulting from IEG expression are characterized by a short half-life. The relative expression of the various IEGs is dependent on the signal. For example, membrane depolarization in PC12 cells results in the following pattern of IEG expression: $\leftrightarrow zif$268, $\leftrightarrow c$-jun, $\uparrow jun$ B, $\uparrow c$-fos, and $\uparrow nur$77. In contrast, activation of the NGF receptor results in $\uparrow zif$268, $\uparrow c$-jun, $\uparrow jun$ B, $\uparrow c$-fos, and $\leftrightarrow nur$77 (Naranjo et al., 1990; Thompson et al., 1990). The expression of the various IEGs results in the translation of a variety of IEG proteins. These proteins, which are subject to post-translational modification (e.g., homo- and heterodimerization), are referred to as third messengers. These third-messenger proteins can interact with nuclear DNA to regulate, negatively or positively, the transcription of those genes that are believed to affect the long-term neuronal responsiveness (Diamond et al., 1990).

With respect to metal exposure, the importance of $[Ca^{2+}]_i$ in mediating the expression of certain IEGs cannot be overemphasized, as illustrated by c-fos expression. Depolarization-induced c-fos expression is mediated by Ca^{2+}-bound (activated) calmodulin, which in turn activates calmodulin-dependent kinases (e.g., CalM-kinases I & II) (Curran and Morgan, 1986). The calmodulin-kinases phosphorylate the Ca^{2+}-responsive element (CRE)-binding protein (CREB), which then binds to the CRE site located in the c-fos promoter (Curran and Morgan, 1990; Thompson et al., 1990). Phosphorylated CREB binds with greater affinity at the c-fos CRE site than at AP1/CRE consensus binding sites. Other signaled kinases, specifically the cAMP-activated kinases (e.g., protein kinase A), also phosphorylate at this site on CREB. Protein kinase C does not phosphorylate CREB, but may phosphorylate the internal domains of specific receptors/ion channels to modulate other aspects of neuronal signalling. In addition, protein kinase C apparently phosphorylates the serum-responsive factor (SRF) protein that acts at the serum-responsive element (SRE) regulatory site in the *c-fos* promoter region. The SRE site is required for *c-fos* induction by NGF (Naranjo *et al.,* 1990). There may also be regulatory sites within the gene (e.g., FIRE); however, little is known about the regulation at such sites. Further regulation results from autoregulation of *c-fos* expression by the FOS protein.

4.7. Transcription: Interaction with DNA and DNA-Binding Proteins

Since neurons do not divide, the ability of the metals to alter DNA replication is only of concern in the developing nervous system. However, the interaction of metals with DNA and/or DNA-binding proteins may affect the rate and/or the fidelity of transcription. With the exception of IEGs, changes in the transcription of certain genes could be considered a "long-term" response that the neuron makes to particular signals. The observation that Hg can influence the conformation of nuclear proteins to induce transcription in bacteria (Frantz and O'Halloran, 1990) suggests that heavy metals could possibly interact directly with DNA-binding proteins in neurons to affect transcription. Some neuronal DNA-binding proteins are receptors for specific chemical signals, such as steroid hormones (Chandler *et al.,* 1983). Some proteins, such as NGF, are internalized and may influence transcription, as suggested by the existence of specific nuclear NGF binding sites (Yanker and Shooter, 1979). In the case of glucocorticoid hormones, for example, the steroid interacts with a cytoplasmic receptor protein, which then enhances or represses transcription by associating selectively with DNA sequences termed either *glucocorticoid response elements* (GREs) or *negative GREs* (nGREs) (Sakai *et al.,* 1988). The glucocorticoid receptor belongs to a class of DNA-binding Zn^{2+} proteins referred to as Zn^{2+}-*twist proteins* (Vallee *et al.,* 1991). The ability of certain neurotoxic metals to interact with protein Zn^{2+}-binding sites suggests that DNA-binding Zn^{2+} proteins (i.e., Zn^{2+} fingers, Zn^{2+} clusters, and Zn^{2+} twists) may be a probable site of metal interaction; for example, Cd^{2+} can replace Zn^{2+} in the GAL4 transcription factor without a loss of specific DNA binding (Pan and Coleman, 1990). Some of the metals may interact directly with DNA to alter DNA conformation, thus interfering with gene expression.

5. INTERACTIONS OF VARIOUS NEUROTOXIC METALS WITH SIGNALLING PROCESSES

Each of the neurotoxic metals described below can potentially interact with various aspects of neuronal signalling processes. The following descriptions of such interactions are not meant to be an exhaustive review of the literature, but rather are focused on those signalling processes that, based on current evidence, have the greatest potential for being factors in the neurotoxicity of these metals. Whether and how such interactions are of a functional and/or toxicological concern is difficult to ascertain from existing knowledge. The conditions and/or biological models of exposure used in many of the studies are often not a good reflection of the human exposure scenario (Davis *et al.,* 1990). For example, inferences to the developing mammalian CNS are sometimes made on the basis of the acute effects of a metal in an *in vitro* biological system. Thus the toxicological consequences resulting from specific interactions of each of these metals with specific signalling processes remains elusive.

5.1. Lead (Pb^{2+})

No other metal has created as much health concern as Pb^{2+}, which, despite recent limitations on its use, remains a significant environmental problem. Infants and young children are most susceptible to the subtle neurobehavioral insults induced by Pb^{2+} exposure, probably as the result of increased gastrointestinal absorption of Pb^{2+}, increased distribution of Pb^{2+} to the CNS, as well as increased vulnerability of the developing nervous system to Pb^{2+}. The neurochemical effects of Pb^{2+} toxicity have been the subject of a number of reviews (Audesirk, 1985; Bressler and Goldstein, 1991; Minnema, 1989; Moore *et al.*, 1986; Shellenberger, 1984; Winder and Kitchen, 1984). The impact of Pb^{2+} on the developing CNS may be indirect, perhaps reflecting insult to the hematopoietic system, or the complex processes that regulate growth/appetite (Hammond and Dietrich, 1990). Direct effects on the CNS, however, are inferred from studies in which rats, exposed to Pb^{2+} either prenatally or neonatally, exhibit decreased CNS synapse formation and synaptic density (Averill and Needleman, 1980; Campbell *et al.*, 1982; McCauley *et al.*, 1979). Additionally, Pb^{2+} may alter neuronal growth, either by delaying the normal conversion of embryonic NCAM to its adult (desialylated) form (Cookman *et al.*, 1987; Regan, 1989) or by inducing precocious glial cell differentiation (Cookman *et al.*, 1988). A study with neuroblastoma cells indicates that Pb^{2+} may act directly to impair neuronal differentiation (Gotti *et al.*, 1987). Some *in vivo* exposure studies suggest that hippocampal processes may be selectively sensitive to Pb^{2+}-induced injury (Alfano and Petit, 1981; Sato *et al.*, 1984a). There are many reports of specific neurotransmitter/neuromodulatory systems that have been compromised by Pb^{2+} exposure. Some recent examples of such reports involve the effects of Pb^{2+} on dopaminergic, cholinergic, and enkephalinergic systems. The reported impairment of opioid-induced antinociception in rats perinatally exposed to Pb^{2+} (Jackson and Kitchen, 1989) may be associated with a Pb^{2+}-induced change in the signalled expression of various opioid processes. This interaction of Pb^{2+} with opioid processes is suggested by studies demonstrating that the CNS of developing rats chronically exposed to low levels of Pb^{2+} exhibited a decrease in the binding of [^{3}H]enkephalin to the δ-opioid receptor (McDowell and Kitchen, 1988) and/or an increase in hypothalamic pro-opiomelanocortin gene expression (Rosen and Polakiewicz, 1989). Similarly, the supersensitivity of postnatally Pb^{2+}-exposed rats to dopamine agonists apparently reflects increases in dopamine receptor number (Cory-Slechta and Widzowski, 1991). A study using neuroblastomas suggests that Pb^{2+} is a potent blocker of the inward current (e.g., Na^+ influx) mediated by the nicotinic cholinergic receptor (Oortgiesen *et al.*, 1990). *In vitro* studies with a variety of neurotransmitter substances indicate that Pb^{2+} has generalized effects on transmitter release in that Pb^{2+} attenuates depolarization-evoked release while increasing spontaneous transmitter release (Minnema and Cooper, 1990). The attenuation of depolarization-evoked release results from blockage of Ca^{2+} influx by Pb^{2+} at voltage-dependent Ca^{2+} channels (Audesirk, 1990; Nachshen, 1984).

Although those aspects of the developing nervous system that are selectively altered by Pb^{2+} leading to a diminution of neurobehavioral performance still remain unresolved, it is possible to speculate regarding the basis of the involvement of specific signalling processes in Pb^{2+} toxicity. Most of the interactions of Pb^{2+} with signalling processes may be ultimately related to Pb^{2+}-Ca^{2+} interactions (Simons, 1986). Neuronal development is greatly dependent on a number of signalling processes, particularly those involving trophic factors, many of which are involved with, or influence, $[Ca^{2+}]_i$ (Johnson et al., 1989; Koike et al., 1989). The interaction of Pb^{2+} with neuronal Ca^{2+} homeostatic processes indicates that Pb^{2+} has a great potential for affecting many aspects of neuronal development. Pb^{2+} may act to increase the intraneuronal Ca^{2+} signal by acting as a Ca^{2+} mimetic and/or by increasing $[Ca^{2+}]_i$. A Ca^{2+}-mimetic action of Pb^{2+} is supported by studies showing that Pb^{2+} can directly stimulate calmodulin, protein kinase C, and/or transmitter release (Chao et al., 1984; Habermann et al., 1983; Markovac and Goldstein, 1988a, 1988b; Mills and Johnson, 1985; Shao and Suszkiw, 1991). An increase in $[Ca^{2+}]_i$ induced by Pb^{2+} has been demonstrated in neuroblastoma cells using ^{19}F-NMR (Schanne et al., 1989) and has been suggested by Pb^{2+}-induced increases in mitochondrial Ca^{2+} efflux (Chavez et al., 1987; Kapoor and Van Rossum, 1984). A Pb^{2+}-induced increase in synaptosomal [45]Ca efflux is consistent with both a Pb-induced increase in $[Ca^{2+}]_i$ as well as a Ca^{2+}-mimetic action of Pb^{2+} (Minnema et al., 1988). Ca^{2+} is also important in stabilizing membranes (Rubin, 1982). Although there is evidence that Pb^{2+} can damage membranes (Bondy, 1988), it has recently been shown that Pb^{2+} is capable of affecting neuronal function (e.g., increasing spontaneous transmitter release) without increasing neuronal membrane permeability (Minnema et al., 1991).

5.2. Organolead (Triethyllead, TEL)

TEL, the major metabolite of tetraethyllead, is apparently responsible for tetraethyllead-induced neurotoxicity, which is characterized by behavioral changes, analgesic effects, ataxia, and convulsive seizures (Bondy, 1988; Cremer, 1959; Tilson et al., 1982; also see Chapter 14). Trialkyllead compounds inhibit mitochondrial respiration, oxidative phosphorylation, ATP synthesis, as well as brain glucose oxidation and creatine phosphate synthesis (Aldridge, 1984; Cremer, 1962). Synaptosomal studies indicate that TEL in vitro increases $[Ca^{2+}]_i$ (Komulainen and Bondy, 1987). This increase in $[Ca^{2+}]_i$ is dependent on $[Ca^{2+}]_e$ (Komulainen and Bondy, 1987), most probably reflecting TEL-induced increases in synaptosomal membrane permeability (Minnema et al., 1991). Inhibition of neuronal energetics, changes in $[Ca^{2+}]_i$, and/or disruption of membrane integrity could affect synaptic function, including transmitter release. Indeed, several studies have noted that trialkyllead compounds in vitro increase the spontaneous release of neurotransmitter (Bondy et al., 1979a, 1979b; Minnema et al., 1991). Komulainen and Tuomisto (1982) attributed an observed net decrease in [3H]transmitter uptake to an increase in transmitter release. In all these studies, a greater effect of TEL on [3H]dopamine (DA) release, relative to other transmitter systems, was observed. The Na^+ channel blocker, tetrodotoxin (TTX), blocks the TEL-induced increase in $[Ca^{2+}]_i$ (Komulainen and Bondy, 1987) and delays (but does not inhibit) the TEL-induced increase in synaptosomal transmitter release (Minnema et al., 1991), indicating that TEL interacts with the membrane Na^+ channel to some extent. The differential sensitivity of [3H]DA release by TEL may be due, in part, to the differential means by which the release of DA is regulated by the membrane Na^+ gradient (Minnema *et al.*, 1991). In addition to effects on transmitter release, TEL may also have direct effects on other membrane processes, as suggested by the decrease in [^{3}H]GABA uptake into cortical synaptosomes resulting from a direct action of TEL on GABA uptake sites (Seidman *et al.*, 1987; Seidman and Verity, 1987).

5.3. Mercury (Hg^{2+})

Long-term exposure to Hg^{2+}, in addition to its effects on the kidney, can produce behavioral alterations and tremor (Smith, 1972). Most Hg^{2+}-induced CNS toxicity is the result of exposure to vapors of elemental Hg (Hg^o), which readily distributes to the CNS, where it is converted to Hg^{2+}. Data obtained from studies employing rat-brain synaptosomes suggests that Hg^{2+} can influence neuronal activity in a number of ways, including enzyme inhibition, membrane depolarization, alteration in $[Ca^{2+}]_i$ homeostasis, and perhaps, direct Ca^{2+}-mimetic activity. The interaction of Hg^{2+} with plasma membrane proteins that contain sulfhydryl groups is well established (Kinter and Pritchard, 1977) and may be the basis for the increase in spontaneous transmitter release observed following *in vitro* Hg^{2+} exposure (Minnema and Cooper, 1990). The Hg^{2+}-induced increase in transmitter release could be the result, in part, of membrane depolarization (Minnema, unpublished observation). Hg^{2+} could depolarize the membrane either by altering the ability of the cell to extrude Na^+ by inhibiting membrane Na,K-ATPase (Hare *et al.*, 1989; Rothstein, 1973) and/or by producing an increase in membrane permeability (Hare *et al.*, 1989, 1990). Membrane depolarization would increase $[Ca^{2+}]_i$ due to an increase in neuronal Ca^{2+} influx. Increases in $[Ca^{2+}]_i$ could also result from intracellular actions of Hg^{2+}, as suggested by the Hg^{2+}-induced increase in $[Ca^{2+}]_i$ observed in cultured renal tubular cells (Smith *et al.*, 1987). For example, Hg^{2+} could be affecting Ca^{2+} uptake and/or efflux from intraneuronal Ca^{2+} stores (Binah *et al.*, 1978). Hg^{2+} can also inhibit the activity of, and binding of regulatory ligands to, protein kinase C (Speizer *et al.*, 1989).

5.4. Organomercury (Methylmercury, MeHg)

In adults, MeHg neurotoxicity is best illustrated by Minamata disease, which is characterized by extensive neurological involvement, including paresthesia; impairment of vision, hearing, and speech; ataxia; and muscular weakness. In addition, MeHg is a well-recognized neuroteratogen. Neuronal proliferation and migration appear to be targets for MeHg (Komulainen, 1988). Studies with MeHg have shown a variety of neuronal insults, including alterations in protein, RNA and DNA synthesis, changes in phospholipid and phosphoprotein metabolites, abnormalities in mitochondrial function, and perturbations in membrane permeability. Many of these effects may be the result of MeHg binding to sulfhydryl groups (Clarkson, 1972) and/or MeHg-induced lipid peroxidation (Yonaha *et al.*, 1983). For example, the neuroteratogenic effects of MeHg may reflect decreased mitotic activity resulting from the interaction of MeHg with microtubule sulfhydryl groups (Vogel *et al.*, 1985). Exposure to MeHg *in vivo* has been shown to affect a number of neurotransmitter systems (Komulainen, 1988). *In vitro* studies employing rat-brain synaptosomes indicate that MeHg increases spontaneous transmitter release (Minnema and Cooper, 1990), which may reflect, in part, increased membrane permeability (Minnema *et al.*, 1989; Walum, 1982). Increased membrane permeability would increase transmitter release by increasing neuronal Na^+ influx, causing the membrane to depolarize (Quandt *et al.*, 1982); increasing $[Ca^{2+}]_i$, due to the influx of Ca^{2+} down its concentration gradient, as well as through Ca^{2+} channels opened by depolarization (Komulainen and Bondy, 1987); and/or transmitter leakage (Minnema *et al.*, 1989). It has been suggested that the abnormal intracellular ionic composition (resulting from increased membrane permeability) contributes to the MeHg-induced inhibition of protein synthesis (Komulainen, 1988; Sarafian *et al.*, 1984). In addition to increasing membrane permeability, MeHg also increases $[Ca^{2+}]_i$ by increasing Ca^{2+} efflux from intraneuronal organelles (e.g., mitochondria) (Komulainen and Bondy, 1987; Levesque and Atchison, 1988; Minnema *et al.*, 1989). The increase in mitochondrial Ca^{2+} efflux may reflect a MeHg-induced increase in the permeability of the mitochrondrial inner membrane (Salvaterra *et al.*, 1973). Increased permeability of the mitochrondrial inner membrane to K^+ could also explain the inhibition of respiration (e.g., energy metabolism) associated with MeHg exposure (Verity *et al.*, 1975).

5.5. Triethyltin (TET)

Organotin neurotoxicity has been the subject of several recent reviews (Bierkamper and Buxton, 1990; Walsh and deHaven, 1988). TET exposure can produce progressive muscular weakness, decreased body weight, decreased body temperature, and decreased heart rate and blood pressure, all of which are believed to be a consequence of insult to the nervous system. The neurotoxicity of TET appears to result mainly from the interaction of TET with myelin. High-affinity binding of TET to myelin is believed to alter ion transport, which in turn alters fluid movement, resulting in edema of myelinated fiber tracts. The ability of CDTD [2'-chloro-2,4-dinitro-5',6-di(trifluoromethyl)diphenylamine] a potent uncoupler of oxidative phosphorylation in brain mitochondria, to mimic TET neurotoxicity in rats suggests that TET mediates its effects by interfering with energy metabolism (Aldridge *et al.*, 1977; Lock, 1979). *In vitro* studies indicate that TET selectively inhibits ATPases (Aldridge and Cremer, 1955; Moore and Brady, 1961). This generalized effect of TET on energy metabolism, in addition to injuring those cells supplying myelin, may explain the alterations in most major neurotransmitter systems that have been observed following TET exposure. Although a TET-induced reduction in ACh release (Allen *et al.*, 1980; Bierkamper and Valdes, 1982) and nerve depolarization (Millington and Bierkamper, 1982) have been attributed to an effect on cellular bioenergetics (Bierkamper *et al.*, 1984), other studies suggest that the magnitude and time course of TET's actions on neurotransmission cannot be explained solely by inhibition of energy production/utilization (Beani *et al.*, 1966; Birks and Cohen, 1968). Alternatively, TET may be affecting the phosphorylation of specific proteins that are involved in neurotransmission (e.g., synaptophysin), as well as enzymes participating in energy production (e.g., pyruvate dehydrogenase) (Neumann and Taketa, 1987). Alterations in transmembrane chloride movement (Bierkamper *et al.*, 1984) and/or alterations in the calcium conductance of the nerve membrane (Allen *et al.*, 1980) could also alter neurotransmission. Several studies suggest that both of these hypotheses are consistent with a TET-induced increase in membrane permeability to small ions (Laurie *et al.*, 1991; Selwyn *et al.*, 1970).

5.6. Trimethyltin (TMT)

Exposure of humans to TMT is associated with seizures, sleep disturbances, depression, disorientation, aggressiveness, sensory disruptions, and memory perturbations. All these symptoms are consistent with perturbation of the limbic system. Animal studies have confirmed that the hippocampus is a major site of TMT-induced insult. However, the regional distribution of the TMT-induced hippocampal lesions is species and age dependent (Chang *et al.*, 1983; Reuhl and Cranmer, 1984). Prenatal exposure studies suggest that differentiated neurons must be present for TMT to induce certain neurohistopathological effects (Paule *et al.*, 1986). Neonatal exposure studies indicate certain age periods during which the brain is more vulnerable (with respect to the adult brain) to TMT neurotoxicity (Reuhl *et al.*, 1983). TMT appears to interact with Zn^{2+}, which is normally sequestered in relatively high amounts by the mossy fibers in the hippocampus. This TMT-Zn^{2+} interaction is suggested by the depletion of hippocampal (mossy fiber) Zn^{2+} observed following TMT exposure (Chang and Dyer, 1984; Dyer *et al.*, 1982). If we assume that hippocampal Zn^{2+} is largely associated with cytoplasmic Zn^{2+}-binding proteins (Sato *et al.*, 1984b), then TMT has the potential to alter the activity of these proteins, including DNA-binding proteins. This decrease in Zn^{2+} may be the critical factor in the reported decrease in protein synthesis that results from either *in vivo* or *in vitro* TMT exposure (Brown *et al.*, 1984; Costa and Sulaiman, 1986). A TMT-induced decrease in protein synthesis may reduce the activity of specific populations of neurons (possibly GABAergic transmission, Valdes *et al.*, 1983). Consistent with a TMT-induced decrease in the activity of inhibitor transmitter systems is the hypothesis that TMT induces seizure activity, or hyperexcitability, in certain hippocampal pathways (e.g., dentate granule cells), resulting in a marked increase in the release of excitatory amino acid transmitters (e.g., glutamate and/or aspartate). Excitotoxic transmitters may be responsible for at least some of the TMT-induced hippocampal damage (e.g., pyramidal cells) (Chang, 1986; Ray, 1981; Sloviter *et al.*, 1986). Supporting such a hypothesis of TMT toxicity are those reports demonstrating that hippocampal CA3 pyramidal cells are extremely vulnerable to hyperexcitation-induced damage (Sloviter and Damiano, 1981).

5.7. Aluminum (Al^{3+})

Al^{3+} has been identified as the causative factor of "dialysis dementia/encephalopathy" occurring in humans undergoing long-term hemodialysis. Dialysis victims exhibit a 10- to 20-fold increase in brain Al levels. In addition, there has been a lot of concern that chronic exposure to Al^{3+} may be involved in neurological diseases often associated with the geriatric population, including the amyotrophic lateral sclerosis and Parkinsonism-dementia (ALS/PD) of Guam disease and Alzheimer's disease (see reviews by Petit, 1989; Sturman and Wisniewski, 1988). Although brain Al concentrations increase about two-fold over the human life span, no consistent elevation in brain Al concentration has been observed in Alzheimer patients. Even though neurofibrillary tangles (NFT) have been observed in both Alzheimer's disease and in "Al^{3+}-sensitive" animals exposed to high Al^{3+} levels, it is clear that the NFTs induced by these two conditions are very different, both structurally and chemically. NFTs have not been observed in victims of "dialysis encephalopathy" or "dialysis dementia" in humans, despite the resulting high brain Al concentrations. However, Al^{3+} may be an interacting or associated, factor in Alzheimer's disease (Crapper McLachlan *et al.*, 1989; Chapter 4). Although Al^{3+} appears to be selectively stored in the nuclei of NFT neurons, and increased Al^{3+} is selectively associated with senile plaques, no clear cause-and-effect relationship has yet been established. Alterations in a variety of neuronal metabolic, structural, and transport processes have been implicated following Al^{3+} exposure. Most interesting with respect to the signalling processes is the interaction of Al^{3+} with $[Ca^{2+}]_i$ homeostasis, G-proteins, and nuclear material (DNA). The observation that Al^{3+} affects a number of DNA/RNA processes (rate of DNA synthesis, DNA replication errors, mRNA pool size, and RNA polymerase A and B activity) suggests that Al^{3+} might interfere with those mechanisms mediating DNA conformational changes that are necessary for gene expression (Crapper-McLachlan, 1986). Additionally, Al^{3+} may be reducing transcription of certain genes by electrostatically crosslinking DNA and histone proteins (Crapper-McLachlan *et al.*, 1989; Lukiw *et al.*, 1987). Al^{3+} also affects $[Ca^{2+}]_i$ in several ways. Al^{3+} binds to calmodulin to disrupt its activity (e.g., Ca^{2+}-ATPase) (Siegel and Haug, 1983; Suhayda and Haug, 1984). Al^{3+} can displace Ca^{2+} from membrane phospholipid binding sites (Deleers, 1985) and can inhibit Ca^{2+} uptake at voltage-dependent Ca^{2+} channels (Koenig and Jope, 1987). In a cell-free system, Al^{3+} potentiated the ability of F^- to inhibit Golgi stacking, a hallmark indicative of activation of the regulatory Gs (stimulatory) protein (Melancon *et al.*, 1987). Inhibition of both Gs and Gi (inhibitory) proteins by F^- appears to be enhanced synergistically by Al^{3+}, whereas Al^{3+} alone only slightly inhibits GTPase activity ($\uparrow$ G protein activity is reflected by $\downarrow$ GTPase activity) (Kanaho *et al.*, 1985). It appears that Al^{3+} enhances F^--induced dissociation of the G-alpha from the G-beta/G-gamma subunits, thus inhibiting GTP→GDP exchange (i.e., GTP hydrolysis), and thereby maintaining the G-protein in an active state. This action of Al^{3+} on G-proteins may explain the increases in cAMP levels, and to a lesser extent, cGMP levels, in rat brain regions following *in vivo* Al^{3+} exposure (Johnson and Jope, 1987).

5.8. Manganese (Mn^{2+})

The neurotoxic effects of Mn^{2+} are characterized by temporally distinct components that parallel both psychiatric ("Mn psychosis") and neurodegenerative (extrapyramidal motor) disorders (see reviews by Barbeau, 1984; Seth and Chandra, 1988). Although the pathophysiological mechanisms of Mn^{2+} neurotoxicity are unknown, most data indicate that dopaminergic transmission is involved. While some evidence suggests the degeneration of dopamine (DA) neurons of the nigrostriatal tract is responsible for the extrapyramidal symptoms, a recent study suggests that the Mn^{2+}-induced insult occurs in pathways postsynaptic to the nigrostriatal neurons (Wolters *et al.*, 1989). If Mn^{2+} is inducing degeneration of nigrostriatal DA neurons as a result of an excess production of toxic free radicals (Archibald and Tyree, 1987), then signalling processes may not be involved. However, several *in vivo* and *in vitro* studies have demonstrated that Mn^{2+} acts directly as a modulator of DA receptors (Creese, 1978; Scheuhammer and Cherian, 1985;

Usdin *et al.*, 1980). An increase in the density of striatal DA receptors was observed in rats subchronically exposed to $MnCl_2$ in their drinking water (Agrawal *et al.*, 1986; Seth *et al.*, 1981). Likewise, *in vitro* studies have demonstrated that exposure to 1 μM Mn^{2+} increases the specific binding of DA ligands to DA receptors in rat striatal tissue (Usdin *et al.*, 1980). One limitation to these studies is that they merely measure the effects of Mn^{2+} on DA receptor binding kinetics and do not address the biological outcome of these effects in terms of activation (or inhibition) of second messenger systems and other cellular responses. Mn^{2+} has also been shown to mimic the activation of calmodulin by Ca^{2+}, although in this respect it is not as potent as Pb^{2+} (Chao *et al.*, 1984; Habermann, 1983). In addition to mimicking Ca^{2+}, Mn^{2+} ($\sim$1 μM) has been shown to substitute partially for Mg^{2+}, as well as to synergize with Mg^{2+}, in the activation of protein kinase C (Hannun and Bell, 1990). Since Mn^{2+} shares the uniport mechanism of mitochondrial Ca^{2+} influx, Mn^{2+} may also have the potential to alter intraneuronal Ca^{2+} homeostasis by altering mitochondrial Ca^{2+} fluxes (Gavin *et al.*, 1990; Konji *et al.*, 1985). Mn^{2+} may also affect the production of cAMP, as demonstrated by the interaction of Mn^{2+} with adenylate cyclase. Specifically, Mn^{2+} appears to be a potent inducer of a conformational change in the catalytic subunit of adenylate cyclase that binds "P-site" agonists (e.g., adenosine, an inhibitor of adenylate cyclase activity) (Johnson *et al.*, 1989; Johnson and Shoshani, 1990).

5.9. Cadmium (Cd^{2+})

Although the kidney is usually considered the critical organ for Cd^{2+} toxicity (Cherian and Goyer, 1989), under certain conditions Cd^{2+} may be considered a neurotoxicant (Babitch, 1988). Some neurological symptoms have been associated with Cd^{2+} exposure in adults. The reported ability of Cd^{2+} to induce anosmia may be related to its selective accumulation in the olfactory bulb (Clark *et al.*, 1985). The developing nervous system of children appears to be most vulnerable to potential insult by Cd^{2+}. Cd^{2+} body burden has been positively correlated with cognitive dysfunction, mental retardation, and behavioral anomalies in children (Bonithon-Kopp *et al.*, 1986; Lester *et al.*, 1982; Marlowe *et al.*, 1983; Moon *et al.*, 1985; Rimland and Larson, 1983). There is little information as to how Cd^{2+} may be affecting the nervous system. Cd^{2+} has the potential to interact with Ca^{2+}-mediated processes. Cd^{2+} is a potent blocker of Ca^{2+} movement through membrane voltage-dependent Ca^{2+} channels (Blaxter and Carlen, 1985), accounting for the ability of Cd^{2+} to attenuate neurotransmitter release (Suszkiw *et al.*, 1984). Cd^{2+} also substitutes for Ca^{2+} at the Ca^{2+}-binding site of a number of proteins, including calmodulin (Haberman *et al.*, 1983). Cd^{2+} can form complexes with proteins by interacting with adjacent sulfhydryl groups or collections of carboxylate residues (Webb, 1979). Such interactions may account for Cd^{2+}-induced inhibition of adenylate cyclase and cAMP phosphodiesterase (Ewers and Erbe, 1980; Nathanson and Bloom, 1976), reduction in brain transmitter (cholinergic, dopaminergic, and serotoninergic) receptors (Hedlund *et al.*, 1979; Huang *et al.*, 1986; Scheuhammer and Cherian, 1985), and inhibition of ATPases (Magour *et al.*, 1981; Rajanna *et al.*, 1981). Cd^{2+} may also interact with Zn^{2+}-binding domains of proteins involved in the regulation of transcription (Miller *et al.*, 1985). Cd^{2+} could also affect transcription by interacting directly with DNA (Jacobson and Turner, 1980).

5.10. Organoplatinum (Cisplatin)

The neurotoxicity of the cancer chemotherapeutic agent cisplatin (*cis*-diam-minedichloroplatinum II) is characterized as a "side effect" resulting from clinical exposure to this agent. While the major neurotoxicity associated with cisplatin is described as a peripheral sensory neuropathy, there are reports of CNS involvement (e.g., seizures, visual loss, and other neurological deficits) (Berman and Mann, 1980; Roelofs *et al.*, 1984). There is limited information as to the mechanisms of neurotoxicity, due to the difficulty in producing neuropathies in an animal model of cisplatin exposure (Tomiwa *et al.*, 1986). While rats exposed to cisplatin showed no hisotopathological nerve damage or symptoms of neuropathy (Blizard, personal communication), a decrease in the sensory component of the rat sciatic nerve conduction velocity was observed (De Koning *et al.*, 1987a). Using this electrophysiological measure as an indicator of cisplatin's neuropathological potential, it was observed that cisplatin neurotoxicity could be prevented by the concomitant administration of an ACTH(4-9) neuropeptide analog, ORG 2766 (De Koning *et al.*, 1987b). Although the mechanism of protection by ORG 2766, which is devoid of ACTH, corticotrope, or melanotrope activity, is unknown, preliminary evidence suggests that this neuropeptide is clinically effective in reducing cisplatin neurotoxicity (Gerritsen van der Hoop *et al.*, 1990). Cisplatin-induced neuropathy has been observed in the frog, in which a single injection of 10 mg/kg cisplatin produced generalized seizures within 35 days (Blisard and Harrington, 1989). A histological examination of the frog's CNS revealed vacuolations, consisting of swollen astrocytic processes in the anterior gray horns of the spinal cord. It is possible that cisplatin's neurotoxicity arises from the same mechanisms that account for its antineoplastic activity. The cytotoxicity of cisplatin is believed to be the result of DNA-intrastrand crosslinks, although some DNA-interstrand and DNA-protein crosslinks occur (Eastman, 1987). However, in the rat, it appears that cisplatin-induced changes in nerve conduction velocity are not associated with cisplatin interactions with nuclear DNA in either nerve cells (dorsal root ganglion) or their supporting satellite cells (Terheggen *et al.*, 1989). Although the critical cytotoxic step resulting from cisplatin-induced DNA-intrastrand crosslinks is believed to be an inhibition of DNA synthesis (at least in non-neuronal tissues), recent evidence suggests that this may not be the case. Rather, cisplatin-induced cytotoxicity may be due to a signalled cell death (apoptotic) process (Sorenson *et al.*, 1990). The ability of cyclosporin A to alter the expression of certain signalling-responsive genes (e.g., *c-fos, c-H-ras, c-myc*), as well as to restore cisplatin cytotoxicity in a cisplatin-resistant cell line (Kashani-Sabet, 1990), suggests that cisplatin acts through signal-mediated processes.

6. SUMMARY AND CONCLUSIONS

There are a number of sites at which the various neurotoxic metals can potentially interact to affect neuronal signalling processes. In many cases the effects of any given metal are not limited to a single process, but rather encompass a number of signalling processes. A number of metals have been shown to alter intraneuronal Ca^{2+} homeostasis and/or to interact with Ca^{2+}-mediated processes. Similarly, many of the metals, particularly the organometals, can affect membrane permeability, which in turn can affect a variety of signalling processes. The relationship between the functional consequences of metal exposure and the interactions of metals with specific aspects of neuronal signalling processes remains elusive. However, the potential for insult, particularly in the developing nervous system, ensures that the interaction of metals with the biochemical processes involved in neuronal signalling will be an area of continued investigation.

REFERENCES

Agrawal, A., Hussain, T., Chandra, S., and Seth, P., 1986, Effects of coexposure of lead and manganese on neurotransmitter uptake and binding in subcellular fractions of rat brain, *Biochem. Arch.* 2:279–285.

Aldridge, W., 1984, Effects on mitochondria and other enzyme systems, in: *Biological Effects of Organolead Compounds* (Grandjean, P., and Grandjean, E., eds.), CRC Press, Boca Raton, FL, pp. 137–144.

Aldridge, W., and Cremer, J., 1955, The biochemistry of organotin compounds: Diethyldichloride and triethyltin sulphate, *Biochem. J.* 61:406–418.

Aldridge, W., Street, B., and Skilleter, D., 1977, Oxidative phosphorylation: Halid-dependent and halid-independent effects of triorganotin and triorganolead compounds on mitochondrial functions, *Biochem. J.* 168:353–364.

Alfano, D., and Petit, T., 1981, Behavioral effects of postnatal lead exposure: Possible relationship to hippocampal dysfunction, *Neural Biol.* 32:319–333.

Alkon, D., and Nelson, T., 1990, Specificity of molecular changes in neurons involved in memory storage, *FASEB J.*, 4:1567–1576.

Allen, J., Gage, P., Leaver, D., and Leow, A., 1980, Triethyltin depresses evoked transmitter release at the mouse neuromuscular junction, *Chem. Biol. Intl.* 32:227–231.

Archibald, F., and Tyree, C., 1987, Manganese poisoning and the attack of trivalent manganese upon catecholamines, *Arch. Biochem. Biophys.* 256:638–650.

Audesirk, G., 1985, Effects of lead exposure on the physiology of neurons, *Prog. Neurobiol.* 24:199–231.

Audesirk, G., 1990, Effects of heavy metals on neuronal calcium channels, in: *Biological Effects of Heavy Metals*, Volume I (Foulkes, E., ed.), CRC Press, Boca Raton, FL, pp. 1–17.

Augustine, G., Charlton, M., and Smith, S., 1987, Calcium action in synaptic transmitter release, *Annu. Rev. Neurosci.* 10:633–693.

Averill, D., and Needleman, H., 1980, Neonatal lead exposure retards cortical synaptogenesis in the rat, in: *Low Level Lead Exposure: Clinical Implications of Current Research* (Needleman, H., ed.), Raven Press, New York, pp. 201–210.

Aw, T., Nicotera, P., Manzo, L., and Orrenius, S., 1990, Tributyltin stimulates apoptosis in rat thymocytes, *Arch. Biochem. Biophys.* 283:46–50.

Azar, C., Scavarda, N., Reynolds, C., and Brodeur, G., 1990, Multiple defects of the NGF receptor in human neuroblastomas, *Cell Growth Different.* 1:421–428.

Babitch, J., 1988, Cadmium neurotoxicity, in: *Metal Neurotoxicity* (Bondy, S., and Prasad, K., eds.), CRC Press, Boca Raton, FL, pp. 141–166.

Baker, P., and Crawford, A., 1975, A note on the mechanisms by which inhibitors of the sodium pump accelerate spontaneous release of transmitter from motor nerve terminals, *J. Physiol.* 247:209–226.

Baptista, C., Gershon, T., and Macagno, R., 1990, Peripheral organs control central neurogenesis in the leech, *Nature* 346:855–858.

Barbeau, A., 1984, Manganese and extrapyramidal disorders, *Neurotoxicology* 5:13–36.

Beani, L., Bianchi, C., and Ledda, F., 1966, The effect of 2,4-dinitrophenol on neuromuscular transmission, *Br. J. Pharmacol.* 27:299–312.

Berman, I., and Mann, M., 1980, Seizures and transient cortical blindness associated with cis-platinum (II) diamminedichloride (PDD) therapy in a thirty-year-old man, *Cancer*, 45:764–766.

Berridge, M., and Irvine, R., 1989, Inositol phosphates and cell signalling, *Nature* 341:197–205.

Bierkamper, G., Aizenman, E., and Millington, W., 1984, Neuromuscular function and organotin compounds, *Neurotoxicology* 5:245–265.

Bierkamper, G., and Buxton, I., 1990, Neurotoxicology of organotin compounds, in: *Biological Effects of Heavy Metals*, Volume I (Foulkes, E. ed.), CRC Press, Boca Raton, FL, pp. 97–170.

Bierkamper, G., and Valdes, J., 1982, Triethyltin intoxication alters acetylcholine release from rat phrenic nerve-lemidiaphragm, *Neurobehav. Toxicol. Teratol.* 4:251–254.

Binah, O., Meiri, U., and Rahamimoff, H., 1987, The effects of HgCl$_2$ and mersalyl on mechanisms regulating intracellular calcium and transmitter release, *Eur. J. Pharmacol.* 51:453–458.

Birks, R., and Cohen, M., 1968, The action of sodium pump inhibitors on neuromuscular transmission, *Proc. R. Soc. Lond.* 170:381–399.

Blaxter, T., and Carlen, P., 1985, Pre- and postsynaptic effects of baclofen in the rat hippocampal slice, *Brain Res.* 341:195–199.

Blisard, K., and Harrington, D., 1989, Cisplatin-induced neurotoxicity with seizures in frogs, *Ann. Neurol.* 26:336–341.

Bondy, S., 1988, The neurotoxicity of organic and inorganic lead, in: *Metal Neurotoxicity* (Bondy, S., and Prasad, K., eds.), CRC Press, Boca Raton, FL, pp. 1–17.

Bondy, S., Anderson, C., Harrington, M., and Prasad, K., 1979a, Effect of organic and inorganic lead and mercury on neurotransmitter high-affinity transport and release mechanisms, *Environ. Res.* 19:102–111.

Bondy, S., Harrington, M., Anderson, C., and Prasad, K., 1979b, Effect of low concentrations of an organic lead compound on the transport and release of a putative neurotransmitter, *Tox. Lett.* 3:35–41.

Bonithon-Kopp, C., Huel, G., Moreau, T., and Wendling, R., 1986, Prenatal exposure to lead and cadmium and psychomotor development of the child at 6 years. *Neurobehav. Toxicol. Teratol.* 8:307–310.

Bressler, J., and Goldstein, G., 1991, Mechanisms of lead neurotoxicity, *Biochem. Pharmacol.* 41:479–488.

Brown, A., Cavanagh, J., Verschoyle, R., Gysbers, M., Jones, H., and Aldridge, W., 1984, Evolution of the intracellular changes in neurons caused by trimethyltin, *Neuropath. Appl. Neurobiol.* 10:267–283.

Campbell, J., Wooley, D., Vijayan, V., and Overmann, D., 1982, Morphometric effects of postnatal lead exposure on hippocampal development of the 15-day-old rat, *Dev. Brain Res.* 3:595–612.

Chandler, V., Maler, B., and Yamamoto, K., 1983, DNA sequences bound specifically by glucocorticoid receptor *in vitro* render a heterologous promoter hormone response *in vivo*, *Cell* 33:489–499.

Chang, L., 1986, Neuropathology of trimethyltin: A proposed pathogenesis mechanism, *Fundam. Appl. Toxicol.* 6:217–232.

Chang, L., and Dyer, R., 1984, Trimethyltin induced zinc depletion in rat hippocampus, in: *The Neurobiology of Zinc: Part B, Deficiency, Toxicology, and Pathology* (Frederickson, C., Howell, G., and Kasarskis, E., eds.), Alan R. Liss, New York, pp. 275.

Chang, L., Wenger, G., McMillan, D., and Dyer, R., 1983, Species and strain comparison of acute neurotoxic effects of trimethyltin in mice and rats, *Neurobehav. Toxicol. Teratol.* 5:337–350.

Chao, S., Suzuki, Y., Zysk, J., and Cheung, W., 1984, Activation of calmodulin by various metal cations as a function of ionic radius, *Mol. Pharmacol.* 26:75–82.

Chavez, E., Jay, D., and Bravo, C., 1987, The mechanism of lead-induced mitochondrial Ca^{2+} efflux, *J. Bioenerg. Biomembr.* 19:285–290.

Cherain, M., and Goyer, R., 1989, Cadmium toxicity, *Comm. Toxicol.* 3:191–206.

Clark, D., Nation, J., Bourgeois, A., Hare, M., Baker, D., and Hinderberger, E., 1985, The regional distribution of cadmium in the brains of orally exposed adult rats, *Neurotoxicology* 6:109–114.

Clarkson, T., 1972, The pharmacology of mercury compounds, *Annu. Rev. Pharmacol.* 12:375–406.

Cookman, G., Hemmens, S., Keane, G., King, W., and Regan, C., 1988, Chronic low level lead exposure precociously induces rat glial development *in vitro* and *in vivo*, *Neurosci. Lett.* 86:33–37.

Cookman, G., King, W., and Regan, C., 1987, Chronic low-level lead exposure impairs embryonic to adult conversion of the neural cell adhesion molecule, *J. Neurochem.* 49:399–403.

Cory-Slechta, D., and Widzowski, D., 1991, Lead induces functional D_1 and D_2 dopaminergic supersensitivity, *Toxicologist* 11:114.

Costa, L., and Sulaiman, R., 1986, Inhibition of protein synthesis by trimethyltin, *Toxicol. Appl. Pharmacol.* 86:189–196.

Crapper-McLachlan, D., 1986, Cellular mechanisms of aluminium toxicity, *Neurobiol. Aging* 7:525–528.

Crapper-McLachlan, D., Lukiw, W., and Kruck, T., 1989, New evidence for an active role of aluminum in Alzheimer's disease, *Can. J. Neurol. Sci.* 16:490–497.

Creese, I., Prosser, T., and Snyder, S., 1978, Dopamine receptor binding: Specificity, localization and regulation by ions and guanyl nucleotides, *Life Sci.* 23:495–500.

Cremer, J., 1959, Biochemical studies on the toxicity of tetraethyl lead and other organolead compounds, *Br. J. Ind. Med.* 16:191–199.

Cremer, J., 1962, The action of triethyl tin, triethyl lead, ethyl mercury, and other inhibitors on the metabolism of brain and kidney slices *in vitro* using substrates labeled with ^{14}C, *J. Neurochem.* 9:289–298.

Curran, T., and Morgan, J., 1986, Barium modulates c-*fos* expression and post-translational modification, *Proc. Natl. Acad. Sci., USA* 83:8521–8524.

Curran, T., and Morgan, J., 1990, Neurotransmitters, oncogenes, transcription factors, neuropeptides. Paper presented at FIDIA Research Foundation Symposium, St. Louis, MO.

Davis, J., Otto, D., Weil, D., and Grant, L., 1990, The comparative developmental neurotoxicity of lead in humans and animals, *Neurotoxicol. Teratol.* 12:215–229.

De Koning, P., Neyt, J., Jennekens, F., and Gispen, W., 1987a, Evaluation of *cis*-diamminedichloroplatinum(II) (cisplatin) neurotoxicity in rats, *Toxicol. Appl. Pharmacol.* 89:81–87.

De Koning, P., Neyt, J., Jennekens, F., and Gispen, W.H., 1987b, ORG.2766 protects from cisplatin induced neurotoxicity in rats, *Exp. Neurol.* 97:746–750.

Deleers, M., 1985, Cationic atmosphere and cation competition binding at negatively charged membranes: Pathological implications of aluminum, *Res. Commun. Chem. Pathol. Pharmacol.* 49:277–294.

Diamond, M., Miner, J., Yoshinaga, S., and Yamamoto, K., 1990, Transcription factor interactions: Selectors of positive or negative regulation from a single DNA element, *Science* 249:1266–1272.

Dyer, R., Walsh, T., Wonderlin, W., and Bercegeay, M., 1982, The trimethyltin syndrome in rats, *Neurobehav. Toxicol. Teratol.* 4:127–133.

Eastman, A., 1987, The formation, isolation and characterization of DNA adducts produced by anticancer platinum complexes, *Pharmacol. Ther.* 34:155–166.

Ewers, V., and Erbe, R., 1980, Effects of lead, cadmium and mercury on brain adenylate cyclase, *Toxicology* 16:227–237.

Frantz, B., and O'Halloran, T., 1990, DNA distortion accompanies transcriptional activation by the metal-responsive gene-regulatory protein MerR, *Biochemistry* 29:4747–4751.

Fujita, K., Lazarovici, P., and Guroff, G., 1989, Regulation of the differentiation of PC12 pheochromocytoma cells, *Environ. Health Perspect.* 80:127–142.

Gant, D., Eldefrawi, M., and Eldefrawi, A., 1987, Cyclodiene insecticides inhibit GABA$_A$ receptor-regulated chloride transport, *Toxicol. Appl. Pharmacol.* 88:313–321.

Gavin, C., Gunter, K., and Gunter, T., 1990, Manganese and calcium efflux kinetics in brain mitochondria: Relevance to manganese toxicity, *Biochem. J.* 266:329–334.

Gerritsen van der Hoop, R., Vecht, C.J., van der Burg, M.E.L., Elderson, A., Boogerd, W., Heimans, J.J., Vries, E.P., van Houwelingen, J.C., Jennekens, F.G.I., Gispen, W.H., and Neijt, J.P., 1990, Prevention of cisplatin neurotoxicity with an ACTH (4-9) analogue in patients with ovarian cancer, *N. Engl. J. Med.* 322:89–94.

Gotti, C., Cabrini, D., Sher, E., and Clementi, F., 1987, Effects of long-term *in vitro* exposure to aluminum, cadmium, or lead on differentiation and cholinergic receptor expression in a human neuroblastoma cell line, *Cell Biol. Toxicol.* 3:431–440.

Habermann, E., Crowell, K., and Janicki, P., 1983, Lead and other metals can substitute for Ca^{2+} in calmodulin, *Arch. Toxicol.* 54:61–70.

Hammond, P., and Dietrich, P., 1990, Lead exposure in early life: Health consequences, *Rev. Environ. Contam. Toxicol.* 115:91–124.

Hannun, Y., and Bell, R., 1990, Rat brain protein kinase C: Kinetic analysis of substrate dependence, allosteric regulation, and autophosphorylation, *J. Biol. Chem.* 265:2962–2972.

Hare, M., Minnema, D., Cooper, G., and Michaelson, I., 1989, Effects of mercuric chloride on [^{3}H]dopamine release from rat brain striatal synaptosomes, *Toxicol. Appl. Pharmacol.* 99:266–275.

Hare, M., Rezazadeh, S., Cooper, G., Minnema, D., and Michealson, I., 1990, Effects of inorganic mercury on [^{3}H]dopamine release and calcium homeostasis in rat striatal synaptosomes, *Toxicol. Appl. Pharmacol.* 102:316–330.

Hedlund, B., Gamarra, M., and Bartfai, T., 1979, Inhibition of striatal muscarinic receptors *in vivo* by cadmium, *Brain Res.* 168:216–218.

Hooper, C., 1990, Apoptosis: The birth of cell death, *J. NIH Res.* 2:46–48.

Huang, E., Pickett, J., Siegal, J., and Andorn, A., 1986, Cations decrease specific [^{3}H]spiroperidol binding in human prefrontal cortex, *Life Sci.* 38:1369–1373.

Jackson, H., and Kitchen, I., 1989, Perinatal lead exposure impairs opioid but not non-opioid stress-induced antinociception in developing rats, *Br. J. Pharmacol.* 97:1338–1342.

Jacobson, K., and Turner, J., 1980, The interaction of cadmium and certain other metal ions with proteins and nucleic acids, *Toxicology* 16:1–37.

Johnson, E., Chang, J., Koike, T., and Martin, D., 1989, Why do neurons die when deprived of trophic factor?, *Neurobiol. Aging* 10:549–552.

Johnson, G., and Jope, R., 1987, Aluminum alters cyclic AMP and cyclic GMP levels but not presynaptic cholinergic markers in rat brain *in vivo*, *Brain Res.* 413:1–6.

Johnson, R., and Shoshani, I., 1990, Kinetics of "P"-site-mediated inhibition of adenylyl cyclase and the requirements for substrate, *J. Biol. Chem.* 265:11595–11600.

Johnson, R., Yeung, S., Stubner, D., Bushfield, M., and Shoshani, I., 1989, Cation and structural requirements for P site-mediated inhibition of adenylate cyclase, *Mol. Pharmacol.* 35:681–688.

Kanaho, Y., Moss, J., and Vaughan, M., 1985, Mechanisms of inhibition of transduction GTPase activity by fluoride and aluminum, *J. Biol. Chem.* 260:11493–11497.

Kapoor, S., and Van Rossum, J., 1986, Effects of Pb^{2+} added *in vitro* on Ca^{2+} movements in isolated mitochondria and slices of rat kidney cortex, *Biochem. Pharmacol.* 33:1771–1778.

Kashani-Sabet, M., Wang, W., and Scanlon, K., 1990, Cyclosporin A suppresses cisplatin-induced *c-fos* expression in ovarian carcinoma cells, *J. Biol. Chem.* 265:11285–11288.

Kater, S., Mattson, M., and Guthrie, P., 1989, Calcium-induced neuronal degeneration: A normal growth cone regulating signal gone awry(?), *Ann. N.Y. Acad. Sci.* 568:252–261.

Kennedy, M., 1989, Do activity-dependent changes in expression of regulatory proteins play a role in the progression of central nervous system neuronal degeneration?, *Ann. N.Y. Acad. Sci.* 568:193–197.

Kinter, W., and Pritchard, J., 1977, Altered permeability of cell membranes, in: *Handbook of Physiology* (Lee, D., Falk, H., and Murphy, S., eds.), American Physiological Society, Washington, D.C., p. 563.

Klein, R., Jing, S., Nanduri, V., O'Rourke, E., and Barbacid, M., 1991, The *trk* proto-oncogene encodes a receptor for nerve growth factor, *Cell* 65:189–197.

Koenig, M., and Jope, R., 1987, Aluminum inhibits the fast phase of voltage-dependent calcium influx into synaptosomes, *J. Neurochem.* 49:316–320.

Koike, T., Martin, D., and Johnson, E., 1989, Role of Ca^{2+} channels in the ability of membrane depolarization to prevent neuronal death induced by trophic factor deprivation: Evidence that [Ca^{2+}]$_i$ determines nerve growth factor dependence of sympathetic ganglion cells, *Proc. Natl. Acad. Sci. USA* 86:6421–6425.

Komulainen, H., 1988, Neurotoxicity of methylmercury: Cellular and subcellular aspects, in: *Metal Neurotoxicity* (Bondy, S. and Prasad, K., eds.), CRC Press, Boca Raton, FL, pp. 167–182.

Komulainen, H., and Bondy, S., 1987, Increased free intrasynaptosomal Ca^{2+} by neurotoxic organometals: Distinctive mechanisms, *Toxicol. Appl. Pharmacol.* 88:77–86.

Komulainen, H., and Tuomisto, J., 1982, Effects of heavy metals on monoamine uptake and release in brain synaptosomes and blood platelets, *Neurobehav. Toxicol. Teratol.* 4:647–649.

Konji, V., Montag, A., Sandri, G., Nordenbrand, K., and Ernster, L., 1985, Transport of Ca^{2+} and Mn^{2+} by mitochondria from rat liver, heart and brain, *Biochimie* 67:1241–1250.

Laurie, R., Cooper, G., and Minnema, D., 1991, Triethyltin: Effects on cholinergic transmission *in vitro*, *Neurotoxicol. Teratol.* (unpublished results).

Lester, M., Thatcher, R., and Monroe-Lord, L., 1982, Refined carbohydrate intake, hair cadmium levels and cognitive functioning in children, *Nutr. Behav.* 1:3–13.

Levesque, P., and Atchison, W., 1988, Effect of alteration of nerve terminal Ca^{2+} regulation on increased spontaneous quantal release of acetylcholine by methylmercury, *Toxicol. Appl. Pharmacol.* 94:55–65.

Lock, E., 1979, Toxic action of 2'-chloro-2,4-dinitro-5',6-di(trifluoromethyl)-diphenylamine in the rat, *Chem. Biol. Interact.* 28:35–46.

Lukiw, W., Kruck, T., and Crapper McLachlan, D., 1987, Alteration in human linker histone-DNA binding in the presence of aluminum salts *in vitro* and in Alzheimer's disease, *Neurotoxicology* 8:291–302.

Lynch, G., 1986, *Synapses, Circuits, and the Beginnings of Memory*, MIT Press, Cambridge, MA.

Magour, S., Kristof, V., Baumann, M., and Assmann, G., 1981, Effect of acute treatment of cadmium on ethanol anesthesia, body temperature and synaptosomal Na^+,K^+-ATPase of rat brain, *Environ. Res.* 26:381–391.

Manalis, R., and Suszkiw, J., 1988, Effects of heavy metal ions on transmitter release, in: *Presynaptic Regulation of Transmitter Release* (Feigenbaum, J., and Hanani, M., eds.), Freund Publishing, Tel Aviv.

Markovac, J., and Goldstein, G., 1988, Lead activates protein kinase C in immature rat brain microvessels, *Toxicol. Appl. Pharmacol.* 96:14–23.

Markovac, J., and Goldstein, G., 1988, Picomolar concentrations of lead stimulate brain protein kinase C, *Nature* 334: 71–73.

Marlowe, M., Errera, J., and Jacobs, J., 1983, Increased cadmium and lead burdens among mentally retarded children, *Am. J. Ment. Defic.* 87:477–483.

McCauley, P., Bull, R., and Lutkenoff, S., 1979, Association of alterations in energy metabolism with lead-induced delays in rat cerebral cortical development, *Neuropharmacology* 18:93–101.

McCobb, D., and Kater, S., 1988, Membrane voltage and neurotransmitter regulation of neuronal growth motility, *Dev. Biol.* 130:599–609.

McConkey, D., Hartzell, P., Nicotera, P., and Orrenius, S., 1989, Calcium-activated DNA fragmentation kills immature thymocytes, *FASEB J.* 3:1843–1849.

McDowell, J., and Kitchen, I., 1988, Perinatal lead exposure alters the development of δ- but not μ-opioid receptors in rat brain, *Br. J. Pharmacol.* 94:933–937.

Melancon, P., Glick, B., Malhotra, V., Weidman, P., Serafini, T., Gleason, M., Orci, L., and Rothman, J., 1987, Involvement of GTP-binding "G" proteins in transport through the Golgi stack, *Cell* 51:1053–1062.

Miller, J., McLachlan, A., and Klug, A., 1985, Repetitive zinc-binding domains in the protein transcription factor IIIA from *Xenopus* oocytes, *EMBO J.* 4:1609–1614.

Miller, M., 1986, Effects of alcohol on the generation and migration of cerebral cortical neurons, *Science* 233:1308–1311.

Millington, W., and Bierkamper, G., 1982, Chronic triethyltin exposure reduces the resting membrane potential of rat soleus muscle, *Neurobehav. Toxicol. Teratol.* 4:255–257.

Mills, J., and Johnson, J., 1985, Metal ions as allosteric regulators of calmodulin, *J. Biol. Chem.* 260:15100–15105.

Minnema, D., 1989, Neurochemical alterations in lead intoxication: An overview, *Comm. Toxicol.* 3:207–224.

Minnema, D., and Cooper, G., 1990, Assessment of the effects of lead and mercury *in vitro* on neurotransmitter release, in: *Biological Effects of Heavy Metals*, Volume I (Foulkes, E. ed.), Boca Raton, FL, pp. 19–57.

Minnema, D., Michaelson, I., and Cooper, G., 1988, Calcium efflux and neurotransmitter release from rat hippocampal synaptosomes exposed to lead, *Toxicol. Appl. Pharmacol.* 92:351–357.

Minnema, D., Cooper, G., and Greenland, R., 1989, Effects of methylmercury on neurotransmitter release from rat brain synaptosomes, *Toxicol. Appl. Pharmacol.* 99:510–521.

Minnema, D., Cooper, G., and Schamer, M., 1991, Differential effects of triethyllead on synaptosomal [³H]dopamine vs. [³H]acetylcholine and [³H]gamma-aminobutyric acid release, *Neurotoxicol. Teratol.* 13:257–265.

Moon, C., Marlowe, M., Stellern, J., and Errera, J., 1985, Main and interaction effects of metallic pollutants on cognitive functioning, *J. Learn. Disabil.* 18:217–221.

Moore, K., and Brady, T., 1961, The effect of triethyltin on oxidative phosphorylation and mitochondrial adenosine triphosphate activation, *Biochem. Pharmacol.* 6:125–133.

Moore, M., McIntosh, M., and Bushnell, I., 1986, The neurotoxicology of lead, *Neurotoxicology* 7:541–556.

Nachshen, D., 1984, Selectivity of the Ca binding site in synaptosome Ca channels: Inhibition of Ca influx by mutivalent metal cations, *J. Gen. Physiol.* 83:941–967.

Naranjo, J., Mellstrom, B., Auwerx, J., Mollinedo, F., and Sassone-Corsi, P., 1990, Unusual *c-fos* induction upon chromaffin PC12 differentiation by sodium butyrate: Loss of *fos* autoregulatory function, *Nucleic Acids Res.* 18:3605–3610.

Nathanson, J., and Bloom, F., 1976, Heavy metals and adensonine 3',5'-monophosphate metabolism: Possible relevance to heavy metal toxicity, *Mol. Pharmacol.* 12:390–398.

Nelson, T., and Alkon, D., 1990, Protein changes underlying long-term facilitation in *Aplysia*, *Bioessays* 11:106–108.

Neumann, P., and Taketa, F., 1987, Effects of triethyltin bromide on protein phosphorylation in subcellular fractions from rat and rabbit brain, *Brain Res.* 388:83–87.

Nicholls, D., 1986, Intracellular calcium homeostasis, *Br. Med. J.* 42:353–361.

Olney, J., 1990, Excitotoxic amino acids and neuropsychiatric disorders, *Annu. Rev. Pharmacol. Toxicol.* 30:47–71.

Oortgiesen, M., van Kleef, R., Bajnath, R., and Vijverberg, H., 1990, Nanomolar concentrations of lead selectively block neuronal nicotinic acetylcholine responses in mouse neuroblastoma cells, *Toxicol. Appl. Pharmacol.* 103:165–174.

Oppenheim, R., 1985, Naturally occurring cell death during neural development, *Trends Neurosci.* 17:487–493.

Pan, T., and Coleman, J., 1990, GAL4 transcription factor is not a "zinc finger" but forms a $Zn(II)_2Cys_6$ binuclear cluster, *Proc. Natl. Acad. Sci. USA* 87:2077–2081.

Paule, M., Reuhl, K., Chen, J., Ali, S., and Slikker, W., 1986, Developmental toxicology of trimethyltin in the rat, *Toxicol. Appl. Pharmacol.* 84:412–417.

Petit, T., 1989, Issues in aluminum neurotoxicology, *Comm. Toxicol.* 3:225–238.

Quandt, F., Kato, E., and Narahashi, T., 1982, Effects of methylmercury on electrical responses of neuroblastoma cells, *Neurotoxicology* 3:205–220.

Rajanna, B., Chaptatwala, K., Vaishnav, D., and Desaiah, D., 1981, Changes in ATPase activities in tissues of rats fed on cadmium, *J. Environ. Biol.* 2:1–9.

Rasmussen, H., Barrett, P., Zawalich, W., Isales, C., Stein, P., Smallwood, J., McCarthy, R., and Bollag, W., 1989, Cycling of Ca^{2+} across the plasma membrane as mechanism for generating a Ca^{2+} signal for cell activation, *Ann. N.Y. Acad. Sci.* 568:73–80.

Ray, D., 1981, Electroencephalographic and evoked release correlates of trimethyltin induced neuronal damage in the rat hippocampus, *J. Appl. Toxicol.* 1:145–148.

Regan, C., 1989, Lead-imparied neurodevelopment. Mechanisms and threshold values in the rodent, *Neurotoxicol. Teratol.* 11:533–537.

Reichardt, L., and Kelly, R., 1983, A molecular description of nerve terminal function, *Ann. Rev. Biochem.* 52:871–926.

Reuhl, K., and Cranmer, J., 1984, Developmental neuropathology of organotin compounds, *Neurotoxicology* 5:187–204.

Reuhl, K., Smallridge, E., Chang, L., and MacKenzie, D., 1983, Developmental effects of trimethyltin intoxication in the neonatal mouse, I. Light microscopy studies, *Neurotoxicology* 4:19–28.

Ridkin, B., Lazarovini, P., Levi, B., Abe, Y., Fujita, K., and Guroff, G., 1989, Cell cycle-specific action of nerve growth factor in PC12 cells: Differentiation without proliferation, *EMBO J.* 8:3319–3325.

Rimland, B., and Larson, G., 1983, Hair mineral analysis and behavior. An analysis of 51 studies, *J. Learn. Disabil.* 16:279–285.

Roelofs, R., Hrushesky, W., Rogin, J., and Rosenberg, L., 1984, Peripheral sensory neuropathy and cisplatin chemotherapy, *Neurology* 34:934–938.

Rothstein, A., 1973, Mercaptans, the biological target for mercurials, in: *Mercury, Mercurials, and Mercaptans* (Miller, M. and Clarkson, T., eds.), Charles C. Thomas, Springfield, IL.

Rosen, H., and Polakiewicz, R., 1989, Increase in hypothalamic pro-opiomelanocortin gene expression in response to prolonged low level lead exposure, *Brain Res.* 493:380–384.

Rubin, R., 1982, *Calcium and Cellular Secretion*, Plenum Press, New York.

Rutishauser, U., Acheson, A., Hall, A., Mann, D., and Sunshine, J., 1988, The neural cell adhesion molecule (NCAM) as a regulator of cell-cell interactions, *Science* 240:53–57.

Sakai, D., Helms, J., Carlstedt-Duke, J., Gustafsson, J., Rottman, F., and Yamamoto, K., 1988, Hormone-mediated repression of transcription: A negative glucocorticoid response element from the bovine prolactin gene, *Genes Dev.* 2:1144–1154.

Salvaterra, P., Lown, B., Morganti, J., and Massaro, E., 1973, Alterations in neurochemical and behavioral parameters in the mouse induced by low doses of methylmercury, *Acta Pharmacol. Toxicol.* 33:177–183.

Sarafian, T., Cheung, M., and Verity, M., 1984, *In vitro* methylmercury inhibition of protein synthesis in neonatal cerebellar perikarya, *Neuropathol. Appl. Neurobiol.* 10:85–92.

Sato, S., Frazier, J., and Goldberg, A., 1984a, Perturbation of a hippocampal zinc-binding pool after postnatal lead exposure in rats, *Exp. Neurol.* 85:620–630.

Sato, S., Frazier, J., and Goldberg, A., 1984b, A kinetic study of the *in vivo* incorporation of ^{65}Zn into the rat hippocampus. *J. Neurosci.* 4:1671–1675.

Schanne, F., Moskal, J., and Gupta, R., 1989, Effect of lead on $[Ca^{2+}]_i$ in a presynaptic neural model: ^{19}F-NMR study of NG108-15 cells, *Brain Res.* 503:308–311.

Scheuhammer, A., and Cherian, M., 1985, Effects of heavy metal cations, sulphydryl reagents and other chemical agents on striatal D_2 dopamine receptors, *Biochem. Pharmacol.* 34:3405–3413.

Scott, R., Florine, D., Wille, J., and Yun, K., 1982, Coupling of growth arrest and differentiation at a distinct state in the G_1 cell cycle, *Proc. Natl. Acad. Sci. USA* 79:845–849.

Seidman, B., and Verity, M., 1987, Selective inhibition of gamma-aminobutyric acid uptake by triethyllead: Role of energy transduction and chloride ions, *J. Neurochem.* 48:1142–1149.

Seidman, B., Olsen, R., and Verity, M., 1987, Triethyllead inhibits gamma-aminobutyric acid binding to uptake sites in synaptosomal membranes, *J. Neurochem.* 49:415–420.

Selwyn, M., Dawson, A., Stockdale, M., and Gains, N., 1970, Chloride-hydroxide exchange across mitochondrial, erythrocyte and artificial lipid membranes mediated by trialkyl- and triphenyltin compounds, *Environ. J. Biochem.* 14:120–126.

Seth, P., and Chandra, S., 1988, Neurotoxic effects of manganese, in: *Metal Neurotoxicity* (Bondy, S. and Prasad, K., eds.), CRC Press, Boca Raton, FL, pp. 19–33.

Seth, P., Hong, J., Kilts, C., and Bondy, S., 1981, Alteration of cerebral neurotransmitter receptor function by exposure of rats to manganese, *Toxicol. Lett.* 9:247–255.

Simons, T., 1986, Cellular interactions between lead and calcium, *Br. Med. Bull.* 42:431–440.

Shao, Z., and Suszkiw, J., 1991, Ca^{2+}-surrogate action of Pb^{2+} on acetylcholine release from rat brain synaptosomes, *J. Neurochem.* 56:568–574.

Shellenberger, M., 1984, Effects of early lead exposure on neurotransmitter systems in the brain: A review with commentary, *Neurotoxicology* 5:177–212.

Siegel, N., and Haug, A., 1983, Aluminum interaction with calmodulin: Evidence for altered structure and function from optical and enzymatic studies, *Biochim. Biophys. Acta* 744:36–45.

Sloviter, R., and Damiano, B., 1981, On the relationship between kainic acid-induced epileptiform activity and hippocampal neuronal damage, *Neuropharmacology* 20:1003–1011.

Sloviter, R., Von Knebel Doeberitz, C., Walsh, T., and Dempster, D., 1986, On the role of seizure activity in the hippocampal damage produced by trimethyltin, *Brain Res.* 367:169–182.

Smith, M., Ambudkar, I., Phelps, P., Regec, A., and Trump, B., 1987, HgCl₂-induced changes in $[Ca^{2+}]_i$ of cultured rabbit renal tubular cells, *Biochim. Biophys. Acta* 931:130–142.

Smith, R., 1972, Dose-response relationship associated with known mercury absorption at low dose levels of inorganic mercury, in: *Environmental Mercury Contamination* (Hartung, R., and Dinman, B., eds.), Ann Arbor Science Publishers, Ann Arbor, MI, pp. 207–222.

Snelling, R., and Nicholls, D., 1985, Calcium efflux and cycling across the synaptosomal plasma membrane, *Biochem. J.* 226:225–231.

Snyder, S., and Narahashi, T., 1990, Receptor-channel alterations in disease: Many clues, few causes, *FASEB J.* 4:2707–2708.

Speizer, L., Watson, M., Kanter, J., and Brunton, L., 1989, Inhibition of phorbol ester binding and protein kinase C activity by heavy metals, *J. Biol. Chem.* 264:5581–5585.

Sorenson, C., Barry, M., and Eastman, A., 1990, Analysis of events associated with cell cycle arrest at G_2 phase and cell death induced by cisplatin, *J. Natl. Cancer Inst.* 82:749–755.

Sturman, J., and Wisniewski, H., 1988, Aluminum, in: *Metal Neurotoxicity* (Bondy, S., and Prasad, K., eds.), CRC Press, Boca Raton, FL, pp. 61–85.

Suhayda, C., and Haug, A., 1984, Organic acids prevent aluminum-induced conformational changes in calmodulin, *Biochem. Biophys. Res. Commun.* 119:376–381.

Suszkiw, J., Toth, G., Murawsky, M., and Cooper, G., 1984, Effects of Pb^{2+} and Cd^{2+} on acetylcholine release and Ca^{2+} movements in synaptosomes and subcellular fractions from rat brain and *Tordedo* electric organ, *Brain Res.* 323:31–46.

Sweadner, K., 1985, Ouabain-evoked norepinephrine release from intact rat sympathetic neurons: Evidence for carrier-mediated release, *J. Neurosci.* 5:2397–2406.

Terheggen, P., Van der Hoot, R., Floot, B., and Gispen, W., 1989, Cellular distribution of *cis*-diamminedichloroplatinum(II)-DNA binding in rat dorsal root spinal ganglia: Effect of the neuroprotecting peptide ORG.2766, *Toxicol. Appl. Pharmacol.* 99:334–43.

Thomas, L., Hartung, K., Langosch, D., Rehm, H., Bamberg, E., Franke, W., and Betz, H., 1988, Identification of synaptophysin as a hexameric channel protein of the synaptic vesicle membrane, *Science* 242:1050–1053.

Thompson, T., Sheng, M., and Greenberg, M., 1990, Neurotransmitter regulation of *c-fos* proto-oncogene transcription, Paper presented at FIDIA Research Foundation Symposium, St. Louis, MO.

Tilson, H., Mactutus, C., McLamb, R., and Burne, T., 1982, Characterization of triethyllead chloride neurotoxicity in adult rats, *Neurobehav. Toxicol. Teratol.* 4:671–681.

Tomiwa, K., Nolan, C., and Cavanagh, J., 1986, The effects of cisplatin on rat spinal ganglia: A study by light and electron microscopy and by morphometry, *Acta Neuropathol.* 69:295–308.

Usdin, T., Creese, I., and Snyder, S., 1980, Regulation by cations of [³H]spiroperidol binding associated with dopamine receptors of rat brain, *J. Neurochem.* 34:669–676.

Vallee, B., Coleman, J., and Auld, D., 1991, Zinc fingers, zinc clusters, and zinc twists in DNA-binding protein domains, *Proc. Natl. Acad. Sci. USA* 88:999–1003.

Valdes, J., Mactutus, C., Santos-Anderson, R., Dawson, R., and Annau, Z., 1983, Selective neurochemical and histological lesions in rat hippocampus following chronic trimethyltin exposure, *Neurobehav. Toxicol. Teratol.* 5:357–361.

Van der Hoot, R., Vecht, C., Van der Burg, M., Elderson, A., Boogerd, W., Heimans, J., Vries, E., Van Houwelingen, J., Jennekens, F., Gispen, W., *et al.*, 1990, Prevention of cisplatin neurotoxicity with an ACTH(4-9) analogue in patients with ovarian cancer, *N. Engl. J. Med.* 322:89–94.

Verity, M., Brown, W., and Cheung, M., 1975, Organic mercurial encephalopathy: *In vivo* and *in vitro* effects of methylmercury on synaptosomal respiration, *J. Neurochem.* 25:759–767.

Vogel, D., Margolis, R., and Mottet, N., 1985, The effects of methylmercury binding to microtubules, *Toxicol. Appl. Pharmacol.* 80:473–486.

Walsh, T., and DeHaven, D., 1988, Neurotoxicity of the alkyltins, in: *Metal Neurotoxicity* (Bondy, S., and Prasad, K., eds.), CRC Press, Boca Raton, FL, pp. 87–107.

Walum, E., 1982, Membrane lesions in cultured mouse neuroblastoma cells exposed to metal compounds, *Toxicology* 25:67–74.

Webb, M., 1979, Interactions of cadmium with cellular components, in: *The Chemistry, Biochemistry and Biology of Cadmium* (Webb, M., ed.), Elsevier/North Holland, New York, pp. 285–340.

Winder, C., and Kitchen, I., 1984, Lead neurotoxicity: A review of the biochemical, neurochemical and drug-induced behavioural evidence, *Prog. Neurobiol.* 22:59–87.

Wolters, E., Huang, C., Clark, C., Peppard, R., Okada, J., Chu, N., Adam, M., Ruth, T., Li, D., and Calne, D., 1989, Positron emission tomography in manganese intoxication, *Ann. Neurol.* 26:647–651.

Yanker, B., and Shooter, E., 1979, Nerve growth factor in the nucleus: Interactions with receptors on the nuclear membrane, *Proc. Natl. Acad. Sci. USA* 76:1269–1273.

Yonaha, M., Saito, M., and Sagai, M., 1983, Stimulation of lipid peroxidation by methylmercury in rats, *Life Sci.* 32:1507–1514.

Zucker, R., 1989, Short-term synaptic plasticity, *Ann. Rev. Neurosci.* 12:13–31.

Chapter 7

Cognitive, Neural, and Behavioral Effects of Low-Level Lead Exposure

Julie A. Riess and *Herbert L. Needleman*

1. INTRODUCTION

Lead toxicity has been recognized since antiquity, and warnings about its neurotoxic properties have been issued throughout history. Recent advances in the neurotoxicology and epidemiology of lead exposure have drawn a clear picture of the extent and nature of the disease. It is now acknowledged that the consequences of exposure to lead constitute the most serious environmental problem of American children. It is also clear that this disease is totally preventable.

The Center for Disease Control's (CDC) current guidelines recommend medical intervention when a child's blood lead level exceeds 25 µg/dl (U.S. Center for Disease Control, 1985). Revisions being drafted of CDC's guidelines will recommend intervention at 15 µg/dl. In 1988, 34 million American children, or 17%, had blood lead levels above 15 µg/dl. Fifty-five percent of poor black children had blood lead levels over 15 µg/dl [Agency for Toxic Substances and Disease Registry (ATSDR), 1988]. Lead toxicity at these levels can lower IQ scores and produce a wide range of behavioral disorders (Davis and Svendsgaard, 1987).

This chapter will focus on recent advances in understanding the effects of low-level lead exposure. The term *low-level* refers to exposures below those at which clinical signs

Julie A. Riess and *Herbert L. Needleman* • University of Pittsburgh School of Medicine, Pittsburgh, Pennsylvania 15213.

The Vulnerable Brain and Environmental Risks, Volume 2: Toxins in Food, edited by Robert L. Isaacson and Karl F. Jensen. Plenum Press, New York, 1992.

of lead poisoning are apparent. We will briefly review potential sources of lead, studies of school-age children from the United States and other countries, prenatal risks, neurobiology, the interaction of nutrition and lead, and related behavioral disorders. We will also examine some of the complexities of scientific and methodological approaches to studying low-level lead exposure. Finally, we will suggest future research areas in lead toxicology.

2. SOURCES OF LEAD

The discovery of lead dates back to at least 3500 B.C., when it was used in cosmetics and jewelry. The Romans used lead in their extensive aqueduct system (Lin-Fu, 1985). Gilfillan (1965) theorized that the Roman's extensive use of lead in wine production and culinary vessels lead to the aristocracy's declining birthrate, increasing mortality rate, and contributed to the decline of the Empire.

As society has become increasingly industrialized, lead usage has steadily increased (Lin-Fu, 1985). From 1946 to 1970, annual U.S. leaded gasoline use rose 500%, from 50,000 to over 250,000 metric tons (Mushak, 1991). During the 1970s and 1980s, the United States Environmental Protection Agency (U.S. EPA) set guidelines for the leaded gasoline phase-down program (Hays, 1992). Blood lead levels of inner-city children have decreased in close parallel (Mielke *et al.* 1983; U.S. EPA, 1986). However, leaded gasoline, primarily for farm vehicle use, still accounts for nearly 20% of gasoline sold in the United States (Sills *et al.*, 1991).

Lead is a nonbiodegradable, toxic metal. It remains in the soil indefinitely. Ingestion of lead from food and water is a concern for the entire population. Lead contaminates food from airborne sources (such as farming vehicles and factory exhaust), the use of lead-bearing water in processing, lead-based solder in canning and food-processing equipment, and culinary vessels.

The concentration of lead in food varies with the contamination source. For example, the amount of lead is more than twice as high in exposed produce or leafy produce compared to lead in protected* produce (U.S. EPA, 1984). While voluntary food-industry guidelines are aimed at eliminating lead solder from canning, about 20% of domestically filled food cans are soldered with lead (ATSDR, 1988). On average, a person in 1984–1985 choosing fresh-frozen food over canned food reduced their daily dietary lead intake from 40 μg to 17 μg (U.S. EPA, 1984).

The most pervasive sources of lead poisoning in children are old paint, dust, and water. Although the passage of the 1971 Lead-Based Paint Poisoning Prevention Act and its later revisions in 1972 and 1977 banned the sale of leaded paint for household use, an estimated 6 million dwellings, which house 2 million young children, contain deteriorated lead-painted surfaces (ATSDR, 1988). It is not necessary to eat paint to raise one's blood lead level. Peeling paint or careless paint removal creates toxic lead dust particles that are inhaled or ingested. Toddlers playing on the floor accumulate leaded dust on their hands and ingest lead by ordinary hand-to-mouth activity.

The major source of lead in drinking water is plumbing. Pipes connecting from the street main to household plumbing may contain lead, or lead solder joints within the home

---

*Protected produce consists of crops whose edible portions are naturally covered (i.e., carrots, corn). Leafy produce includes all vegetables in which the leaf is consumed (i.e., broccoli, lettuce). Exposed produce includes all nonleafy fruits and vegetables whose edibles are naturally exposed (i.e. apples, tomatoes).

may contribute to lead in water. Acidic or soft water can leach out lead from the plumbing, especially if the water has been standing in the pipes for an extended period. The U.S. EPA (1987) estimated that 16% of household water supplies have concentrations of lead over the proposed standard of 20 μg/dl.

The United States uses 1.204 million metric tons of lead annually. Transportation (mainly batteries) accounts for 70.67% of U.S. lead usage. Other uses include cable sheathing (11.51%), chemicals (5.61%), ammunition (3.90%), construction (2.60%), and gasoline (2.20%) (Mushak, 1991). These sources pose occupational health risks to workers manufacturing these products and long-term environmental health risks.

3. LOW-LEVEL EXPOSURE AND SCHOOL-AGE CHILDREN

Childhood lead poisoning was first described in Brisbane, Australia in the pioneering work of A.J. Turner (1897) and J. Lockhart Gibson (1904). They reported that the environmental cause was paint on the porch railings of homes. As late as the 1940s, it was widely believed that a child who survived acute lead poisoning was left without sequelae. In 1943, Byers reported that 19 of 20 children followed up after acute intoxication had behavioral disorders or learning disabilities. The question was raised: How many cases of school failure or behavioral disorders were caused by missed cases of lead poisoning?

In the past decade and a half, studies from several countries have reported cognitive and behavioral effects of lead exposure at increasingly lower concentrations. Most of these modern studies have used large samples and have included children from higher socioeconomic backgrounds. Some investigators have examined blood lead values, which reflect recent exposure. Others have examined tooth lead values, which reflect cumulative exposure, even after the blood lead level has returned to normal.

Needleman and colleagues (1979) screened 2335 first- and second-grade children in the Boston public school system. They analyzed shed deciduous teeth for lead. Children in the highest and lowest tooth lead decile were assessed with measures of psychometric intelligence, speech and language ability, attention, and classroom behavior. After adjusting for covariates, the high-lead group (>20 ppm) scored significantly lower than the low-lead group (>10 ppm) on intelligence quotient (IQ), speech and language processing, and attention. Teacher ratings of nonadaptive classroom behaviors were related in a dose-response fashion to tooth lead levels.

Silva et al. (1988) studies 579 urban New Zealand children at age 11. The sample was socioeconomically advantaged and was under-representative of other Polynesian children. The mean blood lead was 11.1 μg/dl. Only two children had levels above 30 μg/dl. Boys had significantly higher mean blood leads than girls (11.4 μg/dl vs. 10.4 μg/dl). Controlling for several covariates, lead was significantly associated with increases in children's behavioral problems and hyperactivity, as reported by both parents and teachers. Although the relationship between blood lead and IQ was inverse, it did not reach statistical significance at p = .05.

Fergusson et al. (1988) studied a sample of more than 650 children from the longitudinal Christchurch, New Zealand child development project at ages 8 and 9. The mean dentine lead level was just over 6 μg/g. After adjusting for covariates, higher tooth lead levels were significantly related to lower reading scores, poorer spelling, lower mathematics scores, and poorer handwriting. Because of the narrow range of tooth lead levels, this is a conservative estimate of the effect of lead.

Fulton *et al.* (1987) studied 501 middle-class children aged 6–9 years in Edinburgh. The mean blood lead was 11.5 μg/dl. Only 10 children had blood lead concentrations above 25 μg/dl. Controlling for 33 covariates, higher blood lead levels were significantly associated with lower scores on the British Ability Scales (BAS), math and reading skills. There was a dose-response relationship between blood lead scores and cognitive ability scores, with no evidence of a threshold.

Behavioral ratings for this Edinburgh sample were made by teachers and parents using the Rutter behavioral scales (Thomson *et al.*, 1989). An extensive home interview with one parent was also conducted. Controlling for 30 possible covariates, higher blood lead levels were significantly associated with lower teacher ratings on the total Rutter scores and on the aggressive/antisocial and hyperactive subscales. There was a dose-response relationship between blood lead levels and behavior ratings, with no evidence of a threshold. Inspection time, a measure of sustained attention, was also negatively associated with blood lead levels (Raab *et al.*, 1990).

It has been suggested that children with cognitive deficits or behavioral problems may be more likely to behave in ways that increase their exposure to lead (e.g., playing outside in dirt, being careless of hygiene). This hypothesis of reverse causation assumes that the child's behavior or level of cognitive functioning is the cause, rather than the result, of lead exposure. Lead in drinking water is an important source of exposure in Edinburgh (Raab *et al.*, 1987), affecting children regardless of their behavior. Thus, reverse causation is an unlikely explanation for Edinburgh study results.

Hatzakis *et al.* (1987) studied 509 primary school children near a smelter site in Lavrion, Greece. The mean blood lead level was 23.7 μg/dl. Controlling for 17 covariates, blood lead levels were inversely related to full-scale IQ scores on the Weschler Intelligence Scale for Children—Revised (WISC-R) (p = .00007). The decline in cognitive functioning was approximately 2.5 IQ scale points for every 10 μg/dl increase in blood lead. The adjusted full-scale IQ difference between "high" lead (> 45 μg/dl) and "low" lead (<15 μg/dl) was 9.1 IQ scale points.

Hansen *et al.* (1989) studies 162 first-grade children from Denmark. This middle-class sample lived in an area of high-quality housing and no major source of lead pollution. The mean dentine lead level for the "high" lead group (>18.7 μg/g) was 26.8 μ/g and 3.25 μg/g for the "low" lead group (<5 μg/g). The groups were matched by gender and socioeconomic status. The high-lead group scored lower on the full-scale (p < .01) and the verbal (p < .001) WISC scales. Lead exposure was negatively associated with performance on the Bender Visual Motor Gestalt Test (p < .001) and with a behavioral rating scale (p < .01).

Bergomi *et al.* (1989) studies 216 seven-year-old children from northern Italy. The mean tooth lead level for 115 children was 6.05 μg/g; the 95th percentile equaled 12.7 μg/g. The mean blood level was 10.9 μg/dl; the 95th percentile equaled 17.9 μg/dl. After covariate adjustment, tooth lead was significantly related to full-scale and verbal WISC-R scores and performance on the Toulouse Pieron Test (a measure of attention). They found no significant relationships between blood lead and the psychometric measures.

Needleman *et al.* (1990) conducted an 11-year follow-up of 132 children from the 1979 study. The mean age at the time of retesting in 1988 was 18.4 years. Young adults with high dentine lead levels (>20 ppm) at ages 6 or 7 had a sevenfold increased risk for dropping out of high school and a sixfold increased risk for reading disabilities as compared to those with low dentine lead levels (<10 ppm). Higher lead levels were also associated with lower class standing in high school, increased absenteeism, lower vocabulary and grammatical-reasoning scores, longer reaction times, poorer hand-eye coordination, and slower finger tapping. Lead levels were also inversely correlated to self-reports of minor delinquent activity. The investigators concluded that lead exposure, even in children who were asymptomatic, may have an enduring effect on their success in life.

Many of these studies concluded that the size of the effects, while significant, is small. Needleman and Gatsonis (1990) included several of these studies in their meta-analysis of the relationship between lead and IQ. Of the initial 24 studies reviewed, 12 were excluded because they did not control for covariates or use multivariate analysis. The 12 remaining studies were classified by tissue (tooth or blood). The sign of the lead coefficient was negative for 11 of 12 studies. The negative partial r's for lead ranged from $-.27$ to $-.003$. The power to find an effect was below .6 in 7 of the 12 studies. The joint p values for the blood lead studies were less than .0001. The joint p values for the tooth lead studies were less than .004. The effect was robust with the removal of any study.

4. PRENATAL LEAD EXPOSURE AND EARLY DEVELOPMENT

Lead readily passes through the placenta, and maternal and fetal blood levels are highly correlated (Graziano et al., 1990). Lead has been measured in the fetal brain as early as 13 weeks gestation time and increases with brain growth. The immature blood–brain barrier and the absence of protein complexes that sequester lead in mature tissues result in increased vulnerability of the fetal brain to lead (Goyer, 1990).

Lead at high levels has an ancient history as a reproductive toxin (Gilfillan, 1965; Silbergeld, 1983). Female industrial lead workers of the early 20th century experienced an increase in the incidence of infertility, abortion, stillbirth, and fetal death associated with industrial lead exposure (Oliver, 1911).

Case studies of fetal and neonatal outcomes at maternal toxicity levels greater than 50 μg/dl have found the following: a tendency toward premature birth, reduced birth weights, intrauterine growth retardation, failure to thrive, signs of neurological dysfunction, and significant language delays (Bellinger and Needleman, in press). Recent evidence suggests that many of these outcomes may be present at much lower levels of maternal exposure (Bellinger et al., 1991b; Dietrich et al., 1986; McMichael et al., 1986).

The sources of maternal lead exposure during pregnancy and lactation are both exogenous and endogenous. Blood lead levels tend to remain stable or to decline slightly over the course of pregnancy, despite pregnancy-related changes that might be expected to reduce blood lead levels (e.g., increased plasma volume, physiologic anemia, and increased glomerular filtration rate) (Bellinger and Needleman, in press; Goyer, 1990). This may be due to lead mobilization during pregnancy, when maternal hormones mobilize calcium from the bone to support fetal development. Lead resembles calcium and follows the fate of calcium in the bloodstream. Thus, the mother's lifetime lead burden stored in the bone becomes an endogenous source of lead toxicity during pregnancy and lactation. (Silbergeld, 1986; Thompson et al., 1985).

Investigations of low-level prenatal lead exposure on development are optimally conducted using forward, or prospective, methodologies in order to better determine the direction of causality. In forward studies, subjects are recruited prior to birth and are assessed at regular intervals thereafter. Three currently investigated areas of developmental outcome in low-level prenatal exposure are structural malformation, growth retardation, and cognitive functioning.

Structural malformation, or minor physical anomalies (MPAs), are congenital abnormalities with no cosmetic or medical significance (e.g., low-set ears, skin tags, extra digits). However, the presence of two or more minor anomalies may be an important marker of impaired neurological development occurring during the first prenatal trimester (Pomeroy et al., 1988). In an urban study of more than 4000 births, umbilical cord blood leads were analyzed, and the presence of several minor physical anomalies was measured. Controlling for covariates, lead was found to be associated with increased risk for minor physical anomalies in a dose-related fashion (Needleman et al., 1984). Two attempts to replicate this finding were unsuccessful (Ernhart et al. 1986; McMichael et al., 1986). Smaller sample sized reduced the statistical power of these latter studies.

Markers of growth retardation in prenatal development include premature delivery and low birth weight for gestational age. Several studies report an association between increased prenatal lead levels and preterm delivery (Dietrich et al., 1986; McMichael et al., 1986), reduced birth weight (Bornschein et al., 1989; Ward et al., 1990), low birth weight for gestational age (Bellinger et al., 1991b), reduced head circumference (Routh et al., 1979; Ward et al., 1990), and reduced length (Bornschein et al., 1989). Some of these findings have not been replicated (Bellinger et al., 1991; Ernhart et al., 1986).

In a forward study of 260 infants from birth to 15 months, Shukla et al. (1989) showed that growth over the interval of 3–15 months in infants with "high" prenatal exposures (>8 µg/dl) was inversely related to postnatal exposure. Infants with "high" prenatal exposure but "low" postnatal lead levels tended to have particularly rapid postnatal growth rates. Infants with ongoing elevated postnatal lead levels continued to exhibit suppressed growth rates. The authors infer that in utero growth is affected by lead and that infants not exposed to lead postnatally exhibit a catch-up growth rate.

Prospective studies examining the association between prenatal and postnatal blood lead levels and cognitive functioning have been conducted in Boston, Cincinnati, Cleveland, and Port Pirie (Bellinger et al., 1987, 1991a, 1991b; Dietrich et al., 1987, 1991; Ernhart et al., 1985, 1986, 1987, 1989; McMichael et al., 1985, 1988). These studies report significant, although somewhat differing, patterns of associations between blood lead levels in the first 4 years of life and later cognitive functioning.

The Boston study provides some evidence that the effects of prenatal lead exposure may be attenuated by environmental enrichment (Bellinger et al., 1987, 1990). The cohort was unusual in comparison to most studies in that the majority of the children were from middle- or upper-middle class families and the exposure was higher in the higher classes. The study included 249 children from three exposure groups: low (PbB <3 µg/dl), middle (PbB 6–7 µg/dl), and high (PbB >10- µg/dl). Children were evaluated at 1, 6, 12, 18, 24, and 57 months of age. Controlling for several covariates, higher umbilical cord blood lead levels were associated with lower scores on the Bayley Scales of Infant Development at all epochs between 6 and 24 months of age. An increase in blood lead level at age 24 months was associated with a decrease in the General Cognitive Index (GCI) from the McCarthy Scales of Children's Abilities. The investigators administered the GCI at 57 months of age and did not find an association between prenatal exposure and cognitive functioning at 57 months (Bellinger et al., 1991). However, the effect of lead continued to be significant for children of lower socioeconomic status, for boys, and for children whose exposure at 24 months was high. The degree of recovery was mediated by socioeconomic status, maternal IQ, and the quality of the rearing environment.

The Cincinnati study followed a cohort of about 300 urban, mostly black, children from single-parent, low-income households (Dietrich *et al.*, 1987, 1991). Prenatal lead exposure was associated with later decrements in performance on the Bayley scales. At 6 months of age, boys demonstrated an 8.7 point decrease in the Mental Development Index (MDI) for every 10 µg/dl increase in blood lead. These findings were no longer significant at 24 months of age. However, language development at 39 months was inversely associated with prenatal lead levels. Early postnatal lead exposure (10-day) was inversely associated with performance at age 4 years on the Simultaneous Processing subscale of the Kaufman Assessment Battery for Children (K-ABC).

The Cleveland study followed approximately 250 families from an impoverished urban cohort initially recruited for a study of fetal alcohol effects (Ernhart *et al.*, 1985). Cord blood lead levels were associated with abnormal neonatal reflexes (Ernhart *et al.*, 1986). Maternal blood lead level was inversely associated with infants' scores at age 6 months on the Bayley Scales and the Kent Infant Development Scale (Ernhart *et al.*, 1987). No associations were apparent at later ages (Ernhart *et al.*, 1987, 1989). Interpretation of these findings is difficult because half the mothers were selected for positive histories of alcohol abuse.

The Port Pirie study followed over 600 children from birth to 4 years of age. Postnatal blood lead levels rose sharply in this population of children who lived near a smelter site, averaging 21 µg/dl at 2 years of age (McMichael *et al.*, 1985). The authors reported a significant relationship between 6-month blood levels and Bayley MDI scores at 24 months of age (McMichael *et al.*, 1988). At 48 months, GCI scores were significantly related to an index of cumulative postnatal exposure.

The Port Pirie study did not find significant associations between prenatal blood lead levels and cognitive functioning at ages 2 or 4. Prenatal exposure effects may have been overwhelmed by ongoing postnatal exposure. In addition, measurements of cognitive functioning were not obtained until 2 years of age, making detection of a prenatal effect prior to 2 years of age impossible.

A summary report of these studies stated that the slopes (changes in cognitive scores per µg/dl increase in blood lead) reflecting greater cognitive impairment with higher blood levels appeared steeper for prenatal than postnatal exposure (Gradient Corporation, 1990). The decline in cognitive functioning was approximately 1 IQ scale point for each 2 µg/dl increase in prenatal blood lead and 3 IQ points for each 10 µg/dl increase in postnatal blood lead (Bellinger and Needleman, in press). While most studies do not report the data in a way that permits a clear calculation of threshold levels, the linear relationship of lead exposure and cognitive impairment extends over a range of exposures.

The Agency for Toxic Substances and Disease Registry (ATSDR) states ". . . the available evidence for a potential risk of developmental toxicity from lead exposure of the fetus in pregnant women also points towards a Pb-B level of 10 to 15 µg/dl, and perhaps even lower" (1988, p. 3). According to the ATSDR, approximately 400,000 pregnancies are at risk for maternal lead levels greater than µg/dl in a given year (Crocetti *et al.*, 1990). White and black women of childbearing age between 20 and 44 years had an estimated risk of 9.7% and 19.7%, respectively.

Age 2 may be an important developmental epoch for examining the relationship between age at exposure and specific neurobehavioral deficits. Children's blood lead levels tend to peak between 2 and 3 years of age (Mahaffey *et al.*, 1982). The Boston study found that lead levels at age 2 were a significant predictor of cognitive functioning at 57 months of age (Bellinger and Needleman, 1991). Shaheen (1984) noted that the deficits of children poisoned prior to age 2 were primarily linguistic, while the deficits of those poisoned between ages 2 and 3 primarily involved visual-spatial skills. In the Boston and Port Pirie studies, children's visual-motor and visual-spatial performance appeared to be the most strongly related to lead exposure in the second and third years.

5. BIOLOGICAL EFFECTS OF LEAD

Lead is a divalent cation of extreme reactivity. Its propensity to bind sulfhydryl groups on proteins has long been recognized. As a result, lead alters the shape and activity of many enzymes, including d-aminolevulinic acid dehydratase, at an early step in heme conjugation (Hernberg, 1973), ferrochelatase, 1-25 vitamin D hydroxylase (Rosen et al., 1980), and Na and K ATPase (Hasan et al., 1967). It also has been demonstrated to uncouple oxidative phosphorylation (Holtzman et al., 1978) and to interfere with the activity of brain cytochromes (Bull et al., 1979). Brain adenylate cyclase activity is decreased at low concentrations of lead (Nathanson and Bloom, 1975).

A group of new studies have identified other toxic mechanisms for lead that may have as great importance as sulfhydryl binding. Brown et al. (1983) have shown that lead cleaves the phosphoribose backbone of tRNA at specific sites, and thus can interfere with translation. This activity is catalytic and has no threshold.

Markovac and Goldstein (1988) have demonstrated that lead binds to brain protein kinase C with extreme avidity, and at picomolar concentrations lead stimulates this second messenger. Goldstein has speculated that this mechanism, by altering the cellular response to a given stimulus, could interfere with the normal pace of pruning back of dendrites that takes place during brain development and could account for the altered reactivity of lead-exposed individuals (Goldstein, 1992).

In a series of studies of the ontogeny of the endogenous opiate system, a group of neurobiologists from Surrey has shown that early lead exposure reduces the levels of endogenous opoid precursors (Winder and Kitchen, 1984) and that the pain-killing activity of morphine was reduced by low levels of lead (Kitchen et al., 1984). These findings may have implications for the relationship between lead and substance abuse. Nation et al. (1986) have shown that the ordinarily observed aversive properties of alcohol for rodents is extinguished by the administration of lead to pups.

6. INTERACTION OF LEAD AND NUTRITION

Lead interacts with several nutrients. Nutritional status can alter lead uptake and can modify the toxic effects of lead. The interaction between lead and nutrients has been investigated primarily in carefully controlled animal studies. Important nutrients include calcium, iron, phosphate, vitamin D, lipids, zinc, and copper.

Overall patterns and frequency of foot intake influence the absorption of lead from the gastrointestinal tract. Lead ingested during fasting is absorbed at a much higher rate than lead ingested with food. This may be particularly relevant for lead industry workers, where lead is present on the job and workers may have irregular eating patterns (Mahaffey, 1990).

Diets low in calcium increase lead absorption and toxicity. This has been demonstrated in a number of species, including rats (Barltrop and Khoo, 1975; Barton et al.,

1978a, Mahaffey *et al.*, 1973), pigs (Hsu *et al.*, 1975), horses (Willoughby *et al.*, 1972), lambs (Morrison *et al.*, 1977), and domestic fowl (Berg *et al.*, 1980). Lead affects the activity of 1,25 vitamin D hydroxylase at extremely low concentrations and through this mechanism can have profound effects on bone metabolism and growth (Rosen *et al.*, 1980).

Lead can be remobilized from the bone during conditions of high calcium demand, such as pregnancy, lactation, menopause, and osteoporosis. Therefore, calcium deficiency may act to promote the redistribution of lead. Mobilization of long-term stores of lead during pregnancy and lactation may increase the transfer of lead to the fetus and infant (Mahaffey, 1990).

Iron deficiency increases the uptake and susceptibility to lead toxicity at the cellular level. Because lead and iron compete for critical binding sites, iron deficiency results in increased vulnerability to lead toxicity, and the presence of lead can exacerbate iron deficiency.

Lead transfer during pregnancy and lactation was enhanced when dams were maintained on low-iron diets (Cerklewski, 1980). Rodents maintained on iron-deficient diets have increased tissue levels of lead (Barton *et al.*, 1978b; Mahaffey-Six and Goyer, 1972). The effect of changes in lead level on iron absorption is less clear. Flanagan *et al.* (1979) reported that lead reduced iron absorption, while other investigators found no effect (Barton *et al.*, 1978b; Dobbins *et al.*, 1978).

Lead uptake occurs at the same site as phosphate (Smith *et al.*, 1978). Low dietary phosphate has been shown to enhance lead retention in rats (Quarterman and Morrison, 1975), increasing lead uptake by a factor of nearly three (Barltrop and Khoo, 1975). Conflicting results have been reported on the relationship between reduced dietary phosphate and skeletal lead mobilization (Barton and Conrad, 1981; Quarterman and Morrison, 1975).

Early studies indicated a potentially positive relationship between dietary vitamin D and lead uptake (Sobel *et al.*, 1938, 1940). Barton and his colleagues (1980) reported that lead absorption in the rat is increased with either deficient or excessive amounts of dietary vitamin D. Lead uptake in the femur and kidney has also been reported in rat diets deficient of vitamin D (Hart and Smith, 1981).

Lipids are positively associated with lead absorption in rats. By increasing the lipid (corn oil) content of the rat diet from 5 to 40%, Barltrop and Khoo (1975) demonstrated a 13.6-fold increase in blood lead levels, and parallel lead increases were measured in kidney, femur, and carcass. The chemical composition of the lipid was a significant factor in affecting lead absorption (Barltrop, 1982).

Zinc-deficient diets promote lead absorption, while repletion with zinc reduces lead uptake (Cerklewski and Forbes, 1976; El-Gazzar *et al.*, 1978). In a study of zinc-lead interactions in rats during pregnancy and lactation, zinc-deficient diets resulted in more transfer of lead through milk to rat pups (Cerklewski, 1979). Rats fed a low-zinc diet with lead had significantly higher retention of lead in the brain and calvarium compared to those fed a high-zinc diet (Bushnell and Levin, 1983).

Low dietary copper has been shown to enhance lead absorption in rats fed a high-lead or moderate-lead diet (Klauder *et al.*, 1973; Klauder and Petering, 1975). Reduced copper intake enhances the hematological effects of lead (Klauder and Petering, 1977), suggesting that both copper and iron deficiencies must be addressed to restore hemoglobin levels to normal.

Children having multiple nutrient deficiencies are at greater risk for deleterious effects from lead exposure (U.S. EPA, 1986). Mahaffey and Michaelson (1980) summarized three national nutritional status surveys for infants and young children. Iron deficiency was the most prevalent nutritional problem in children under 2 years of age, particularly those from low-income groups. Other common nutritional deficiencies in low-income groups included zinc, vitamins A and C, and calcium (Hambidge, 1977; Owen and Lippman, 1977). Several observational studies on infants and children have noted an inverse relationship between blood lead level and calcium intake (Johnson and Tenuta, 1979; Mahaffey et al., 1976; Sorrell et al., 1977; Ziegler et al., 1978), vitamin D intake (Rosen et al., 1980, 1981; Sorrel et al., 1977), zinc intake (Chisolm, 1981; Johnson and Tenuta, 1979; Markowitz and Rosen, 1981), and iron intake (Chisolm, 1981; Yip et al., 1981).

Nutrition has been discussed as an intervention strategy to reduce the impact of lead exposure (Mahaffey, 1990). While high-level lead exposure cannot be treated by nutritional modifications, low-level lead exposure may respond to nutritional supplements. This issue requires systematic study. The relevant nutritional guidelines are consistent with the general recommendations for a healthful diet. This is not to suggest, as the lead industry did in the 1950s and early 1960s, that the solution to lead problems is to assure that those exposed had proper nutrition (Hays, 1992). Primary prevention is the only cure for lead poisoning.

7. SCIENTIFIC AND METHODOLOGICAL ISSUES

The controversy over the relationship between low-level lead exposure and neurobehavioral deficits has involved certain methodological issues. Human studies are limited to observational designs. Making causal inferences from nonexperimental studies requires particular care in balancing the opposing risks of type I and type II errors. A type I error means that the experimenter accepts spurious associations in the data as causal (e.g., lead poisoning is not the cause of the deficit but the researcher identifies it as such). A type II error means that the experimenter misses the true causal association (e.g., lead poisoning is the cause of the deficit, but is not identified as such).

Traditionally, scientific rigor emphasizes avoiding type I errors, thus reducing spurious claims in a given body of literature. Needleman and Bellinger (1991) identified six factors contributing to systematic reduction of the risk of type I errors at the increased risk of type II errors.

1. Assigning an arbitrary p value criterion. Statistical significance is often defined as achieving the criterion of $p < .05$. Studies reporting results above this criterion accept the null hypothesis and thus dismiss the possibility of a causal association. This criterion is an arbitrary threshold and is dependent on sample size and effect size.

2. Postulating unidentified covariates. Covariates are factors that independently affect the results and are associated with the hypothesized causal factor in a study. In nonexperimental studies, subjects are not randomized across treatment groups. Many nonrandomized factors may act as covariates to influence the outcome of a study. While the effect of an identified covariate can be statistically estimated, an unidentified covariate may reduce the effect size of the hypothesized causal factor to zero. In the case of lead and child development, an unidentified (or improperly measured) covariate with lead could reduce the reported effect size for lead. However, the literature on factors affecting

children's cognitive and behavioral outcomes is sufficiently established to minimize the possibility of a completely unidentified covariate.

3. Building inaccurate causal models. Building causal models requires applying knowledge or theoretical principles about the topic under study. A variable can have more than one position in the causal chain: It can modify an effect, or be both an independent and dependent factor. For example, mothers of children with elevated lead levels and deficits tend to score lower on IQ tests; thus, maternal rearing incompetence is given as the cause of the child's deficit. In fact, a mother's rearing skill might be influenced by her own lead exposure as a child, as suggested by animal research findings (Barrett and Livesey, 1983). Likewise, building a causal model that controls for factors possibly related to lead exposure, such as hyperactivity or developmental delay, clearly over-controls and reduces the estimate of the true effect size for lead.

4. Inadequate sample size and statistical power. The statistical power of a study is defined as the probability of finding a true effect. This is determined by the number of subjects, the desired effect size, and the alpha level set by the researcher. Nonexperimental studies require large sample sizes to achieve adequate power to find an effect. Many lead studies reporting no effect have small sample sizes and weak statistical power (Needleman and Gatsonis, 1990).

5. Underestimating the significance of a "small" effect size. Differences among groups are often reported as mean or median scores. Some scientists interpret small group differences as inconsequential. However, this does not accurately describe variations of effects throughout the population distribution. For example, in most studies the difference between mean IQ scores in exposed and unexposed lead groups is approximately 4–7 IQ points, with the partial r for lead in multiple regression at about .14 (Needleman and Bellinger, 1991). For lead-exposed children, the rate of severe deficit (i.e., IQ <80) is four times greater in the high-lead group (16% vs. 4%). The maximum IQ score in the high-lead group in the study by Needleman *et al.* (1979) was 125; however, 5% of children in the low-lead group scored above 125. Lead exposure may prevent about 5% of this population from achieving truly superior function.

6. Limitations of causality. Scientific studies cannot prove causality (Hume, 1894). Scientists are faced with limitations of variate and covariate precision, financial and practical restrictions in the number of subjects that can be tested, and selecting optimal, but not all, possible variates. Instead of attempting to prove causality, epidemiologists focus on specific canons that permit drawing causal inferences (Kenny, 1979). These canons include (1) time precedence of the hypothesized cause (addressed with the use of forward studies); (2) biological plausibility (based on current animal and human studies); (3) a dose-response relationship between the independent and dependent variable; (4) non-spuriousness (addressed by careful control of covariates and parallel findings in experimentally designed animal work); and (5) consistency of findings across studies (addressed by current literature reviews and meta-analysis).

8. FUTURE DIRECTIONS

Most studies on low-level lead exposure have focused on cognitive and neurological effects. Little attention has been given to higher order behaviors, such as social functioning with peers and functioning within society. There is growing evidence from both animal and human studies that lead interferes with attentional processes (Fergusson *et al.*, 1988; Gilbert and Rice, 1987; Needleman *et al.*, 1979; Thomson *et al.*, 1989) and may be associated with aggressiveness (Lansdown *et al.*, 1983). Attention-deficit disorder with hyperactivity combined with antisocial behavior is a strong predictor of criminality (Magnusson *et al.*, 1983; Moffitt, 1990). Several factors are associated with both criminality and lead exposure (Needleman and Bellinger, 1991). We are currently exploring the relationship of lead exposure, attention-deficit disorder, and juvenile delinquency.

Additional work is needed on contributing factors in prenatal lead exposure. Studies examining exogenous and endogenous factors in maternal exposure, particularly mobilization of lead during pregnancy and lactation, are needed. Evidence from animal studies suggests that lead is a reproductive toxin for both males and females (Silbergeld, 1983). Paternal exposure to lead and its effects on the father, male reproduction, and the fetus are virtually unexplored (Needleman and Bellinger, 1988, 1991).

Lead mobilization from the bone is also a concern for the aged. With aging, the bone demineralizes, providing a possible ongoing endogenous source of lead (Silbergeld *et al.*, 1988). Research is needed on the sites of redistribution of bone lead and its possible relationship to cognitive and neurological dysfunction in the aged.

While there are many opportunities for future research investigations, scientists and society must also ask why we have not focused on eradicating this totally preventable disease. Factors slowing the removal of lead from the human environment include the following: The belief that the disease is limited to poor minorities; the belief that the gasoline and paint legislation of the 1970s has solved the problem; the obstructionism of the lead industry; the lack of medical interest in this "low technology" disease; and the lack of commitment of governmental resources (Needleman and Bellinger, 1991).

REFERENCES

Agency for Toxic Substances and Disease Registry, 1988, *The Nature and Extent of Lead Poisoning in Children in the United States: A Report to Congress.* Department of Health and Human Services, Atlanta.

Barltrop, D., 1982, Nutritional and maturational factors modifying the absorption of inorganic lead from the gastrointestinal tract, in: *Environmental Factors in Human Growth and Development* (V.R. Hunt, M.K. Smith, and D. Worth, eds.), Cold Spring Harbor Laboratory Press, Cold Spring Harbor, NY, pp. 35–41.

Barltrop, D., and Khoo, H.E., 1975, The influence of nutritional factors on lead absorption, *Postgrad. Med. J.* 51:795–800.

Barrett, J., and Livesey, P.J., 1983, Lead induced alterations in maternal behavior and offspring development in the rat, *Neurobehav. Toxicol. Teratol.* 5:557–563.

Barton, J.C., and Conrad, M.E., 1981, Effect of phosphate on the absorption and retention of lead in the rat, *Am. J. Clin. Nutr.* 34:2192–2198.

Barton, J.C., Conrad, M.E., Harrison, L., and Nuby, S., 1978a, Effects of calcium on the absorption and retention of lead, *J. Lab. Clin. Med.* 91:366–376.

Barton, J.C., Conrad, M.E., Harrison, L., and Nuby, S., 1978b, Effects of iron on the absorption and retention of lead, *J. Lab. Clin. Med.* 92:536–547.

Barton, J.C., Conrad, M.E., Harrison, L., and Nuby, S., 1980, Effects of vitamin D on the absorption and retention of lead, *Am. J. Physiol.* 238:G124–G130.

Bellinger, D., and Needleman, H.L., 1992, Lead, in: *Prenatal Exposure to Environmental Toxicants: Developmental Consequences* (H.L. Needleman, and D. Bellinger, eds.), Johns Hopkins Press, Baltimore (in press).

Bellinger, D., Leviton, A., Waternaux, C., Needleman, H., and Rabinowitz, M., 1987, Longitudinal analyses of pre- and postnatal lead exposure and early cognitive development, *N. Engl. J. Med.* 316:1037–1043.

Bellinger, D., Leviton, A., and Sloman, J., 1990, Antecedents and correlates of improved cognitive performance in children exposed in utero to low levels of lead, *Environ. Health Perspect.* 89:5–11.

Bellinger, D., Sloman, J., Leviton, A., Rabinowitz, M., Needleman, H., and Waternaux, C., 1991a, Low level lead exposure and children's cognitive function in the preschool years, *Pediatrics* 87:219–227.

Bellinger, D., Leviton, A., Rabinowitz, M., Allred, E., Needleman, H., and Schoenbaum, S., 1991b, Weight gain and maturity in fetuses exposed to low levels of lead, *Environ. Res.* 54:151–158.

Berg, L.R., Nordstrom, J.O., and Ousterhout, L.E., 1980, The prevention of chick growth depression due to dietary lead by increased dietary calcium and phosphorus levels, *Poult. Sci.* 59:1860–1863.

Bergomi, M., Borella, P., Fantuzzi, G., Vivoli, G., Sturloni, N., Cavazzuti, G., Tampieri, A., and Tartoni, P.L., 1989, Relationship between lead exposure indicators and neuropsychological performance in children, *Dev. Med. Child Neurol.* 31:181–190.

Bornschein, R.L., Grote, J., Mitchell, T., Succop, P., Dietrich, K.M., Krafft, K., and Hammond, P., 1989, Effects of prenatal and postnatal lead exposure on fetal maturation and postnatal growth, in: *Lead Exposure and Child Development: An International Assessment* (M. Smith, L. Grant, and A. Sors, eds.), Kluwer Academic Publishers, Boston, pp. 307–319.

Brown, R.S., Hingerty, B.E., Dewan, J.C., and Klug, A., 1983, Pb(II)-catalysed cleavage of the sugar-phosphate backbone of yeast tRNA(Phe)—implications for lead toxicity and self-splicing RNA, *Nature* 303:543–546.

Bull, R.J., Lutkenhoff, S.D., McCarty, G.E., and Miller, R.G., 1979, Delays in the postnatal increase of cerebral cytochrome concentrations in lead-exposed rats, *Neuropharmacology* 18:83–92.

Bushnell, P.J., and Levin, E.D., 1983, Effects of zinc deficiency on lead toxicity in rats, *Neurobehav. Toxicol. Teratol.* 5:283–288.

Byers, R.K., and Lord, E.E., 1943, Late effects of lead poisoning on mental development, *Am. J. Dis. Child.* 66:471–483.

Cerklewski, F.L., 1979, Influence of dietary zinc on lead toxicity during gestation and lactation in the female rat, *J. Nutr.* 109:1703–1709.

Cerklewski, F.L., 1980, Reduction in neonatal lead exposure by supplemental dietary iron during gestation and lactation in the rat, *J. Nutr.* 110:1453–1457.

Cerklewski, F.L., and Forbes, R.M., 1976, Influence of dietary zinc on lead toxicity in the rat, *J. Nutr.* 106:689–696.

Chisolm, J.J., Jr., 1981, Dose-effect relationships for lead in young children: Evidence in children for interactions among lead, zinc, and iron, in: *Environmental Lead: Proceedings of the Second International Symposium on Environmental Lead Research, December, 1978, Cincinnati, OH* (D.R. Lynam, L.G. Piantanida, and J.F. Cole, eds.), Academic Press, New York, pp. 1–7.

Crocetti, A., Mushak, P., and Schwartz, J., 1990, Determination of numbers of lead-exposed women of child-bearing age and pregnant women: An integrated summary of a report to the U.S. Congress on childhood lead poisoning, *Environ. Health Perspect.* 89:121–124.

Davis, J.M., and Svendsgaard, D.J., 1987, Lead and child development, *Nature* 329:287–300.

Dietrich, K., Krafft, K., Shukla, R., Bornschein, R., and Succop, P., 1986, The neurobehavioral effects of prenatal and early postnatal lead exposure, in: *Toxic Substances and Mental Retardation: Neurobehavioral Toxicology and Teratology* (S. Schroeder, ed.), American Association on Mental Deficiency, Washington, D.C., pp. 71–95.

Dietrich, K., Krafft, K., Bornschein, R., Hammond, P., Berger, O., Succop, P., and Bier, M., 1987, Low-level fetal lead exposure effect on neurobehavioral development in early infancy, *Pediatrics* 80:721–730.

Dietrich, K., Succop, P., Berger, O., Hammond, P., and Bornschein, R., 1991, Lead exposure and the cognitive development of urban preschool children: The Cincinnati Lead Study cohort at age 4 years, *Neurotoxicol. Teratol.* 13:203–211.

Dobbins, A., Johnson, D.R., and Nathan, P., 1978, Effect of exposure to lead on maturation of intestinal iron absorption of rats, *J. Toxicol. Environ. Health* 4:541–550.

El-Gazzar, R.M., Finelli, V.N., Boiano, J., and Petering, H.G., 1978, Influence of dietary zinc on lead toxicity in rats, *Toxicol. Lett.* 1:226–234.

Ernhart, C., Wolf, A., Brittenham, G., and Erhard, P., 1985, Fetal lead exposure: Antenatal factors, *Environ. Res.* 38:54–66.

Ernhart, C., Wolf, A., Kennard, M., Erhard, P. Filipovich, H., and Sokol, R., 1986, Intrauterine exposure to low levels of lead: The status of the neonate, *Arch. Environ. Health* 41:287–291.

Ernhart, C., Morrow-Tlucak, M., Marler, M., and Wolf, A., 1987, Low level lead exposure in prenatal and early preschool periods: Early preschool development, *Neurotoxicol. Teratol.* 9:259–270.

Ernhart, C., Morrow-Tlucak, M., Wolf, A., Super, D., and Drotar, D., 1989, Low level lead exposure in the prenatal and early preschool periods: Intelligence prior to school entry, *Neurotoxicol. Teratol.* 11:161–170.

Fergusson, D.M., Fergusson, J.E., Horwood, L.J., and Kinzett, N.G., 1988, A longitudinal study of dentine lead levels, intelligence, school performance and behaviour: Part III: Dentine lead levels and attention/activity, *J. Child. Psychol. Psychiat.* 29(6):811–824.

Flanagan, P.R., Hamilton, D.L., Haist, J., and Valnerg, L.S., 1979, Inter-relationships between iron and absorption in iron-deficient mice, *Gastroenterology* 77:1074–1080.

Fulton, M., Raab, G., Thomson, G., Laxen, D., Hunter, R., and Hepburn, W., 1987, Influence of blood lead on the ability and attainment of children in Edinburgh, *Lancet* 1:1221–1226.

Gibson, J.L., 1904, A plea for painted railings and painted walls of rooms as the source of lead poisoning among Queensland children, *Austr. Med. Gaz.* 23:149–153.

Gilbert, S.G., and Rice, D.C., 1987, Low-level lifetime lead exposure produced behavioral toxicity (spatial discrimination reversal) in adult monkeys, *Toxicol. Appl. Pharmacol.* 91:484–490.

Gilfillan, S.C., 1965, Lead poisoning and the fall of Rome, *J. Occup. Med.* 7:53–60.

Goldstein, G., 1992, Developmental neurobiology of lead toxicity, in: *Human Lead Exposure* (H.L. Needleman, ed.), CRC Press, Boca Raton, FL.

Goyer, R.A., 1990, Transplacental transport of lead, *Environ. Health Perspect.* 89:101–105.

Gradient Corporation, 1990, *The Relationship Between Blood Lead and Cognitive Development Scores: Evidence from Prospective Epidemiological Studies,* Cambridge, MA.

Graziano, J., Popovac, D., Factor-Litvak, P., Shrout, P., Kline, J., Murphy, M., Zhao, Y., Mehmeti, A., Ahmedi, X., Rajovic, B., Zvicer, Z., Nenezic, D., Lolacono, N., and Stein, Z., 1990, Determinants of elevated blood lead during pregancy in a population surrounding a lead smelter in Kosovo, Yugoslavia, *Environ. Health Perspect.* 89:95–100.

Hambidge, K.M., 1977, The role of zinc and other trace metals in pediatric nutrition and health, *Pediatr. Clin. North Am.* 24:95–106.

Hansen, O.N., Trillingsgaard, A., Beese, I., Lyngye, T., and Grandjean, P., 1989, A neuropsychological study of children with elevated dentine lead level: Assessment of the effect of lead in different socio-economic groups, *Neurotoxicol. Teratol.* 11:205–213.

Hart, M.H., and Smith, J.L., 1981, Effect of vitamin D and low dietary calcium on lead uptake and retention in rats, *J. Nutr.* 111:694–698.

Hasan, J., Vihko, V., and Hernberg, S., 1967, Deficient red cell membrane /Na$^+$ +K$^+$/ATPase in lead poisoning, *Arch. Environ. Health* 14:313–318.

Hatzakis, A., Kokkevi, A., Katsouyanni, K., Maravelias, K., Salaminios, F., Kalandidi, A., Koutselinis, A., Stefanis, K., and Trichopoulos, D., 1987, Psychometric intelligence and attentional performance deficits in lead-exposed children, in: *Heavy Metals in the Environment: International Conference, New Orleans* (S.E. Lindberg and T.C. Hutchinson, eds.), CEP Consultants, Edinburgh, pp. 204–209.

Hays, S., (1992), The role of values in science and policy: The case of lead, in: *Human Lead Exposure* (H.L. Needleman, ed.), CRC Press, Boca Raton, FL.

Hernberg, S., 1973, Biological effects of low lead doses, in: *Proc. International Symposium: Environmental Health Aspects of Lead, Amsterdam, The Netherlands, 1972* (D. Barth, A. Berlin, R. Engel, P. Recht, and J. Smeets, eds.), Commission of the European Communities, Centre for Information and Documentation, Luxembourg.

Holtzman, D., Hsu, J.S., and Mortell, P., 1978, The pathogenesis of lead encephalopathy in the rat pup: Effects of maternal PbCO$_3$ feedings from birth, *Ped. Res.* 12:1077–1082.

Hsu, F.S., Krook, L., Pond., W.G., and Duncan, J.R., 1975, Interactions of dietary calcium with toxic levels of lead and zinc in pigs. *J. Nutr.* 105:112–118.

Hume, D., 1894, *Enquiry Concerning Human Understanding*, Claredon Press, Oxford.

Johnson, N.E., and Tenuta, K., 1979, Diets and lead blood levels of children who practice pica, *Environ. Res.* 18:369–376.

Kenny, D.A., 1979, *Correlation and Causality*, Wiley, New York.

Kitchen, I., McDowell, J., Winder, C., and Wilson, J.M., 1984, Low-level lead exposure alters morphine antinociception in neonatal rats, *Toxicol. Lett.* 22:119–123.

Klauder, D.S., and Petering, H.G., 1975, Protective value of dietary copper and iron against some toxic effects of lead in rats, *Environ. Health Perspect.* 12:77–80.

Klauder, D.S., and Petering, H.G., 1977, Anemia of lead intoxication: A role for copper, *J. Nutr.* 107:1779–1785.

Klauder, D.S., Murthy, L., and Petering, H.G., 1973, Effect of dietary intake of lead acetate on copper metabolism in male rats, in: *Trace Substances in Environmental Health VI: Proc. of University of Missouri's 6th Annual Conference on Trace Substances in Environmental Health; June, 1972; Columbia, MO* (D.D. Hemphill, ed.), University of Missouri, Columbia, MO, pp. 131–136.

Lansdown, R., Yule, W., Urbanowicz, M., and Miller, I., 1983, Blood lead, intelligence, attainment and behavior in school children: Overview of a pilot study in: *Lead versus Health* (M. Rutter, and R.R. Jones eds.), John Wiley, London, pp. 267–296.

Lin-Fu, J.S., 1985, Historical perspective on health effects of lead, in: *Dietary and Environmental Lead: Human Health Effects* (K. Mahaffey, ed.), Elsevier Science, New York.

Magnusson, D., Stottin, H., and Duner, A., 1983, Aggression and criminality in a longitudinal perspective, in: *Antecedents of Aggression and Antisocial Behavior* (K.T. Van Dusen, and S.A. Mednick, eds.), Kluwer-Nijhoff, Boston, pp. 277–302.

Mahaffey, K.R., 1990, Environmental lead toxicity: Nutrition as a component of intervention, *Environ. Health Perspect.* 89:75–78.

Mahaffey, K.R., and Michaelson, I.A., 1980, The interaction between lead and nutrition, in: *Low Level Lead Exposure: The Clinical Implications of Current Research* (H.L. Needleman, ed.), Raven Press, New York, pp. 159–200.

Mahaffey, K.R., Goyer, R., and Haseman, J.K., 1973, Dose-response to lead ingestion in rats fed low dietary calcium, *J. Lab. Clin. Med.* 82:92–100.

Mahaffey, K.R., Treloar, S., Banks, T.A., Peacock, B.J., and Parekh, L.E., 1976, Differences in dietary intake of calcium, phosphorus and iron of children having normal and elevated blood lead concentrations, *J. Nutr.* (Abstr.) 106(7):xxx.

Mahaffey, K.R., Annest, J., Roberts, J., and Murphy, R., 1982, National estimates of blood lead levels: United States, 1976–1980: Association with selected demographic and socioeconomic factors, in *N. Engl. J. Med.* 307:573–579.

Mahaffey-Six, K., and Goyer, R.A., 1972, The influence of iron deficiency on tissue content and toxicity of ingested lead in the rat, *J. Lab. Clin. Med.* 79:128–136.

Markovac, J., and Goldstein, G.W., 1988, Picomolar concentrations of lead stimulate brain protein kinase C. *Nature* 334:71–73.

Markowitz, M.E., and Rosen, J.F., 1981, Zinc (Zn) and copper (Cu) metabolism in CaNa$_2$ EDTA-treated children with plumbism, *Pediatr. Res.* 15:635.

McMichael, A., Baghurst, P., Robertson, E., Vimpani, G., and Wigg, N., 1985, The Port Pirie Cohort Study: Blood lead concentrations in early childhood, *Med. J. Austr.* 143:499–503.

McMichael, A., Vimpani, G., Robertson, E., Baghurst, P., and Clark, P., 1986, The Port Pirie Cohort Study: Maternal blood lead and pregnancy outcome, *J. Epidemiol. Commun. Health* 40:18–25.

McMichael, A., Baghurst, P., Wigg, N., Vimpani, G., Robertson, E., and Roberts, R., 1988, The Port Pirie Cohort Study: Environmental exposure to lead and children's abilities at the age of four years, *N. Engl. J. Med.* 319:468–475.

Mielke, H.W., Blake, B., Burroughs, S., and Hassinger, N., 1983, Lead concentrations in inner-city soils as a factor in the child lead problem, *Am. J. Public Health* 73:1366–1369.

Moffitt, T.E., 1990, Juvenile delinquency and attention deficit disorder: Boys' developmental trajectories from age 3 to age 15, *Child Dev.* 61:893–910.

Morrison, J.N., Quarterman, J., and Humphries, W.R., 1977, The effect of dietary calcium and phosphate on lead poisoning in lambs, *J. Comp. Pathol.* 87:417–429.

Mushak, P., 1991, Defining lead as a critical environmental health issue: Criteria and their quantitative application, *Proceedings of 12th Annual Uosherc Symposium, "Getting the Lead Out: Priorities for the 1990s,"* Rutgers University, Piscataway, NJ.

Nathanson, J.A., and Bloom, F.E., 1975, Lead-induced inhibition of brain adenyl cyclase, *Nature* 255:419–420.

Nation, J.R., Baker, D.M., Taylor, B., and Clark, D.E., 1986, Dietary lead increases ethanol consumption in the rat, *Behav. Neurosci.* 100:525–530.

Needleman, H.L., and Bellinger, D., 1988, Commentary: Recent developments, *Environ. Res.* 46:190–191.

Needleman, H.L., and Bellinger, D., 1991, The health effects of low level exposure to lead, *Annu. Rev. Public Health* 12:111–140.

Needleman, H.L., and Gatsonis, C.A., 1990, Low-level lead exposure and the IQ of children: A meta-analysis of modern studies, *JAMA* 263:673–678.

Needleman, H.L., Gunnoe, C., Leviton, A., Reed, R., and Peresit, H., 1979, Deficits in psychological and classroom performance of children with elevated dentine lead levels, *N. Engl. J. Med.* 300:689–95.

Needleman, H.L., Rabinowitz, M., Leviton, A., Linn, S., and Schoenbaum, S., 1984, The relationship between prenatal exposure to lead and congenital anomalies, *JAMA* 25:2956–2959.

Needleman, H.L., Schell, A., Bellinger, D., Leviton, A., and Allred, E.N., 1990, The long-term effects of exposure to low doses of lead in childhood: An 11-year follow-up report, *N. Engl. J. Med.* 322:83–88.

Oliver, T., 1911, Lead poisoning and the race, *Br. Med. J.* 1:1096–1098.

Owen, G., and Lippman, G., 1977, Nutritional status of infants and young children: U.S.A., *Pediatr. Clin. North Am.* 24:211–227.

Pomeroy, J.C., Sprafkin, J., and Gadow, K.D., 1988, Minor physical anomalies as a biologic marker for behavior disorders, *J. Am. Acad. Child Adoles. Psychol.* 27:466–473.

Quarterman, J., and Morrison, J.N., 1975, The effects of dietary calcium and phosphorus on the retention and excretion of lead in rats, *Br. J. Nutr.* 34:351–362.

Raab, G.M., Laxen, D.P.H., and Fulton, M., 1987, Lead from dust and water as exposure sources for children, *Environ. Geochem. Health* 9:80–85.

Raab, G.M., Thomson, G.O.B., Boyd, L., Fulton, M., and Lazen, D.P.H., 1990, Blood lead levels, reaction time, inspection time and ability in Edinburgh children, *Br. J. Dev. Psychol.* 8:101–118.

Rosen, J.F., Chesney, R.W., Hamstra, A.J., DeLuca, H.F., and Mahaffey, K.R., 1980, Reduction in 1,25-dihydroxyvitamin D in children with increased lead absorption, *N. Engl. J. Med.* 302:1128–1131.

Rosen, J.F., Chesney, R.W., Hamstra, A.J., DeLuca, H.F., and Mahaffey, K.R., 1981, Reduction in 1,25-dihydroxyvitamin D in children with increased lead absorption, in: *Organ-Directed Toxicity: Chemical Indices and Mechanisms* (S.S. Brown, and D.S. Davis, eds.), Pergamon Press, New York, pp. 91–95.

Routh, D., Mushak, P., and Boone, L., 1979, A new syndrome of elevated blood lead and microenphaly, *J. Pediatr. Psychol.* 4:67–76.

Shaheen, S., 1984, Neuromaturation and behavior development: The case of childhood lead poisoning, *Develop. Psychol.* 20:542–550.

Shukla, R., Bornschein, R., Dietrich, K., Buncher, C., Berger, O., Hammond, P., and Succop, P., 1989, Fetal and infant lead exposure: Effects on growth in stature, *Pediatrics* 84:604–612.

Silbergeld, E., 1983, Effects of lead on reproduction: Review of experimental studies, in: *Lead Versus Health* (M. Rutter, and R.R. Jones, eds.), John Wiley, London, pp. 217–227.

Silbergeld, E., 1986, Maternally-mediated exposure of the fetus: In utero exposure to lead and other toxins, *Neurotoxicology* 7:557–568.

Silbergeld, E., Schwartz, J., and Mahaffey, K., 1988, Lead and osteoporosis: Mobilization of lead from bone in postmenopausal women, *Environ. Res.* 47:79–94.

Sills, M.R., Mahaffey, K.R., and Silbergeld, E.K., 1991, Letter to the editor, *N. Engl. J. Med.,* 324:416–417.

Silva, P.A., Hughes, P., Williams, S., and Faed, J., 1988, Blood lead, intelligence, reading attainment, and behaviour in eleven-year-old children in Dunedin, New Zealand, *J. Child. Psychol. Psychiatry* 29:43–52.

Smith, C.M., DeLuca, H.F., Tanaka, Y., and Mahaffey, K.R., 1978, Stimulation of lead absorption by vitamin D administration, *J. Nutr.* 108:843–847.

Sobel, A.E., Gawron, O., and Kramer, B., 1938, Influence of vitamin D in experimental lead poisoning, *Proc. Soc. Exp. Biol. Med.* 38:433–435.

Sobel, A.E., Yuska, H., Peters, D.D., and Kramer, B., 1940, The biochemical behavior of lead: I. Influence of calcium, phosphorus, and vitamin D on lead in blood and bone, *J. Biol. Chem.* 132:239–265. Reprinted 1981 in *Nutr. Rev.* 39:374–377.

Sorrell, M., Rosen, J.F., and Roginsky, M., 1977, Interactions of lead, calcium, vitamin D, and nutrition in lead-burdened children, *Arch. Environm. Health* 32:160–164.

Thompson, G.N., Robertson, E.F., and Fitzgerald, S., 1985, Lead mobilization during pregnancy, *Med. J. Aust.* 143:131.

Thomson, G.O.B., Raab, G.M., Hepburn, W.S., Hunter, R., Fulton, M., and Laxen, D.P.H., 1989, Blood-lead levels and children's behavior: Results from the Edinburgh lead study, *J. Child Psychol. Psychiatry* 30:515–528.

Turner, A.J., 1897, Lead poisoning among Queensland children, *Austr. Med. Gaz.* 30:515–528.

U.S. Centers for Disease Control, 1985, *Preventing Lead Poisoning in Young Children: A Statement by the Centers for Disease Control,* January, No. 99–2230. U.S. Department of Health and Human Services, Atlanta.

U.S. Environmental Protection Agency, Office of Radiation Programs, 1984, *An Estimation of the Daily Food Intake Based on Data from the 1977-78 USDA Nationwide Food Consumption Survey, Tables 1 and 3,* U.S. Environmental Protection Agency, Washington, D.C.

U.S. Environmental Protection Agency, June, 1986, *Air Quality Criteria for Lead,* Environmental Criteria and Assessment Office, Research Triangle Park, NC.

U.S. Environmental Protection Agency, 1987. *Reducing Lead in Drinking Water: A Benefit Analysis.* U.S. Environmental Protection Agency, Washington, DC.

Ward, N., Durrant, S., Sankey, R., Bound, J., and Bryce-Smith, D., 1990, Elemental factors in human fetal development, *J. Nutr. Med.* 1:19–26.

Willoughby, R.A., Thirapatsakun, T., and McSherry, B.J., 1972, Influence of rations low in calcium and phosphorus on blood and tissue lead concentrations in the horse, *Am. J. Vet. Res.* 33:1165–1173.

Winder, C., and Kitchen, I., 1984, Lead neurotoxicity: A review of the biochemical, neurochemical and drug induced behavioral evidence, *Prog. Neurobiol.* 22:59–87.

Yip, R., Norris, T.N., and Anderson, A.S., (1981) Iron status of children with elevated blood lead concentrations, *J. Pediatr.* 98:922–925.

Ziegler, E.E., Edwards, B.B., Jensen, R.L., Mahaffey, K.R., and Fomon, S.J., 1978, Absorption and retention of lead by infants, *Pediatr. Res.* 12:29–34.

Chapter 8

Lead Poisoning, Toxocariasis, and Pica

Links to Neurobehavioral Disorders

Peter J. Donovick and *Richard G. Burright*

1. INTRODUCTION

In this chapter we will explore relationships among environmental toxins and an eating disorder in which individuals (infants, children, and adults) mouth, taste, and ingest a variety of strange and often inedible substances, which may include sand, dirt, insects, animal excreta, hair, and cloth, among other things. This eating disorder is known as *pica*. A more complete discussion of pica will follow; however, it should be obvious that such eating habits can lead to exposure to toxins, parasites, bacterial infections, and other causes of disease. Similarly, there are many "conditions" that may lead to and/or exacerbate pica. In addition, we will examine the neurobehavioral consequences of the ingestion of harmful environmental toxins and pathogens. More specifically, we will present a necessarily selective review of the animal and human literature related to environmental neuropsychology using lead poisoning and a parasitic disease, toxocariasis, as examples of pathologies often related to the eating of inappropriate matter (i.e., pica).

We will argue that pathologies such as metal toxicity and/or parasitic infections may underlie a variety of neurobehavioral disorders, including pica itself, at many levels of analysis. Certainly, pica may lead to disease, or disease to pica; thus, we intend to emphasize how individuals may become entrapped in a "vicious cycle": pica/disease → disease/pica → pica/disease, etc. Indeed, we hope to convince the reader that pursuing a better understanding of the implied processes and mechanisms—at all levels of analysis,

Peter J. Donovick and *Richard G. Burright* • Environmental Neuropsychology Laboratory, Department of Psychology, State University of New York, Binghamton, New York 13902.
The Vulnerable Brain and Environmental Risks, *Volume 2: Toxins in Food,* edited by Robert L. Isaacson and Karl F. Jensen. Plenum Press, New York, 1992.

including the behavioral level—is extremely important, not only for basic research in all facets of the neurosciences, but also for creating meaningful public health policies.

The Environmental Protection Agency (EPA) recently labeled lead and its compounds "toxic enemy #8" (*Sci. News,* 1991). "Once mined, lead is everywhere, and never goes away" (C. Patterson, quoted by S. Blakeslee, 1990, p. 72); and once absorbed, lead circulates widely within the mammalian system, affects many organs (including the brain), and often becomes stored in bone.

The impact of many inorganic or organic environmental toxins, including lead, on the central nervous system (CNS) is diverse and may be observed at many levels of analysis. Thus, such influences are of interest to the neurosciences in general and to the neurobehavioral psychologist in particular (Needleman, 1991: see also Chapter 7). The National Institute of Mental Health (NIMH) recently announced a program intended to generate a better understanding of the development, maintenance, and pathology of cognition over an individual's lifetime. Similarly, the National Institute of Aging (NIA) inaugurated a program this year encouraging scientists to broaden their investigations of cognition, and to apply theoretical and experimental advances to understanding what happens to cognition as people grow older. Certainly, the documented impact of environmental toxins on cognitive functions is, at best, poorly understood at virtually any level of analysis.

In addition, the specific effects of any pathogen on any organ system depend on a broad array of factors, which involve not only the nature, quantity, and cumulative impact of exposure to them, but also all aspects of an individual's experiential history across his or her life span. "Experience" can be logically defined only in terms of dynamic, continually ongoing coactions of any organism's genome and its environment(s) (Donovick and Burright, 1984). Therefore, influencing variables include the developmental period during which exposure may have occurred and the psychophysically determined (both consciously perceived and unconsciously received) conditions under which an individual is tested.

2. PICA: AN EATING BEHAVIOR DISORDER

The third, revised *Diagnostic and Statistical Manual of the American Psychiatric Association* (DSM-III-R) defined pica as ". . . the persistent eating of a non-nutritive substance. Infants with the disorder typically eat paint, plaster, string, hair, or cloth. Older children may eat animal droppings, sand, insects, leaves, or pebbles. There is no aversion to food" (p. 69). The DSM-III-R diagnostic criteria are "A. Repeated eating of a non-nutritive substance for at least one month. B. Does not meet the criteria for either Autistic Disorder, Schizophrenia, or Kleine-Levin syndrome" (p. 69).

As Landrigan (1990) points out, modern society has come to recognize that industrial/chemical developments in the 20th century have led to an increasing number of "environmental illnesses." But, the potential role in disease of relatively common human behavioral patterns, such as eating, or even the act of breathing, is less well known and poorly understood at most, if not all, levels of scientific analysis. Obviously, part of the problem lies in the speed with which technological advances have caused changes in the environment. In many cases, neither biological patterns of adaptation nor psychosocial accommodation have been effective in meeting new or changed circumstances. Failures to "adapt" to relatively rapid changes in the environment, while by no means unique, are in striking contrast to what typically are much longer term evolutionary adjustments.

Indeed, it has been argued that pica could represent a behavioral strategy to help overcome nutritional deficiencies. Certainly, any beneficial consequences of pica could be based on the ingestion of needed trace substances and/or "placebo effects" derived from shared belief systems in given cultures. However, any benefits resulting from pica must be weighed against the costs of such behavior; e.g., the severity of poisoning from exposure to toxins and the implications of any subsequent conditioned food aversion(s) that might develop in the individual. In any case, the literature is very sparse when it comes to knowledge concerning the behavior of sick individuals of any species, and is quite limited with respect to understanding the role of behavior in human or animal disease processes.

Lacey (1990) indicates that definitions of pica may include a broad spectrum of abnormal consummatory behavior, ranging from the ingestion of substances with little or no nutritive value to the excessive eating of typical foodstuffs; indeed, some aspects of addictive behaviors might be considered a form of pica. Thus, whether a given behavior pattern is considered to represent pica depends on the nature and amount of the substance(s) ingested, whether or not the consumption seems to be in response to taste preferences typical of the culture, and whether or not the eating behavior appears to be compulsive.

Feldman's (1986) review suggests that pica is most common in (1) children under 7 years of age, (2) mentally disabled populations (McAlpine and Singh, 1986), and (3) pregnant women. Furthermore, children from families with pets are at increased risk for pica, and over 20% of children seen in urban clinics may exhibit the disorder (Feldman, 1986). Sayetta (1986) suggests that perhaps half of all children between the ages of 1 and 3 develop pica, and that such behavior is most likely to be seen in undernourished individuals, especially those whose intake of calcium or iron is inadequate.

The more frequently consumed nonfood substances are paint chips, clay, and laundry starch, and individuals diagnosed with pica often overeat food-related substances, such as ice and raw potatoes. In the United States, pica is most common in young children, pregnant women, southern or inner-city black women, and retarded individuals. According to Lacey (1990), depending on socioeconomic factors, estimates of geophagia (eating clay or dirt) range between 25% and 75% of pregnant women, and the prevalence of pica may be as high as 50% for black children and 35% for white children. Even if pica represents a behavioral strategy to help overcome nutritional deficiencies and/or to produce positive placebo effects derived from shared belief systems in given cultures, any benefits resulting from pica must be weighed against the costs of such behavior; e.g., the severity of poisoning from exposure to toxins/pathogens and the implications of any subsequent conditioned food aversion(s) that might develop in the individual.

Clearly, as Lacey (1990) points out, there are at least four potentially adverse effects of pica: (1) toxicity of the ingested substances themselves; (2) obstruction of the gastrointestinal tract (and attendant physiological effects) as the result of eating large amounts of nondigestible substances; (3) increased caloric intake (e.g., when eating starch); and (4) under- and/or malnutrition (Winick, 1976) resulting from the ingestion of large quantities of non-nutritive substances and the subsequent suppression of appetite. Lacey also points to the relation between iron deficiency, pica, and lead poisoning; i.e., anemia is far more common in individuals who eat clay. Both clay and starch absorb iron, and thus interfere with the absorption of iron from the gastrointestinal tract. Furthermore, there may be a similar process involved in the intestinal absorption of both iron and lead.

Feldman (1986) suggests that between 70% and 90% of children presenting with serious lead poisoning have a history of pica and that more than 30% of children known to exhibit pica have elevated body burdens of lead. Obviously, pica potentially results in exposure to other toxic substances, such as mercury and lead, as well as pathogens such as *T. canis* (Donovick and Burright, 1987; Glickman *et al.*, 1981).

Barnes (1990) has reported that variability in estimates of soil intake may range from 10 mg/day to 10,000 mg/day. Any determination of the amount due to pica per se obviously must discriminate between exposure as the result of eating vs. breathing, touching, or other forms of contact with nonfood and/or toxic elements. In addition, many ingested substances are differentially absorbed and/or stored in various body tissues, and their release may occur over very long periods of time as a function of various circumstances, thus making determination of the source(s) of exposure most difficult.

Furthermore, while the sample results reported by Barnes (1990) suggest that greater amounts of soil are ingested by adults than by children, he does not consider intake-to-body weight to be issues. In his sample of 64 children (from the Amherst, Massachusetts area), the median daily intake of soil was 26 mg. However, insignificant amounts of soil were deemed to have been ingested by at least 20% of the children, whereas 5 of the 64 children ingested very large amounts; e.g., one probably took in a total of 49–54 g of soil in a week. Barnes (1990) also suggests that estimates made by parents (or care-givers) of where and how long children play in various environments are quite inaccurate; thus, such indicators of possible sources of contamination are poor at best.

2.1. Cravings

Although a variety of hypotheses have been presented to explain the origins of pica, none have adequate documentation. For example, Feldman (1990) points out that some have suggested that nutritional deficiency increases "cravings" for specific substances. But other work (Bengelloun *et al.*, 1976; Donovick *et al.*, 1973; Rozen, 1989) implies that a better explanation may be found in increased ingestive exploration of environmental substances as a consequence of nutritional deficiency. Certainly, cultural norms might be expected to influence such behavior; thus, groups that traditionally eat clay during pregnancy (or tolerate the behavior) are more likely to exhibit pica than individuals from groups in which such behavior is taboo or alien.

While most of us have an intuitive knowledge of "craving," objective criteria frequently are lacking. For instance, the presence of a craving may be assessed by consummatory behavior; but circularly, the reason for the observed consummatory pattern may often be ascribed to a craving. Despite the difficulties in defining cravings, a large proportion of people report having them, and thus the concept is likely to be an important one (Weingarten and Elston, 1990). The Weingarten and Elston review points out that explanations of craving often suggest that abstinence from, or need of, a substance underlies the perceived craving; and thus, environmental cues may provide the eliciting stimuli. Furthermore, complete satiation of the craving typically is achieved by the specific, desired substance, and not some surrogate.

Weingarten and Elston (1990) also note that some have hypothesized a common neurochemical effect of substances that satisfy a given craving, while other theories depend more directly on a variety of environmental cues. Cuing theories suggest that the degree of similarity among stimuli associated with ingestion of the craved substance itself, and any alternative substance should predict the degree to which the surrogate will satisfy the craving.

But commonly desired foodstuffs (e.g., chocolate, dill pickles, clay) typically are not related to metabolic deficiencies. Thus, theories arguing that cravings are the consequence of need states fail to explain why pica is not necessarily reduced or eliminated by "appropriate" dietary supplements, or why some substances, though relatively rich in the needed nutrient, are not always preferred to other foods that are quite capable of satisfying the craving, despite being relatively poor in the required substance(s).

2.2. Normal or Abnormal Eating?

Although young children frequently have their hands in their mouths, it is very difficult to obtain estimates of the amount of dirt and other nonfood stuffs that are actually consumed (Barnes, 1990). For instance, people often may be reluctant to discuss aberrant eating behavior, and such reluctance may be exacerbated by racial, cultural, and/or socioeconomic differences between the interviewer and the subject/patient. In addition, individuals typically do not complain of geophagia or pica to a consultant/physician, but instead complain of other, often systemic ailments; thus, a diagnosis of pica results only from its discovery via other means (Feldman, 1986).

Barnes (1990) has suggested that a distinction can, and should, be made between "normal" mouthing (i.e., "involuntary" ingestion) of inedible substances and pica, essentially because he feels pica represents an abnormal craving to "voluntarily" eat clay, paint, chalk, or similar substances. However, this distinction seems to us rather arbitrary, and certainly is hard to substantiate or even to instantiate.

In any case, it is apparent that individuals who engage in pica, for whatever reason(s), i.e., the curiosity and exploration of the environment by the "normal" child, or the result of some illness/deficiency, may be "doomed" to a vicious cycle of illness (perhaps the result of pica), which may lead to (further) cravings, which in turn result in increased pica. Thus, a consequence of pica is the exposure of the individual to environmental toxins and pathogens, including lead, parasites, bacteria, viruses, etc.

There is a gray area between the dynamic, gene-environment coactions that lead to the development of taste aversions capable of protecting the individual from lethal poisons and eating habits defined so rigidly that access to needed nutrients is markedly limited (Schneirla, 1965). In this latter context, it is worth considering briefly the role that taste (as a psychophysically determined experience) may play in the phenomenon of pica.

2.3. Taste

In addition to those gustatory projections to thalamocortical neurons that are thought to conduct the discriminative qualities of taste, there is a major projection system to the ventral forebrain limbic system (Isaacson, 1982; van Hoesen, et al., 1972). This latter projection system may be a component of a hypothetical "comparator mechanism," which serves to integrate information derived from the "external milieu" with information derived from the "internal milieu" (Donovick, et al., 1979).

The response profile of neurons involved in the gustatory system of mammals can be organized along a nutritive-to-toxic, bipolar continuum, and there appears to be a parallel, hedonic continuum of acceptance-to-rejection (Scott and Giza, 1990; Scott and Mark,

1986, 1987). Furthermore, such parallel behavioral and neurophysiological profiles can be observed prenatally. Thus, in accord with suggestions of Schnierla (1965), there is a "genetic predisposition," which helps the organism to avoid life-threatening substances and to approach those beneficial to its survival. The neural encoding necessary for the behavioral, hedonically related approach-avoidance continuum appears to occur in those brainstem structures involved in the integration of taste and visceral responses.

Obviously, structures higher in the CNS, especially in the limbic system, play a modulatory role over the brainstem system. The comparator processes involved necessarily relate to the immediate sensory experiences associated with consumption, the physiological consequences of ingestion, and the experiential history of the organism (Donovick et al., 1979). Recall that experience must be defined as the result of continually ongoing, dynamic coactions among the individual's genes and the environment.

It is well established that the basic hedonic profile of tastants can be modified by experience (Scott and Mark, 1986). Both conditioned preferences and aversions have been shown. For instance, both a reduction in acceptability of a previously palatable solution and a change in the pattern of neuronal firing have been seen using the conditioned-aversioned paradigm. Further, in addition to changes in consumption that develop when a previously acceptable substance is paired with illness, the relative acceptability of the substance is also modified by the motivational state of the organism, e.g., satiety decreases the palatability of sucrose. Scott and Mark (1986) also note that specific hungers, such as for sodium or thiamine, increase cravings for that substance. However, the change in acceptability of previously unacceptable concentrations and/or substances is not unique to the needed substance (Donovick, et al., 1973).

Adams and Dawborn (1972) found that rats maintained on a potassium-poor diet ingested normally unpalatable concentrations of various salt solutions. Similarly, we found (Bengelloun et al., 1976) that normal and brain-damaged rats that had been maintained on a sodium-deficient diet increased their willingness to ingest unpalatable solutions of quinine- and potassium-hydrochloride (QHCl and KHCl), as well as sodium chloride (NaCL) (Burright et al., 1974; O'Kelly, 1963; Strouthes, 1971; Young, 1967, 1977).

In keeping with such findings, Scott and Mark (1986) report that the suppressive effect of stomach distension on firing of neurons in the nucleus of the tractus solitarius was diminished in rats that were food deprived for between 24 and 48 hr prior to the manipulation. Furthermore, injection of either glucose or insulin decreased food consumption, depressed the reactivity of sweet-sensitive neurons, and increased the responsiveness of neurons normally reactive to unpalatable substances. Interestingly, not all factors associated with satiety (e.g., cholecystokinin) have such effects on taste neurons.

Clearly, past experience alters consummatory behavior. For instance, exposure to a bitter drinking solution (QHCl), or to unavoidable foot shock, suppressed feeding in rats (Dees, et al., 1989). After such exposure, feeding returned to baseline levels, but body weight appeared to stabilize at a lower level than before. Providing the animal with the ability to control the electrical shock reduced the effect produced by the foot shock (Dees et al., 1989; see also Kavanau, 1967; Zuromski et al., 1972).

Dees and Chapman (1990) further explored this stress-induced finickiness, and again reported that inescapable shock increased the finickiness of rats. In addition, they found a moderate, positive correlation between initial body weight and acceptance of a low concentration of quinine; i.e., heavier rats tended to drink more of the available quinine solution than lighter rats.

In a parallel study of college students, Dees and Chapman (1990) also reported that the ability to detect weak QHCl solutions tended to be poorer in heavier than in lighter students; i.e., acceptance of QHCl was greater in heavier students, just as it was in the male rats tested in the animal-analog work. However, this correlation between acceptance of bitter tastes and body weight was significant in male students, but not in female students. These findings provide an example of the types of sexually dimorphic behaviors often observed—when carefully looked for—in both the animal and human research literature.

In addition, Dees and Chapman (1990) gave the Beck Depression Inventory (BDI) to the students in their nondepressed population. Interestingly, they found that BDI scores were positively correlated to both body weight and QHCl thresholds in males, but that a negative correlation existed between BDI scores and body weight in females.

3. NONLETHAL LEAD POISONING

The EPA estimates that people, even in low-lead environments, take in at least 10 µg of lead per day from food alone. In addition, developing children may absorb up to 50% more of the lead to which they are exposed than do adults, and evidence is mounting that lead may be harmful to humans in much smaller amounts than previously thought. For example, the "danger" threshold for lead levels in children's blood, established by the Centers for Disease Control (CDC), has steadily decreased over the past few decades. Recently, the blood-lead danger level has been 25 µg/dl and the CDC is considering reducing it to as low as 10 µg/dl for children (Lindner, 1990).

The 1988 U.S. Public Health Service (PHS) report to the U.S. Congress on lead poisoning in children cited evidence of reduced IQ scores, delayed intellectual development, and impaired hearing in children with blood levels of 10–15 µg/dl. The same report estimated that 3–4 million American children under 9 years of age have enough lead in their blood to cause such problems. Such concerns regarding environmental lead pollution, also expressed by the EPA and the Office of Safety and Health Administration (OSHA), apparently need to be heightened even further, as evidenced in the problems surrounding battery factories in areas such as Throop, Pennsylvania (Murphy, 1991; Wylam, 1990).

Once absorbed, lead circulates widely and affects many organ systems. Lead crosses the placenta readily (Moore, 1988), affecting the fetus both directly and indirectly through its impact on the mother's well-being (Dietrich, 1991). After birth, lead also can have direct effects on the infant through the mother's milk. Of course, specific effects of lead on each organ system depend on a myriad of factors; these include the individual's genenome, age at exposure, duration of exposure, and conditions (including age) under which testing occurs (Bellinger *et al.*, 1989; Donovick and Burright, 1987, 1989).

The impact of lead on the CNS is multifaceted and appears at diverse levels of analyses; therefore, it is of particular interest to the neurobehavioral scientist. Attempts to understand the behavioral consequences of lead in humans is complicated considerably by the confounding effects of many socioeconomic variables that correlate with exposure to lead (Bornschein *et al.*, 1985). Thus, while the risk of nonlethal lead poisoning is increasing for all forms of life throughout the world, the risk of such exposure is much higher, for example, among the urban and rural poor (often racial minorities) in America. However, some remarkable contamination of wine and milk stored in lead-crystal decanters or bottles has recently been reported (Raloff, 1991).

In addition, even if chelating agents are used to return a child's blood lead levels to "normal," some children have bone lead levels three to five times higher than children who have not been poisoned by lead (Blakeslee, 1990). Furthermore, bone stores of lead may be released into the circulatory system many years after initial exposure, and after years during which blood lead levels may have appeared normal. Also, we know of no work that has studied the behavioral effects of chelating agents themselves; such studies clearly should be done if such agents are to become routinely used.

The accelerating impact of this environmental lead problem on the world's eco-system(s) can be appreciated from a study by Grandjean and Jorgensen (1990); they compared the amount of lead found in 5000-year-old teeth (from Nubia) or 500-year-old teeth (from Greenland) with that found in samples from present-day Denmark. Their data suggested a 30-fold increase in lead in "modern" teeth relative to those from earlier times; presumably that increase is associated with increases in environmental pollution.

There is no doubt that in humans, as in other primates and mammals, lead is capable of altering the behavior of both the developing organism, the adult, and the aged, albeit often in different situations and/or amounts. For instance, Seeber et al. (1990) reported that both digit-symbol and reaction-time performance correlated with lead levels in urine from factory workers exposed to antiknock gasoline additives. Given the multiplicity of lead's effects on the CNS, it is not surprising that the concomitant effects of that toxicant on the "final common path" of behavior are quite complex.

3.1. Animal Studies

Much of the animal work in our Environmental Neuropsychology Laboratory in the Department of Psychology here at SUNY-Binghamton has used the Binghamton Hetero-geneous (HET) stock of mice, developed by John Fuller (Donovick and Horowitz, 1982; Fuller, 1979), as an animal model for examining the behavioral effects of nonlethal lead poisoning, as well as the parasitic disease, toxicariasis.

In our hands, lead exposure has been achieved by providing a 0.50% lead-acetate solution as the only available drinking fluid. This lead-exposure regime typically has resulted in blood lead levels of about 100 μg/dl in our young-adult HET mice. Its behavioral effects sometimes have been ephemeral, always quite puzzling, and clearly complex (Burright et al., 1983).

3.2. Activity

How an organism moves around in and explores its environment necessarily influ-ences the probability that it will encounter hazards. Thus, as lead exposure changes patterns of activity, it also alters patterns of exposure to other chemical and/or biological agents that may further threaten the individual's well-being.

In 1973, Silbergeld and Goldberg observed that mice exposed to a lead-contaminated drinking fluid from birth were more active than control animals. Since that time there have been conflicting results regarding the effects of lead on patterns of rodent activity. Various investigators have reported hyperactivity (Sauerhoff and Michaelson, 1973), hypoactivity (Reiter *et al.*, 1975), and no change in activity (Dolinsky *et al.*, 1981b; Hastings *et al.*, 1977; Silbergeld and Goldberg, 1974).

Other studies of changes in activity as a function of lead administration have indicated that specific conditions of testing are critical to the specific pattern of observed behavioral changes (Mullenix, 1980; Zimering *et al.*, 1982). In addition, the time of testing during the day-night cycle (Dolinsky *et al.*, 1981b; Donovick and Burright, 1986), and the stage of development during which both exposure and testing occurred, also can be critical determinants of behavioral effects (Crofton *et al.*, 1980; Dolinsky *et al.*, 1983; Draski *et al.*, 1989).

3.3. Social Behavior/Aggression

As we have seen, exposure to lead alters how the organism interacts with the (inanimate) physical world. Not surprisingly, the exposed individual's interactions with its social milieu are affected as well. Thus, pre- and continued postnatal exposure to lead alters a variety of social behaviors (Cutler, 1977). For example, Bushnell and Bowman (1979) showed that play and social contact between young monkeys and their mothers were disrupted with prolonged pre- and postnatal lead administration. In rats, postnatal exposure reduced aggression observed in shock-induced, aggression tests between males (Hastings *et al.*, 1977).

When we exposed male HET mice to lead via our standard regime for 15 weeks, either beginning in young adulthood (ca. 60 days of age) or at an older age (ca. 325 days old), and then paired them with male, control mice of the same age, the young adult, lead-treated animals typically were subordinate. However, in older adults, the isolation-induced aggression tests showed that the lead-exposed mice usually were dominant over their like-aged control "combatants" (Burright *et al.*, 1983). Subsequently, we found that when similarly treated male mice were paired against one another, only older, lead-treated pairs showed a markedly reduced latency to aggression compared to older, water-control pairs (Engellener *et al.*, 1986).

Partly because of the emphasis on males in the aggression literature, and to further explore the effects of our lead exposure regime on the social behavior of both genders, we exposed young-adult, female, HET mice either to lead or to water as their sole source of fluid from their birth, through their weaning (at 21 days of age), their mating (at ca. 50 days of age), their pregnancy, and the subsequent birth of their offspring (Burright *et al.*, 1989).

Eight days after giving birth to their first litter, postpartum aggression tests (with a similarly treated, but unfamiliar male intruder) were conducted. The intruder mouse was introduced to the primiparous dam's home/nesting cage, and behavioral interactions were observed for 10 min. In pairs that fought, the intensity of fighting was greater in lead-exposed pairs than water controls. However, both the percentage of pairs that displayed aggressive behavior and the average latency to initial contact were similar, regardless of exposure history.

We also obtained plasma prolactin levels of these females; the prolactin results implied that lead exposure *alone* decreased circulating prolactin levels in primiparous HET dams, 8 days postpartum. But direct confrontation with an unfamiliar male intruder (whether or not outright fighting occurred) reduced plasma prolactin levels in water-control dams to levels similar to those seen in the lead-exposed females under any circumstances.

The pattern of plasma prolactin we observed was not consistent with observations that lead exposure decreases dopamine levels (Govani et al., 1984; Lashley and Lane, 1988), because lead exposure would be expected to remove dopamine's normally inhibitory effects on prolactin release. To account for the low prolactin levels in controls, one may argue that these mothers released dopamine in response simply to the (presumably) stressful encounter with a male intruder, even if no overt fighting occurred. The (assumed) increase of dopamine would inhibit prolactin release in these intact, HET-control, primiparous dams.

However, to account for the low levels of plasma prolactin seen in lead-exposed dams, regardless of whether or not they encountered a male intruder, is more problematic; that is, given the results of both Govani et al. (1984) and Lashley and Lane (1988), we must assume that ingested lead (by male rats) is capable of interfering with dopamine's known inhibitory effect on prolactin release. But in this context, it is important to note that (1) lead can "competitively inhibit" calcium in several biological systems, (2) interactions between lead and calcium in the brain depend on the neurotransmitters involved (Silbergeld, 1977), and (3) a decrease in intracellular concentrations of free-ionized calcium results in *decreased* prolactin secretion (Meno et al., 1985). For other, recent indications of the calcium-lead "connection(s)," see Blakeslee (1990), Lindner (1990), and Chapter 5 in this volume.

Indeed, Meno and coworkers have argued (1985) that dopamine inhibits the influx of extracellular calcium to achieve its inhibitory/regulatory role in prolactin release. Thus, if lead levels are high enough to at least partially block calcium channels, then any other effects it might have on dopamine would be inconsequential, because the lead itself would inhibit prolactin release.

Obviously, many factors could have contributed to the apparent discrepancy between our results and those reported by Govani et al. (1984) and Lashley and Lane (1988) for male rats. However, while both of those studies used protocols similar to ours for exposing animals to lead, both used drinking solutions lower in lead-acetate concentration than our 0.5% "standard," and both reported blood-lead levels in their male rats lower than the 100+ µg/dl levels that our protocol typically produces (DeLuca et al., 1982; Draski et al., 1989; Rasile, 1990; Zimering et al., 1982). That is, Govani et al. reported blood lead levels of ca. 70 µg/dl, whereas Lashley and Lane observed lower blood lead levels (ca. 36 µg/dl).

To more fully explore sex differences in terms of social/agonistic responses to lead exposure, we (Hahn et al., 1991) examined the effects of lead in both male-male and female-female, food-competition situations. While lead-exposed mice of both sexes spent more time than controls in social contact with one another, and also in possession of the bit of food available, very little truly aggressive behavior took place in either the water-control or lead-exposed, same-sex, food-competition situation.

In the same study (Hahn et al., 1991), we also tested the same HET mice used in food competition in a cricket-predation test. The results suggested that lead-exposed males attacked the cricket more quickly than water-control males, and that lead-exposed females initially attacked the cricket's legs more than any other group.

In fact, suggestions of sex × treatment interactions occurred in both the food-competition and cricket-predation data. Given the results of Hahn et al. (1991) and

Burright *et al.* (1989), in conjunction with other aspects of both the animal and human literature, and recognizing that statistical tests of interaction(s) have relatively little power, we believe that it is important to further explore the potentially differential effects that lead exposure probably has on males and females of all species, including humans.

3.4. Learning and Performance

Given the alterations in how the lead-exposed organism interacts with its psychophysically determined world, it is not surprising that there is an extensive literature suggesting that such exposure also alters patterns of learning and/or performance. Changes in performance following exposure to lead have been observed in a number of complex tasks in both animals and humans (Snowdon, 1973; Winneke *et al.*, 1977). More specifically, lead has been reported to affect a variety of standard, animal-learning paradigms, i.e., discrimination acquisition (Zenick *et al.*, 1978), reversal learning (Bushnell and Bowman, 1979), and extinction (Taylor *et al.*, 1982). As expected, the degree to which learning is affected appears related to both the "dose" (Bushnell and Bowman, 1979) and to the complexity of the task(s) employed (Winneke *et al.*, 1977).

4. HUMAN STUDIES

Cognition and Performance

Recently, Dietrich and coworkers (1990) reported a significant relationship in humans between pre- and neonatal blood lead levels and development as assessed by Bayley Mental Development Scores (BMDSs); but, at least with the scores used, the observed relationship seemed to disappear by the time the children were 2 years of age. However, the Dietrich *et al.* data are in contrast to those reported by Bellinger and coworkers (1988), who found a consistent relationship between their set of BMDSs and blood lead levels.

Furthermore, in a large, prospective study reported by McMichael *et al.* (1988), a statistically, and apparently substantively, significant negative relationship was seen between prenatal blood lead levels and McCarthy Scales of Children's Abilities scores in 4-year-old children. In fact, a negative influence of lead exposure on general levels of functioning has been reported consistently from different geographical regions and ethnic/racial groups [e.g., black school children in North Carolina (Schroeder *et al.*, 1985); school-aged children from the Boston area (race unspecified; Bellinger *et al.*, 1985); and both black and white children from the Cleveland vicinity (Ernhart *et al.*, 1987, 1989)].

Typical of such findings are results of data recently collected in eight European countries and reported by Winneke *et al.* (1990). The collaborating researchers correlated blood lead levels in children with the children's performance on a battery of neuropsychological tests. The strongest inferred negative effects of lead were on those performance tasks that presumably demand either sustained attention or require visual-motor integration (as interpreted in a version of the Bender–Gestalt test).

These effects are apparent after the influence of other socioeconomic factors are statistically "removed" (Needleman and Gatsonis, 1990). Thus, while a correlation between socioeconomic factors and risk of exposure to lead exists, when such variables are statistically "factored out," the data indicate a direct, negative impact of lead on intellectual functioning (McMichael *et al.*, 1988; Needleman, 1991). Even so, controversy remains as to which functions are affected, the degree to which performance is impaired, and what the relationships are among "effective" dose, period of exposure, and behavior (Ernhart and Greene, 1990).

Data from the workplace support the contention that adults also are at risk of adverse effects from rather low-level exposure to heavy metals, including lead. For example, Seeber *et al.* (1990) reported that both digit symbol and reaction time correlated with the urine lead levels of factory workers exposed to antiknock gasoline additives. In addition, Yokoyama and coworkers (1988) administered the performance subtests of the Japanese version of the Wechsler Adult Intelligence Scale—Revised (WAIS-R); they found a negative relationship between blood lead level and scores on the picture-completion subtest. Two years later, following improvement of working conditions, and a reduction in blood lead levels, performance of those subjects who originally had the highest blood lead levels was improved.

5. DIETARY CONSIDERATIONS (ANIMAL AND HUMAN)

As noted earlier, nutritional factors influence the gastrointestinal absorption of lead. For instance, diets low in iron (Six and Goyer, 1972), calcium (Mahaffey, 1974), or phosphorus (Baltrop and Koo, 1973), or high in vitamin D (Sobel *et al.*, 1940), milk (Kello and Kostial, 1973), or fat (DeLuca *et al.*, 1982) can all increase the gastrointestinal uptake of lead. Obviously, pica could influence such dietary patterns. However, less is known about how lead exposure alters patterns of food and fluid consumption (also see earlier section devoted to pica).

Hammond *et al.* (1990) provide evidence that even relatively short exposure to lead may have long-term, depressive effects on food consumption. We found that HET mice maintained on our lead-exposure regimen increased their consumption of a highly palatable saccharin solution, as did control mice. In contrast, the lead-exposed mice drank more of a highly unpalatable QHCl solution than controls (Donovick *et al.*, 1981; see also Burright *et al.*, 1974, Donovick *et al.*, 1979).

Environmental temperature affects food and water consumption also. Not surprisingly, although mice maintained on a 0.5% lead-acetate solution also responded to changes in temperature, their pattern of reactivity was different from that seen in control animals (DeLuca *et al.*, 1989; see also Czech and Hoium, 1984; Donovick *et al.*, 1981; Kutscher and Yamamoto, 1979; Morrison *et al.*, 1974).

Parasites

Pica not only results in exposure to inorganic toxins, but to a variety of biological pathogens as well. Indeed, pica may constitute a common route of exposure to a variety of parasites. Interestingly, although perhaps as many as a billion people worldwide have been exposed to one or more animal parasites, little is known about the behavioral consequences of such exposure. Diagnosis of parasitic infection today is also complicated by the increased mobility and global travel of individuals who may subsequently exhibit disease symptoms uncommon for people in their home region. Moreover, in a particular area, both parasites and potential hosts develop behavioral and physiological adaptations to promote their own survival (Hart, 1990). For instance, there is evidence from both animal and human literature on assortative mating suggesting that (at least some) illnesses, perhaps especially those that alter behavior, influence mate selection.

In addition to exposure to parasites secondary to ingestion of substances such as dirt, Hart also points out that behavioral patterns such as self- and/or allo-grooming may be examples of behavior designed to help avoid or reduce the full impact of parasites on the host. Given that grooming in may species includes mouthing of both edible and inedible substances, grooming behavior might even be viewed as an evolutionary precursor of pica. An example of a parasite in which pica *may* play a central role in human exposure is the common roundworm of dogs, *Toxocara canis* (Donovick and Burright, 1987).

6. TOXOCARIASIS

In the dog, *T. canis* larvae may be sequestered in somatic tissue. Pregnancy in female dogs activates larvae, which migrate through the placenta into (fetal) pups. The adult stage of the parasite may be found in the intestinal tract of newborn pups, and it is only there that *T. canis* is susceptible to antiparasitic treatments. The parasite's eggs are passed in the feces, and thus become available to infect other dogs and other animals. In aberrant mammalian hosts, including humans and mice, second-stage larvae migrate through various organs and can remain viable for long periods of time. The brain is a primary target of second-stage *T. canis* in aberrant hosts (Hill *et al.*, 1985; Summers *et al.*, 1983).

Apparently the dog differs from aberrant hosts in the prenatal effect of *T. canis* on the fetus. Akao *et al.* (1990) reported that female BALB/c mice infected with 500 embryonated *T. canis* eggs prior to mating delivered fewer offspring than noninfected controls. We also have examined the question of parasitic infection of HET mice both prior to and during pregnancy and weaning (Cypess *et al.*, submitted) and found that cross-placental infection is quite rare, but exposure via mother's milk is common.

In our laboratory, exposure to *T. canis* typically has been accomplished by gastrointestinal intubation of 1000 embryonated *T. canis* eggs. This intubation procedure has resulted in a considerable body burden of the parasite, as indicated by recovery of second-stage larvae from various somatic tissues, including the brain (Summers *et al.*, 1983). The procedure also produces enlarged spleens and has provided other indications (Draski *et al.*, 1987) that the immune system of the host is involved. In addition, we found that *T. canis* intubation altered a broad spectrum of behaviors, including exploration of the environment, reactivity to tastants, and changes in performance of learned tasks (Donovick and Burright, 1987). In addition, the combined effects of lead exposure and *T. canis* intubation are neither simple, nor additive (Dolinsky *et al.*, 1981a).

Behavioral changes in mice may precede significant neuropathology. This indicates that the pattern of behavioral symptoms can be a by-product of changes in both central and peripheral tissues. Such findings may, in part, explain early reports that rats or mice infected with *Schistosoma mansoni* display altered patterns of performance on learning tasks. Early investigators chose to work with *S. mansoni* because they believed that it had minimal effect on the CNS. More recently, we failed to find marked changes in either the levels of activity or the spatial-learning performance of HET mice infected with *S. mansoni* (Rajachandran *et al.*, submitted).

These data suggest that toxocariasis in mice can have major behavioral consequences. But one still might ask if this parasitic infection presents a significant health problem for humans. A survey of American households found that about 38% had dogs (Jacobs, 1979). The prevalence of intestinal toxocariasis in dogs is estimated to be 15% (Glickman and Schantz, 1981). But Glickman and Schantz (1981) also reported that in a sample of 143 dog litters, 99.6% of the pups were born infected. Ten to 30% of soil samples taken in U.S. parks and playgrounds were contaminated with *T. canis* eggs. Duwel (1984) found such contamination in 27 of 31 sandboxes sampled in Frankfurt, Germany.

The high prevalence, and long-term viability of *T. canis* eggs in the environment, and their resistance to agents such as temperature and sewage treatment, suggests that this parasite may present a health risk for many people, and especially those prone to pica. In fact, Herrman *et al.* (1985) found that 4.6–7.3% of children from different regions in the United States exhibited antibodies to *T. canis* and that 30% of black children from lower socioeconomic groups also were seropositive. We believe that toxocariasis in mice can be viewed as a useful model system to examine the effects of parasitic infection on behavior and on other levels of analysis as well.

It would be surprising if there are not complex interactions among factors such as nutritional state, genotype of the host, and the consequences of exposure to a variety of biological and/or inorganic environmental toxins. Indeed, we have reported some such complexities (Donovick and Burright, 1987). In addition, Nelson (1979) suggests that there may be crossprotection among infections from related organisms, but changes in responsiveness to infections are not restricted to similar parasitic or bacterial/viral infections. For instance, we found that exposure to lead may diminish the behavioral consequences of infection with *T. canis* (Dolinsky *et al.*, 1981a), but the degree of CNS neuropathology observed using light microscopy was similar in both the HET mice that were exposed only to the parasite and in those exposed to *T. canis* in combination with lead. The observed damage was confined primarily to myelinated tracts (white matter) in the brains of both groups of animals intubated with the parasite (Summers *et al.*, 1983).

Of course, naturally occurring exposure to parasites and other toxins is likely to be the result of repeated exposures to the challenging agent(s). Individuals tend to live in and explore a relatively constant environment. Children play repeatedly in the same playgrounds and sandboxes. Because of this, we examined the impact on HET mice of single vs. multiple exposures to *T. canis*. Based on prior observations that the distribution of larvae differed as a function of the "dosage" regime, we anticipated that mice infected repeatedly would show a more heightened and sustained immune response to subsequent infection than would those infected only once. Indeed, both the observed pathology and the behavior patterns of the mice were influenced by the intubation regime. This supported our hypothesis that prior exposure could protect the organism against subsequent *T. canis* exposure (Draski *et al.*, 1987). However, these results also indicate the complex interactions between the host and the parasite: Factors such as "dose" (Burright *et al.*, 1982), time of testing, exposure to other toxins, and the patterns of repeated infection are all capable of dynamically and interactively altering the nature and extent of changes in the behavior of the infected individual.

In 1985, Ader reviewed work suggesting that conditioning may significantly alter immune reaction(s) to pathogens. Available data indicated that both increased and decreased immune competency may result as a function of conditioning history. In the same issue of *The Behavioral and Brain Sciences* (1985), several authors criticized Ader's interpretation of the data, and only recently have others come to recognize the importance of "behavioral neuroendoimmunogenetics" as an interdisciplinary science. Data such as Ader's obviously influence how disease processes, including toxocariasis, lead poisoning, and pica, must be viewed.

Clearly, the available data suggest that toxocariasis can have a major effect on brain and behavior. There is now a small, but growing body of literature that suggests other forms of infection, such as toxoplasmosis (Koskiniemi *et al.*, 1989) and herpes simplex, (McFarland and Hotchin, 1987; McGarland, 1989) may have long-term behavioral effects.

7. CONCLUSIONS

As we have seen, there is a tight interplay between behavior and general well-being. How a living individual, regardless of species, interacts with its environment is a result of the continually dynamic, ongoing coactions of the organism's genenome and its ever-changing, multilevel (i.e., molecular to cultural) environment(s). An individual's characteristics at any moment in time influence the organism's response to its environment at that moment, which in turn may influence what aspects of the environment may alter the individual in the next moment.

As a result, a *sick* organism may seek out (explore) aspects of its environment that it might otherwise avoid (Fuller, 1979b). Thus, along with immediate behavioral changes that may be associated with being ill (e.g., reduced activity; Hart, 1988, 1990), changes in eating behavior may result in pica and subsequent exposure to physical, chemical, and/or biological hazards. In turn, exposure to potentially harmful/toxic agents may further alter the behavior of the individual, placing that individual at increased risk of further illness as the result of new infection and/or additional poisoning. Relatively low levels of exposure to toxins or pathogens may result in insidious health problems, which could masquerade as any number of nonspecific illnesses, such as "the flu," "the common cold," "runny nose," or "allergies" (Cypess, 1978).

Reactions to such exposure may well be quite idiosyncratic, even within a species, because they represent a relatively momentary adaptation of the individual based on the unique, two-way interplay of the genenome and environment at those infinitely many prior moments in time. In contrast, analysis at the species level may allow one to view environmental risk factors as relatively constant. In such cases, it may well be possible to discern more generalized patterns of adaptation. But, as we've seen, the literature is sparse when it comes to knowledge concerning the behavior of sick individuals of any species, and very limited with respect to understanding the role of behavior in human or animal health and disease.

The influences of disease processes, and any associated psychobiological processes, change across the entire life span of an organism. For instance, cravings may be influenced by factors such as the menstrual cycle and pregnancy. Not surprisingly, there are hormonal influences on environmental exploration and patterns of ingestion; these effects are particularly important because many toxins/pathogens, including lead and *T. canis*, can and do cross the placenta and/or are passed through mother's milk (Cypess *et al.*, submitted; Dietrich *et al.*, 1987; Wide, 1985). Furthermore, lead, for example, is capable of influencing spermatogenesis in males (Uzych, 1985) and gonadotrophin binding in females (Wiebe *et al.*, 1988). Thus, there are cross-generational implications and consequences of eating behavior (Rasile, 1990) and other avenues of exposure to environmental hazards.

Individual variation, both within an individual over time and among individuals in a physically constant external milieu, are, or should be, the province of psychology (Donovick and Burright, 1989). But there are many other disciplines that could benefit by concerning themselves with these matters. Clearly, factors such as genotype and gender, experiential history, stage of development, and situational/task specificity are important at all levels of analysis.

Unfortunately, while much of the variance attributable to "individual differences" necessarily is represented in *experimental error*, such error is too often treated simply as "error," even by otherwise highly competent scientists. But experimental error must be recognized as representing—primarily and importantly—differences among individuals (even of a common species or gender) on common trials, *and* differences within the same individual(s) among different trials (Donovick and Burright, 1984, 1989).

The environmental dangers we have discussed are real, probably increasing, and clearly include many hazards other than lead and *T. canis*. Furthermore, the links to neurobehavioral disorders that we've examined—via behavior in general and pica in particular—also are of critical importance. In any case, we believe that the issues we have attempted to consider in this paper represent matters in need of being seriously addressed at many levels of analysis, including the behavioral level, if humankind expects to continue to know and enjoy living in this world as it is experienced today by ". . . all creatures, great and small."

REFERENCES

Adams, W.R., and Dawson, J.K. 1972, Effect of potassium depletion on mineral appetite in the rat, *J. Comp. Physiol. Psychol.* 78:51–58.

Ader, R. and Cohen, N., 1985, CNS-immune system interactions: Conditioning phenomena (with commentaries), *Behav. Brain Sci.* 8:379–426.

Akao, N. Desowitz, R.S., and Kondo, K., 1990. Decrease in litter size of female mice with *Toxocara canis*, *Trans. R. Soc. Trop. Med. Hygeine* 84:724.

Baltrop, D., and Khoo, H.E., 1975, The influence of nutritional factors on lead and absorption, *Postgrad. Med. J.* 51:797–800.

Baltrop, D., and Khoo, H.E., 1976, The influence of dietary minerals and fat on the absorption of lead, *Sci. Total Environ.* 6:265–273.

Barnes, R.M., 1990, Childhood soil ingestion: How much dirt do kids eat?, *Anal. Chem.* 62:1023A–1033A.

Bayley, N., 1949, Consistency and variability in the growth of intelligence from birth to 18 years, *J. Genetic Psychol.* 75:165–196.

Bellinger, D., Leviton, A., Waternaux, C., and Allred, E., 1985, Methodological issues in modeling the relationship between low-level lead exposure and infant development: Examples from the Boston lead study, *Environ. Res.* 38:119–129.

Bellinger, D., Leviton, A., Waternaux, C., Needleman, H., and Rabinowitz, M., 1988, Low-level lead exposure, social class, and infant development, *Neurotoxical. Teratol.* 10:497–503.

Benetou-Marantidou, A., Nakou, S., and Micheloyannis, J., 1988, Neurobehavioral estimation of children with life-long increased lead exposure, *Arch. Environ. Health* 43:392–395.

Bengelloun, W.A., Burright, R.G., and Donovick, P.J., 1976, Nutritional experience and spacing of shock opportunities alter the effects of septal lesions on passive avoidance acquisition by male rats. *Physiol. Behav.* 16:583–587.

Bernard, C., 1859, *Lecons sur les Propieties Physiologiques et les Alterations Pathologiques des Liquides de l'Organisme*, 2 volumes, Balliere, Paris.

Blakeslee, S., 1990, The lead-calcium time bomb, *Am. Health: Fitness of Body and Mind, IX*, Nov, 68–75.

Bornschein, R.L., Succop, P., Dietrich, K.N., Clark, C.S., Que Hee, S., and Hammond, P.B., 1985, The influence of social and environmental factors on dust lead, hand lead, and blood lead levels in young children, *Environ. Res.* 38: 108–118.

Bower, B., 1991, Questions of mind over immunity, *Sci. News* 139:216–217.

Burright, R.G., Donovick, P.J., and Zuromski, E.S., 1974, Septal lesion and experiential influences on saline and saccharin preference-aversion functions, *Physiol. Behav.* 12:951–959.

Burright, R.G., Engellenner, W.J., and Donovick, P.J., 1983, Lead exposure and agonistic behavior of adult mice of two ages, *Physiol. Behav.* 30:285–288.

Burright, R.G., Donovick, P.J., Dolinsky, Z., Hurd, Y., and Cypess, R.H., 1982, Behavioral changes in mice as a function of dose of *Toxocara canis, J. Toxicol Environ. Health* 10:621–626.

Burright, R.G., Donovick, P.J., Michaels, K., Fanelli, R.J., and Dolinsky, Z.S., 1982, Effects of amphetamine and cocaine on seizure susceptibility in lead-treated mice of different brain weights, *Pharm. Biochem. Behav.* 16:631–635.

Burright, R.G., Engellenner, W.J., and Donovick, P.J., 1989, Postpartum aggression and plasma prolactin levels in mice exposed to lead, *Physiol. Behav.* 46:889–893.

Bushnell, P.J., and Bowman, R.E., 1979, Effects of chronic lead ingestion on social development in infant rhesus monkeys, *Neurobehav. Toxicol.* 1:207–219.

Caho, C.C., Peterson, P.K., Filice, G.A., Pomeroy, C., and Sharp, B.M., 1990, Effects of immobilization stress on the pathogenesis of acute murine toxoplasmosis, *Brain Behav. Immun.* 4:162–169.

Childs, J.E., 1985, The prevalence of *Toxocara* species ova in backyards and gardens of Baltimore, Maryland, *Am. J. Public Health* 75:1092–1094.

Crofton, K.M., Taylor, D.H., Bull, R.J., Sivulka, D.J., and Lutkenhoff, S.D., 1980, Developmental delays in exploration and locomotor activity in male rats exposed to low level lead, *Life Sci.* 26:823–831.

Cutler, M.G., 1977, Effects of exposure to lead on social behaviour in the laboratory mouse, *Psychopharmacology* 52:279–282.

Cypess, R.H., 1978, Visceral larva migrans, *Cornell Vet.* 68:283–288.

Cypess, R.H., and Glickman, L.T., 1976, Visceral larva migrans: A significant zoonosis?, *Mod. Vet. Pract.* 57:462–464.

Cypess, R.H., Karol, M.H., Zidian, J.L., Glickman, L.T., and Gitlin, D., 1977, Larva-specific antibodies in patients with visceral larva migrans, *J. Infect. Dis.* 135:633–640.

Cypess, R.H., Donovick, P.J., and Burright, R.G., 1992, Transplacental and galactogenic transmission of *T. canis* larvae to brains of neonatal mice (submitted).

Czech, D.A., and Hoium, E., 1984, Some aspects of feeding and locomotor activity in adult rats exposed to tetraethyl lead, *Neurobehav. Toxicol. Teratol.* 6:357–361.

Dees, N.K., and Chapman, C., 1990, Individual differences in taste, body weight, and depression in the "helplessness" rat model and in humans, *Brain Res. Bull.* 24:669–676.

Dees, N.K., Minor, T.R., and Brewer, J., 1989, Suppression of feeding and body weight by inescapable shock: Modulation by quinine adulteration, stress, reinstatement, and controllability, *Physiol. Behav.* 45:975–983.

DeLuca, J., Hardy, C., Burright, R.G., Donovick, P.J., and Tuggey, R.L., 1982, The effects of dietary fat and lead ingestion on blood-lead levels in mice, *J. Toxicol. Environ. Health* 10:441–447.

DeLuca, J., Burright, and Donovick, P.J., 1989, Effects of genotype and food deprivation on lead-induced hyperactivity; *Behav. Genet.* 19:171–181.

DeLuca, J., Donovick, P.J., and Burright, R.G., 1989, Lead exposure, environmental temperature, nesting and consummatory behavior in adult mice of two ages, *Neurobehav. Toxicol. Teratol.* 11:7–11.

Diagnostic and Statistics Manual: DSM-III-R, 1987, American Psychiatric Association, Washington, D.C.

Dietrich, K.N., 1991, Human fetal lead exposure: Intrauterine growth, maturation, and postnatal neurobehavioral development, *Fundam. Appl. Toxicol.* 16:17–19.

Dietrich, K.N., Krafft, K.M., Bornschein, R.L., Hammond, P.B., Berger, O., Succop, P.A., and Bier, M., 1987, Low-level fetal lead exposure effect on neurobehavioral development in early infancy, *Pediatrics* 80:721–730.

Dietrich, K.N., Succop, P.A., Bornschein, R.L., Krafft, K.M., Berger, O., Hammond, P.B., and Buncher, C.R., 1990, Lead exposure and neurobehavioral development in late infancy, *Environ. Health Perspect.* 89:13–19.

Dolinsky, Z.S., Burright, R.G., Donovick, P.J., Glickman, L.T., Babish, J., Summers, B., and Cypess, R.H., 1981, Behavioral effects of lead and *Toxocara canis* in mice, *Science* 213:1142–1144.

Dolinsky, Z., Fink, E., Burright, R.G., and Donovick, P.J., 1981, The effects of lead, d-amphetamine, and time of day on activity levels in the mouse, *Pharm. Biochem. Behav.* 14:877–880.

Dolinsky, Z.S., Burright, R.G., and Donovick, P.J., 1983, Behavioral changes in mice following lead administration during several stages of development, *Physiol. Behav.* 30:583–589.

Dolinsky, Z., Hardy, C., Burright, R.G., and Donovick, P.J., 1985, The progression of behavioral and pathological effects of the parasite *Toxocara canis* in the mouse, *Physiol. Behav.* 35:33–42.

Donovick, P.J., and Burright, R.G., 1984, Roots to the future: Gene-environment coaction and individual vulnerability to neural insult, in: *Early Brain Damage* (C.R. Almli, and S. Finger, eds.), Academic Press, New York.

Donovick, P.J., and Burright, R.G., 1986, Short-term lead exposure, age and good deprivation: Interactive effects on wheel-running behavior of adult male mice, *Exper. Aging Res.* 12:163–168.

Donovick, P.J., and Burright, R.G., 1987, The consequence of parasitic infection for the behavior of the mammalian host, *Environ. Health Perspect.* 73:247–250.

Donovick, P.J., and Burright, R.G., 1989, An odyssey in behavioral neuroscience: The search for common factors underlying individual differences in response to brain damage, in *Preoperative Events: Their Effects on Behavior Following Brain Damage* (J. Schulkin, ed.), Lawrence Erlbaum, Hillside, NJ.

Donovick, P.J., and Horowitz, G.P., 1982, On the choice of subject populations for research in neurobehavioral toxicology, *J. Toxicol. Environ. Health* 10:1–9.

Donovick, P.J., Bliss, D.K., Burright, R.G., and Wertheim, L.M., 1973, Effect of pinealectomy or septal lesions on intake of unpalatable fluids in rats given sodium deplete or replete diets. *Physiol. Behav.* 10:1095–1099.

Donovick, P.J., Burright, R.G., and Bengelloun, W.A., 1979, The septal region and behavior: An example of the importance of genetic and experiential factors in determining effects of brain damage, *Neurosci. Biobehav. Rev.* 3:83–96.

Donovick, P.J., Dolinsky, Z.S., Perdue, V.P., Burright, R.G., Summers, B., and Cypess, R.H., 1981, *Toxocara canis* and lead alter consummatory behavior in mice, *Brain Res. Bull.* 7:317–323.

Draski, L.J., Summers, B., Cypess, R.H., Burright, R.G., and Donovick, P.J., 1987, The impact of single versus repeated exposures of mice to *Toxocara canis, Physiol. Behav.* 40:301–306.

Draski, L.J., Burright, R.G., and Donovick, P.J., 1989, The influence of prenatal and/or postnatal exposure to lead on behavior of preweanling mice, *Physiol. Behav.* 45:711–715.

Duwel, D., 1984, The prevalence of *Toxocara* eggs in the sand in children's playgrounds in Frankfurt, *Ann. Trop. Med. Parasitol.* 78:633–636.

Ehle, A.L., and McKee, D.C., 1990, Neuropsychological effect of lead in occupationally exposed workers: A critical review, *Crit. Rev. Toxicol.* 20:237–255.

Engellener, W.J., Burright, R.G., and Donovick, P.J., 1986, Lead, age and aggression in male mice, *Physiol. Behav.* 36:823–828.

Ernhart, C.B., and Greene, T., 1990, Low-level lead exposure in the prenatal and early preschool periods: Language development, *Arch. Environ. Health* 45:342–354.

Ernhart, C.B., Morrow-Tlucak, M., Wolf, A.W., Super, D., and Drotar, D., 1989, Low-level lead exposure in the prenatal and early preschool periods: Intelligence prior to school entry, *Neurotoxicol. Teratol.* 11:161–170.

Feldman, M.C., 1986, Pica: Current perspectives, *Psychosomatics* 27:519–523.

Fuller, J.L., 1979a, Fuller BWS lines: History and results, in: *Development and Evolution of Brain Size: Behavioral Implications* (M.E. Hahn, C. Jensen, and B.C. Dudek, eds.), Academic Press, New York.

Fuller, J.L., 1979b, The taxonomy of psychophenes, in: *Theoretical Advances in Behavior Genetics* (J.R. Royce, and L.P. Moss, eds.), Sijthoff & Noordhoff, Alphen aan der Rijn, Netherlands.

Glickman, L.T., and Schantz, P.M., 1981, Epidemiology and pathogenesis of zoonotic toxocariasis, *Epidemio. Rev.* 3:230–250.

Glickman, L.T., and Summers, B.A., 1983, Experimental *Toxocara canis* infection in cynomolgus macaques (*Macaca fascicularis*), *Am. J. Vet. Res.* 44:2347–2354.

Glickman, L.T., Chaudry, I.U., Costantino, J., Clack, F.B., Cypess, R.H., and Winslow, L., 1981, Pica patterns, toxocariasis, and elevated blood lead in children, *Am. J. Trop. Med. Hygiene,* 30:77–80.

Govani, S., Lucchi, L. Battaini, F., Spano, P.F., and Trabucchi, M., 1984, Chronic lead treatment affects dopaminergic control of prolactin secretion in rat pituitary, *Toxicol. Lett.* 20:237–241.

Grandjean, P., and Jorgensen, P., 1990, Retention of lead and cadmium in prehistoric and modern teeth, *Environ. Res.* 53:6–15.

Hahn, M.E., Burright, R.G., and Donovick, P.J., 1991, Lead effects on food competition and predatory aggression in Binghamton HET mice, *Physiol. Behav.* 50:757–764.

Hammond, P.B., Minnema, D.J., and Shulka, R., 1990, Lead exposure lowers the set point for food consumption and growth in weanling rats. *Toxicol. Appl. Pharm.* 106:80–87.

Hart, B., 1988, Biological basis of the behavior of sick animals, *Neurosci. Biobehav. Rev.* 12:123–137.

Hart, B.J., 1990, Behavioral adaptations to pathogens and parasites: Five strategies, *Neurosci. Biobehav. Rev.* 14: 273–294.

Hastings, L., Cooper, G.P., Bornschein, R.L. and Michaelson, I.A., 1977, Behavioral effects of low-level neonatal lead exposure, *Pharm. Biochem. Behav.* 7:37–42.

Herrmann, N., Glickman, L.T., Schantz, P.M., Weston, M.G., and Domanski, L.M., 1985, Seroprevalence of zoonotic toxocariasis in the United States: 1971–1973, *Am. J. Epidemiol.* 122:890–896.

Hill, I.R., Denham, D.A., and Scholtz, C.L. 1985, *Toxocara canis* larvae in the brain of a British child, *Trans. R. Soc. Trop. Med. Hygiene* 79:351–354.

Isaacson, R.L., 1982, *The Limbic System,* Plenum Press, New York.

Jacobs, D., 1979, Man and his pets, in *Parasites and Western Man* (R.J. Donaldson, ed.), MTP Press, Lancaster, England.

Jordan, C., Whitman, R.D., Harbut, M., and Tanner, B., 1990, Memory deficits in workers suffering from hard metal disease, *Toxicol. Lett.* 54:241–243.

Kavanau, J.L., 1967, Behavior of captive white-footed mice, *Science* 155:1623–1639.

Kello, D., and Kostial, K., 1973, The effect of milk diet on lead metabolism in rats, *Environ. Res.* 6:355–360.

Koskiniemi, M., Lappalanien, M., and Hedman, K., 1990, Toxoplasmosis needs evaluation, *Am. J. Dis. Child.* 143:724–728.

Kutscher, C.L., and Yamamoto, B.K., 1979, Altered saccharin preference during chronic dietary administration of lead in adult rats, *Neurobehav. Toxicol.* 1:259–262.

Lacey, E.P., 1990, Broadening the perspective of pica: Literature review *Public Health Rep.* 105:29–35.

Landrigan, P.J., 1990, Prevention of toxic environmental illness in the twenty-first century, *Environ. Health Perspec.* 86:197–199.

Landrigan, P.J., Baker, E.D., Whitworth, R.H., and Feldman, R.G., 1980, Neuroepidemiological evaluations of children with chronic increased lead absorption, in: (M.L. Needleman, ed.), *Low-Level Lead Exposure: The Clinical Implications of Current Research,* Raven Press, New York.

Laraque, D., McCormick, M., Norman, M., Taylor, A., Weller, S.C., and Karp, J., 1990, Blood lead, calcium status, and behavior in preschool children, *Am. J. Dis. Child.* 144:186–189.

Lashley, S.M., and Lane, J.D., 1988. Diminished regulation of mesolimbic dopaminergic activity in rat after chronic inorganic lead exposure, *Toxicol. Appl. Pharm.,* 95:474–483.

Lindner, L. 1990, Getting the lead out, *Am. Health: Fitness of Body and Mind, IX*, Nov., 70–71.

Mahaffey, K.R., 1974, Nutritional factors and susceptibility to lead toxicity, *Environ. Health Perspect.* 7:107–112.

Mahaffey, K.R., 1983, Biotoxicity of lead: Influence of various factors, *Fed. Proc.* 42:1730–1734.

Marlow, M., Stellern, J., Moon, C., and Errera, J., 1985, Main effects and interaction effects of metallic toxins on aggressive classroom behavior, *Aggress. Behav.* 11:41–48.

McAlpine, C., and Singh, N.N., 1986, Pica in institutionalized mentally retarded persons, *J. Ment. Defic. Res.* 30:171–178.

McFarland, D.J., 1989, Temporal development of the behavioral effects of herpes encephalitis in mice, *Psychobiology* 17:276–280.

McFarland, D.J., and Hotchin, J., 1987, Animal models in behavioral neurovirology, in: *Viruses, Immunity, and Mental Disorders* (E. Kurstak, Z.J. Lipowski, and P.V. Morozov, eds.), Plenum Press, New York.

McMichael, A.J., Baghurst, P.A., Wigg, N.R., Vimpani, G.V., Robertson, E.F., and Roberts, R.J., 1988, Port Pirie cohort study: Environmental exposure to lead and children's abilities at the age of four years, *N. Engl. J. Med.* 319:468–475.

Meno, M., Carbonni, E., Trabucchi, M., Carruba, M., and Spano, P.F., 1985, Dopamine inhibition of neurotensin-induced increase in Ca[2+] influx into rat pituitary cells. *Brain Res.*, 253–257.

Morrison, J., Olton, D.S., Goldberg, A.M., and Silbergeld, E.K., 1974, Alterations in consummatory behavior of mice produced by dietary exposure to inorganic lead, *Devel. Psychobiol.* 8:389–396.

Mullenix, P., 1980, Effect of lead on spontaneous behavior, in: *Low-Level Lead Exposure: The Clinical Implications of Current Research*. (H. L. Needleman, ed.), Raven Press, New York, pp. 211–220.

Murphy, J., 1991, Marjol cleanup site grim reminder of toxic disaster, *The Sunday Times*, Scranton, PA, A10.

Needleman, H.L., 1991, Seminar on the neural and behavioral effects of lead poisoning on children. The Federation of Behavioral, Psychological and Cognitive Sciences 10th Annual Capitol Hill Science Seminars, Mar. 8. *Fed. News* March 8, 1991.

Needleman, H.L., and Gatsonis, C.A., 1990, Low-level lead exposure and the IQ of children: A meta-analysis of modern studies, *JAMA* 263:673–678.

Needleman, H.L., Gunnoe, A., Reed, R., Peresie, H.H., Maher, C., and Barrett, P., 1979, Deficit in psychologic and classroom performance of children with elevated dentine lead levels, *N. Engl. J. Med.* 300:689–695.

Nelson, G.S., 1979, The parasite and the host, In: *Parasites and Western Man* (R.J. Donaldson, ed.), MTP Press, Lancaster, England.

O'Kelly, L.I., 1963, The psychophysiology of motivation, *Ann. Rev. Psychol.* 14:57–92.

Rajachandran, L., Donovick, P.J., Burright, R.G., and Siddiqi, H., 1992, Behavioral consequences of schistosomiasis in heterogeneous (HET) stock male mice (submitted).

Rankin, H., Hodgson, R., and Stockwell, T., 1979, The concept of craving and its measurement, *Behav. Res. Ther.* 17:389–396.

Raloff, J., 1991, Beverages intoxicated by lead in crystal, *Sci. News* 139:54.

Rasile, D.A., 1990, Cross-Generation Effects of Low-Level Lead Exposure on Development and Behavioral Activity in Male and Female Binghamton Heterogeneous Stock Mice, Unpublished M.A. Thesis, SUNY-Binghamton.

Reiter, L., Anderson, G., Laskey, J., and Cahill, D., 1975, Developmental and behavioral changes in the rat during chronic exposure to lead, *Environ. Health Perspect.* 12:119–123.

Reynolds, R.D., Binder, H.J., Miller, M.B., Chang, W.W.Y., and Horan, S., 1968, Pagophagia and iron deficiency anemia, *Ann. Intern. Med.* 69:435–440.

Rozin, P., 1989, Disorders of food selection, in: (L.H., Schneider, S.J. Cooper, and K.A. Halmi, eds.), *The Psychobiology of Human Eating Disorders: Preclinical and Clinical Perspectives, Ann. N.Y. Acad. Sci.* 575:376–386.

Sauerhoff, M.W., and Michaelson, A.I., 1973, Hyperactivity and brain catecholamines in lead exposed developing rats, *Science* 182:1022–1024.

Sayetta, R.B., 1986, Pica: An overview, *Am. Fam. Pract.* 33:181–185.

Schneider, L.H., Cooper, S.J., and Halmi, K.A., (eds.), 1989, *The Psychobiology of Human Eating Disorders, Ann. N.Y. Acad. Sci.* 575.

Schneirla, T.A., 1965, Aspects of stimulation and organization in approach/withdrawal processes underlying vertebrate behavioral development, in: *Advances in the Study of Behavior* (D.S. Lehrman, R.A. Hinde, and E. Shaw, eds.), Academic Press, New York.

Schroeder, S.R., Hawk, B., Otto, D.A., Mushak, P., and Hicks, R.E., 1985, Separating the effects of lead and social factors on IQ, *Environ. Res.* 38:144–154.

Science News, 1991, EPA targets 17 toxins, 139:101.

Scott, T.R., and Giza, B.K., 1990, Coding channels in the taste system of the rat, *Science* 249:1585–1587.

Scott, T.R., and Mark, G.P., 1986, Feeding and taste, *Prog. Neurobiol.* 27:293–317.

Scott, T.R., and Mark, G.P., 1987, The taste system encodes stimulus toxicity, *Brain Res.* 414:197–203.

Scrimgeour, E.M., and Gajdusek, D.C., 1985, Involvement of the central nervous system in *Schistosoma mansoni* and *S. haematobium* infection: A review, *Brain* 108:1023–1038.

Seeber, A., Kiesswetter, E., Neidhart, B., and Blaszkewicz, M., 1990, Neurobehavioral effects of a long-term exposure to tetraalkylead, *Neurotoxicol. Teratol.* 12:653–655.

Silbergeld, E.K., 1977, Interactions of lead and calcium on the synaptosome uptake of dopamine and choline, *Life Sci.* 20:309–318.

Silbergeld, E.K., and Goldberg, A.M., 1973, A lead induced behavior disorder, *Life Sci.* 13:1275–1282.

Silbergeld, E.K., and Goldberg, A.M., 1974, Lead induced behavioral dysfunction: An animal model of hyperactivity, *Exper. Neurol.* 42:146–157.

Singhal, E.L., and Thomas, J.E., eds., 1980, *Lead Toxicity,* Urban and Schwarzenberg, Baltimore.

Six, K.M., and Goyer, R.M., 1972, The influence of iron deficiency on tissue content and toxicity of ingested lead in the rat, *J. Lab. Clin. Med.* 79:128–136.

Snowdon, C.T., 1973, Learning deficits in lead-injected rats, *Pharmacol. Biochem. Behav.* 1:599–603.

Sobel, A.E., Yuska, H., Peters, D.D., and Kramer, B., 1940, The biochemical behavior of Pb. I: Influence of calcium phosphorus and vitamin D on lead in blood and bone, *J. Biol. Chem.* 132:239–265.

Strouthes, A., 1971, Thirst and saccharine preference in rat, *Physiol. Behav.* 6:289–292.

Summers, B., Cypess, R.H., Dolinsky, Z.D., Burright, R.G., and Donovick, P.J., 1983, Neuropathological studies of experimental toxocariasis in lead exposed mice, *Brain Res. Bull.* 10:547–550.

Taylor, D.H., Noland, E.A., Brubaker, C.M., Crofton, K.M., and Bull, R.J., 1982, Low level lead (Pb) exposure produces learning deficits in young rat pups, *Neurobehav. Toxicol. Teratol.* 4:311–314.

Uzych, L., 1985, Teratogenesis and mutagenesis associated with the exposure of human males to lead: A review, *Yale J. Biol.* 58:9–17.

van Hoesen, G.W., Pandya, D.P., and Butters, N., 1972, Cortical afferents to the entorhinal cortex of the rhesus monkey, *Science* 175:1471–1473.

Weingarten, H.P., and Elston, D., 1990, The phenomenology of food cravings, *Appetite* 15:231–246.

Wide, M., 1985, Lead exposure on critical days of fetal life affects fertility in the female mouse, *Teratology* 32: 375–380.

Wiebe, J.P., Barr, K.J., and Buckingham, K.D., 1988, Effect of prenatal and neonatal exposure to lead on gonadotrophin receptors and steroidogenesis in rat ovaries, *J. Toxicol. Environ. Health* 24:461–476.

Winick, M., 1976, *Malnutrition and the Brain,* Oxford University Press, New York.

Winneke, G., Brockhaus, A., and Baltissen, R., 1977, Neurobehavioral and systemic effects of long term blood-lead elevation in rats, *Arch. Toxicol.* 37:247–263.

Winneke, G., Brockhaus, A., Ewers, U., Kramer, U., and Neuf, M., 1990, Results from the European multicenter study on lead neurotoxicity in children: Implications for risk assessment, *Neurotoxicol. Teratol.* 12:553–559.

Wylam, M.A., 1990, Throop lead tests ominous, *The Morning Times,* Scranton, PA, May 4, 1990, A1–A3.

Yokoyama, K., Araki, S., and Aono, H., 1988, Reversibility of psychological performance in subclinical lead absorption, *Neurotoxicology* 9:405–410.

Young, P.T., 1967, Palatability: Hedonic response to food stuffs in: *Handbook of Physiology, Section 6, Alimentary Canal: Volume 1* (C.F. Code, ed.), American Physiology Society, Washington, D.C.

Young, P.T., 1977, The role of hedonic processes in the development of sweet taste preferences, in: *Taste and Development: The Genesis of Sweet Preference* (J.M. Weiffenbach, ed.), DHEW, Bethesda, MD, Publication No. (NIH) 771068, pp. 399–417.

Yuhl, D.E., Burright, R.G., Donovick, P.J., and Cypess, R.H., 1985, Behavioral effects of early lead exposure and subsequent toxocariasis in mice, *J. Toxicol. Environ. Health* 16:315–321.

Zenick, H., and Goldsmith, M., 1981, Drug discrimination learning in lead-exposed rats, *Science* 212:569–571.

Zenick, H., Padich, R., Tokacek, T., and Aragon, P., 1978, Influence of prenatal and postnatal lead exposure on discrimination learning in rats, *Pharm. Biochem. Behav.* 8:347–350.

Zimering, R.T., Burright, R.G., and Donovick, P.J., 1982, Effects of prenatal and continued lead exposure on activity levels in the mouse, *Neurobehav. Toxicol. Teratol.* 4:9–14.

Zuromski, E.S., Donovick, P.J., and Burright, R.G., 1972, The late effect of septal lesions on the albino rat's ability to regulate light, *J. Comp. Physiol. Psychol.* 78:83–90.

Chapter 9

Nocardia

An Environmental Bacterium Possibly Associated with Neurodegenerative Diseases in Humans

Blaine L. Beaman

1. INTRODUCTION

The genus *Nocardia* is composed of gram-positive strictly aerobic bacteria belonging to the order Actinomycetales in the class Thallobacteria (Lechevalier, 1989; Murray, 1989). These organisms are ubiquitous in the environment, and they are part of the normal microflora of fertile soils worldwide (Lechevalier, 1989). In addition, they have been isolated from numerous aquatic sources as well as the ocean floor (Williams *et al.*, 1983).

There are more than nine species of *Nocardia* recognized, and numerous additional species have been proposed (Lechevalier, 1989). Of these, *Nocardia asteroides* is the most frequently recognized to cause disease in humans and a large variety of animals (Beaman, 1992). The types of disease caused by this organism may vary from a self-limited, subclinical infection to a progressive pulmonary infection with dissemination to other regions of the body. Pulmonary or systemic disease of this type is referred to as nocardiosis, in contrast to the more localized cutaneous infections that may give rise to nocardial mycetomas (actinomycetoma) (Beaman, 1992). It is important to emphasize that nocardial infections, regardless of the type of disease they cause or the location of the initial site affected, can invade through blood vessels and gain entry into the bloodstream

Blaine L. Beaman • Department of Medical Microbiology and Immunology, University of California School of Medicine, Davis, California 95616.
The Vulnerable Brain and Environmental Risks, Volume 2: Toxins in Food, edited by Robert L. Isaacson and Karl F. Jensen. Plenum Press, New York, 1992.

(Beaman, 1992). Once the nocardiae enter the blood, they are disseminated to other regions of the body. The brain represents the primary target of blood-borne dissemination (Beaman, 1992). Therefore, nocardiae should be considered as pathogens of the central nervous system.

2. NOCARDIAL INFECTIONS OF THE ALIMENTARY SYSTEM

Pathogenic species of *Nocardia [N. asteroides, N. brasiliensis,* and *N. otiditiscaviarum (N. caviae)]* can be isolated from fertile soils, water, and vegetation (Williams *et al.,* 1983). As a consequence, the human may come in contact with these organisms through both food and water. Nocardiae probably do not colonize the normal mucous membranes or healthy skin for extended periods of time, even though they can be transiently isolated from these sources. Therefore, the persistence of *Nocardia* in a specific body site should be considered an infectious process, even in the absence of clinical signs (i.e., *Nocardia* should never be considered as part of the normal flora). These silent or subclinical infections in "healthy" individuals may represent an important, but unrecognized, source for dissemination of the organisms to the central nervous system or other regions of the body (Beaman, 1992).

Terezhalmy and Bottomley (1978) reported a case of infection of the oral cavity in which *N. asteroides* was isolated from the periodontal pockets of the mandibular anterior area. This 34-year-old male patient was a chronic alcoholic who had iron-deficiency anemia secondary to alcohol abuse. He indicated that he had fallen several times and experienced soil contamination of the oral cavity. This patient then developed pneumonia within the left upper lobe of the lung. *N. asteroides* was isolated from this pulmonary lesion, and it was found to be the same as the strain isolated from the periodontal pockets (unpublished data). Therefore, this case represented pulmonary nocardiosis secondary to soil contamination of the oral cavity.

There are reports of nocardial infections of the face with involvement of the oral cavity (Lampe *et al.,* 1981). Lampe *et al.* (1981) described three cases of cervicofacial nocardiosis in three previously healthy children that were shown not to have any form of immunodeficiency. In each case, the submandibular region was affected, there was no report of trauma preceding the infection, and in two of the children it involved the left naris, whereas the ear was infected in one of the children (Lampe *et al.,* 1981).

N. asteroides can cause chronic, undefined infections of the upper aerodigestive tract (Burton and Burgess, 1990). Adair *et al.* (1987) reported a nocardial peritonsillar abscess in a previously healthy 22-year-old male who had a history of recurrent pharyngitis and sore throat that persisted for 5 years. Katz and Fauci (1987) reported a case of a *N. asteroides*-induced fever for a period of at least 1 year in a healthy 39-year-old woman. It was shown that she had developed a sinusitis in the maxillary sinus that was responsible for this prolonged fever of unknown origin. Although the cases described above involved an infection that probably originated in the oral cavity, the mechanism of exposure, especially the possible relationship to food or water, was not addressed. However, there was a definite relationship established between food and a pulmonary infection in a 68-year-old, healthy male who choked on a small piece of lettuce while eating a salad. Over a period of several months following the choking episode, the individual developed a progressive lung abscess that had to be removed surgically. Pathological analysis revealed that fragments of a foreign material, which appeared to be a piece of lettuce, were embedded in the abscessed tissue, and *N. asteroides* was the only organism isolated from the abscess (unpublished data).

There are several reports of laryngeal and pharyngeal nocardiosis, gastrointestinal involvement, and disseminated nocardial infections, with the appendix, colon, ileum, and jejunum as the probable portals of entry (Adair *et al.*, 1987; Burdon, 1971; Burton and Burgess, 1990; Cockerill *et al.*, 1984; Cox and Hughes, 1975, Gibb and Williams, 1986, Hathaway and Mason, 1962; Katz and Fauci, 1977; List *et al.*, 1954; Munslow, 1954; Petri *et al.*, 1988; Young *et al.*, 1971). Finally, *N. asteroides* has been isolated from the stools of individuals with disseminated disease (unpublished data). The data from these reports suggest that the gastrointestinal (GI) tract may be a focus for nocardial entry into the bloodstream.

Although a specific food has not been identified as a source for nocardiae in the GI tract, there are several that could be involved. All foods that have direct contact with the soil (i.e., vegetables) would likely have nocardiae on their surface. Therefore, raw vegetables that have not been adequately washed, peeled, or cooked could be a source for nocardial contamination of the GI tract. Milk and dairy products represent another potential source for pathogenic strains of *Nocardia* (Beaman and Sugar, 1983; Stark and Anderson, 1990).

It is well documented that virulent strains of *N. asteroides* and *N. caviae* cause mastitis in dairy cows and goats (Beaman and Sugar, 1983). These organisms represent a serious problem in dairy animals in many regions of the world, and in the central valley of California, *Nocardia* is one of the major causes of mastitis in dairy herds (Bushnell *et al.*, 1979). In at least one instance, more than 10^6 colony forming units (CFU) of *N. asteroides* per milliliter of milk were being excreted by a prized, registered Holstein. The injection of 0.1 ml of this milk intravenously into Swiss Webster mice resulted in significant animal death, and the mice that survived this injection expressed a variety of neurologic disorders (unpublished data).

It is clear that there is a potential risk for acquiring nocardiae by ingesting contaminated food, water, or milk. However, it should be pointed out that the documentation of infection by *Nocardia* following ingestion of contaminated materials has never been studied adequately. There are no reports of infecting animals experimentally with pathogenic strains of nocardiae by the oral route.

3. NOCARDIAL INFECTIONS OF THE CENTRAL NERVOUS SYSTEM OF HUMANS

The first case of nocardial infection in the brain of a human was described by Eppinger in 1891. The organism isolated from the cerebral abscess of this fatal disease was later named *N. asteroides* (Eppinger, 1891; Lechevalier, 1989). During the next 100 years, there have been several hundred case reports of CNS nocardiosis described in the literature. Obviously, it is not possible to discuss each of these in this review. Instead, 150 randomly selected, well-described cases were chosen for further analysis (see reference numbers 2–13; 23–31; 35–42; 44; 45; 47–66; 69–83; 85–89; 91–93; 95–97; 99–110; 112–122; 124–135; 137–146; 148–153; 155–157; 159–168; 170–174). These will be combined with our own experiences involving several unpublished case reports of nocardial infections of the central nervous system.

There are several misconceptions concerning various aspects of CNS nocardiosis presented in the literature that must be addressed. These include the nature of the disease, the incidence of infection, the opportunistic aspects of the organism, and the recognition and diagnosis of CNS nocardiosis.

It is generally thought that nocardial infections of the CNS represent dissemination from a pulmonary focus that resulted from inhalation of the organisms. Based upon an analysis of the selected cases in which adequate information is provided, 43% (64/150) had no evidence of prior pulmonary infection. In fact, in some of these CNS infections the portal of entry for the organism may have been through the GI tract. Most reports indicate that nocardiosis occurs in compromised individuals; however, of the 150 cases in this study, 59 (39.3%) were healthy individuals with no identifiable predisposing factor. The number of males with brain infections (104) outnumbered females (46) by 226% (2.26:1). The age of the patients with CNS nocardiosis ranged from a young 2 months to 77 years; however, the average age was 42.4 ± 15 years. Of the total 150 cases described, 79 (52.6%) died, whereas 71 (47.4%) of the patients were described as surviving their brain infection. Patients described prior to 1970 had a higher rate of mortality (approximately 70%) than those who were presented after 1970 (approximately 45%). Individuals who had no identifiable predisposing factor were only slightly more successfully treated (32/59 = 54% survived) than those who had an underlying condition that predisposed them to nocardial infection (39/91 = 42.8% survived). The sex of the patient did not influence the survival rate. Thus, 48% of the males (50/104) and 46% of the females (21/46) survived their infection. The most frequently identified species of *Nocardia* isolated from CNS infections was *N. asteroides* (123/150), followed by *N. brasiliensis* (8/150), *N. caviae* (6/150), one *N. farcinica,* and a small number identified only as *Nocardia* (2–13; 23–31; 35–42; 44; 45; 47–66; 69–83; 85–89; 91–93; 95–97; 99–110; 112–122; 124–135; 137–146; 148–153; 155–157; 159–168; 170–174).

4. CLINICAL PRESENTATION OF CNS NOCARDIOSIS

The signs and symptoms expressed by individuals who have nocardial infection of the brain are variable. These infections may be silent with no outward neurological manifestations (recognized only at autopsy), or they may be easily recognized as causing an abscess in any location within the brain. Additionally, there may be meningitis with or without evidence of involvement of the deeper regions of the brain. Occasionally, the spinal cord represents the only site of CNS infection. The clinical presentation may be that of an acute and rapidly developing infection; however, most often, nocardial infection of the brain has an insidious onset, with a gradual progression of a variety of neurologic deficits over a period of months to years. Often there is no fever and no shift in the blood-cell differential to signal a bacterial infection, especially during the early stages of disease. CNS infection in the compromised patient is generally more rapidly progressive than when seen in the normal person with no identifiable predisposing condition wherein CNS nocardiosis is indeed insidious and slowly progressive (2–13; 23–31; 35–42; 44; 45; 47–66; 69–83; 85–89; 91–93; 95–97; 99–110; 112–122; 124–135; 137–146; 148–153; 155–157; 159–168; 170–174).

Ajax (1964) described the progression of a nocardial brain abscess in a previously healthy 41-year-old male farmer. The first signs of a possible CNS problem in this individual were several episodes of "blurred vision," which occurred over an 8-month period. After 6 months, these episodes were then accompanied by a transitory loss of balance, mental confusion, and difficulty writing with the right hand. The patient developed a weakness of the right arm and leg, and had an episode of "twitching." Eight months after the initial signs, the individual developed pulmonary signs with a productive cough and a left hilar mass. A pure culture of *N. asteroides* was isolated from a granuloma removed by thoracotomy from the left hilar region. The patient was treated with cycloserine and sulphonamides (Hoeprich *et al.*, 1968); nevertheless, 1 month later he developed both a weakness and numbness of the right leg and arms with an associated "twitching." This progressed to a generalized convulsion and the patient became confused. Although his speech was intact, he was not able to read, write, perform calculations, or discriminate between right and left. He developed a mild hemiparesis on the right. He had decreased ability to feel or sense solid objects, and decreased graphesthesia on the right side, but he had no impairment of vision. A brain scan was done and a craniotomy performed. A large abscess caused by *Nocardia* was excised from the posterior temporal and adjacent parietal areas, and the patient continued antibiotic therapy. He gradually improved; however, his acquired dyslexia was permanent. He never regained the ability to read, and 1 year after successful therapy he exhibited agraphia, expressive aphasia, impairment of the ability to perform calculations, and a loss in dexterity of the right hand. With the exception of temporary blurred vision, there were no vision defects in this patient (Ajax, 1964). However, this is often not the case in other patients, since various forms of papilledema and hemianopia have been described in approximately 35% of individuals with CNS nocardiosis.

Nocardial infections of the brain can result in a variety of personality and behavioral alterations. For example, Jacobson and Cloward (1948) described a 28-year-old woman who was admitted to the hospital because of manic-depressive psychosis with atypical features of hysteria and schizophrenia that developed over a period of 1½ years. During a period of 18 months, this person became overtalkative, distractable, sleepless, and hyperactive. She later developed a belligerent and combative personality. For these, she underwent electric shock treatment with some temporary success. During the next several months, she remained hyperactive, restless, and exhibited marked hysterical symptoms. She constantly complained of headaches, backaches, pains in the neck, and astasia abasia (unwillingness or inability to stand or walk). A lump 1 cm in diameter was noted on her neck, which she claimed had appeared there about 2 years previously. Most physicians considered the lump as an enlarged lymph node and that "nothing was wrong." No biopsy of the lump was ever performed. Neurological examination was completely normal, and the patient was physically well. About 2 months later the patient began to complain more vehemently than before about her backache and neck pains. At this time she developed a fever and examination revealed positive Kernig and Brudzinski signs, both of which are indicative of meningitis. Lumbar puncture confirmed a diagnosis of meningitis. No organisms were seen or recovered from the spinal fluid at this time, but she was placed on penicillin and sulfadiazine, and after no improvement, streptomycin was added. One week following therapy, the patient developed bilateral papilledema. A ventriculogram was done and ventricular fluid removed. The roentgenogram revealed cerebral edema without abscess. She improved following drainage and antibiotic therapy. After 3 weeks she was considered clinically well. After repeated attempts, *Nocardia* was finally isolated from the CSF, and the cerebral infection was confirmed as being caused by *N. asteroides*. Five months after successful therapy, the woman recovered completely from all signs of mental illness as well as the meningitis.

Recently, an individual was encountered who had a nocardial-induced lesion that resulted in significant changes in personality that developed over a period of 2–3 years (unpublished data). A previously healthy woman in her mid-30s developed a variety of subtle changes in personality that slowly progressed to manifest themselves as psychotic. She expressed manic depression for about 18 months with a development of schizophrenia. She was initially a very pleasant, quiet person with a very pleasing personality, and a good sense of humor. During the following 3 years, her personality became more aggressive and hostile. In an interview 1 year after successful therapy, she stated that she did not like the person she had become, and it was like being on the outside watching her personality change, not liking what she saw, but at the same time, being unable to stop the process. The personality changes progressed with a gradual development of physical signs being expressed primarily on the left side of the body. She gradually developed a left-sided weakness and hemiparesis. There was a numbness that developed in the left extremities, and later she had difficulty walking. One morning she fell and was unable to stand. She was hospitalized and a complete medical examination revealed a healthy woman with no fever and no evidence of infection (the blood analysis revealed normal results). A CAT scan demonstrated a mass in the right upper cerebral hemisphere. Since there was no evidence of an infectious process, a diagnosis of brain tumor was made. Because of the favorable location, the patient underwent surgery and the entire tumor was removed and sent to the pathologist for analysis. Much to everyone's surprise, the tumor was in fact a purulogranulomatous lesion, and a pure culture of *N. asteroides* was isolated from this mass. The patient was then placed on trimethoprim-sulfamethoxazole for 1 year with complete recovery. Two years after the surgery (February 1991), she was found to be very healthy, and her personality had returned to normal. Thus, she is now a very pleasant, quiet woman who has a sparkling smile and a jovial personality, with no significant neurological deficits.

There are numerous additional reports in the literature of nocardial CNS infections resulting in alterations in personality that range from manic depression to schizophrenia, dyslexia, amnesia, and palilalia. In addition to mental disorders, cerebral nocardiosis results in a variety of physical disabilities. These include hemiparesis, body tremors, Parkinsonian features, seizures, epilepsy, palsy, convulsions, coma, retropulsion, and ataxia (2–13; 23–31; 35–42; 44; 45; 47–66; 69–83; 85–89; 91–93; 95–97; 99–110; 112–122; 124–135; 137–146; 148–153; 155–157; 159–168; 170–174).

The following cases are presented as a brief representation of the types of physical disabilities that may be encountered following infection of the CNS by *Nocardia*. Richter *et al.* (1968) described a 39-year-old male who was initially treated for inflammation of the eye, but 3 months later he presented with a fever, and muscle and joint pain. Several days later he complained of a stiff neck and a lumbar puncture was done. The material was cultured for fungi, bacteria, and *Mycobacterium,* but all tests were negative. He received a wide range of antimicrobial agents, but his condition worsened. He became progressively confused. Over a period of the next several weeks he became disoriented, experienced visual hallucinations, and a severe tremulousness developed. He was later transferred to another hospital, at which time he had a fever of 102.8°F; he was confused, disoriented, and made frequent, inappropriate remarks. His face was mask-like and his speech was dysarthric. He had a stiff neck and a positive Kernig sign. There was no evidence of pulmonary involvement, no lymphadenopathy, and the liver and spleen were not palpable. His gait was wide-based and ataxic; and there was a generalized muscle wasting and weakness, even though muscle tone was increased. Hyper-reflexia with bilateral patellar and ankle clonus were noted. This patient exhibited course and irregular at-rest tremors of all extremities, with head and truncal tremors. An extensive infectious disease workup was negative for bacteria, fungi, viruses, and parasites. The lungs were completely clear. The cerebral spinal fluid had a very high white blood cell content, with 98% PMN leukocytes. From this CSF sample, *N. asteroides* was isolated. Two months after his illness began, the patient was placed on sulfadiazine, and he gradually improved. More than 1 year later, the sulfadiazine levels were reduced and the patient was able to return to work (Richter *et al.,* 1968).

In a clinicopathological conference of the Mayo Clinic (1967), the case of a previously healthy 34-year-old woman who was a farmer's wife in Illinois was discussed. She developed persistent headaches, and previously she had the "flu" with a low-grade fever, headache, and blood-streaked sputum. She experienced an unsteadiness when she moved her head, vomited, and developed a slurred speech and difficulty answering questions. She had a long-term history of nervousness and episodic palpitations with weakness. For years, she complained of bifrontal headaches in the early evenings, and 6 months prior to the hospitalization she had an episode of uncontrolled crying spells and severe depression. She never felt well after the crying episodes. Over a period of months she became more lethargic, with slow, thick speech. Her gait was unsteady and reeling, and she had difficulty standing on one leg. Her headaches increased in number and severity, and she developed left-ankle clonus, impairment of sensation to touch on the left hand, and a right facial weakness. She had left hyper-reflexia. A brain biopsy of the left posterior region was interpreted as showing a "degenerating brain" and some cerebral edema, with no evidence of an infectious process. All cultures for bacteria and fungi were negative. Following the brain biopsy she developed a severe right facial weakness and paralysis of the right arm. Her condition continued to deteriorate until she died. At autopsy, *N. asteroides* was cultured from the brain, and there were diffuse lesions in the medulla, pons, cerebellum, and cerebrum (Clinicopathologic Conference, 1967).

Recently, a previously healthy female in her mid 60s who was living in the country was seen by her physician because of a "flu" that persisted. A tentative diagnosis of mycoplasmal pneumonia was reached, and she was treated with antibiotics. Her condition did not improve. After several weeks she began to show signs of neurological deficits without improvement of the pulmonary disease. An open lung biopsy was performed because all other attempts to culture the etiology of the pulmonary infection had failed. *N. asteroides* was isolated from this biopsy. Shortly afterwards, the woman became comatose and a diffuse brain infection caused by *Nocardia* was identified. She remained comatose while on chemotherapy for several days then she gradually improved, but remained paralyzed from the waist downward with only partial use of the upper extremities. Over a period of several years these features remained; however, her physicians noted the development of tremors of all extremities while at rest. She was described by her physicians as developing a "Parkinsonian-like syndrome" (unpublished observations).

5. AN EXPERIMENTAL MODEL FOR NOCARDIAL-INDUCED NEURODEGENERATION

Developing an experimental animal model in order to study a disease in humans depends on the ability of the agent to induce the same response in both systems. For an infectious agent such as *Nocardia*, it is necessary for the model to express the same variety of clinical manifestations that are recognized when this organism infects humans. In an effort to understand both the mechanisms of nocardial pathogenesis and host resistance to *Nocardia*, murine models for human nocardiosis and mycetomas have been established (Beaman and Maslan, 1977; Beaman *et al.*, 1978a, 1978b). Nocardial infections in a variety of mice have been studied extensively. In each system, it was shown that the mouse expressed the same process that a particular strain of *Nocardia* demonstrated in the human from which it was originally isolated (Beaman and Maslan, 1977; Beaman and Scates, 1981; Beaman *et al.*, 1978, 1980a, 1980b, 1982).

It is well established that cells of *Nocardia* often enter the blood-stream either from an infectious focus elsewhere in the body or directly by traumatic inoculation (Hadley *et al.*, 1988; Peterson *et al.*, 1978; Vanderstigel *et al.*, 1986; Wilson *et al.*, 1989). Therefore, it is important to establish a murine model to investigate the consequences to the host of blood-borne nocardiae. It was demonstrated that mice that were infected by an intravenous route developed a variety of signs that were the result of invasion of the brain (Kohbata and Beaman, 1991). Animals that survived an acute infectious dose of *Nocardia* (i.e., more than 1 week) frequently expressed a variety of signs indicative of neurological damage. These mice can be grouped into categories based upon the specific set of symptoms and signs that are expressed over a period of several weeks or months. Some of these categories are summarized in Table 1. It is clear that most of the types of physical disabilities described above for cerebral nocardiosis in humans are reproduced in this murine model.

In humans, central nervous system infection with *Nocardia* is currently recognized by the development of a progressive lesion that is usually an abscess, but it may occasionally be a granuloma. Furthermore, this progressive form of infection in the CNS is more often diagnosed in immunocompromised patients (e.g., 91/150 cases described; see list of references cited above). Since diagnosis of nocardiosis in humans requires cultivation and identification of the recovered bacterium from the infected tissue, inapparent or subclinical infections would be diagnosed only by serendipity (Beaman, 1992). By injecting either a sufficiently large dose of nocardial cells with certain strains of *Nocardia*, or by using mice immunosuppressed with corticosteroids, a progressive abscess can be induced in the brains of mice (Beaman and Maslan, 1977; Beaman and Scates, 1981, Schofield, 1985). However, if the inoculum dose is sufficiently small and mice are not immunocompromised, a self-limited, often subclinical or inapparent, infection of the brain is produced. Nevertheless, most of these mice still develop signs of neurological damage that are progressive and permanent (Table 1) (Kohbata and Beaman, 1991).

Microscopic analysis of sections of the brains of mice following intravenous injection of single cells of log-phase (filamentous form) *N. asteroides* reveals that these

TABLE 1. Categories of Signs of Neurological Damage Expressed in Female BALB/c Mice After a Self-Limited, Subclinical Infection of the Brain with *Nocardia*

Category I:	Mice have a deviation of the head to one side and a one-sided weakness with a tendency to roll ("hemiparesis"). These mice spin in a circular motion when suspended by the tail. They may have a gait disturbance, and they may express retropulsion on a smooth surface. They tend to be hypoactive. These signs are not improved when the mice are treated with L-dopa and carbidopa.
Category II:	The mice do not have a deviation of the head; but instead, they express a rhythmic tremor or vertical shake of the head several times per second. They have a stooped posture, which becomes exaggerated when suspended by the tail (they do not spin in a circular motion). They have a tremulous movement when walking and the hind feet are often splayed. There is rigidity in the extremities. They are hypoactive and usually express retropulsion when placed on a smooth surface. The headshake, as well as many of the other signs, become visibly improved when the mice are treated with L-dopa and carbidopa. Some mice may even appear normal. This response to L-dopa is temporary and lasts about 2 hr. The headshake signs are permanent and may be progressive.
Category III:	The same as Category II above, except the mice are hyperactive instead of hypoactive. They show an exaggerated restlessness and agitation. They may be "jittery." The headshake signs are L-dopa responsive.
Category IV:	Mice in this category show mixed signs that combine features of Categories I, II, and III above. They have "hemiparesis" and a deviation of the head with a vertical headshake that is L-dopa responsive. They have ataxic movement. They usually spin when suspended by the tail, but a stooped posture may also be expressed. They tend to be both hyperactive and hypoactive at times. The "hemiparesis" signs often improve or disappear over a period of weeks to months, with the headshake signs remaining constant. They may or may not express retropulsion on a smooth surface.
Category V:	These mice do not have a rhythmic vertical headshake, but instead, they express a rapid horizontal headshake, have tremulous moement (often ataxic) with severe hyperactivity (always on the run) and exaggerated restlessness. Posture may be stooped, but it is usually normal when suspended by the tail. Sometimes they will spin. The ears of these mice are rigid and overly erect (response to L-dopa not known).
Category VI:	These mice may have a slight deviation of the head. They are characteristically hyperactive and run rapidly in circles (chasing their tail). They never seem to rest. Often many features from the above categories are combined or expressed, although mice in this category may appear relatively normal, except for running in circles.
Category VII:	These mice express either a variety of mixed features as described above or no abnormalities, with the exception of periodic episodes of seizures that are aggravated by an outside stimulus. These seizures are temporary and last for a few seconds. Occasionally the seizure may precede death.
Category VIII:	The animals in this category may not express signs, except for partial or total paralysis of the limbs, usually restricted to the lower half of the body. They will drag themselves around the cage and appear as though they have a broken back. This paralysis is permanent and often progressive. Mice with this type of paralysis may live up to 1 year, but they usually die within a few months.
Category IX:	These mice are severely debilitated with total paralysis, often with twitching, and they look quite ill (ruffled hair). They usually die within weeks of onset, probably because of their inability to eat or drink.
Category X:	The mice in this category have been infected but they appear to remain normal or express only a transitory, mild set of signs that disappear with time. They have antibody to *Nocardia,* and there is neurochemical evidence of damage in the brain, but outward signs are not obvious.

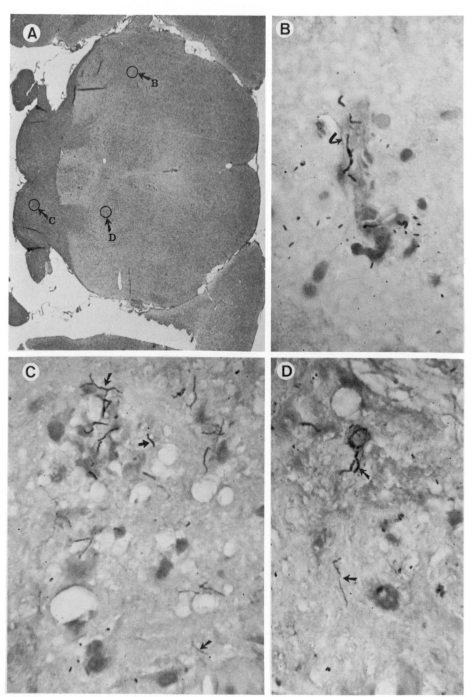

FIGURE 1. Light micrographs of coronal sections of the murine brain 24 hr after injection of *N. asteroides* GUH-2. (A) Low magnification of H and E stained sections, with inserts B, C, and D showing areas of nocardial invasion in the brain. Note a lack of inflammatory response. B, C, and D are high-magnification micrographs of a Gram stain of the adjacent serial section shown in A. Arrows point to nocardial filaments growing within each region of the brain. (B) Nocardial growth in the substantia nigra pars compacta region. (C) Extensive nocardial growth in the pons region. (D) Nocardial growth in the red nucleus region. The upper arrow notes nocardial cells inside a probable neuron. From Kohbata and Beaman (1991), with permission.

bacteria adhere to the surface of the endothelial cells in the capillaries (Kohbata and Beaman, 1991). The nocardiae may then grow along the capillary, forming a tangled filamentous mass that can occlude the blood vessel. This will often result in an aneurysm, which may rupture, resulting in petechial hemorrhages. During the first 24 hr of this process, there is surprisingly little or no inflammatory response observable at these sites (Figure 1). In many regions, the nocardial cells do not block the blood vessel, but instead grow through the capillary wall, invading the brain tissue (Figure 1). At 24 hr after infection there is a rapid growth of the nocardiae within the cells and neurons of various regions of the brain. Furthermore, there is no inflammatory reaction at these sites of proliferation (i.e., no polymorphonuclear neutrophils or monocytes are observed) (Figure 1). As indicated above, if the inoculum dose is sufficiently small (i.e., less than 500 bacterial cells per brain), then the growth subsides after 24–48 hours, with a persistence of the organisms within the brain tissue for a week (Kohbata and Beaman, 1991). The bacterial counts then decrease so that 10–14 days after infection the brain becomes sterile. At this point in time (10–14 days postinfection), the neurological manifestations presented in Table 1 become apparent. These signs will progress for several days before they stabilize to a level that usually remains constant or gradually worsens over the rest of the life of the mouse (in some instances, more than 1 year) (Kohbata and Beaman, 1991).

Microdissection of the brain followed by quantitation of viable cells of *Nocardia* within specific regions indicate that nocardiae adhere to capillaries throughout the brain. However, both the level and rate of growth is specific for a given region (Ogata and Beaman, unpublished data). By using mutants of *N. asteroides,* it was shown that there are specific binding sites that nocardial cell-surface receptors recognize (Ogata and Beaman, unpublished data). Furthermore, preliminary data suggest that the categories of neurological signs presented in Table 1 represent growth and neuron damage within specific regions of the brain.

Thus, category II (Table 1) represents mice that have an L-dopa-responsive headshake, tremulous movement, hypoactivity, and stooped posture (especially when suspended by the tail). These mice appear to have many signs that are similar to those seen in Parkinson's disease in humans. In an effort to determine whether similar neurodegenerative mechanisms are involved in this murine model, Kohbata and Beaman (1991) studied the brains of these animals. It was demonstrated that mice with the L-dopa-responsive headshake have a significantly decreased number of neurons in the substantia nigra that stain for Nissl substance (Figure 2). Furthermore, there is decreased staining reactivity in the substantia nigra pars compacta and ventral tegmental region for tyrosine hydroxylase (Figure 3). The headshake signs last for the life span of the mouse and may progressively worsen with time. Hyalin inclusion bodies are observed in the neurons in the brains of mice 6 weeks to 1 year after the initial infection (1 month after onset of signs) (Figure 4). These inclusion bodies may be similar to Lewy bodies seen in neurons in patients with idiopathic Parkinson's disease (Kohbata and Beaman, 1991).

The results of these studies support the view that a subclinical or silent infection of the brain by certain strains of *Nocardia* results in damage to neurons that may be both permanent and progressive. If this damage is localized in the substantia nigra, then a Parkinson's-like process is induced. On the other hand, if this neurodegenerative response is localized in a different region of the brain, then other neurological signs become manifest. It appears that the self-limited, subclinical infection of the murine brain by nocardiae may serve as a model for studying a variety of neurodegenerative diseases, such as Parkinson's disease. Furthermore, based upon the ability of nocardiae to invade the human brain, it is tempting to speculate that this organism may be etiologically associated

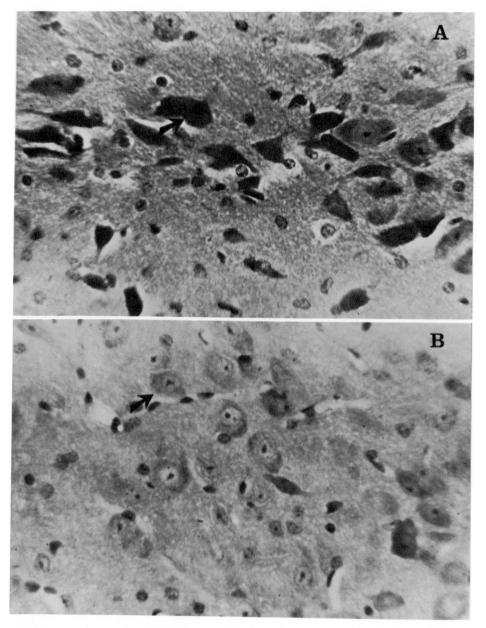

FIGURE 2. Photomicrographs of Nissl-stained sections of the substantia nigra pars compacta of the murine brain. (A) Coronal section of an age-matched control mouse that was not exposed to *Nocardia*. Arrows point to neuron cells that stained dark with the Nissl stain. Note the large number of neurons with prominently stained Nissl bodies. (B) Coronal section of an age-matched mouse (as in A above) 14 days after i.v. injection of *N. asteroides* GUH-2. This mouse developed frequent vertical head-shakes. The sections in both A and B are at approximately the same level and orientation within the brain. Most neurons in the injected mouse do not show Nissl granules, but instead remain unstained and appear swollen (arrows; compare A and B). From Kohbata and Beaman (1991), with permission.

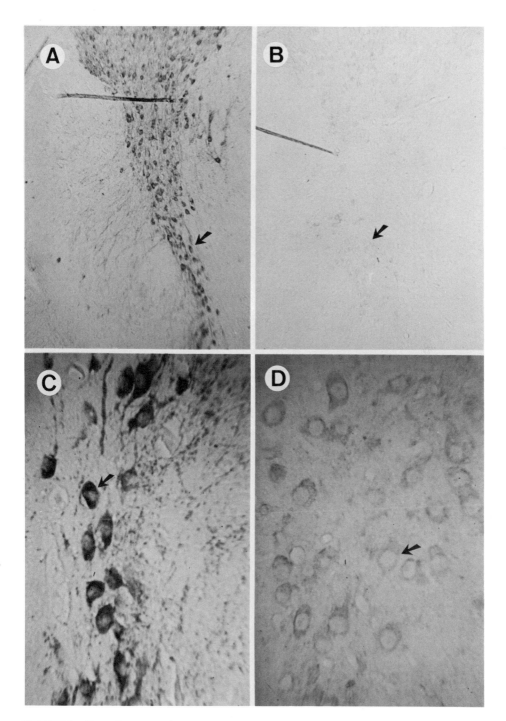

FIGURE 3. Photomicrographs of tyrosine hydroxylase stained sections of the substantia nigra pars compacta region of the brain. (A) Low magnification of a coronal section of an age-matched control mouse that was not exposed to *Nocardia*. The arrow points to the heavily labeled neurons in the substantia nigra pars compacta region. (B) Low magnification of a coronal section of an age-matched mouse (as in A above) 14 days after i.v. injection of *N. asteroides* GUH-2. This mouse had developed rapid vertical head-shakes. Both sections A and B are at approximately the same level and orientation within the brain. The arrow points to neurons of the substantia nigra pars compacta region (note the reduction of tyrosine hydroxylase). (C) A high magnification of A above (control). The arrow points to heavily labeled neuron cells. (D) A high magnification of B above (nocardial infected). The arrow points to neurons with significantly reduced tyrosine hydroxylase. From Kohbata and Beaman (1991), with permission.

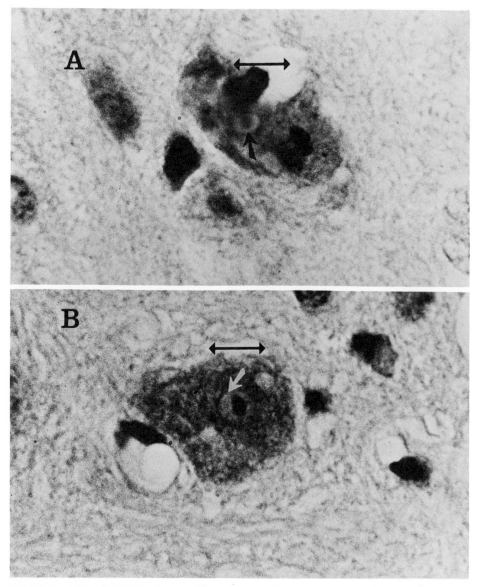

FIGURE 4. Light micrographs of hematoxylin and eosin stained coronal sections of the murine brain after injection of *N. asteroides* GUH-2. (A). High magnification of thalamus region of the brain of a mouse with rhythmic headshake 6 weeks after infection with *Nocardia*. The arrow points to a hyalin, Lewy-like inclusion in a neuron. (B). High magnification of the substantia nigra region of the brain of a mouse with rhythmic headshake 8 months after infection with *Nocardia*. The arrow points to a hyalin, Lewy-like inclusion in a neuron. Magnification bars represent 10 μm. From Kohbata and Beaman (1991), with permission.

with a variety of neurodegenerative diseases in humans, including Parkinson's disease. Clearly, more research in this area is required.

6. CONCLUSIONS

Nocardia is a genus of filamentous bacteria that are ubiquitous in soil and water worldwide. They cause serious disease in humans and animals, and they have a specific ability to invade the brain of most mammals. In this review, evidence is presented that subclinical or inapparent infections in humans may be a relatively common occurrence. Furthermore, these silent infections would never be recognized. Using a murine model, it was shown that nocardiae can silently invade the brain, grow within neurons, and cause neurodegenerative damage after the bacteria appear to have been eliminated from the brain tissue. The mechanisms for this neuronal damage after the microorganism has "exited from the scene" are not clear. There are several possible mechanisms that may be involved in nocardial-induced neurodegeneration. These include the following: induction of an autoimmune response to components in the brain; nocardial products that may have neurotoxic properties (i.e., similar to that seen with MPTP); persistence of the nocardiae within the brain tissue in an altered or cryptic cellular form (i.e., L-forms); the early nocardial-induced alterations may be exacerbated by a normal aging process or by repeated exposures to the nocardia from the environment; or there may be a persisting nidus of nocardial infection that remains hidden.

What can be done to prevent nocardial-induced neurodegeneration? Avoiding exposure to the organism is not feasible, and our preliminary data suggest that immunization against the organism is ineffective for protecting against neuron damage induced by the nocardiae. Furthermore, chemotherapy with antibiotics would not be a practical solution, and probably it would not be effective. Therefore, the solution to this problem must rely on early detection of these silent infections with an ability to determine the propensity of them for inducing specific neurodegenerative responses. Therefore, research should be directed towards immunodiagnosis using antigens that are characteristic for strains that produce specific types of neurodegeneration. Not all pathogenic strains of *Nocardia* induce neurodegenerative changes; therefore, it is essential to identify those nocardial components that are associated with these responses. Preliminary data indicate that this is a feasible approach. If the nocardial process is detected early, then appropriate procedures may be developed to present further neuron damage.

ACKNOWLEDGMENTS.   The research presented in this review was supported by a Public Health Service Grant RO1-AI 20900 from the National Institute of Allergy and Infectious Diseases.

I thank the American Society for Microbiology for permitting me to reproduce the figures presented in this manuscript. I thank Lynn Diaz for typing this manuscript.

REFERENCES

1. Adair, J.C., Amber, I.J., and Johnston, J.M., 1987, Peritonsillar abscess caused by *Nocardia asteroides, J. Clin. Microbiol.* 25:2214–2215.
2. Adair, J.C., Beck, A.C., Apfelbaum, R.I., and Baringer, J.R., 1987, Nocardial cerebral abscess in the acquired immunodeficiency syndrome, *Ar. Neurol.* 44:548–550.

3. Adams, A.R., Jackson, J.M., Scopa, J. Lane, and Wilson, R., 1971, Nocardiosis: Diagnosis and management, with a report of three cases, *Med. J. Aust.* 581–674.
4. Ajax, E.T., 1964, Acquired dyslexia: A comparative study of two cases, *Arch. Neurol.* 11:66–72.
5. Andriole, V.T., Ballas, M., and Wilson, G.L., 1964, The association of nocardiosis and pulmonary alveolar proteinosis, *Ann. Intern. Med.* 60:266–274.
6. Arroyo, J.C., Nichols, S., and Carrol, G.F., 1977, Disseminated *Nocardia caviae* infection, *Am. J. Med.* 62:409–412.
7. Awad, I., Bay, J.W., and Peterson., 1984, Nocardial osteomyelitis of the spine with epidural spinal cord compression, *Neurosurgery* 15:254–256.
8. Baddour, L.M., Baleski, V.S., Herr, M.J., Christensen, G.D., and Bisno, A.L., 1986, Nocardiosis in recipients of renal transplants: Evidence for nosocomial acquisition, *Am. J. Infect. Control* 14:214–219.
9. Bagchi, A.K., 1983, Infections and infestations of the central nervous system in India, *Neurosurg. Rev.* 6:93–101.
10. Baikie, A.G., MacDonald, C.B., and Mundy, G.R., 1970, Systemic nocardiosis treated with trimethoprim and sulfamethoxazole, *Lancet* 2:261.
11. Barmeir, E., Mann, J.H., and Marcus, R.H., 1981, Cerebral nocardiosis in renal transplant patients, *Br. J. Radiol.* 54:1107–1109.
12. Barnicoat, M.J., Wierzbicki, A.S., and Norman, P.M., 1989, Cerebral nocardiosis in immunosuppressed patients: Five cases, *Q. J. Med. New Series.* 72:689–698.
13. Bauman, J.M., Osenback, R., Hartshorne, M.F., Youngblood, L., Crooks, L., Landry, A.J., and Cawthon, M.A., 1986, Positive indium 111 leukocyte scan in *Nocardia* brain abscess, *J. Nucl. Med.* 27:60–72.
14. Beaman, B.L., 1992, Nocardial infections, in: *Fungal Infections and Immune Responses* (J. Murphy, M. Bendinelli, and H. Friedman, eds.), Plenum, New York (in press).
15. Beaman, B.L., Gershwin, M.E., and Maslan, S., 1978a, Infectious agents in immunodeficient murine models: Pathogenicity of *Nocardia asteroides* in congenitally athymic (nude) and hereditarily asplenic (Dh/+) mice, *Infect. Immun.* 20:381–387.
16. Beaman, B.L., Gershwin, M.E., Scates, S., and Ohsugi, Y., 1980a, Immunobiology of germfree mice infected with *Nocardia asteroides, Infect. Immun.* 29:733–743.
17. Beaman, B.L., Gershwin, M.E., Ahmed, A., Scates, and Deem, R., 1982, Response of CBA/N X DBA2/F mice to *Nocardia asteroides, Infect. Immun.* 35:111–116.
18. Beaman, B.L., Goldstein, E., Gershwin, M.E., Maslan, S., and Lippert, W., 1978b, Lung response of congenitally athymic (nude) heterozygous, and Swiss Webster mice to aerogenic and intranasal infection by *Nocardia asteroides, Infect. Immun.* 22:867–877.
19. Beaman, B.L., and Maslan, S., 1977, The effect of cyclophosphamide on experimental *Nocardia asteroides* infection in mice, *Infect. Immun.* 16:995–1004.
20. Beaman, B.L., Maslan, S., Scates, S., and Rosen, J., 1980b, Effect of route of inoculation on host resistance to *Nocardia, Infect. Immun.* 28:185–189.
21. Beaman, B.L., and Scates, S.M., 1981, Role of L-forms of *Nocardia caviae* in the development of chronic mycetomas in normal and immunodeficient murine models, *Infect. Immun.* 33:893–907.
22. Beaman, B.L., and Sugar, A.M., 1983, *Nocardia* in naturally acquired and experimental infections in animals, *J. Hyg.* 91:393–419.
23. Berd, D., 1973, *Nocardia brasiliensis* infection in the United States: A report of nine cases and a review of the literature, *Am. J. Clin. Pathol.* 60:254–258.
24. Bergstrom, R., Edebo, L., Fors, B., and Tegner, K.B., 1966, Systemic *Nocardia* infection, *Scand. J. Resp. Dis.* 47:75.
25. Berkey, P., and Bodey, G.P., 1989, Nocardial infection in patients with neoplastic disease, *Rev. Infect. Dis.* 11:407–412.
26. Bertoldi, R.V., and Sperling, M.R., 1984, *Nocardia* brain stem abscess: Diagnosis and response to medical therapy, *Bull. Clin. Neurosci.* 49:99–104.
27. Bishburg, F., Fog, R.H., Slim, J., Perez, G., and Johnson, F., 1989, Brain lesions in patients with acquired immunodeficiency syndrome, *Arch. Intern. Med.* 149:941–943.
28. Bradsher, R.W., Monson, T.P., and Steele, K.W., 1982, Brain abscess due to *Nocardia caviae, Am. J. Clin. Pathol.* 78:124–127.
29. Brine, J.A.S., 1965, Human nocardiosis: A developing clinical picture, *Med. J. Aust.* 1:339–342.
30. Bross, J.E., and Gordon, G., 1991, Nocardial meningitis: Case reports and review, *Rev. Infect. Dis.* 13:160–165.
31. Buggy, B.P., 1987, *Nocardia asteroides* meningitis without brain abscess, *Rev. Infect. Dis.* 9:228–231.
32. Burdon, D.W., 1971, Nocardiosis after appendectomy, *Br. Med. J.* 1:538.
33. Burton, D.M., and Burgess, L.P.A., 1990, Nocardiosis of the upper aerodigestive tract, *Ear, Nose, Throat. J.* 69:350–353.
34. Bushnell, R.B., Pier, A.C., Fichtner, R.E., Beaman, B.L., Boos, H.A., and Salman, M.D., 1979, Clinical diagnostic aspects of herd problems with nocardial and myobacterial mastitis, *Am. Assoc. Vet. Lab. Diagnost.* 22nd Ann. Proc., pp. 1–12.
35. Byrne, E., Brophy, B.P., and Perrett, L.V., 1979, Nocardial cerebral abscess: New concepts in diagnosis and prognosis, *J. Neurol. Neurosurg. Psych.* 42:1038–1045.
36. Carlile, W.K., Holley, K.E., and Logan, G.B., 1963, Fatal acute disseminated nocardiosis in a child, *JAMA* 184:477–480.
37. Carlsen, E.T., Hill, R.B., Jr., and Rowlands, D.T., 1964, Nocardiosis and pulmonary alveolar proteinosis, *Ann. Intern. Med.* 60:275–281.

38. Causey, W.A., Arnell, P., and Brinker, J., 1974, Systemic *Nocardia caviae* infection, *Chest.* 65:360–362.
39. Chapman, S.W., and Wilson, J.P., 1990, Nocardiosis in transplant patients, *Semin. Resp. Infect.* 5:74–79.
40. Clapp, M.P., and Williams, M.J., 1955, Nocardiosis: Discussion of two cases with emphasis on diagnostic features, *Texas, Rep. Biol. Med.* 13:11–22.
41. Claveria, L.E., DuBoulay, G.H., and Moseley, I.F., 1976, Intracranial infections: Investigations by computerized axial tomography, *Neuroradiology* 12:59–71.
42. Clinicopathologic Conference, 1967, Pulmonary lesion, headache and neurologic deficit. Resume of a case, *Mayo Clinic Proc.* 42:565–582.
43. Cockerill, F.R., Edson, R.S., Roberts, G.D., and Waldorf, J.C., 1984, Trimethoprim/sulfamethoxazole-resistent *Nocardia asteroides* causing multiple hepatic abscesses, *Am. J. Med.* 77:558–560.
44. Cosnett, J.E., Moodley, M., Bill, P., and Bullock, R., 1988, Operculum syndrome from brain abscess in a left hander, *J. Neurol. Neurosurg. Psychiat.* 51:307–308.
45. Cox, F., Hall, J.F., Ballenger, C.F., and Leshner, R.T., 1986, *Nocardia asteroides* brain abscess following mastiodectomy, *Ped. Neurol.* 7:183–184.
46. Cox, F., and Hughes, W.T., 1975, Contagious and other aspects of nocardiosis in the compromised host, *Pediatrics,* 55:135–138.
47. Cross, R.M., and Binford, C.H., 1962, Infections by fungi that are commonly primary pathogens: Is *Nocardia asteroides* an opportunist? *Lab. Invest.* 11:1103–1109.
48. Cupp, C.M., Edwards, W.M., Walton, M.E., and Cleve, E.A., 1960, Nocardiosis of the central nervous system: Report of two fatal cases, *Ann. Intern. Med.* 52:223–226.
49. Curry, W.A., 1980, Human nocardiosis: A clinical review with selected case reports, *Arch. Intern. Med.* 140:818–826.
50. DeLouvois, J., 1984, Antimicrobial therapy in the treatment of brain abscess. *J. Antimicrob. Chemother.* 12:205–207.
51. Dietlein, F., Firsching, R., and Peters, G., 1988, Therapy of brain abscess caused by *Nocardia farcinica, Medizinsche Klinik* 83:613–614.
52. Ellner, J.J., and Bennett, J.E., 1976, Chronic meningitis, *Medicine* 55:341–369.
53. Eppinger, H., 1891, Über eine neue pathogene *Cladothrix* und eine durch sie hervorgerufene Pseudotuberculosis, *Wein Klin. Wschr.* 3:321–323.
54. Epstein, S., Holden, M., Feldshuh, J., and Singer, J.M., 1963, Unusual cause of spinal cord compression: Nocardiosis, *N.Y. State J. Med.* 63:3422–3427.
55. Erchul, J.W., and Koch, M.L., 1955, Cerebral nocardiosis with coexistent pulmonary tuberculosis, *Am. J. Clin. Pathol.* 25:775–781.
56. Fernandez, P.M., Paredes, P.L., Castillo, G.M., and Donoso, S.A., 1987, Nocardiosis: Aspectos clinicos y bacteriologicos experiencia en 16 casos, *Rev. Med. Chile* 115:1053–1060.
57. Fernandez-Guerrero, M.L., Torres, A., Diaz Curiel, M., and Soriano, F., 1985, Successful treatment of nocardial thigh abscess and possible brain abscess with Co-trimoxazole, *Eur. J. Clin. Microbiol.* 4:430–431.
58. Finkemeyer, H., Tzonos, T., and Stanisic, M., 1967, Ein *Nocardia*-granulom des ganglion des gaperi, *Zbl. Neurochis.* 28:137–146.
59. Fontaneda-Lopez, P., Corrales-Rodriguez de Temhlegise, M., Fernandez-Ortega, F., Sarasa Corral, J.L., Gomez-Garcas, J., and Fernandez-Guerrero, M., 1989, Nocardiosis: Clinical observations apropos of 9 cases, *Revista Clinica Espanola* 185:454–458.
60. Frazier, A., Rosenow, E.C., and Roberts, G.D., 1975, Nocardiosis: A review of 25 cases occurring during 24 months, *Mayo Clin. Proc.* 50:657–663.
61. Fried, J., Hinthorn, D., Ralstin, J., Gerjarusak, P., and Liu, C., 1988, Cure of brain abscess caused by *Nocardia asteroides* resistant to multiple antibiotics, *South Med. J.* 81:412–413.
62. Geiseler, P.J., and Anderson, B.R., 1979, Results of therapy in systemic nocardiosis, *Am. J. Med. Sci.* 278:188–194.
63. Germain, P., Remy, G., Deville, J., Strady, A., Dropsy, G., Guyot, J.F., and Puot, M., 1974, Nocardiosis, osseous and cerebral locations. Apropos of 2 cases, *Ann. Med. Interne. (Paris)* 125:201–206.
64. Gibb, W., and Williams, A., 1986, Nocardiosis mimicking Wegener's granulomatosis, *Scand. J. Infect. Dis.* 18:583–585.
65. Gilligan, B.S., Williams, I., and Perceval, A.K., 1962, Nocardial meningitis: Report of a case with bacteriological studies, *Med. J. Aust.* 49:747–752.
66. Goldstein, F.W., Hautefort, B., and Acar, J.F., 1987, Amikacin containing regimens for treatment of nocardiosis in immunocompromised patients, *Eur. J. Clin. Microbiol.* 6:190–200.
67. Gombert, M.E., Aulicino, T.M., deBouchet, L., Silverman, G.E., and Sheinbaum, W.M., 1986, Therapy of experimental cerebral nocardiosis with imipenem, amikacin, trimethoprim-sulfamethoxazole, and minocycline, *Antimicrob. Agents Chemother.* 30:270–273.
68. Goodfellow, M., 1989, Suprageneric classification of actinomycetes, in: *Bergey's Manual of Systematic Bacteriology,* Volume 4 (S.T. Williams, M.E. Sharpe, and J.G. Holt, eds.), Williams and Wilkins, Baltimore, pp. 2333–2339.
69. Goodman, J.S., and Koenig, M.G., 1970, *Nocardia* infections in a general hospital, *Ann. N.Y. Acad. Sci.* 174:552–567.
70. Guidon-Attali, C., Bertrando, J., Sethian, M., Perez, R., Pellissier, J.F., and Peragut, J.C., 1988, Nocardiose cerebrale isolee une observation, *Presse Medicale* 17:1649.
71. Hadley, M.N., Spetzler, R.F., Martin, N.A., and Johnson, P.C., 1988, Middle cerebral artery aneurysm due to *Nocardia asteroides:* Case report of aneurysm exicision and extracranial-intracranial bypass, *Neurosurgery* 22:923–928.
72. Hall, W.A., Martinez, A.J., Dummer, J.S., and Lunsford, L.D., 1987, Nocardial brain abscess: Diagnostic and therapeutic use of stereotactic aspiration, *Surg. Neurol.* 28:114–118.

73. Hall, W.A., Martinez, A.J., Dummer, J.S., Griffith, B.P., Hardesty, R.I., Babrson, H.T., and Lunsford, I.D., 1989, Central nervous system infections in heart-lung transplant recipients, *Arch. Neurol.* 46:173–177.

74. Hargrove, M.D., Matthews, W.R., and McIntyre, P.A., 1967, Intestinal lymphangiectasia with response to corticosteroids, *Arch. Intern. Med.* 119:206–220.

75. Hathaway, B.M., and Mason, K.N., 1962, Nocardiosis: Study of fourteen cases, *Am. J. Med.* 32:903–909.

76. Herkes, G.K., Fryer, J., Rushworth, R., Pritchard, R., Wilson, R.McL., and Joffe, R., 1989, Cerebral nocardiosis-clinical and pathological findings in three patients, *Aust. N.Z. J. Med.* 19:475–478.

77. Hershewe, G.L., Davis, L.E., and Bicknell, J.M., 1988, Primary cerebellar brain abscess from nocardiosis in a heroin addict, *Neurology* 38:1655–1656.

78. Hinokuma, K., Shimoyama, I., Ninchoji, T., and Uemura, K., 1984, *Nocardia asteroides* brain abscess. Case report, *Neurol. Med. Chir. (Tokyo)* 24:135–138.

79. Hoeprich, P.P., Brandt, D., and Parker, R.H., 1968, Nocardial brain abscess cured with cycloserine and sulfonamides, *Am. J. Med. Sci.* 255:208–216.

80. Holtz, H.A., Lavery, D.P., and Kapila, R., 1985, Actinomycetes infection in the acquired immunodeficiency syndrome, *Ann. Intern. Med.* 102:203–205.

81. Hutter, R.V.P., and Collins, H.S., 1962, The occurrence of opportunistic fungus and infection in a cancer hospital, *Lab. Invest.* 11:1035–1042.

82. Jacobs, S.I., and Gibson, R.M., 1963, A fatal case of cerebral abscess due to *Norcardia asteroides*, *J. Neurol. Neurosurg. Psychiatry* 26:363–367.

83. Jacobson, J.R., and Cloward, R.B., 1948, Actinomycosis of the central nervous system, *JAMA* 137:769–771.

84. Katz, P., and Fauci, A.S., 1977, *Nocardia asteroides* sinusitis: Presentation as a trimethoprim-sulfamethoxazole response fever of unknown origin, *JAMA* 238:2397–2398.

85. Kaufman, N., and Prieto, L.C., 1952, Cerebral nocardiosis, *Arch. Pathol.* 53:379–384.

86. Kepes, J.J., and A. Schoolman, 1965, Post-traumatic abscess of the medulla oblongata containing *Nocardia asteroides*, *J. Neurosurg.* 22:511–514.

87. Khalili, A.H., 1982, Nocardial brain abscess: A case report, *J. Neurol.* 227:115–120.

88. King, R.B., Stoops, W.C., Fitzgibbons, J., and Bunn, P., 1966, *Nocardia asteroides* meningitis: A case successfully treated with large doses of sulfadiazine and urea, *J. Neurosurg.* 24:749–751.

89. Kirmani, N., Tuazon, C.U., Ocuin, J.A., Thompson, A.M., Kramer, N.C., and Geelhoed, G.W., 1978, Extensive cerebral nocardiosis cured with antibiotic therapy alone, *J. Neurosurg.* 49:924–928.

90. Kohbata, S., and Beaman, B.L., 1991, L-dopa-responsive movement disorder caused by *Nocardia asteroides* localized in the brains of mice, *Infect. Immun.* 59:181–191.

91. Kremer, E.P., 1972, Pulmonary and cerebral nocardial abscess, *Med. J. Aust.* 59:538–540.

92. Krone, A., Schaal, K.P., Brawanski, A., and Schuknecht, B., 1989, Nocardial cerebral abscess cured with imipenem/amikacin and enucleation, *Neurosurg. Rev.* 12:333–340.

93. Krueger, E.G., Norsa, L., Kenney, M., and Price, P.A., 1954, Nocardiosis of the central nervous system, *J. Neurosurg.* 11:226–233.

94. Lampe, R.M., Baker, C.J., Septimus, E.J., and Wallace, R.J., 1981, Cervicofacial nocardiosis in children, *J. Pediatr.* 99:593–595.

95. Larsen, M.C., Diamond, H.D., and Collins, H.S., 1959, *Nocardia asteroides* infection, *Arch. Intern. Med.* 103:712–725.

96. Law, B.J., and Marks, M.I., 1982, Pediatric nocardiosis, *Pediatrics* 70:560–565.

97. Leaker, B., Hellyar, A., Neild, G.H., Rudge, C., Mansell, M., and Thompson, F.D., 1989, *Nocardia* infection in a renal transplant unit, *Transplant. Proc.* 21:2103–2104.

98. Lechevalier, H.A., 1989, Nocardioform *Actinomycetes*, in: *Bergey's Manual of Systematic Bacteriology*, Volume 4 (S.T. Williams, M.E. Sharpe, and J.G. Holt, eds.), Williams and Williams, Baltimore, pp. 2348–2404.

99. List, C.F., Williams, J.F., Beaman, C.B., and Payne, C.A., 1954, Nocardiosis with multiocular cerebellar abscess: Report of a cured case, *J. Neurosurg.* 11:394–398.

100. Lope, E.S., and Gutierrez, D.C., 1977, *Nocardia asteroides* primary cerebral abscess and secondary meningitis, *Acta Neurochir.* 37:139–145.

101. Lovett, I.S., Houang, E., Burge, S., Turner-Warwick, M., Thompson, F.D., Harrison, A.R., Joekes, A.M., and Parkinson, M.C., 1981, An outbreak of *Nocardia asteroides* infection in a renal transplant unit, *Q. J. Med. New Series L* 198:123–135.

102. Lundmerer, K.M., and Kissane, J.M., (eds.), 1989, Headache, mental status, changes, and death in a 36-year old woman with lupus, *Am. J. Med.* 86:94–102.

103. Maderazo, E., and Quintiliani, R., 1974, Treatment of nocardial infections with trimethoprim and sulfamethoxazole, *Am. J. Med.* 57:671–675.

104. Manz, H.J., 1983, Pathobiology of neurosarcoidosis and clinicopathologic correlation, *Can. J. Neurol. Sci.* 10:50–55.

105. McAndrew, G.M., 1965, Cerebral nocardiosis, *Postgrad. Med. J.* 41:639–642.

106. Mestre, C., Nares, E., Fernandez, G.M., and Boixados, J.R., 1983, Multiple cerebral abscesses caused by *Nocardia asteroides*, *Rev. Clin. Esp.* 171:185–190.

107. Mills, V.A., Cleary, T.G., Frankel, L., Miner, M.E., Wallace, R.J., and Silva-Sosa, M., 1982, Central nervous system *Nocardia* infection, *Clin. Pediatr.* 21:248–250.

108. Munslow, R.A., 1954, Actinomycotic (*Nocardia asteroides*) brain abscess with recovery: Case report, *J. Neurosurg.* 11:399–402.

109. Murray, J.F., Finegold, S.M., Froman, S., and Will, D.W., 1961, The changing spectrum of nocardiosis, *Am. Rev. Resp. Dis.* 83:315–330.

110. Murray, K.J., Ackerman, S.K., Chow, S.N., and Douglas, S.D., 1977, Hypogammaglobulinemia and *Nocardia* brain abscess, *Neurosurgery* 1:297–299.

111. Murray, R.G.E., 1989, The higher taxa, or, a place for everything . . . . . ?, in: *Bergey's Manual of Systematic Bacteriology,* Volume 4 (S.T. Williams, M.E. Sharpe, and J.G. Holt, eds.), Williams and Wilkins, Baltimore, pp. 2333–2339.

112. Natarajan, M., Muthu, A.K., and Arumugham, K., 1974, Nocardial extradural granuloma causing spinal cord compression, *Neurology (India)* 22:97–99.

113. Nauta, H.J.W., Contreras, F.L., Weiner, R.L., and Crofford, M.J., 1987, Brain stem abscess managed with computed tomography-guided sterotactic aspiration, *Neurosurgery* 20:476–480.

114. Norden, C.W., Ruben, F.L., and Selker, R., 1983, Nonsurgical treatment of cerebral nocardiosis, *Arch. Neurol.* 40:594–595.

115. Oda, Y., Kamijyo, Y., and Kang, Y., 1986, *Nocardia* brain abscess and ventriculitis, *No Shinkai Geka Neurol. Surg.* 14:140–144.

116. Opsahl, M.S., and O'Brien, W.F., 1983, Systemic nocardiosis in pregnancy, *J. Reprod. Med.* 28:621–623.

117. Palmer, D.L., Harvey, R.L., and Wheeler, J.K., 1974, Diagnostic and therapeutic considerations in *Nocardia asteroides* infection, *Medicine* 53:391–401.

118. Parmentier, J.C., Vanlanduyt, H.W., Prignot, J.J., and Tanghe, W., 1968, A case of disseminated nocardiosis, *Br. J. Dis. Chest* 62:46–51.

119. Pavillard, E.R., 1973, Treatment of nocardial infection with trimethoprim-sulfamethoxazole, *Med. J. Aust.* 60 (Suppl):65–69.

120. Peabody, J.W., Jr., and Seaburg, J.H., 1960, Actinomycosis and nocardiosis, *Am. J. Med.* 28:99–115.

121. Peacock, J.E., McGinnis, M.R., and Cohen, M.S., 1984. Persistent neutrophilic meningitis, *Medicine* 63:379–395.

122. Peterson, D.L., Hudson, L.D., and Sullivan, K., 1978, Disseminated *Nocardia caviae* with positive blood cultures, *Arch. Intern. Med.* 138:1164–1165.

123. Petri, M., Katzenstein, P., and Hellman, 1988, Laryngeal infection in lupus: Report of nocardiosis and review of laryngeal involvement in lupus, *J. Rheumatol.* 15:1014–1015.

124. Pizzolato, P., Ziskind, J., Derman, H., and Buff, E.E., 1961, Nocardiosis of the brain. Report of three cases, *Am. J. Clin. Pathol.* 36:151–156.

125. Poutz, D.M., Smith, M.N., and Park, C.H., 19795, Intracranial suppuration secondary to trauma infection with *Nocardia asteroides,* *JAMA* 232:730–731.

126. Rahy, N., Forbes, F., and Williams, R., 1990, *Nocardia* infection in patients with liver transplants or chronic liver disease: Radiologic findings, *Radiology* 174:713–716.

127. Rankin, P., and Javid, M., 1955, Nocardiosis of the central nervous system, *Neurology* 5:815–820.

128. Richter, R.W., Silva, M., Neu, H.C., and Silverstein, P.M., 1968, The neurological aspects of *Nocardia asteroides* infection, *Assoc. Res. Nervous Mental Dis.: Infect. Nerv. Syst.* 44:424–444.

129. Rifkind, D., Marchioro, T.L., Schneck, S.A., and Hill, R.B., 1967, Sytemic fungal infections complicating renal transplantation and immunosuppressive therapy, *Am. J. Med.* 43:28–38.

130. Roquer, J., Pou, A., Herraiz, J., Campodarve, I., Sequeira, T., Vilato, J., Alameda, F., and Serrano, R., 1990, Primary cerebral abscess due to *Nocardia* presenting as "ghost tumor," *Eur. Neurol.* 30:254–257.

131. Rosenblum, M.L., and Rosegay, 1979, Resection of multiple nocardial brain abscesses: Diagnostic role of computerized tomography, *Neurosurgery* 4:315–318.

132. Rosett, W., and Hodges, G.R., 1978, Recent experience with nocardial infections, *Am. J. Med. Sci.* 276:279–285.

133. Saltzman, H.A., Chick, E.W., and Conant, N.F., 1962, Nocardiosis as a complication of other diseases, *Lab. Invest.* 11:1110–1117.

134. Savage, M.W., Clarke, C.E., and Yuill, G.M., 1990, Silent *Nocardia* cerebral abscesses in treated dermatomyositis, *Postgrad. Med. J.* 66:582–583.

135. Schmid, A., Traupe, H., Todt, H.C., and Trittmacher, S., 1987, Intracerebral *Nocardia brasiliensis* infection, *Neurosurg. Rev.* 10:315–319.

136. Schofield, G.M., Organotropism in mice of two strains of *Nocardia asteroides,* *Ann. Microbiol.* 35:221–229.

137. Sharer, L.R., and Kapila, R., 1985, Neuropathologic observations in acquired immunodeficiency syndrome (AIDS), *Acta Neuropathol.* 66:188–198.

138. Shashikala, C.A., Ramani, P.S., Ambekar, V.A., and Deodhar, K.P., 1985, Cerebral nocardiosis, *JAPI* 33:182–183.

139. Shuster, M., Klein, M.M., Pribor, H.C., and Kozub, W., 1967, Brain abscess due to *Nocardia, Arch. Intern. Med.* 120:610–614.

140. Siao, P., McCabe, P., and Yagnik, P., 1989, Nocardial spinal epidural abscess, *Neurology* 39:996.

141. Smego, R.A., and Gallis, H.A., 1984, The clinical spectrum of *Nocardia brasiliensis* infection in the United States, *Rev. Infect. Dis.* 6:164–180.

142. Smego, R.A., Moeller, M.B., and Gallis, H.A., 1983, Trimethoprim-sulfamethoxazole therapy for *Nocardia* infections, *Arch. Intern. Med.* 143:711–710.

143. Smith, R.W., Steinkraus, G.E., and Hendricks, B.W., 1980, CNS nocardiosis: Response to sulfamethoxazole-trimethoprim, *Arch. Neurol.* 37:729–730.

144. Spehn, J., Grosser, S., Jessel, A., Essen, J.V., and Klose, G., 1986, Hochdosierte cotrimoxazol-therapie einer disseminierten *Nocardia brasilliensis* infektion, *D.M.W.* 111:215–218.

145. Stallworth, J.R., Perira, D., Boykin, D., Young, F.H., and Porter, R.C., 1985, Central nervous system nocardiosis associated with traumatic, polymicrobial brain abscess, *Pediatr. Infect. Dis.* 4:411–413.

146. Stamm, A.M., McFall, D.W., and Dismukes, W.E., 1983, Failure of sulfonamides and trimethoprim in the treatment of nocardiosis: Report of a patient with pneumonia and empyeme due to *Nocardia brasiliensis* and disseminated disease due to *Nocardia asteroides*, *Arch. Intern. Med.* 143:383–385.

147. Stark, D.A., and Anderson, N.G., 1990, A case control study of *Nocardia* mastitis in Ontario dairy herds, *Can. Vet. J.* 31:197–201.

148. Stevens, H., 1953, Actinomycosis of the central nervous system, *Neurology* 3:761–772.

149. Sullivan, M.J., and Drake, M.E., Jr., 1984, Unilateral pruritis and *Nocardia* brain abscess, *Neurology* 34:828–829.

150. Supena, R., Karlin, D., Strate, R., and Cramer, P.G., 1974, Pulmonary alveolar proteinosis and nocardial brain abscess, *Arch. Neurol.* 30:266–268.

151. Taleghani-far, M., Barber, J.B., Sampson, C., and Harden, K.A., 1964, Cerebral nocardiosis and alveolar proteinosis, *Am. Rev. Resp. Dis.* 89:561–565.

152. Talwar, P., Chakrabarti, A., Ayyagari, A., Nayak, N., Khosla, V.K., Minz, M., and Yadav, R.V.S., 1989, Brain abscess due to *Nocardia*, *Mycopathology* 108:21–23.

153. Tang, I.M., and Hsi, M.S., 1989, Nocardial cerebral abscess: Report of a case, *Taiwan i Hsueh Hui Tsa Chih J. Formosan Med. Assoc.* 88:186–188.

154. Terezhalmy, G.T., and Bottomley, W.K., 1978, Pulmonary nocardiosis associated with primary nocardial infection of the oral cavity, *Oral Surg.* 45:200–206.

155. Turner, E., and Whitby, J.L., 1969, Nocardial cerebral abscess with systemic involvement successfully treated with aspiration and sulphonamides, *J. Neurosurg.* 31:227–229.

156. Turner, O.A., 1954, Brain abscess caused by *Nocardia asteroides*, *J. Neurosurg.* 11:312–318.

157. Tyson, G.W., Welsh, J.E., Butler, A.B., Jane, J.A., and Winn, H.R., 1979, Primary cerebellar nocardiosis, *J. Neurosurg.* 51:408–414.

158. Vanderstigel, M., Leclercq, R., Brun-Buisson, C., Schaeffer, A., and Duval, J., 1986, Blood-borne pulmonary infection with *Nocardiae asteroides* in a heroin addict, *J. Clin. Microbiol.* 23:175–176.

159. Viroslav, J., and Williams, T.W., 1971, Nocardial infection of the pulmonary and central nervous system: Successful treatment with medical therapy, *South. Med. J.* 64:1382–1385.

160. Walker, D.A., and McMahon, S.M., 1986, Pulmonary alveolar proteinosis complicated by cerebral abscess: Report of a case, *J. Am. Osteopath. Assoc.* 86:497–450.

161. Webster, B.H., 1956, Pulmonary nocardiosis, *Am. Rev. Tubercul.* 73:485–489.

162. Weed, L.A., Anderson, H.A., Good, C.A., and Baggenstoss, A.H., 1955, Nocardiosis: Clinical, bacteriologic and pathological aspects, *N. Engl. J. Med.* 253:1137–1139.

163. Weintraub, M.I., and Glaser, G.H., 1970, Nocardial brain abscess and pure motor hemoplegia, *N.Y. State J. Med.* 70:2717–2721.

164. Weiss, M.H., and Jane, J.A., 1969, *Nocardia* brain abscess successfully treated by enucleation: Case report, *J. Neurosurg.* 30:83–86.

165. Welsh, J.D., Rhoades, E.R., and Jaques, W., 1961, Disseminated nocardiosis involving spinal cord, *Arch. Intern. Med.* 108:141–147.

166. Whelan, M.A., Stern, J., and deNapoli, R.A., 1981, The computed tomographic spectrum of intracranial mycosis: Correlation with histopathology. *Radiology* 141:703–707.

167. Whitmore, D.N., Gresham, G.A., and Grayson, M.J., 1961, Nocardiosis in anemic patients given steroids, *J. Clin. Pathol.* 14:259–263.

168. Wichelhausen, R.H., Robinson, L.B., Mazzara, J.R., and Everding, C.J., 1954, Nocardiosis, *Am. J. Med.* 16:295–303.

169. Williams, S.T., Lanning, S., and Wellington, E.M.H., 1983, Ecology of actinomycetes, in: *The Biology of the Actinomycetes* (M. Goodfellow, M. Mordarski, and S.T. Williams, eds.), Academic Press, London, pp. 481–528.

170. Wilson, J.P., Turner, H.K., Kirchner, K.A., and Chapman, W.W., 1989, Nocardial infections in renal transplant patients, *Medicine* 68:38–54.

171. Wolinetz, E., and LeBeau, J., 1969, Abces cerebral a *Nocardia asteroides*, *Rev. Neurol.* 121:464–467.

172. Wren, M.V., Savage, A.M., and Alford, R.H., 1979, Apparent cure of intracranial *Nocardia asteroides* infection by minocycline, *Arch. Intern. Med.* 139:249–250.

173. Yamaguchi, Y., Miyoke, H., Nakahara, N., and Masuzawa, T., 1989, Nocardial brain abscess: Case report. *No Shinkei Geka, Neurol. Surg.* 17(3):285–289.

174. Young, L.S., Armstrong, D., Blevins, A., and Lieberman, P., 1971, *Nocardia asteroides* infection complicating neoplastic disease, *Am. J. Med.* 50:356–367.

Part II

Toxicants

Chapter 10

Neurotoxicity of Polychlorinated Biphenyls

The Role of *Ortho*-Substituted Congeners in Altering Neurochemical Function

Richard F. Seegal and *William Shain*

1. BACKGROUND

Polychlorinated biphenyls (PCBs) are members of a large class of organic compounds known as halogenated aromatic hydrocarbons. This class of compounds also includes 2,3,7,8-tetrachlorodibenzo-*p*-dioxin (TCDD) and 2,3,7,8-tetrachlorinated dibenzofuran (TCDF) (Fig. 1). These latter compounds are often contaminants of environmental and commercial mixtures of PCBs because small quantities of them may be produced either during the manufacturing process or when PCBs are heated in the absence of oxygen (Erickson, 1986a).

PCBs were first manufactured in 1930 by the chemical reaction of chlorine gas with biphenyl (National Research Council, 1979) and gained widespread industrial use because of their physical and chemical properties. PCBs were used in the electrical industry, primarily in capacitors and transformers, in die and machine cutting oils, as heat-exchange fluids in the preparation of edible oils, in paints and plastics, in carbonless copy paper, and in sealants for cement silos (Hutzinger *et al.*, 1974).

Richard F. Seegal and *William Shain* • New York State Department of Health, Wadsworth Center for Laboratories and Research, Albany, New York 12201, and School of Public Health, State University of New York at Albany, Albany, New York 12203.

The Vulnerable Brain and Environmental Risks, Volume 2: Toxins in Food, edited by Robert L. Isaacson and Karl F. Jensen. Plenum Press, New York, 1992.

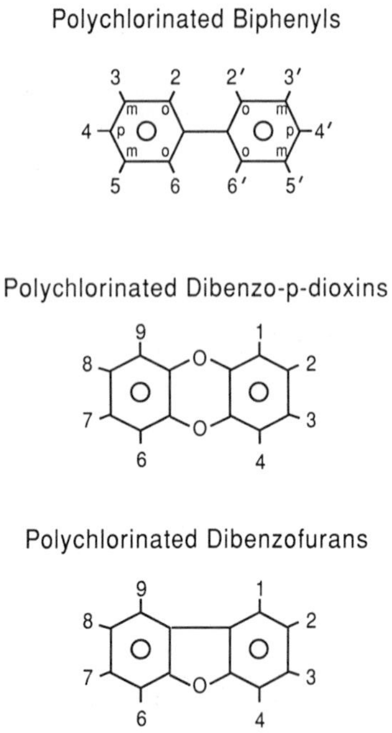

Polychlorinated Biphenyls

Polychlorinated Dibenzo-p-dioxins

Polychlorinated Dibenzofurans

FIGURE 1. Structure of chlorinated biphenyls, dibenzo-*p*-dioxins, and dibenzofurans. Chlorine atoms can be substituted at any of the numbered positions. o = ortho; m = meta; p = para.

PCBs can be chlorinated in any of 10 positions on the biphenyl ring (Fig. 1), resulting in isomers or congeners ranging from monochlorinated to decachlorinated biphenyls. Although the combination of chlorination patterns allows for 209 theoretically possible congeners (Mullin *et al.*, 1984), commercial synthesis yielded approximately 135 congeners (Erickson, 1986b). In the United States PCBs were manufactured primarily by the Monsanto Corporation under the trademark of Aroclor®. PCB mixtures included Aroclors 1016, 1221, 1232, 1242, 1248, 1254, 1260, 1262, 1268, and 1270. Except for Aroclor 1016, which was produced by the distillation of Aroclor 1242, the last two digits in the Aroclor designation indicate the weight percent chlorine in the commercial mixture (Brinkman and de Kok, 1980). Aroclor mixtures differ in their physicochemical properties. The viscosity of Aroclor 1016 is similar to water, Aroclor 1254 is similar to honey and Aroclor 1268 is a solid wax (Erickson, 1986a).

It has been estimated that more than 1.2×10^9 kg of PCBs have been manufactured in the last 50 years (Erickson, 1986a). In the mid-1960s it became evident that, because of their chemical stability and extensive industrial use, PCBs were also widespread environmental contaminants (Safe *et al.*, 1987) with approximately one third of the total world production being present in mobile reservoirs, including atmospheric, fresh, and marine waters and sediments and sewage sludge (Hansen, 1987). Indeed, PCBs are now so ubiquitous that remote regions of the world have measurable concentrations of PCBs in soil, snow, or water (World Health Organization, 1976). Concentrations of PCBs in antarctic snow range from 0.3 to 1 ng/liter (Tanabe *et al.*, 1983), while polar bears and other arctic-dwelling animals have significant body burdens (Norstrom *et al.*, 1988). Because these regions are so remote, it is highly likely that the contamination of these animals and their habitats results from atmospheric deposition due to the evaporation of PCBs from the surfaces of contaminated bodies of water, such as the Great Lakes

(Mackay *et al.*, 1983). In support of this argument, ambient air concentrations of PCBs are highest over the Hudson River (140 ng/m^3) (Bush *et al.*, 1986) and the Great Lakes (0.1–5 ng/m^3) (Mackay *et al.*, 1983), and are considerably lower when measured over the Atlantic Ocean (<0.05–1.6 ng/m^3) or the Pacific Ocean (0.54 ng/m^3) (Erickson, 1986a). Atmospheric concentrations of PCBs are also elevated over highly industrialized regions (5–20 ng/m^3) (Erickson, 1986a). Thus, in addition to the more classical sources of human exposure (e.g., contaminated landfills, industrial spills, consumption of contaminated foodstuffs), atmospheric deposition of PCBs may be an additional route of exposure. Consistent with this interpretation is the observation that levels of PCBs in fetal cord blood and breast milk from women in upstate New York (Bush *et al.*, 1984) are not significantly different from those reported in a population of women who consumed contaminated fish from Lake Michigan (Jacobson *et al.*, 1984a).

2. MODIFICATION OF PCB CONGENER PATTERNS

2.1. Environmental Modification of PCBs

The congener patterns observed in aquatic plants, aquatic and marine invertebrates, aquatic and marine fish and mammals, and ultimately humans (Bush *et al.*, 1985a, 1985b, 1986; Spagnoli and Skinner, 1979; Wasserman *et al.*, 1979) do not, necessarily, reflect the congener patterns found in the original commercial mixtures. The reasons why these differences exist between the original mixtures and environmental samples involve the physical and chemical properties of PCBs and the extensive metabolic changes that occur when PCBs are ingested.

First, PCBs differ in their solubility in water, ranging from 5.9 ppm for 2-mono-chlorobiphenyl (Hutzinger *et al.*, 1974) to 0.00011 ppm for 2,3,4,5,6,2′,3′,4′,5′-nona-chlorobiphenyl (Yalkowsky *et al.*, 1983). Thus, in sediments contaminated with PCBs ranging from di- to heptachlorinated biphenyls, the water column above the sediments will be selectively enriched for the more hydrophilic lightly chlorinated congeners, result-ing in greater bioavailability of the lightly chlorinated congeners. This phenomenon has also been reproduced in a laboratory study where water passed over PCB-contaminated sediment was shown to be selectively enriched for the lightly chlorinated congeners (Bush *et al.*, 1987).

Secondly, environmental degradation of PCBs can also modify the original Aroclor congener pattern. Photolysis of PCBs has been shown to result in dechlorination of hexa- to pentachlorinated congeners (Hutzinger *et al.*, 1974), while aerobic bacterial degrada-tion of lightly chlorinated congeners has been observed by Bedard *et al.* (1986). However, these methods of degradation will not affect the high concentrations of PCBs present in anaerobic settings, such as river and lake sediments. Anaerobic bacterial degradation of PCBs may be a more important process that occurs naturally at low rates and is being considered for remediation of PCB-contaminated dump sites and lake and river beds (Chen *et al.*, 1988). Anaerobic bacteria from PCB-contaminated sediments have been cultured in the laboratory and exposure of contaminated sediments to these cultures results in dechlorination of a wide spectrum of heavily chlorinated congeners to mono- and dichlorinated congeners (Abramowicz, 1990). Although these lightly chlorinated by-products are susceptible to degradation by aerobic bacteria, the high concentration of

2,2'-dichlorobiphenyl and other lightly chlorinated congeners found in the Hudson River (Bush *et al.*, 1985a) argue against the presence of aerobic conversion at rates sufficient to remove these congeners from the aqueous environment.

2.2. Mammalian Metabolism

Mammalian metabolism of PCBs can alter the pattern of congeners that reach the brain. Hepatic metabolism primarily converts the highly lipophilic PCBs to more polar molecules that are readily excreted in either urine or via the biliary route (Matthews, 1981). In general, the lower chlorinated congeners, such as those found in Aroclor 1016, are more readily metabolized than the more heavily chlorinated congeners. However, the degree of metabolism depends on both the species of animal (Sundstrom *et al.*, 1976) and the specific congeners that make up the applied PCB mixture (Safe, 1980). In general, hydroxylation is favored at the para position in the least chlorinated phenyl ring, unless this site is sterically hindered. If two vicinal unsubstituted carbon atoms are present (particularly C4 and C5), oxidative metabolism is facilitated. Thus, 2,3,6,2',3',6'-hexachlorobiphenyl and 2,4,5,2',5'-pentachlorobiphenyl can be metabolized and are therefore only minor contaminants of adipose tissue from occupationally and environmentally exposed humans, whereas 2,4,5,2',4',5'-hexachlorobiphenyl is poorly metabolized and is, therefore, a major constituent in exposed humans and animals (Ryerson *et al.*, 1984). A number of metabolic species of PCBs are formed through dechlorination, hydroxylation, thiolation, methylthiolation, methylthio oxidation, dihydrodiol formation, mercapturic acid formation, and conjugation with glucuronic acid (Bakke *et al.*, 1983).

In summary, both environmentally and metabolically induced changes in congener patterns from the initial Aroclor contaminations may occur. Environmental degradation appears to involve a number of processes, including differential solubility of lightly chlorinated congeners and anaerobic degradation. However, the use of anaerobic degradation of PCBs as an environmentally acceptable means of remediating PCB-contaminated sediments and landfills may result in different potential health consequences. For instance, anaerobic dechlorination results in a two- to sixfold increase in the concentrations of di- and trichlorinated congeners, such as 2,2'-dichlorobiphenyl and 2,6,2'-trichlorobiphenyl (Abramowicz, 1990); however, these congeners are most potent in their ability to alter neurochemical function (see below and Seegal *et al.*, 1990, 1991c).

3. NONNEUROLOGIC EFFECTS OF PCBS: EVIDENCE FOR TWO CLASSES OF PCB CONGENERS

The majority of the work describing the biochemical mechanisms by which PCBs, polychlorinated dibenzo-*p*-dioxins (PCDDs), and polychlorinated dibenzofurans (PCDFs) affect non-nervous system processes (e.g., carcinogenesis, hepatic toxicity, and immunotoxicity) is based on studies carried out primarily by Poland and his coworkers (1976) using TCDD. However, certain PCBs act similarly when either whole animals or *in vitro* hepatic test systems are used. The dioxin-like 3,4,3',4'-tetrachlorobiphenyl (TCB) is frequently most potent (Parkinson and Safe, 1987).

The initial event in these processes requires the binding of the xenobiotic molecule to a cytosolic Ah receptor, which exhibits saturable and high-affinity binding for TCDD and related compounds. Formation of the ligand/receptor complex is followed by activation and accumulation of ligand/receptor complexes in the nucleus that interact with specific DNA sequences and result in the induction of several cytochrome P-450 isozymes (Safe, 1990). When stimulated by TCDD, this process results in a 50- to 100-fold increase in the concentrations of these isozymes (particularly cytochrome P450A1A and P450A2A) and the induction of associated microsomal monooxygenases, including aryl hydrocarbon hydroxylase (AHH) and ethoxyresorufin O-deethylase (EROD) (Parkinson and Safe, 1987; Safe, 1990). By using radiolabelled PCDF, it has been shown that binding of the ligand to the receptor correlates with the biological potency of the ligand (Farrell et al., 1987) and that inbred strains of mice deficient in the Ah receptor exhibit an attenuated response to the ligand (Robertson et al., 1984; Silkworth et al., 1984). In the intact animal these events result in body weight loss, thymic atrophy, immunosuppression, and teratogenic and reproductive toxicity (Safe, 1990). Although the greatest enzyme induction occurs following exposure to dioxins and dibenzofurans, dioxin-like PCB congeners (e.g., 3,4,3′,4′-tetrachlorobiphenyl; 3,4,5,3′,4′-pentachlorobiphenyl; or 3,4,5,3′,4′,5′-hexachlorobiphenyl) also activate cytochrome P450A1A (Parkinson and Safe, 1987), albeit to a lesser extent. Thus, differences between PCDDs, PCDFs, and dioxin-like PCB congeners are related to their potency, rather than to qualitative differences in their mechanisms of action.

However, when single chlorine substitutions are made in either the 2 or 6 positions of PCBs, the ability of the congener to induce P450A1A, AHH, or EROD is reduced, and is entirely absent when di-*ortho*-substituted congeners, such as 2,2′-dichlorobiphenyl or 2,4,5,2′,4′,5′-hexachlorobiphenyl, are tested (Safe, 1990). These results suggest that PCB congeners can be divided into two major classes: (1) dioxin-like congeners that bind to the Ah receptor and induce enzyme activation and (2) di-*ortho*-substituted congeners that do not. We will discuss new data that indicate that this latter class of PCB congeners may be neurotoxic and may play an important role in the induction of psychomotor, cognitive, and movement disorders in both perinatally and adult exposed animals and humans.

4. EFFECTS OF PCBS ON CENTRAL NERVOUS SYSTEM FUNCTION

4.1. Human Health Effects

There have been two major accidental PCB poisoning incidents in humans ("Yusho" and "YuCheng") and two major epidemiological studies of environmentally induced PCB contamination in humans (Michigan and North Carolina).

In Japan PCBs had been used as heat-exchange fluids in the production of edible rice oil. In 1968 approximately 2000 people were exposed to contaminated oil due to leaks in the heating coils used to process the rice oil. This unfortunate incident became known as "Yusho," which in Japanese means oil disease (Kuratsune et al., 1972). Symptoms present in adults exposed to the contaminated oil included chloracne, porphyria, alopecia, increased incidence of headaches, numbness and weakness in limbs, and decreased peripheral nerve-conduction velocities (Kuratsune et al., 1972; Kuroiwa et al., 1969). However, the greatest health effects were observed in infants exposed either in *utero* or during breastfeeding. Perinatally exposed infants showed more frequent somatic signs of poisoning than did control infants, including higher rates of mortality, lower body weights, and dermal evidence of chlorobiphenyl poisoning similar to those seen in adults (Yamaguchi *et al.*, 1971). A subset of the exposed children was clinically described as dull and apathetic and had IQs in the low 70s (Harada, 1976). Follow-up studies conducted 7–8 years after the initial poisoning indicated that PCB levels in serum had dramatically decreased, although neurological signs of poisoning (e.g., headaches, nausea, limb weakness) were still evident. Because the rice oil also contained other chlorinated aromatic hydrocarbons, including dibenzofurans and quaterphenyls, and because these agents were still present in blood, it was suggested that the prolonged effects might be due to these contaminants and not to the PCBs (Kuratsune, 1980).

In 1978 almost 2000 Taiwanese were also exposed to contaminated rice oil. This incident was known as "YuCheng" (Hsu *et al.*, 1985), and dermatological and neurological dysfunctions similar to those seen in "Yusho" were observed in the adult and perinatally exposed populations (Lü and Wong, 1984). Rogan *et al.* (1988) evaluated a cohort of exposed and control children and found that the exposed children also exhibited physical symptoms, including small size; more frequently displayed dermal, nail, and gingival abnormalities; and increased incidence of pneumonia and bronchitis than did control children. Most importantly, the exposed children were delayed in their psychomotor development and performed significantly less well on the Bayley Scales of Infant Development and the performance IQ portion of the Weschler Scale of Infant Development. All of these measures were validated for use in a Chinese-speaking population (Rogan, personal communication).

Thus, high-level exposure to PCBs, and perhaps to related chlorinated aromatic hydrocarbons, has been shown to yield persistent decrements in important aspects of nervous system development and function.

The birth weight and nervous system dysfunctions seen in the above studies have also been observed in infants in the United States whose mothers were exposed to lower levels of PCBs and who did not exhibit signs of overt chlorobiphenyl toxicity. In a series of studies dating from 1984, Jacobson and colleagues have reported lower birth weights and shorter gestational times in infants born to mothers who consumed Lake Michigan fish contaminated with PCBs (Fein *et al.*, 1984). Control and exposed infants from Michigan were given the Brazelton Neonatal Behavioral Assessment Scale; the infants of fish-eating mothers performed less well than control infants. Exposed infants also exhibited more abnormally weak reflexes, were less responsive, and showed more jerky, uncoordinated movements than did control children (Jacobson *et al.*, 1984b). At 7 months of age the infants were given the Fagan test of visual memory recognition, which has been shown to reliably predict school performance (Fagan and McGrath, 1981; Fagan *et al.*, 1986). Cord serum PCB levels and maternal consumption of contaminated fish were associated with significantly poorer performance on the Fagan test by the exposed infants (Jacobson *et al.*, 1985).

Another study has been carried out in North Carolina by Rogan *et al.* on a population of more than 900 PCB-exposed children. Deficits in psychomotor performance, as measured by the Brazelton test, were observed in the highest 5% of the PCB-exposed infants, with developmental delays observed through 24 months of age (Gladen *et al.*, 1988; Rogan *et al.*, 1986).

These epidemiological studies provide strong evidence that exposure to levels of PCBs common in the United States is sufficient to yield long-lasting, if not permanent, changes in psychomotor and cognitive development of children. Given their widespread distribution in the environment and in the food chain, PCBs may be an important environmental contaminant that produces deficits in central nervous system function. However, the conclusions of these epidemiological studies must be interpreted with caution. The ability to unequivocally state that PCBs were the sole toxicant responsible for the observed behavioral dysfunctions is weakened because these studies are correlational in nature and because the "Yusho," "YuCheng" and American infants may have also been exposed to other neurotoxicants (e.g., dibenzofurans, quaterphenyls, DDE). Thus, although the epidemiological data indicate that PCBs may be neurotoxic, especially to the developing nervous system, these data cannot be used to conclusively determine that PCBs are responsible for the central nervous system dysfunctions.

4.2. Animal Studies

The potential neurotoxic actions of PCBs have been investigated using laboratory rodents and nonhuman primates. Results from these studies have confirmed the conclusion obtained from the epidemiological studies that PCBs are important neurotoxicants, as well as permitting the development of experimental strategies to describe the mode of action of PCBs.

4.2.1. Perinatal Exposure

Because many of the effects of PCBs were observed in children of parents exposed to PCBs, the majority of the studies have focused on the effects of PCBs on the developing nervous system. Commercial mixtures of PCBs or 3,4,3',4'-tetrachlorobiphenyl have been used. All of these studies demonstrate that PCB exposure results in changes in central nervous system function. Shiota (1976) exposed rat dams to Kanechlor 500 (20 or 100 mg/kg) during gestational days 8–14 or 15–21. Behavioral testing of the offspring began at 84–91 days of age. Open-field and maze performance were examined. Although no significant effects were observed on the open-field performance, the offspring exposed during both time periods made significantly more errors in a water-maze task, suggesting that in-utero Kanechlor exposure alters the learning ability of rats.

The timing of PCB exposure during development was more critically evaluated by Pantaleoni et al. (1988), who exposed dams to Fenclor 42 at dosage levels of 2–10 mg/kg during (1) the 2-week period before gestation, (2) during gestational days 6–15 (the second trimester), or (3) during lactation. Animals were tested at between 3 and 30 days of age. PCB exposure during lactation decreased cliff avoidance behavior, while exposure during any of the three periods decreased swimming performance and increased circling behavior. Active avoidance learning was also significantly depressed in rats exposed during either the second trimester or lactation.

In another series of experiments, the effects of combined prenatal and lactational exposure to PCBs were studied on the development of the nervous system (Overmann et al., 1987; Shain et al., 1986). Dams were fed Aroclor 1254-adulterated rat chow ad libitum at dose levels of 0, 3, 30, or 300 ppm and behavioral testing was initiated on pups shortly after birth and was continued throughout adulthood. Dose-dependent decreases in body weights and delays in development of the startle response, righting reflex, and negative geotaxis were observed. When animals were tested after 60 days of age, a lack of habituation in the open field was observed in the PCB-exposed pups, while animals more than 125 days of age exhibited circling behavior (Kostas, personal communication). All of these results indicate that PCB exposure during the development of the central nervous system results in prolonged deficits in brain function.

The effects of perinatal exposure of nonhuman primates to PCBs on behavior have also been studied. Pregnant females were exposed to either Aroclor 1016 or Aroclor 1248 in their diets during gestation and offspring were tested beginning at 12 months of age. Several behavioral toxicological outcomes were observed, including changes in locomotor activity (Bowman and Heironimus, 1981b; Bowman et al., 1981a) and deficits in spatial, shape, and color discrimination reversal tasks (Schantz et al., 1989). Thus, perinatal exposure of nonhuman primates to levels of PCBs similar to those found in the environment lead to locomotor and cognitive dysfunctions similar to the behavioral deficits observed in exposed human infants.

Several important observations can be made from these studies. First, every commercial mixture of PCBs tested resulted in behavioral deficits in the offspring; thus, the neurotoxic action of mixtures of PCBs is either associated with congeners that have a common structure and are present in all commercial PCB mixtures, or a common feature of the mixtures is important. If neurotoxicity is associated with a common structure, PCBs may function at a specific site of action. If toxicity is not associated with a common structure, PCBs may be neurotoxic because of their lipophilic properties, e.g., their action as a perturbator of cellular membranes.

Two different approaches have been used to determine the nature of the PCBs responsible for the neurotoxic action. In the first approach, animals were exposed to a single congener, 3,4,3',4'-tetrachlorobiphenyl. When mice were exposed on gestational days 10–16 to 3,4,3',4'-tetrachlorobiphenyl at 32 mg/kg, several teratogenic effects were observed; increases in pup mortality and the percentage of stillborn pups and a decrease in the birth weights. Approximately half of the surviving mice exhibited a syndrome of rapid, uncoordinated circling and were designated "spinners" (Chou et al., 1979). Accompanying these behavioral changes were morphological alterations in the spinal cord and altered responses to dopaminergic agonists and antagonists, suggesting involvement of catecholaminergic neurons.

Tilson (1979) also exposed mice perinatally to 3,4,3',4'-tetrachlorobiphenyl and noted decreased hind-limb strength, hyperactivity, and uncoordinated circling, reminiscent of the spinning observed by Chou. Agrawal (1981), using a similar exposure paradigm, noted persistent (up to 1 year) decreases in striatal concentrations of dopamine and decreased concentrations of dopamine receptor binding sites. More recently, Ericksson (1988) exposed 10-day-old mice to 0.41 or 41 mg/kg of 3,4,3',4'-tetrachlorobiphenyl. When animals were injected with [^{14}C]3,4,3',4'-tetrachlorobiphenyl, the radioactivity in the brain decreased to approximately 20% within 7 days. Exposure to either concentration of PCB resulted in significant decreases in the density of muscarinic acetylcholine receptors in hippocampus, measured using the muscarinic antagonist [^{3}H]QNB.

The results from these perinatal studies in mice clearly indicate that this single congener can produce long-term behavioral and neurochemical changes in brain function and that there may be at least two sites of PCB action; one on dopamine metabolism and a second one affecting muscarinic acetylcholine receptors. These results support the hypothesis that PCBs may have a specific site of action and do not cause their neurotoxic action by a nonspecific action on cell membranes.

The second approach used to determine whether specific PCB congeners are responsible for the observed neurotoxic action was made by exposing animals to complex mixtures of PCBs and then analyzing brain tissue for PCBs to determine which congeners accumulate in brain. When newborn or weanling rat pups were exposed to PCBs via exposure of the dams to adulterated chow, dose-dependent increases in total-brain PCBs were observed (Shain et al., 1986). By using gas chromatography, it was possible to demonstrate selective retention of congeners. Interestingly, no 3,4,3',4'-tetrachlorobiphenyl was detected in the brains of these animals, while several ortho-substituted congeners were found at concentrations as much as 100-fold greater than their concentrations in the adulterated lab chow. If accumulation of congeners in brain tissue is related to toxicity, then these results indicate that PCB neurotoxicity is not mediated via the interaction of dioxin-like congeners, such as 3,4,3',4'-tetrachlorobiphenyl with the Ah receptor.

The perinatal studies clearly demonstrate that the developing nervous system is sensitive to PCB exposure. When lab chow is adulterated with as little as 3 ppm or as little as 0.41 mg/kg is injected, significant effects can be observed. However, the design of these experiments does not allow the investigator to clearly determine which congeners are responsible for the changes in nervous system function or the mechanisms of action.

4.2.2. Adult Exposure

Because of the complexity of the events that occur during development (e.g., possible alterations in maternal behavior, nutritional status), a number of studies have been carried out with adult animals. For the most part, these studies have been designed to examine changes in neurochemical function following PCB exposure.

Adult rats were exposed to a single high dose of Aroclor 1254 (500 or 1000 mg/kg) and were sacrificed 1, 3, 7, or 14 days after exposure to determine the relationship between regional brain concentrations of PCBs and changes in regional brain biogenic amine concentrations (Seegal et al., 1985, 1986b, 1986c). Concentrations of all biogenic amines were reduced on days 1 and 3, and gradually returned to pre-exposure levels by day 14. In addition, brain PCB concentrations, determined by high-resolution glass-capillary gas chromatography, were reduced three- to fourfold after 14 days. In a somewhat similarly designed study, Suenga et al. (1975) demonstrated that exposure of adult rats to 100 mg/kg per day of Kanechlor 400 for 7 days increased norepinephrine concentrations in the cortex and decreased the levels in the cerebellum. Longer-term exposure to 20–50 mg/kg of PCB for 7 weeks resulted in decreases in norepinephrine in both brain areas. The results of these two studies clearly indicate that PCB exposure can cause changes in catecholamine metabolism.

To more clearly correlate changes in catecholamine metabolism and PCB exposure, adult rats were exposed to PCBs for 30 days using adulterated lab chow (500–1000 ppm of Aroclor 1254) and changes in biogenic amines and concentrations of individual PCB congeners were determined (Seegal et al., 1991b). Total brain concentrations of PCBs ranged from 55 to 82 ppm, with no significant differences in PCB concentrations between brain regions. Similar to studies following perinatal exposure (Seegal, 1992), all congeners detected in brain were di-*ortho*-substituted congeners (Table 1). Although brain concentrations of total PCBs were similar to those seen in acute exposure studies (Seegal et al., 1985, 1986b, 1986c), significant neurochemical changes were limited to decreases

TABLE 1. Major *Ortho*-Substituted Congeners Detected in Rat Brain Following Aroclor 1254 Exposure[a,b]

Mono-*Ortho* Congeners	Di-*Ortho* Congeners
2,4,5,3′,4′	2,4,5,2′,4′
2,3,4,3′,4′	2,3,4,2′,4′
2,3,4,5,3′,4′	2,4,5,2′,4′,5′
	2,3,4,2′,4′,5′
	2,3,4,2′,3′,5′
	2,3,4,2′,3′,4′

[a]Congeners constituting more than 1.5% of the total concentration in brain.

[b]Rats were exposed to a diet containing 1000 ppm Aroclor 1254 for 30 days. Brain concentrations were determined by glass capillary gas chromatography with electron capture detection (Bush and Barnard, 1982).

in concentrations of dopamine and its metabolites in the lateral olfactory tract and caudate nucleus (Fig. 2). The regional and neurochemical specificities observed in this study were the first suggestions that dopaminergic neurons, *in situ*, may be differentially sensitive to PCBs.

Long-term Aroclor 1016 and 1260 feeding studies in the adult non-human primate, *Macaca nemestrina*, have also clearly demonstrated that catecholamine metabolism is a possible site of PCB action (Seegal *et al.*, 1991a). Animals were exposed, on a daily basis, to either Aroclor 1016 or 1260, at dosage levels of 0.8, 1.6, or 3.2 mg/kg per day, for a total of 20 weeks. Exposure to PCBs did not affect the body weight of the animals or induce any observable signs of chlorobiphenyl poisoning. However, both Aroclor mixtures caused significant decreases in brain concentrations of dopamine that were restricted to the hypothalamus and basal ganglia. Dopamine concentrations were reduced in the caudate nucleus and putamen of both Aroclor-exposed groups, while dopamine concentrations were significantly reduced in the substantia nigra of the Aroclor 1016-exposed animals (Fig. 3). Total-brain PCB concentrations in the high-dose groups were 6 ppm for the Aroclor 1016-exposed animals and 30 ppm for the Aroclor 1260-exposed animals. PCB congener-specific analysis of brain tissue indicated that all detectable congeners (concentrations greater than 0.5 ppb) were *ortho* substituted. Indeed, for the Aroclor 1016-exposed animals, the findings were even more striking: Out of 27 congeners present in the original Aroclor mixture, only three were detected in brain (i.e., 2,4,4′-trichlorobiphenyl, and 2,5,2′,5′- and 2,4,2′,4′-tetrachlorobiphenyl (Table 2). Although a larger number of congeners were detected in the brains of Aroclor 1260-exposed monkeys, all of them were also *ortho* substituted (Table 3).

To determine whether the effects of PCBs following adult exposure were persistent, as observed following perinatal exposure of nonhuman primates, animals were exposed to 3.2 mg/kg per day of either Aroclor 1016 or Aroclor 1260 for 20 weeks. PCBs were then removed from the animals' diets and serum PCB concentrations were monitored to determine changes in the body burden. Twenty-four weeks after the last PCB exposure, serum concentrations had decreased by approximately 50% (Fig. 4), and brain PCB and biogenic amine concentrations were measured. Brain PCB concentrations, like serum concentrations, declined by approximately 60%; however, dopamine concentrations in the caudate

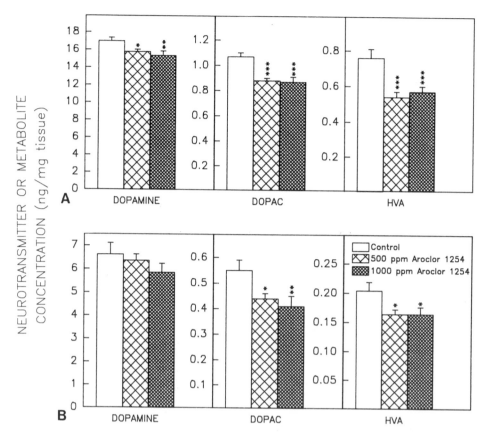

FIGURE 2. Dopamine, DOPAC, and HVA concentrations in (A) caudate nucleus and (B) lateral olfactory tract from rats following 30-day subchronic exposure to a diet containing either 500 or 1000 ppm Aroclor 1254. N = 9 animals/treatment group. *p < 0.05; **p < 0.01; *** p < 0.001.

TABLE 2. Congeners in Nonhuman Primate Brain Following Aroclor 1016 Exposure[a,b]

Congener	% in Brain	% in Aroclor 1016
2,4,4'	76	7
2,4,2',4'	7	5
2,5,2',5'	14	2

[a] Expressed as a percentage of the total concentration in brain and in Aroclor 1016.
[b] Nonhuman primates were exposed to Aroclor 1016 (3.2 mg/kg per day) for 20 weeks. Brain concentrations were determined by glass capillary gas chromatography with electron capture detection (Bush and Barnard, 1982).

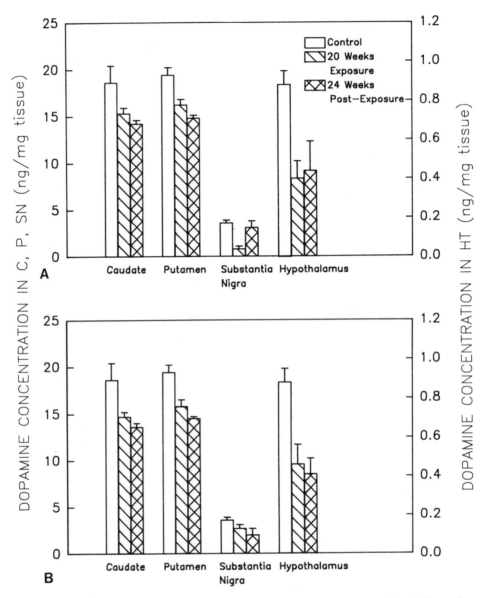

FIGURE 3. Dopamine concentrations in the caudate, putamen, substantia nigra, and hypothalamus from control nonhuman primates, exposed to either (A) Aroclor 1016 or (B) Aroclor 1260 (3.2 mg/kg per day) for 20 weeks, or nonhuman primates 24 weeks after 20-week exposure to either Aroclor 1016 or 1260 (3.2 mg/kg per day). N = 3–4 animals/treatment group.

nucleus, putamen, and hypothalamus of Aroclor 1016-exposed animals and the caudate nucleus, putamen, substantia nigra, and hypothalamus of Aroclor 1260-exposed animals were still depressed to the levels observed in animals immediately after PCB exposure (Figure 3). Thus, prolonged PCB exposure in either adults or during development can result in persistent reductions in dopamine content.

The results from the adult studies indicate (1) that lower level (i.e., ≤ 30 ppm)

TABLE 3.   Major PCB Congeners in Nonhuman
Primate Brain Following Aroclor 1260 Exposure[a,b]

Di-*Ortho* Congeners
2,3,4,2′,4′,5′
2,3,4,5,2′,4′,5′
2,4,5,2′,4′,5′
2,3,4,5,2′,3′,4′
2,3,5,6,2′,4′,5′
2,3,4,5,6,2′,6′
2,3,4,5,6,2′,4′,5′
2,3,4,5,2′,3′,5′,6′
2,3,4,5,2′,3′,4′,5′
2,3,5,6,2′,3′,4′
2,3,4,5,2′,3′
2,3,4,5,2′,3′,6′
2,3,4,6,2′,4′,5′

[a]Congeners constituting more than 2% of the total concentration in
brain.

[b]Nonhuman primates were exposed to Aroclor 1260 (3.2 mg/kg per
day) for 20 weeks. Brain concentrations were determined by glass
capillary gas chromatography with electron capture detection
(Bush and Barnard, 1982).

exposure to PCBs results in neurochemical changes largely restricted to dopamine, (2) that
not all brain regions containing dopamine were affected, (3) that the congeners present in
brain are *ortho* substituted, suggesting that these congeners might be responsible for the
decreases in brain dopamine concentrations, and (4) that the effects of PCB exposure
persist beyond the period of exposure.

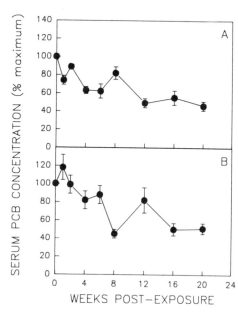

FIGURE 4.   Serum PCB concentrations in nonhuman primates following removal from exposure
[either (A) Aroclor 1016 or (B) Aroclor 1260, 3.2
mg/kg per day for 20 weeks] expressed as a percent of
the maximum concentration at the end of exposure.
N = 5 animals/treatment group.

4.3. Studies with PC12 Cells in Culture

Investigations of PCB neurotoxicity using laboratory animals indicate that PCBs clearly affect dopamine metabolism. However, it is not evident how PCBs may act. They may act directly on dopamine-synthesizing neurons, or they may function via some presynaptic mechanism, resulting in reduced dopamine levels. If PCBs act directly on the neurons that synthesize dopamine, PCBs may reduce dopamine content by altering dopamine synthesis, release, or metabolism. Furthermore, the effects of PCBs may be mediated by membrane receptors, second messenger systems, or by directly affecting proteins or enzymes that regulate dopamine metabolism. Analysis of PCB action using homogenous populations of cells in culture has numerous advantages over experiments with intact animals. First, there is a single cellular target for PCB action. In the intact brain there are many potential targets that may interact to produce a decrease in dopamine content. Unraveling the contributions of these components is a difficult and frequently not satisfactory process. Second, cells in culture provide a direct assay of the action of PCBs. In the culture dish, there is no blood–brain barrier to exclude access to the brain or peripheral components to metabolize PCBs. Third, assays are performed in a small, closed compartment—the culture dish. This has several important experimental implications: (1) only small volumes of test solutions are needed, permitting efficient use of difficult to obtain congeners, and (2) the tissue-culture procedures provide a closed system, permitting ready accounting of dopamine and its metabolites, as well as PCB congeners and their possible metabolites.

Since PCB action in the CNS results in a reduction of dopamine content, cell lines that have a catecholamine phenotype are potential candidates. Several homogenous cell lines were available and were considered. Initial experiments indicated that only PC12 cells would be appropriate (Table 4). This cell line, adapted to culture from a pheochromocytoma, expresses a number of characteristics of catecholamine neurons, including dopamine and norepinephrine synthesis and the release and uptake of dopamine (Greene and Rein, 1977; Greene and Tischler, 1976; Kittner et al., 1987).

4.3.1. Effects of Aroclor Mixtures

We first demonstrated that PCBs cause reductions in cell dopamine content similar to the loss of dopamine observed in our intact animal studies (Seegal et al., 1989). These experiments used Aroclor 1254, a commercial mixture of PCB congeners that contained lightly to heavily chlorinated congeners. Since PCBs are not readily soluble in aqueous

TABLE 4. Cell Lines Reported to Exhibit Biogenic Amine Function[a]

Cell line	Source	L-Dopa	Dopamine	Norepinephrine	Serotonin
NIE-N115	Mouse	+[b]	−	−	−
IMR-32	Human	−	−	−	+
PC12	Rat	+	+	+	−

[a]Cells were grown in mass cultures and analyzed for biogenic amines by high-performance liquid chromatography with electrochemical detection (Seegal et al., 1986a).
[b]Plus signs indicate detection of the product; minus signs indicate no product was observed.

TABLE 5. The Relative Ability of Individual PCB Congeners to Reduce PC12 Cell Dopamine Content[a]

Ortho-substituted		Ortho-, Para-substituted		Para-substituted	
Congener	ED_{50}	Congener	ED_{50}	Congener	ED_{50}
2'	182	2,4,4'	115	4,4	NEO[b]
2,2'	65	2,4,2',4'	196		
2,6,2',6'	NEO	2,4,6,2',6'	93		

Ortho-, Meta-substituted		Meta-, Para-substituted		Ortho-, Meta-, Para-substituted	
Congener	ED_{50}	Congener	ED_{50}	Congener	ED_{50}
2,5,2'	82	3,4,3',4'	NEO	2,4,3',4'	>201
2,5,2',5'	86	3,4,3',4',5'	NEO		
2,3,2',3'	>201				

[a]The effectiveness of individual PCB congeners was determined by calculating the dose of congener required to reduce PC12 cell dopamine content by 50% (ED_{50}).
[b]No effect was observed.

solutions, dimethyl sulfoxide (0.1% final medium concentration) was used as a vehicle. Dimethyl sulfoxide has no significant effect on cell dopamine content. Aroclor 1254 caused time- and concentration-dependent decreases in cell dopamine content (Seegal *et al.*, 1989). Parallelling the decreases in cell dopamine content was a reduction in medium concentrations of the dopamine metabolites homovanillic acid (HVA) and DOPAC. Furthermore, dopamine concentrations in the culture medium did not increase following PCB exposure.

Thus, PCBs cause a decrease in PC12 cell dopamine concentration similar to that observed *in vivo*. In addition, these data indicate that PCBs do not cause an increase in the release of dopamine from PC12 cells or induce greater metabolism of dopamine to HVA or DOPAC. Therefore, PCBs may reduce cell dopamine content by inhibition of dopamine synthesis.

4.3.2. Effects of Individual Congeners

Since PCBs are a mixture of congeners, it is possible that congeners will act with different potencies at one site of action or that there may be several sites of action. Investigation of these issues requires that we describe the action of individual congeners. Only when actions of individual congeners are described will it be possible to describe the mechanisms of action of mixtures of congeners similar to those found in the environment.

We have recently carried out experiments to describe the mode of action of individual PCB congeners. Concentration-dependent decreases in cell dopamine content have been described for more than 50 congeners (Shain *et al.*, 1991), with the more lightly chlorinated congeners studied most completely (Table 5). These data indicate that *ortho*-substituted congeners (Fig. 5) are the most potent congeners, while *para*-substituted, dioxin-like congeners are without effect. These observations indicate that the site of PCB action

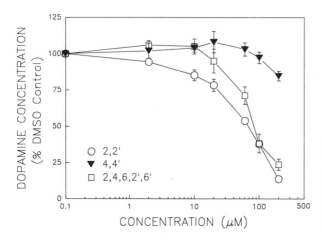

FIGURE 5. Dopamine concentrations in PC-12 cells (expressed as a percent of DMSO control) following 6-hr exposure to 2,2'-dichlorobiphenyl, 4,4'-dichlorobiphenyl, and 2,4,6,2',6'-pentachlorobiphenyl. N = 4–6 wells/data point.

in the CNS differs from its site of action in the periphery. For instance, the actions of PCBs as carcinogens (Hayes, 1987) and immunotoxicants (Silkworth *et al.,* 1986) are associated with their ability to mimic the actions of TCDD via the Ah receptor. The congeners that most effectively act at this site are *para*-substituted congeners, e.g., 3,4,3',4'-tetrachlorobiphenyl, while *ortho*-substituted congeners have little or no effect.

Analysis of the effects of these congeners on dopaminergic function indicates that there may be more than one active site. Three sets of observations support this hypothesis.

The first set is based on the observed potencies of *ortho*-substituted congeners (Table 5), which indicate that 2,2'-dichlorobiphenyl is the most potent congener, while 2,6,2',6'-tetrachlorobiphenyl has no effect on cell dopamine content. However, if a single *para* chlorine substitution is made, the resulting congener, 2,6,2',4',6'-tetrachlorobiphenyl, is very potent. Thus, two sites of action can be described. The first has high specificity for *ortho*-substituted congeners and is not responsive to congeners that have all four *ortho*-chlorine substitutions. The second site will accept congeners with saturation of the *ortho* positions and requires at least a single *para*-chlorine substitution.

The second set of observations also comes from the descriptions of the structure-activity relationships for individual congeners. When *meta*-chlorine substitutions are made on *ortho*-substituted congeners (e.g., 2,2'-dichlorobiphenyl and 2,2',5'-trichlorobiphenyl vs. 2,2',4'-trichlorobiphenyl and 2,4,2',5'-tetrachlorobiphenyl), there is little effect on the potency of the congeners. However, when *meta*-chlorine substitutions are added to *ortho*- and *para*-substituted congeners (e.g., 2,4,2',4'- vs. 2,4,3',4'-tetrachlorobiphenyl), there is a reduction in the potency of the *meta*-substituted congener. These observations indicate that the first site, with preference for *ortho*-substituted congeners, will nearly equally accept congeners with *meta*-substitutions, while the second site, with preference for *ortho*- and *para*-substituted congeners, differentiates between similar congeners and *meta*-substitutions.

The third set of observations comes from a study of congeners found in the brains of nonhuman primates following exposure to Aroclor 1016 (Seegal *et al.,* 1990, 1991c). In these experiments we demonstrated that a mixture of congeners prepared in the laboratory to represent the concentrations of congeners found in brain samples (e.i., 2,4,4'-trichlorobiphenyl; 2,5,2',5'-tetrachlorobiphenyl; and 2,4,2',4'-tetrachlorobiphenyl) was more potent than a similar concentration of each congener (Fig. 6). This observation

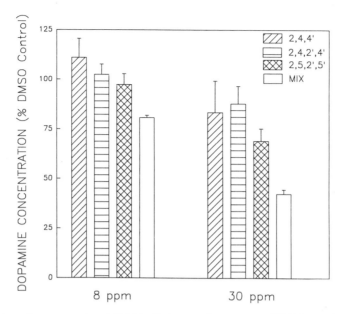

FIGURE 6. Dopamine concentrations in PC-12 cells (expressed as a percent of DMSO control) following 6-hr exposure to either 8 or 30 ppm in media 2,4,4'-trichlorobiphenyl, 2,4,2',4'-tetrachlorobiphenyl, 2,5,2',5'-tetrachlorobiphenyl, or a mixture of the three congeners in the same proportion found in nonhuman primate brain following exposure to Aroclor 1016. N = 4–6 wells/data point.

suggests that, when *ortho-* and *ortho-*, *para*-substituted congeners are applied simultaneously, a synergistic action is observed.

Two important conclusions can be drawn from these observations. First, PCB congeners reduce both cellular and brain dopamine concentrations by inhibiting dopamine synthesis. Second, PCB action occurs at sites with high specificity for congeners with *ortho* chlorine substitutions. The latter conclusion indicates that the neurotoxicant actions of PCBs occur by a mechanism significantly different from peripheral effects, such as immunotoxicity and carcinogenesis, that prefer congeners such as 3,4,3',4'-tetrachlorobiphenyl and 3,4,5,3',4'-pentachlorobiphenyl.

4.3.3. Effects of Structurally Related Hydrocarbons

The specificity of action of PCBs has also been studied using biphenyls where substitutions with bromine, methyl, and hydroxy substitutions have been made. These data (Fig. 7) indicate that polybrominated biphenyl analogs to PCBs are similar in potency to structural PCB analogs, that methyl analogs are somewhat less effective and that hydroxy analogs do not affect cell dopamine content. The structure-activity relationships of these related compounds may be explained by examining physical and chemical differences between the ring substitutions. The brominated compounds are chemically most similar to PCBs and thus follow the same substitution rules as PCBs. The methyl substitutions are less bulky and therefore significantly alter the size of the biphenyl molecule. The hydroxylated biphenyl may be ionized at physiological pH and may thus assume a planar

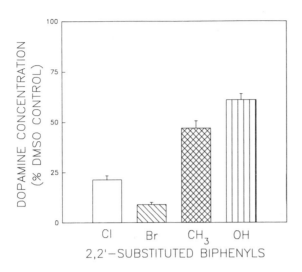

FIGURE 7. Dopamine concentrations in PC-12 cells (expressed as a percent of DMSO control) following 6-hr exposure to 200 μM in media of the different *ortho*-substituted biphenyls (-Cl, -Br, -CH$_3$, -OH). N = 4–6 wells/data point.

conformation if an electron is shared by the carbon atoms in the one position on both phenyl rings. No effect was observed with TCDF at concentrations ≤ 10 nM, indicating the preference of the two proposed sites on the PC12 cells for nonplanar aromatic hydrocarbons.

4.3.4. Role of PCB Metabolites in the Neurotoxic Action of PCBs

The observations discussed above indicate that PCBs are regulators of cell dopamine content; however, they have not directly addressed the issue of whether metabolites of PCBs or the parent congeners are the active agents. Three different series of experiments with PC12 cells addressed this issue.

The first experiments compared the effects of PCBs on dopamine content in PC12 cells and in the brains of nonhuman primates. A mixture of PCB congeners containing 2,4,4'-trichlorobiphenyl and 2,4,2',4'- and 2,5,2',5'-tetrachlorobiphenyls was prepared to have the same content as was measured in brain samples after exposure of the nonhuman primates to Aroclor 1016 (Seegal *et al.*, 1990, 1991c). When PC12 cells were exposed to this mixture, decreases in cell dopamine content were observed that were similar to the decreases in brain dopamine content. Thus, these congeners were able to produce the neurotoxic response observed *in vivo* in a system where metabolism, if it occurs at all, takes place at a significantly lower rate than would occur in the whole animal.

The second series of experiments has described the time courses of action of Aroclor 1254, 2,2'-dichlorobiphenyl, and 2,5,2',5'-tetrachlorobiphenyl on cellular dopamine concentration (Fig. 8). PCBs cause a rapid decrease in cell dopamine content that asymptotically reaches a maximal effect. If a metabolite were responsible for PCB action, one would expect a lag in the time course for the reduction in cellular dopamine, indicating the period of time required for any metabolites to reach a critical concentration. Since no lag is observed, it is likely that the action of the PCB congeners occurs directly and is not mediated by the production of PCB metabolites.

The third series of experiments directly measured the changes in congener concentra-

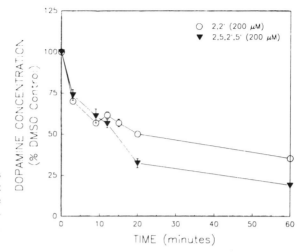

FIGURE 8. Dopamine concentrations in PC-12 cells (expressed as a percent of DMSO control) following exposure to 2,2'-dichlorobiphenyl and 2,5,2',5'-tetrachlorobiphenyl at 200 μM in media. N = 4–6 wells/data point.

tions in cells and media after a 6-hr incubation—a time long enough to observe a maximal effect of PCB exposure on PC12 cell dopamine content. Cells were incubated with 2,2'-dichlorobiphenyl or [14C]-labelled 2,5,2',5'-tetrachlorobiphenyl at the concentrations required to reduce cell dopamine content by 50%. No significant loss of either congener was detected when the amount of congener present in cells + media was compared to the amount of congener present in the media before cell exposure (Fig. 9). To more precisely

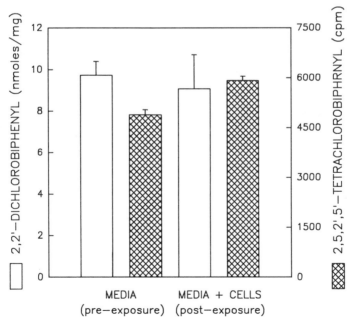

FIGURE 9. Concentrations of 2,2'-dichlorobiphenyl and [14C]-2,5,2',5'-tetrachlorobiphenyl in PC-12 cells following 6-hr incubation and in growth media before and after 6-hr incubation in the presence of cells. N = 3 wells/determination.

analyze for possible PCB metabolites, media, and cell samples from cultures exposed to [^{14}C]-labelled 2,5,2′,5′-tetrachlorobiphenyl for 6 hr were examined by thin-layer chromatography. No metabolites were observed in any of the samples (Shain *et al.*, manuscript in preparation). These results indicate that PCB congeners and not their metabolites are responsible for the observed neurochemical changes in PC12 cells.

4.3.5. Biochemical Mechanism of PCB Action

Since PCBs reduce cell dopamine content without increasing release or metabolism, it is likely that their mode of action may be through regulation of dopamine synthesis. Synthesis requires the action of two enzymes: tyrosine hydroxylase, the rate-limiting enzyme, which converts tyrosine to L-dopa; and aromatic amino-acid decarboxylase, which converts L-dopa to dopamine. We have investigated the effects of 2,2′-dichlorobiphenyl, the most active congener tested, on tyrosine hydroxylase using two different experimental approaches. In the first we used N1E-N115 cells. These cells express high levels of tyrosine hydroxylase activity (see Table 4), but contain no aromatic amino-acid decarboxylase (Amano *et al.*, 1972); therefore, they synthesize high levels of L-dopa, the product of tyrosine hydroxylase, but are unable to convert it to dopamine. Exposure of N1E-N115 cells to 2,2′-dichlorobiphenyl results in a reduction in the production of L-dopa from 1.28 μM/mg per min to 0.11 μM/mg per min (Seegal *et al.*, 1991c). Thus, PCBs may function by reducing tyrosine hydroxylase activity.

Regulation of tyrosine hydroxylase may occur via membrane-mediated events or by a direct action on enzyme activity. When the rate of tyrosine hydroxylase activity is mea-

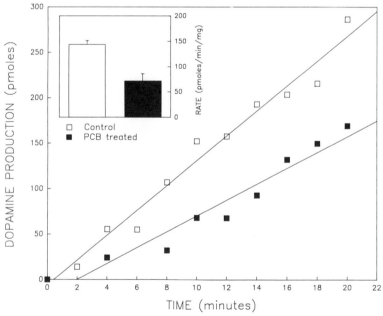

FIGURE 10.   Dopamine (pmoles) in a broken PC-12 cell preparation in the presence and absence of 65 μM 2,2′-dichlorobiphenyl. Inset shows the control and exposed rates of dopamine production. N = 1 assay/data point.

sured using a broken-cell preparation of PC12 cells, 2,2'-dichlorobiphenyl causes a decrease in the rate of L-dopa production (Fig. 10). Thus, the effects of PCBs appear to occur by directly regulating tyrosine hydroxylase activity, clearly demonstrating that PCBs reduce cell dopamine content by direct inhibition of tyrosine hydroxylase activity and not via a cellular receptor or through a second-messenger system.

5. PCBS AND DOPAMINE FUNCTION

Results from animal and cell culture studies clearly indicate that PCBs are neurotoxicants and that dopamine synthesis is reduced. Experimental studies with rodents also demonstrate that circling behavior is induced following perinatal exposure to PCBs [(e.g., Chou's spinners (1979), Pantaleoni's circling "swimmers" (1988), and Tilson's circlers (1979)]. These PCB-induced changes in behavior may occur because of increases in asymmetries of brain dopamine content. Glick et al. (1979) have demonstrated that alterations in central dopaminergic function enhance preexisting asymmetries in striatal dopamine concentrations and result in increased circling (Glick and Shapiro, 1985). Thus, the circling observed following perinatal exposure to PCBs is consistent with dopamine synthesis as a principal site of PCB action.

However, circling has not been reported in humans or in nonhuman primates. A common index of PCB neurotoxicity in these studies is decreased cognitive function, including deficits in spatial discrimination and delayed alternation learning (Levin et al., 1988; Schantz et al., 1989). Deficits in these behaviors may also be consistent with the action of PCBs on dopamine, since Sawaguchi and coworkers (1988, 1989) have recently demonstrated that iontophoretic application of dopaminergic antagonists into prefrontal cortex induces spatial discrimination deficits in nonhuman primates. Thus, when dopaminergic function in the prefrontal cortex is altered, changes in spatial discrimination are observed that are similar to those seen in either perinatally exposed nonhuman primates (Levin et al., 1988; Schantz et al., 1989) or in infants whose mothers consumed contaminated fish from the Great Lakes (Jacobson et al., 1990).

A discussion of PCBs and dopamine function would not be complete however, without discussing the significance of the action of PCBs on specific neuronal sites. These include the apparent selectivity of PCBs for affecting dopamine function, possibly in a related population of neurons, including the A9 dopamine neurons, originating in the substantia nigra, and the A10 dopamine neurons from ventral tegmental area (collectively referred to as the mesotelencephalic dopaminergic system; Lindvall and Björklund, 1983), and the mode of action of perinatal exposure to 3,4,3',4'-tetrachlorobiphenyl in causing circling (Chou et al., 1979; Tilson et al., 1979) and decreasing dopamine content (Agrawal et al., 1981) in mice. This latter point is important because of the apparent discrepancy between our observation that 3,4,3',4'-tetrachlorobiphenyl has no significant effect on dopamine function in PC12 cells and Agrawal et al.'s observation that 3,4,3',4'-tetrachlorobiphenyl decreases dopamine content in perinatally exposed mice.

The results of experiments with N1E-N115 cells and homogenates from PC12 cells indicate that 2,2'-dichlorobiphenyl functions by reducing tyrosine hydroxylase activity, suggesting that PCBs may function by interacting at a specific site. Do PCBs yield their neurochemical effects by interacting at a site unique to PCBs and tyrosine hydroxylase or are PCBs acting opportunistically by affecting tyrosine hydroxylase activity via a binding site for some endogenous compound(s)? For example, specific binding sites have been described in the CNS for a number of exogenous compounds, including morphine, and these investigations have lead to descriptions of the endogenous opioid peptides, the enkephalins and endorphins (Adler, 1980).

However, if the principal action of PCBs is to directly reduce tyrosine hydroxylase activity, then all catecholaminergic neurons should be affected. However, our regional brain analyses indicate that the neurons most sensitive to PCBs are the A9 dopamine neurons that arise in the ventral tegmentum. Because there were no differences in PCB concentrations or congener make-up between brain regions (Seegal et al., 1991a), we are compelled to consider what makes this region vulnerable to the action of PCBs. Indeed, this region is sensitive to the action of several exogenous compounds, including manganese, MPTP, carbon disulfide, and encephalitic flu (Bird et al., 1984; Eadie et al., 1965; Elsworth et al., 1987; Peters et al., 1988). Because of the disparity in the chemical nature of these environmental insults, it is likely that it is the midbrain dopaminergic neurons, and not the particular neurotoxin, that is responsible for the apparent regional specificity of PCBs. Possible mechanisms include the fact that metabolism of catecholamines, and in particular dopamine, occur by the well-known pathways of O-methylation and deamination, as well as by alternate pathways that yield cytotoxic products, including hydrogen peroxide, free radicals, and reactive quinones (Forno, 1982; Graham, 1978). The greater vulnerability of the A9 neurons, compared to other dopaminergic neurons, may be due to the fact that neuromelanin is synthesized from these autoxidation products, increasing the cellular residence times of these toxic intermediate products.

Expression of Parkinson's disease follows decreases in brain dopamine content and PCB exposure results in persistent decreases in brain dopamine content. Thus, PCB exposure may increase the risk to individuals of developing Parkinson's disease. However, at this time it is not known whether the neuropathology that persists following PCB exposure is due to a decrease in the ability of individual cells to synthesize dopamine, or whether there is a decrease in the number of dopaminergic neurons in the substantia nigra, as has been observed with the pathology of Parkinson's disease.

An additional point to be considered is that dioxin-like congeners (e.g., 3,4,3′,4′-tetrachlorobiphenyl) do not alter dopamine concentrations in PC12 cells, although Tilson et al. (1979) and Agrawal et al. (1981) have demonstrated that this congener significantly alters behavior and dopaminergic function in perinatally exposed mice. These findings suggest that direct inhibition of tyrosine hydroxylase activity cannot be the sole mechanism responsible for the changes in nervous system function. There are at least two possible interpretations of these apparently conflicting observations. The simplest is that it is not 3,4,3′,4′-tetrachlorobiphenyl that is causing the effects in the Tilson and Agrawal experiments but rather a metabolite that is produced in the periphery, the liver. Such a metabolite would not be produced in PC12 cultures, and therefore no effect would be observed during 3,4,3′,4′-tetrachlorobiphenyl exposure.

Alternatively, this congener may not directly affect tyrosine hydroxylase but instead may alter endogenous steroidal hormones, such as estrogen, which, in turn, have been shown to affect dopaminergic function (Becker and Beer, 1986; Di Paolo et al., 1982). Indeed, the dioxin-like congeners are antiestrogenic (Gierthy et al., 1987) and when administered perinatally alter behavior and neurochemistry. However, when these congeners are administered to adults, they are inactive (Agrawal et al., 1981). Thus, PCB-induced changes in estrogen function (either changes in circulating concentrations of estrogen or estrogen receptor function) may mediate the changes in dopamine neurochemistry in perinatally exposed rats. Thus, Agrawal's lack of effect in adult mice is consistent with our observation of the ineffectiveness of 3,4,3′,4′-tetrachlorobiphenyl in reducing cellular dopamine in PC12 cells and suggests that the effects of the dioxin-like congeners occur through a different mechanism in perinatally exposed animals. An additional potential mechanism involving the interaction between estrogen and dopamine has been suggested by Panek and Dixon (1985), who have demonstrated that intraventricular injection of either 4- or 6-hydroxycatecholestrogen in adult rats inhibits tyrosine hydroxylase activity.

6. SUMMARY

PCBs are only weak inducers of cytochrome P450 and related isozymes when compared with dioxins and dibenzofurans; therefore, PCBs have until recently been considered to be only minor public health hazards. However, epidemiological observations and laboratory experiments demonstrate that these halogenated hydrocarbons affect brain function.

Epidemiological studies (Gladen and Rogan, 1988; Gladen et al., 1988; Jacobson et al., 1985, 1990) have demonstrated that human exposure to PCBs and related compounds during development yields long-lasting changes in nervous system function. Experimental studies have reported similar changes in learning dysfunctions following perinatal exposure of nonhuman primates to Aroclor mixtures (Bowman and Heironimus, 1981b; Levin et al., 1988; Schantz et al., 1989). Neurochemical analysis of both perinatally exposed (Agrawal et al., 1981) and adult-exposed (Seegal et al., 1986b, 1991a) animals clearly indicate that a principal action of PCBs is to decrease brain dopamine content. Analysis of PCB action using homogeneous populations of cells in culture indicate that ortho- and ortho-, para-substituted congeners are most potent and that these effects may be due to a direct action on tyrosine hydroxylase, the rate-limiting enzyme in dopamine synthesis.

In comparison with the best known environmental neurotoxicant (e.g., lead), research on the health effects of PCBs is still in its infancy. A more detailed characterization of the long-term sequelae of perinatal and adult human exposure to PCBs on central nervous system function, a more complete analysis of the relationship between PCB structure and neurological activity, determination of the biochemical mechanisms by which PCBs alter nervous system function, and increased understanding of the types of interactions between PCBs and other neurotoxicants remain important goals.

ACKNOWLEDGMENTS.   Research support for this work was provided, in part, by NIH grant R01-ESO3884 and EPA grant R-813830 to Richard F. Seegal

REFERENCES

Abramowicz, D.O., 1990, Aerobic and anaerobic biodegradation of PCBs: A review, *Crit. Rev. Biotechnol.* 10:241–251.

Adler, M.W., 1980, Opioid peptides, *Life Sci.* 26:497–510.

Agrawal, A.K., Tilson, H.A., and Bondy, S.C., 1981, 3,4,3′,4′-Tetrachlorobiphenyl given to mice prenatally produces long term decreases in striatal dopamine and receptor binding sites in the caudate nucleus, *Toxicol. Lett.* 7:417–424.

Amano, T., Richelson, E., and Nirenberg, M., 1972, Neurotransmitter synthesis by neuroblastoma clones, *Proc. Natl. Acad. Sci. USA* 69:258–263.

Bakke, J.E., Feil, V.J., and Bergman, A., 1983, Metabolites of 2,4′,5′-trichlorobiphenyl in rats, *Xenobiotica* 13:555–564.

Becker, J.B., and Beer, M.E., 1986, The influence of estrogen on nigrostriatal dopamine activity: Behavioral and neurochemical evidence for both pre- and postsynaptic components, *Behav. Brain Res.* 19:27–33.

Bedard, D.L., Unterman, R., Bopp, L.H., Brennan, M.J., Haberl, M.L., and Johnson, C., 1986, Rapid assay for screening and characterizing microorganisms for the ability to degrade polychlorinated biphenyls, *Appl. Environ. Microbiol.* 51:761–768.

Bird, E.D., Anton, A.H., and Bullock, B., 1984, The effect of manganese inhalation on basal ganglia dopamine concentrations in rhesus monkey, *Neurotoxicology* 5:59–66.

Bowman, R.E., Heironimus, M.P., and Barsotti, D.A., 1981a, Locomotor hyperactivity in PCB-exposed rhesus monkeys, *Neurotoxicology* 2:251–268.

Bowman, R.E., and Heironimus, M.P., 1981b, Hypoactivity in adolescent monkeys perinatally exposed to PCBs and hyperactive as juveniles, *Neurobehav. Toxicol. Teratol.* 3:15–18.

Brinkman, U.A.Th., and de Kok, A., 1980, Production, properties and usage, in: *Halogenated Biphenyls, Terphenyls, Naphthalenes, Dibenzodioxins and Related Products* (R.D. Kimbrough, ed.), Elsevier/North-Holland Biomedical Press, Amsterdam, pp. 1–40.

Bush, B., and Barnard, E.L., 1982, Determination of nonpolar chlorinated hydrocarbons and PCB in microsamples, *Anal. Lett.* 15:1643–1648.

Bush, B., Snow, J., and Koblintz, R., 1984, Polychlorobiphenyl (PCB) congeners, *p,p'*-DDE, and hexachlorobenzene in maternal and fetal cord blood from mothers in upstate New York, *Arch. Environ. Contam. Toxicol.* 13:517–527.

Bush, B., Simpson, K.W., Shane, L., and Koblintz, R.R., 1985a, PCB congener analysis of water and caddisfly larvae (Insecta: Trichoptera) in the upper Hudson River by glass capillary chromatography, *Bull. Environ. Contam. Toxicol.* 34:96–105.

Bush, B., Snow, J., Connor, S., and Koblintz, R., 1985b, Polychlorinated biphenyl congeners (PCBs), *p,p'*-DDE and hexachlorobenzene in human milk in three areas of upstate New York, *Arch. Environ. Contam. Toxicol.* 14:443–450.

Bush, B., Shane, L.A., Wilson, L.R., Barnard, E.L., and Barnes, D., 1986, Uptake of polychlorobiphenyl congeners by purple loosestrife (*Lythrum salicaria*) on the banks of the Hudson River, *Arch. Environ. Contam. Toxicol.* 15:285–290.

Bush, B., Shane, L.A., Wahlen, M., and Brown, M.P., 1987, Sedimentation of 74 PCB congeners in the upper Hudson River, *Chemosphere* 16:733–744.

Chen, M., Hong, C.S., Bush, B., and Rhee, G.-Y., 1988, Anaerobic biodegradation of polychlorinated biphenyls by bacteria from Hudson River sediments, *Ecotoxicol. Environ. Safety* 16:95–105.

Chou, S.M., Miike, T., Payne, W.M., and Davis, G.J., 1979, Neuropathology of "spinning syndrome" induced by prenatal intoxication with a PCB in mice, *Ann. N.Y. Acad. Sci.* 320:373–396.

Di Paolo, T., Poyet, P., and Labrie, F., 1982, Effect of prolactin and estradiol on rat striatal dopamine receptors, *Life Sci.* 31:2921–2929.

Eadie, M.J., Sutherland, J.M., and Doherty, R.L., 1965, Encephalitis: Etiology of parkinsonism in Australia, *Arch. Neurol.* 12:240–245.

Elsworth, J.D., Deutch, A.Y., Redmond, D.E. Jr., Sladek, J.R. Jr., and Roth, R.H., 1987, Effects of 1-methyl-4-phenyl-1,2,3,6-tetrahydropyridine (MPTP) on catecholamines and metabolites in primate brain and CSF, *Brain Res.* 415:293–299.

Erickson, M.D., 1986a, *Analytical Chemistry of PCBs*, Butterworth, Boston, pp. 5–53.

Erickson, M.D., 1986b, *Analytical Chemistry of PCBs*, Butterworth, Boston, pp. 469–475.

Eriksson, P., 1988, Effects of 3,3',4,4'-tetrachlorobiphenyl in the brain of the neonatal mouse, *Toxicology* 49:43–48.

Fagan, J.F., and McGrath, S.K., 1981, Infant recognition memory and later intelligence, *Intelligence* 5:121–130.

Fagan, J.F., Singer, L.T., Montie, J.E., and Shepherd, P.A., 1986, Selective screening device for the early detection of normal or delayed cognitive development in infants at risk for later mental retardation, *Pediatrics* 78:1021–1026.

Farrell, K., Safe, L., and Safe, S., 1987, Synthesis and aryl hydrocarbon receptor binding properties of radiolabeled polychlorinated dibenzofuran congeners, *Arch. Biochem. Biophys.* 259:185–195.

Fein, G.G., Jacobson, J.L., Jacobson, S.W., Schwartz, P.M., and Dowler, J.K., 1984, Prenatal exposure to polychlorinated biphenyls: Effects on birth size and gestational age, *J. Pediatr.* 105:315–320.

Forno, L.S., 1982, Pathology of Parkinson's disease, in: *Movement Disorders* (C.D. Marsden, and S. Fahn, eds.), Butterworth Scientific, London, pp. 25–40.

Gierthy, J.F., Lincoln, D.W., Gillespie, M.B., Seeger, J.I., Martinez, H.L., Dickerman, H.W., and Kumar, S.A., 1987, Suppression of estrogen-regulated extracellular tissue plasminogen activator activity of MCF-7 cells by 2,3,7,8-tetrachlorodibenzo-*p*-dioxin, *Cancer Res.* 47:6198–6203.

Gladen, B., and Rogan, W., 1988, Decrements on six-month and one-year Bayley scores and prenatal polychlorinated biphenyl (PCB) exposure, *Am. J. Epidemiol.* 128:912.

Gladen, B.C., Rogan, W.J., Hardy, P., Thullen, J., Tingelstad, J., and Tully, M., 1988, Development after exposure to polychlorinated biphenyls and dichlorodiphenyl dichloroethene transplacentally and through human milk, *J. Pediatr.* 113:991–995.

Glick, S.D., and Shapiro, R.M., 1985, Functional and neurochemical mechanisms of cerebral lateralization in rats, in: *Cerebral Lateralization in Nonhuman Species* (S.D. Glick, ed.), Academic Press, Orlando, pp. 157–183.

Glick, S.D., Meibach, R.C., Cox, R.D., and Maayani, S., 1979, Multiple and interrelated functional asymmetries in the brain, *Life Sci.* 25:395–400.

Graham, D.G., 1978, Oxidative pathways for catecholamines in the genesis of neuromelanin and cytotoxic quinones, *Mol. Pharmacol.* 14:633–643.

Greene, L.A., and Rein, G., 1977, Release, storage and uptake of catecholamines by a clonal cell line of nerve growth factor (NGF) responsive pheochromocytoma cells, *Brain Res.* 129:247–263.

Greene, L.A., and Tischler, A.S., 1976, Establishment of a noradrenergic clonal line of rat adrenal pheochromocytoma cells which respond to nerve growth factor, *Proc. Natl. Acad. Sci. USA* 73:2424–2428.

Hansen, L.G., 1987, Environmental toxicology of polychlorinated biphenyls, in: *Polychlorinated Biphenyls (PCBs): Mammalian and Environmental Toxicology* (S. Safe, and O. Hutzinger, eds.), Springer-Verlag, New York, pp. 15–48.

Harada, M., 1976, Intrauterine poisoning: Clinical and epidemiological studies of the problem, *Bull. Inst. Const. Med.* 25:1–60.

Hayes, M.A., 1987, Carcinogenic and mutagenic effects of PCBs, in: *Polychlorinated Biphenyls (PCBs): Mammalian and Environmental Toxicology* (S. Safe, and O. Hutzinger, eds.), Springer-Verlag, New York, pp. 77–95.

Hsu, S.-T., Ma, C.-I., Hsu, S.K.-H., Wu, S.-S., Hsu, N.H.-M., Yeh, C.-C., and Wu, S.-B., 1985, Discovery and epidemiology of PCB poisoning in Taiwan: A four-year followup, *Environ. Health Perspect.* 59:5–10.

Hutzinger, O., Safe, S., and Zitko, V., 1974, *The Chemistry of PCB's*, CRC Press, Cleveland, OH.

Jacobson, J.L., Fein, G.G., Jacobson, S.W., Schwartz, P.M., and Dowler, J.K., 1984a, The transfer of polychlorinated biphenyls (PCBs) and polybrominated biphenyls (PBBs) across the human placenta and into maternal milk, *Am. J. Public Health* 74:378–379.

Jacobson, J.L., Jacobson, S.W., Schwartz, P.M., Fein, G.G., and Dowler, J.K., 1984b, Prenatal exposure to an environmental toxin: A test of the multiple effects model, *Dev. Psychol.* 20(4):523–532.

Jacobson, J.L., Jacobson, S.W., and Humphrey, H.E.B., 1990, Effects of in utero exposure to polychlorinated biphenyls and related contaminants on cognitive functioning in young children, *J. Pediatr.* 116:38–45.

Jacobson, S.W., Fein, G.G., Jacobson, J.L., Schwartz, P.M., and Dowler, J.K., 1985, The effect of intrauterine PCB exposure on visual recognition memory, *Child Dev.* 56:853–860.

Kittner, B., Brautigam, M., and Herken, H., 1987, PC12 cells: A model system for studying drug effects on dopamine synthesis and release, *Arch. Int. Pharmacodyn. Ther.* 286:181–194.

Kuratsune, M., 1980, Yusho, in: *Halogenated Biphenyls, Terphenyls, Napthalenes, Dibenzodioxins and Related Products* (R.D. Kimbrough, ed.), Elsevier/North-Holland, Amsterdam, pp. 287–302.

Kuratsune, M., Youshimara, T., Matsuzaka, J., and Yamaguchi, A., 1972, Epidemiologic study on Yusho: A poisoning caused by ingestion of rice oil contaminated with a commercial brand of polychlorinated biphenyls, *Environ. Health Perspect.* 1:119–128.

Kuroiwa, Y., Murai, Y., and Santa, T., 1969, Neurological and nerve conduction velocity studies on 23 patients with chlorobiphenyls poisoning, *Fukuoka Igaku Zasshi* 60:446–462.

Levin, E.D., Schantz, S.L., and Bowman, R.E., 1988, Delayed spatial alteration deficits resulting from perinatal PCB exposure in monkeys, *Arch. Toxicol.* 62:267–273.

Lindvall, O., and Björklund, A., 1983, Dopamine- and noradrenaline-containing neuron systems: Their anatomy in the rat brain, in: *Chemical Neuroanatomy* (P.C. Emson, ed.), Raven Press, New York, pp. 229–255.

Lü, Y.-C., and Wong, P.-N., 1984, Dermatological, medical, and laboratory findings of patients in Taiwan and their treatments, in: *PCB Poisoning in Japan and Taiwan* (M. Kuratsune, and R.E. Shapiro, eds.), Alan R. Liss, New York, pp. 81–115.

Mackay, D., Paterson, S., Eisenreich, S.J., and Simmons, M.S., 1983, *Physical Behavior of PCBs in the Great Lakes*, Ann Arbor Science Publishers, Ann Arbor, MI.

Matthews, H.B., 1981, Disposition of persistent halogenated hydrocarbons in higher animals, in: *Toxicology of Halogenated Hydrocarbons, Health and Ecological Effects* (M.A.Q. Khan, and R.H. Stanton, eds.), Pergamon Press, New York, pp. 259–270.

Mullin, M.D., Pochini, C.M., McCrindle, S., Romkes, M., Safe, S.H., and Safe, L.M., 1984, High-resolution PCB analysis: Synthesis and chromatographic properties of all 209 PCB congeners, *Environ. Sci. Technol.* 18:468–476.

National Research Council, 1979, *Polychlorinated Biphenyls*, National Academy of Sciences, Washington, D.C.

Norstrom, R.J., Simon, M., Muir, D.C.G., and Schweinsburg, R.E., 1988, Organochlorine contaminants in Arctic marine food chains: Identification, geographical distribution and temporal trends in polar bears, *Environ. Sci. Technol.* 22:1063–1071.

Overmann, S.R., Kostas, J., Wilson, L.R., Shain, W., and Bush, B., 1987, Neurobehavioral and somatic effects of perinatal PCB exposure in rats, *Environ. Res.* 44:56–70.

Panek, D.U., and Dixon, W.R., 1985, Effect of intraventricular administration of catechol estrogens on catecholamine content in various brain regions, *Brain Res.* 340:87–90.

Pantaleoni, G., Fanini, D., Sponta, A.M., Palumbo, G., Giorgi, R., and Adams, P.M., 1988, Effects of maternal exposure to polychlorinated biphenyls (PCBs) on F1 generation behavior in the rat, *Fundam. Appl. Toxicol.* 11:440–449.

Parkinson, A., and Safe, S., 1987, Mammalian biologic and toxic effects of PCBs, in: *Polychlorinated Biphenyls (PCBs): Mammalian and Environmental Toxicology* (S. Safe, and O. Hutzinger, eds.), Springer-Verlag, New York, pp. 49–75.

Peters, H.A., Levine, R.L., Matthews, C.G., and Chapman, L.J., 1988, Extrapyramidal and other neurologic manifestations associated with carbon disulfide fumigant exposure, *Arch. Neurol.* 45:537–540.

Poland, A., Glover, E., and Kende, A.S., 1976, A stereospecific, high affinity binding of 2,3,7,8-tetrachlorodibenzo-*p*-dioxin by hepatic cytosol: Evidence that the binding species is the receptor for induction of aryl hydrocarbon hydroxylase, *J. Biol. Chem.* 251:4936–4946.

Robertson, L.W., Parkinson, A., Bandiera, S., Lambert, I., Merrill, J., and Safe, S., 1984, PCBs and PBBs: Biologic and toxic effects on C57BL/6J and DBA/2J mice, *Toxicology* 31:191–206.

Rogan, W.J., Gladen, B.C., McKinney, J.D., Carreras, N., Hardy, P., Thullen, J.D., Tinglestad, J., and Tully, M., 1986, Neonatal effects of transplacental exposure to PCBs and DDE, *J. Pediatr.* 109:335–341.

Rogan, W.J., Gladen, B.C., Hung, K.L., Koong, S.L., Shih, L.Y., Taylor, J.S., Wu, Y.C., Yang, D., Rogan, N.B., and Hsu, C.C., 1988, Congenital poisoning by polychlorinated biphenyls and their contaminants in Taiwan, *Science* 241:334–336.

Ryerson, B.A., Carter, D.E., and Sipes, I.G., 1984, Comparison of 2,2',4,4',5,5'-hexachloro[^{14}C]biphenyl levels in different adipose tissues of dogs and monkeys, *Fundam. Appl. Toxicol.* 4:120–124.

Safe, S., 1980, Metabolism, uptake, storage and bioaccumulation, in: *Halogenated Biphenyls, Terphenyls, Napthalenes, Dibenzodioxins and Related Products* (R.D. Kimbrough, ed.), Elsevier/North Holland Biomedical Press, New York, pp. 81–107.

Safe, S., 1990, Polychlorinated biphenyls (PCBs), dibenzo-*p*-dioxins (PCDDs), dibenzofurans (PCDFs), and related compounds: Environmental and mechanistic considerations which support the development of toxic equivalency factors (TEFs), *CRC Crit. Rev. Toxicol.* 21:51–88.

Safe, S., Safe, L., and Mullin, M., 1987, Polychlorinated biphenyls: Environmental occurrence and analysis, in: *Polychlorinated Biphenyls (PCBs): Mammalian and Environmental Toxicology* (S. Safe, and O. Hutzinger, eds.), Springer-Verlag, Berlin, pp. 1–13.

Sawaguchi, T., Matsumura, M., and Kubota, K., 1988, Dopamine enhances the neuronal activity of spatial short-term memory task in the primate prefrontal cortex, *Neurosci. Res.* 5:465–473.

Sawaguchi, T., Matsumura, M., and Kubota K., 1989, Delayed response deficits produced by local injection of bicuculline into the dorsolateral prefrontal cortex in Japanese macaque monkeys, *Exp. Brain Res.* 75:457–469.

Schantz, S.L., Levin, E.D., Bowman, R.E., Heironimus, M.P., and Laughlin, N.K., 1989, Effects of perinatal PCB exposure on discrimination-reversal learning in monkeys, *Neurotoxicol. Teratol.* 11:243–250.

Seegal, R.F., 1992, Perinatal exposure to Aroclor 1016 elevates brain dopamine concentrations in the rat, *The Toxicologist* 12(1):320.

Seegal, R.F., Bush, B., and Brosch, K.O., 1985, Polychlorinated biphenyls induce regional changes in brain norepinephrine concentrations in adult rats, *Neurotoxicology* 6:13–24.

Seegal, R.F., Brosch, K.O., and Bush, B., 1986a, High-performance liquid chromatography of biogenic amines and metabolites in brain, cerebrospinal fluid, urine and plasma, *J. Chromatogr.* 377:131–144.

Seegal, R.F., Brosch, K.O., and Bush, B., 1986b, Polychlorinated biphenyls produce regional alterations of dopamine metabolism in rat brain, *Toxicol. Lett.* 30:197–202.

Seegal, R.F., Brosch, K.O., and Bush, B., 1986c, Regional alterations in serotonin metabolism induced by oral exposure of rats to polychlorinated biphenyls, *Neurotoxicology* 7:155–166.

Seegal, R.F., Brosch, K., Bush, B., Ritz, M., and Shain, W., 1989, Effects of Aroclor 1254 on dopamine and norepinephrine concentrations in pheochromocytoma (PC-12) cells, *Neurotoxicology* 10:757–764.

Seegal, R.F., Bush, B., and Shain, W., 1990, Lightly chlorinated ortho-substituted PCB congeners decrease dopamine in nonhuman primate brain and in tissue culture, *Toxicol. Appl. Pharmacol.* 106:136–144.

Seegal, R.F., Bush, B., and Brosch, K.O., 1991a, Comparison of effects of Aroclors 1016 and 1260 on nonhuman primate catecholamine function, *Toxicology* 66:145–163.

Seegal, R.F., Bush, B., and Brosch, K.O., 1991b, Sub-chronic exposure of the adult rat to Aroclor 1254 yields regionally-specific changes in central dopaminergic function, *Neurotoxicology* 12:55–66.

Seegal, R.F., Bush, B., and Shain, W., 1991c, Neurotoxicology of ortho-substituted polychlorinated biphenyls, *Chemosphere* 23:1941–1949.

Shain, W., Overmann, S.R., Wilson, L.R., Kostas, J., and Bush, B., 1986, A congener analysis of polychlorinated biphenyls accumulating in rat pups after perinatal exposure, *Arch. Environ. Contam. Toxicol.* 15:687–707.

Shain, W., Bush, B., and Seegal, R.F., 1991, Neurotoxicity of polychlorinated biphenyls: Structure-activity relationship of individual congeners, *Toxicol. Appl. Pharmacol.* 11:33–42.

Shiota, K., 1976, Postnatal behavioral effects of prenatal treatment with PCBs (polychlorinated biphenyls) in rats, *Okajimas Folia Anat. Jpn.* 53:105–114.

Silkworth, J.B., Antrim, L., and Kaminsky, L.S., 1984, Correlations between polychlorinated biphenyl immunotoxicity, the aromatic hydrocarbon locus and liver microsomal enzyme induction in C57BL/6J and DBA/2 mice, *Toxicol. Appl. Pharmacol.* 75:156–165.

Silkworth, J.B., Antrim, L., and Sack, G., 1986, *Ah* receptor mediated suppression of the antibody response in mice is primarily dependent on the *Ah* phenotype of lymphoid tissue, *Toxicol. Appl. Pharmacol.* 86:380–390.

Spagnoli, J., and Skinner, L., 1979, PCBs in fish from selected waters of New York State, *Pesticide Monitoring J.* 11:69–87.

Suenaga, N., Yamada, K., Hidaka, T., and Fukuda, T., 1975, Influences of PCB on the brain catecholamine levels in rats, *Fukuoka Igaku Zasshi* 66:589–592.

Sundstrom, G., Hutzinger, O., and Safe, S., 1976, The Metabolism of chlorobiphenyls—A review, *Chemosphere* 5:267–298.

Tanabe, S., Hidaka, H., and Tatsukawa, R., 1983, PCBs and chlorinated hydrocarbon pesticides in Antarctic atmosphere and hydrosphere, *Chemosphere* 12:277–288.

Tilson, H.A., Davis, G.J., McLachlan, J.A., and Lucier, G.W., 1979, The effects of polychlorinated biphenyls given prenatally on the neurobehavioral development of mice, *Environ. Res.* 18:466–474.

Wasserman, M., Wasserman, D., Cucos, S., and Miller, H.J., 1979, World PCBs map: Storage and effects in man and his biologic environment in the 1970s, *Ann. N.Y. Acad. Sci.* 320:69–124.

World Health Organization, 1976, *Polychlorinated Biphenyls and Terphenyls. Environmental Health Criteria 2*, World Health Organization, Geneva.

Yalkowsky, S.H., Valvani, S.C., and Mackay, D., 1983, Estimation of the aqueous solubility of some aromatic compounds, *Residue Rev.* 85:43–55.

Yamaguchi, A., Yoshimura, T., and Kuratsune, M., 1971, A survey on pregnant women having consumed rice oil contaminated with chlorobiphenyls and their babies, *Fukuoka Igaku Zasshi* 62:112–117.

Chapter 11

Central Nervous System Plasticity and Pathology Induced by Exposure to Organophosphate Pesticides

David H. Overstreet and *Grant D. Schiller*

1. INTRODUCTION

It is now widely accepted that pesticides are an integral part of modern agricultural practices (Zabik, 1987). "The usage of chemical pesticides has increased dramatically over the last 30 years. Today, very few food crops are produced on an economically competitive basis without some type of pesticide input" (Coats, 1987, p. 249). With their increased use have come concerns about the long-term toxicological effects of these pesticides on exposed/overexposed agricultural workers (Rosenstock *et al.*, 1990; Savage *et al.*, 1988) and the possibility of the pesticides and/or their residues contaminating foods and groundwater (e.g., Coats, 1987; Ritter, 1990; Zabik, 1987). It is now quite certain that low levels of pesticides can be detected in groundwater and/or various foods, but there is still a debate about what are the acceptable levels for a particular chemical. In any case, it is clear that almost everyone in the United States will be ingesting some pesticides.

Among the most widely used pesticides are the organophosphates (OP, e.g., para-

David H. Overstreet • Center for Alcohol Studies, Department of Psychiatry, University of North Carolina, Chapel Hill, North Carolina 27599. *Grant D. Schiller* • School of Biological Sciences, Flinders University, Adelaide, S. A. 5001 Australia.
The Vulnerable Brain and Environmental Risks, Volume 2: Toxins in Food, edited by Robert L. Isaacson and Karl F. Jensen. Plenum Press, New York, 1992.

thion) and the carbamates (e.g., carbaryl), which are thought to produce their toxic effects mainly by inhibiting the enzyme acetylcholinesterase (AChE), which is critically important for normal transmission at synapses containing acetylcholine (ACh). Unfortunately, mammalian organisms, including humans, are also quite sensitive to these compounds, and there are numerous instances of acute toxic effects in humans from exposure to these agents. Because OPs appear to be irreversible inhibitors of AChE, their effects can increase with subsequent exposure, and there is thus a high potential for long-term consequences. On the other hand, carbamates tend to be reversible inhibitors and, consequently, possess less potential for long-term consequences. The present study will, therefore, focus on the consequences of short- and long-term exposure to OPs. Reference to carbamates will be made at particular points to emphasize certain principles.

In order to develop a clear understanding of the toxicological potential of OPs, the reader must become more familiar with the cholinergic neurotransmitter system. So this chapter will begin with a brief outline of this system. Then a description of the mechanisms believed to underlie the sensitivity and tolerance of animals to OPs will be given. Finally, the adaptive changes that occur during chronic exposure to low levels of OPs will be discussed, stressing that these changes may have maladaptive consequences.

2. THE CHOLINERGIC SYSTEM

Cholinergic neurons are neurons that utilize ACh as a neurotransmitter. They are widespread throughout the central and peripheral nervous system, including the motor neurons to skeletal muscles, preganglionic autonomic neurons, septo-hippocampal neurons, striatal interneurons, and nucleus basalis-cortical neurons. These central pathways, in particular, have been characterized in part by antibodies against choline acetyltransferase, the enzyme that is involved in the synthesis of ACh and that exists only in cholinergic neurons (Wainer et al., 1984). It has also been established that cholinergic neurons exhibit a sodium-dependent, high-affinity uptake for choline, one of the precursors for ACh. The other precursor for ACh is acetyl CoA, derived from energy metabolism and common to all cells (Russell and Overstreet, 1987).

Upon its release from the presynaptic terminal, ACh may be either rapidly inactivated by the enzyme AChE or may interact with one of two types of receptors, the muscarinic or the nicotinic. The latter receptors are located at the neuromuscular junction, at autonomic ganglia, and in certain brain regions, whereas the former receptors are located at smooth muscles and the heart, at autonomic ganglia, and in many brain regions, the most prominent being the striatum, the hippocampus, and the cerebral cortex (Russell and Overstreet, 1987).

Because AChE rapidly inactivates ACh at cholinergic synapses, which are widely distributed throughout the body, inhibitors of AChE, such as OPs, can have widespread effects on the organism. The effects possible after acute exposure to OPs are listed in Table 1 (Karczmar, 1984; Russell and Overstreet, 1987). It can be seen that the effects are indeed quite varied and involve central nervous system components as well as peripheral muscarinic and nicotinic effects. These effects are normally attributed to the buildup of ACh due to the inhibition of AChE (Taylor, 1980). However, several recent papers have

TABLE 1.   Effects of Organophosphate Agents

1. Effects related to peripheral muscarinic actions
   a. Salivation
   b. Chromodacryorrhea
   c. Diarrhea
   d. Urination
   e. Bradycardia
2. Effects related to peripheral nicotinic actions
   a. Fasciculations
   b. Paralysis
3. Effects related to central (mainly muscarinic) actions
   a. EEG desyncronization
   b. Stimulation of REM sleep
   c. Facilitation of drinking in rodents
   d. Hypothermia
   e. Hypokinesia and catalepsy
   f. Tremors
   g. Convulsions
   h. Hypoalgesia (antinociception)
   i. Facilitation of learning and memory (low doses only)
   j. Anergia and depression in humans

suggested that these compounds may have a direct effect on cholinergic receptors (Katz and Marquis, 1989; Vianna *et al.,* 1988; Volpe *et al.,* 1985).

A potentially very significant feature of the action of OPs is that they inhibit AChE irreversibly. Consequently, the effects of subsequent injections could be magnified; if doses are selected carefully, it is possible to reduce brain AChE activity to very low levels without any obvious changes in the behavior of the organism. Such instances have been reported for people receiving anticholinesterase treatment for glaucoma (DeRoeth *et al.,* 1965), and our laboratory was among the first to report such work in rats (Chippendale *et al.,* 1972). Several more recent papers have replicated our original finding but have conducted more complex behavioral analyses. These studies will be summarized in Section 5.

3. SENSITIVITY AND RESISTANCE

Sensitivity and resistance are concepts that will be used to refer to individuals/animals upon acute exposure to organophosphates. Tolerance and/or adaptation will be used to describe an individual or animal when chronically exposed to OPs. In general, sensitivity and resistance are opposite but relative terms. In other words, when comparing only two individuals, one must necessarily be more sensitive than the other, who can be referred to as the more resistant. Some workers use the term *insensitive* rather than resistant; e.g., insects that develop resistance to organophosphates do so in part because of the development of an insensitive AChE (Zahavi *et al.,* 1971).

3.1. Factors Affecting Sensitivity

It is important to realize that the sensitivity of an organism to OPs is inferred from its response and that there is a wide range of factors that may influence this response. In this section only a small number of these multiple factors will be highlighted. The reader should consult Russell and Overstreet (1987) for a more comprehensive discussion.

Broadly, the factors that influence the response of an individual to OPs can be grouped into four categories. The first group is related to the chemical compound and includes such factors as chemical composition, solubility in biological fluids, and stability. The second group is related to the exposure situation, dose, and duration, etc. The third group is related to the individual and includes such factors as age, sex, and strain/species. The final group is related to the environment and includes such factors as temperature and humidity.

It has become increasingly clear in recent times that sex, age, and genetic background can all play important roles in anticholinesterase sensitivity in rats. Genetic background was known for a long time to be involved because of the well-documented instances of resistance to OPs in insects (Oppenorth and Welling, 1976). However, the development of two lines of rats with differing sensitivity to the anticholinesterase diisopropyl fluorophosphate (DFP) indicated that genetic factors were involved in the rodents' responses as well (Overstreet et al., 1979b). Finally, very recent studies have demonstrated that 24-month-old (aged) rats were more sensitive to the effects of DFP than were 3-month-old rats (Pintor et al., 1988, 1990). An interesting question related to the demonstration of sex, genetic, and age influences on sensitivity is whether the underlying mechanisms are similar. This issue will be considered in detail in the next section.

3.2. Mechanisms Underlying Sensitivity

The following discussion is an adapted and updated consideration of the more detailed treatment by Russell and Overstreet (1987). The focus will be on the Flinders Line rats, which were selectively bred for differences in sensitivity to DFP (Overstreet et al., 1979b). Three responses known to be sensitive to OPs—core body temperature, water intake, and body weight—were used in the selection studies; those rats that exhibited the greatest responses were mated together and those that exhibited the smallest responses were correspondingly mated (Overstreet et al., 1979b). The line more sensitive to DFP (Flinders sensitive line, FSL) is also more sensitive to a range of other drugs (Overstreet et al., 1988) than are their control counterparts, the Flinders resistant line (FRL). When Sprague-Dawley rats, from which the selected lines were derived, were tested under various parallel conditions, they were very similar to the FRL rats (Russell et al., 1982; Overstreet et al., 1986b); thus, FRL rats are not truly resistant, only in comparison with the FSL rats.

3.2.1. Changes in AChE

Since AChE is the target enzyme for OPs, it is likely that changes in this enzyme may account for changes in the sensitivity to OPs in some situations. Indeed, variations in the affinity of OPs for AChE has been reported to underlie many instances of resistance in insects (Andersen *et al.*, 1977; Hama and Hosoda, 1983; Wang and Murphy, 1982; Ugaki *et al.*, 1983; Zahavi *et al.*, 1971).

As indicated above, a line more sensitive to DFP, the FSL rats, has been developed by selective breeding, but not a line more resistant (Overstreet *et al.*, 1979b; Russell *et al.*, 1982). Because insects resistant to OPs have insensitive AChEs, the possibility of FSL rats having more sensitive AChEs was examined. However, similar DFP inhibition profiles for AChE were found *in vitro* (Sihotang and Overstreet, 1983), and the degree of brain levels of AChE activity after *in vivo* administration of the same doses of DFP was similar (Overstreet *et al.*, 1979b; Sihotang and Overstreet, 1983). Thus, changes in AChE may underlie some instances of differences in sensitivity/resistance but not all.

3.2.2. Changes in other Enzymes

There are a range of other enzymes that appear to have special significance in this discussion of mechanisms underlying sensitivity. Serum cholinesterase and carboxylesterase (aliesterase) are nonspecific esterase enzymes that can be inhibited by DFP and other OPs. Consequently, alterations in the levels of these enzymes due to hormones and or drugs can alter the degree of inhibition of AChE by OPs, thereby altering their toxicity (Clement, 1984; Cohen, 1981).

It has been mentioned that sex, age, and genetic background could all influence the sensitivity to OPs. It appears that these nonspecific esterases may underlie some of these influences, but not all. For example, both serum cholinesterase and carboxylesterase activities are higher in females than in males, thereby explaining the relative resistance of females to OPs (Overstreet *et al.*, 1979a, 1990). These sex differences in serum cholinesterases are probably hormonally mediated, because ovariectomized female rats were found to have both reduced, male-like serum cholinesterase activities and increased sensitivity to DFP (Overstreet *et al.*, 1981). There is also some evidence that these enzymes may be elevated in OP-resistant insects (Hama and Hosoda, 1983), thereby accounting for some of the genetic influences on resistance. However, there are no differences in either serum cholinesterase or carboxylesterase activities between FSL and FRL rats, and the degree of inhibition of serum cholinesterase or brain AChE by DFP is similar in the two lines (Overstreet *et al.*, 1979b, 1990). As yet, no one has investigated the potential involvement of these enzymes in aged rats, but one suspects they are not involved, because aged rats appear to be more affected than young rats at similar doses of DFP that produce similar inhibition of brain AChE activity (Pintor *et al.*, 1988, 1990).

In conclusion, changes in enzymes, particularly esterases affecting acetylcholinergic function, can occur in some situations and may contribute to differences in sensitivity/resistance. However, in the selectively bred FSL and FRL rats, neither changes in AChE nor in nonspecific esterases were found, and the evidence for other mechanisms responsible for the differences in sensitivity in these two lines must be considered.

3.2.3. Presynaptic Mechanisms

It is conceivable that animals that vary in their sensitivity to OPs might have altered presynaptic cholinergic function. Among the possible sites/processes for alterations include (1) changes in the concentration of the synthesizing enzyme, choline acetyltransferase; (2) changes in choline uptake processes; (3) changes in metabolic processes, e.g., energy metabolism, which alter the availability of Acetyl CoA; and/or (4) changes in the release of ACh. There are essentially no data on these variables in either insects resistant to OPs or in the FSL rats supersensitive to OPs [see Russell and Overstreet (1987) for a fuller discussion]. Recent unpublished studies failed to detect a difference in choline actyltransferase activity between FSL and FRL rats (Overstreet et al., unpublished observations, 1990). There are a number of studies indicating that OPs can alter energy metabolism (Russell and Overstreet, 1987), but it is not clear whether these changes are primary or secondary responses, and whether they might contribute to differences in sensitivity/resistance.

3.2.4. Postsynaptic Mechanisms

Because it is well documented that rats chronically treated with OPs are both subsensitive to cholinergic agonists (Overstreet et al., 1973, 1974) and exhibit down-regulation of muscarinic acetylcholine receptors (mAChRs) (Schiller, 1979), it was considered possible that postsynaptic mAChRs might contribute to the supersensitivity exhibited by the FSL rats. Early studies did indeed discover that the FSL rats were more sensitive to both indirect agonists, such as physostigmine, and direct agonists, such as oxotremorine (Overstreet and Russell, 1982). Later studies confirmed the increased sensitivity of FSL rats to muscarinic agonists (Overstreet, 1986; Overstreet et al., 1986a, 1986b, 1988).

Direct receptor binding assays have established that these differences in cholinergic sensitivity are associated with differences in mAChR density. The FSL rats exhibit increases in mAChR binding in the striatum and the hippocampus relative to the control, FRL rats (Overstreet et al., 1984; Pepe et al., 1988). There were no significant differences in the cerebral cortex, so the changes were not uniformly seen in the brain. Recent direct receptor binding studies and parallel psychopharmacological challenges suggest that both M1 and M2 subtypes of the mAChR are increased and that these increases are associated with increased sensitivity to both selective M1 and M2 agonists (Schiller et al., 1988). It is quite clear, therefore, that postsynaptic mAChRs are elevated in the FSL rats, which are supersensitive to cholinergic agonists and OPs.

Whether these receptor changes represent the only mechanism underlying muscarinic supersensitivity is unclear. We have detected a strain of rat that appears to be supersensitive to muscarinic agonists without having elevated mAChRs (Overstreet and Crocker, 1991), and others have indicated that genetic differences in OP sensitivity in mice also cannot be accounted for by differences in mAChRs (Smolen et al., 1985; Upchurch and Wehner, 1988). A more conclusive mismatch concerns aged rats, which exhibit increased sensitivity to OPs (Pintor et al., 1988, 1990) and direct agonists (Pedigo, 1988), and a *decrease* in mAChRs. Obviously, there is a need to examine postreceptor mechanisms in these situations. Such studies have basically characterized a range of second-messenger responses to cholinergic stimulation (McKinney and Richelson, 1984), but there have been only limited, unsuccessful attempts to use this approach to relate to the questions of sensitivity/resistance (Cioffi and El-Fakahany, 1988). Certainly more work is necessary.

3.2.5. Involvement of Noncholinergic Systems

A number of investigators have reported alterations in other neurotransmitters in animals treated with OPs and have, at various times, speculated on the involvement of these systems in the effects of OPs. Similarly, in recent years the possibility that non-cholinergic changes might have occurred in the FSL and FRL rats as a result of the selective breeding program for differences in OPs is being explored (Crocker and Over-street, 1991; Pepe et al., 1988; Wallis et al., 1988).

A number of investigators have implicated GABA in the convulsions induced by OPs (Kar and Matin, 1972; Lipp, 1973; Lundy and Magor, 1977; Lundy et al., 1978; Rump et al., 1973). There is even some suggestion that the convulsions induced by OPs are not a direct consequence of inhibition of AChE, because certain phosphorus esters can induce convulsions without inhibiting AChE (Bellet and Casida, 1976), and atropine does not always prevent convulsions induced by OPs (Lundy et al., 1978). Most recently investigators have demonstrated changes in GABA metabolism and/or receptors after OPs and have suggested that changes in GABA may account for the differences between OPs (Sivam et al., 1983a, 1984).

There have also been occasional reports on the alteration of serotonin (Fernando et al., 1984a), dopamine (Fernando et al., 1984b; Glisson et al., 1974; Sivam et al., 1983b), or endogenous opioid peptides (Koehn et al., 1982). However, results have been too isolated for a consistent picture to emerge. The key point of whether these non-cholinergic changes are key determinants of the behavioral and/or physiological effects of OPs or are simply secondary and/or modulatory systems has not been answered [see Russell and Overstreet (1987) for a fuller description of effects].

The FSL rats have been found to be supersensitive not only to OPs and direct cholinergic agonists, but also to a range of other, noncholinergic drugs. For example, they are more sensitive to the hypothermic effects of all of the following compounds: bus-pirone, a serotonin$_{1A}$ agonist; mCPP, a serotonin$_{1B}$ agonist; diazepam, a benzodiazepine agonist; muscimol, a GABA agonist; apomorphine, a dopamine agonist; and quinpirole, a dopamine D$_2$ agonist (Crocker and Overstreet, 1991; Overstreet, 1989; Pepe et al., 1988; Wallis et al., 1988). The FSL rats are also more sensitive to the behavioral depressant effects of both serotonin$_1$ and serotonin$_2$ agonists (Schiller, 1991), but they are less sensitive to the stereotypy-inducing effects of apomorphine and quinpirole (Crocker and Overstreet, 1991). This latter result was quite unexpected, particularly since there were no differences in dopamine receptor binding (Crocker and Overstreet, 1991). The fact that the FSL rats are supersensitive to dopamine agonists for some measures (temperature) but subsensitive for others (stereotypy) suggests that the dopamine sensitivity changes may only be apparent and secondary to the primary changes in the cholinergic system induced by the selective breeding. Studies are underway to examine more closely the serotonergic alterations in the FSL rats.

3.2.6. Neuronal Damage

Recent studies in rats have demonstrated that OPs may produce extensive neuronal degeneration and necrosis; however, these degenerative changes have only been noted in rats surviving single or multiple convulsive seizures (Churchill et al., 1985; Lemercier et *al.*, 1983; Mays *et al.*, 1984; McLeod *et al.*, 1984; Samson *et al.*, 1984). It is quite likely that such findings may be directly relevant to the recent neuropsychological studies on humans, which have reported quite significant behavioral deficits in workers previously exposed to high levels of OPs (Rosenstock *et al.*, 1990; Savage *et al.*, 1988). Unfortunately, there do not appear to be any comparable behavioral data in rats exposed to high doses of OPs. Only a few studies have examined the behavioral effects of withdrawal from OPs (Russell *et al.*, 1971a, 1989), and these did not use high doses, nor did they report on dramatic cognitive effects. However, any significant effects that were observed during withdrawal tended to be in cognitive areas, just as the most obvious effects in the human studies were cognitive ones (Russell *et al.*, 1989; Savage *et al.*, 1988).

4. TOLERANCE

The development of tolerance to OPs has been one of the most commonly reported phenomena in the scientific literature. Tolerance has been most commonly studied as the recovery of a parameter to normal, despite the continued administration of the OPs. However, a number of studies have referred to a state of tolerance when brain AChE levels reached a very low stable level, regardless of whether there have been initial changes in behavioral or physiological processes (Chippendale *et al.*, 1972; Overstreet, 1974; Russell and Overstreet, 1987). Much is known about the processes and the mechanisms involved and many reviews abound (Costa *et al.*, 1982; Overstreet, 1984; Russell, 1982; Russell and Overstreet, 1987). Consequently, this section will not attempt to be comprehensive; rather, important issues will be highlighted and key publications appearing since the 1987 review will be integrated.

4.1. Factors Influencing Tolerance

Among the factors that have been demonstrated to influence the development of tolerance to OPs are the following: (1) sex and age, (2) genetic background, (3) dose and frequency of administration, (4) type of OP, (5) behavioral parameters, and (6) specific task conditions. There have been several others, but a brief discussion of these six should be adequate to give the reader an idea of the complex processes involved.

Female, young, FRL rats tend to develop tolerance to DFP, a typical OP, more readily than male, old, FSL rats (Pintor *et al.*, 1988, 1990; Russell *et al.*, 1983). The reasons for these differences have not been completely elucidated; however, it is important to note that those rats that develop tolerance more readily are also more resistant to the acute effects of DFP. It has been suggested that these findings may be related to the observation that the rate of tolerance development is related to the dose: the lower the dose administered, the faster the rate of tolerance development (Chippendale *et al.*, 1972; Russell and Overstreet, 1987). Thus, although the acutely resistant rats are receiving the same applied dose of the OP, they are receiving a smaller effective dose and should develop tolerance sooner. A number of other recent studies have commented on the importance of dose; if the application rate is too steep (combination of dose and frequency), then animals will die before there is an opportunity for tolerance to develop (Chippendale *et al.*, 1972; Pintor *et al.*, 1990).

4.2. Studies of Development of Tolerance

From the earliest behavioral studies of the development of tolerance to OPs, it was recognized that behavioral task was an important variable. Responses involving relatively simple motor behavior developed tolerance quickly, as did temperature regulation (Overstreet *et al.*, 1973; Russell *et al.*, 1969, 1971a, 1975). On the other hand, more complex behavioral phenomena, which may require the involvement of central cholinergic systems, either took longer to develop tolerance or only partial tolerance developed (Overstreet *et al.*, 1974; Russell *et al.*, 1969, 1971a). Recently Genovese *et al.* (1988a, 1988b, 1990) have reported that the behavioral conditions of testing can also influence the rate of tolerance development to the carbamate antiChE, physostigmine. They also make the important point related to dose. Tolerance was not observed if physostigmine, which has a comparatively short duration of action, was administered only once a day, but was when it was administered three times a day (Genovese, 1990). A last point that should be made about the issue of dose is that it is possible, through judicious use of dose and other treatment conditions, to produce an animal with very low brain AChE activity without any apparent behavioral and/or physiological effects (Bushnell *et al.*, 1991; Chippendale *et al.*, 1972; Raffaele *et al.*, 1990). A key point here is the word *apparent*, as more sophisticated recent studies have revealed behavioral effects of low-dose regiments. These studies will be discussed in detail in Section 5.

4.3. Mechanisms Underlying Tolerance

Theoretically, most of the mechanisms discussed above in relation to sensitivity and resistance could also be involved in the processes underlying tolerance development. However, because these have been given comprehensive treatment in a comparatively recent review (Russell and Overstreet, 1987), we wish only to highlight a few of the most important mechanisms here.

4.3.1. Enzyme Levels

It has been conclusively demonstrated that tolerance development to OPs occurs despite constant levels of AChE, the enzyme that they inhibit (Russell *et al.*, 1975). It also appears that a number of other enzymes, such as the synthesizing enzyme choline acetyltransferase, cytochrome oxidase, alkaline phosphatase, and sodium-potassium activated ouabain-sensitive ATPase, are not related to tolerance development (Russell *et al.*, 1975; Sivam *et al.*, 1984). However, a couple of studies have suggested that the selective recovery of a specific isoenzyme form of AChE may contribute to the recovery of behavioral and physiological processes during acute and chronic treatment with OPs (Meneguz *et al.*, 1981; Michalek *et al.*, 1981, 1982). The degree to which such isoenzymes might contribute to tolerance development must await further confirmatory studies from other laboratories.

4.3.2. Presynaptic Mechanisms

One of the simplest models to account for tolerance development to OPs incorporates the notion of feedback inhibition of the synthesizing enzyme for ACh, choline acetyltransferase. Feedback inhibition is a well-recognized concept, and there is strong evidence that the levels of tyrosine hydroxylase, for example, can be regulated by the levels of dopamine and norepinephrine. However, studies with the cholinergic system suggested that, unlike tyrosine hydroxylase, choline acetyltransferase is not a rate-limiting enzyme (Jope, 1979; Tucek, 1984). In fact, numerous studies have failed to provide any evidence for changes in choline acetyltransferase activity or ACh synthesis in rats treated chronically with OPs (Russell *et al.*, 1975, 1979, 1981; Sivam *et al.*, 1984).

Several of the studies on basic regulation of ACh synthesis suggested that one of the precursors of ACh, choline, which is actively transported into cholinergic neurons, may play a key role in the regulation of ACh synthesis (Jope, 1979; Tucek, 1984). Thus, if a feedback inhibition process were involved in OP tolerance, it might operate at the level of choline uptake. There is mixed information on this model. Yamada *et al.* (1983a, 1983b), using guinea pigs and an *in vitro* approach to choline uptake (in synaptosomes), reported evidence for a decrease in choline uptake, whereas Russell *et al.* (1979, 1981), using an *in vivo* approach in rats, found no evidence for a change in choline uptake during chronic OP treatment. A more recent paper on this topic has clarified the issue somewhat. Using an *in vitro* approach in rats, Lim *et al.* (1987a) confirmed Yamada's findings of decreased choline uptake, but found that this effect had largely disappeared within 24 hr after the last OP administration, i.e., at the time Russell and collaborators normally sacrificed their rats.

Studies on the levels of ACh or its precursor, choline, after acute and chronic DFP treatment have produced varied results. The degree of reported elevation of ACh after OP treatment has varied from 0 (Shih, 1982) to 40% (Russell *et al.*, 1975, 1981; Wecker *et al.*, 1977). The key finding in the earlier studies was that any change found after acute treatment tended to remain constant throughout chronic treatment (Russell *et al.*, 1975, 1981); thus ACh levels could not be related to the mechanisms underlying tolerance development. However, more recently Lim *et al.* (1987b) reported that bound ACh did decrease with chronic OP treatment and concluded that presynaptic alterations in the cholinergic systems could contribute to tolerance development to OPs. The levels of choline are also increased by acute or chronic OP treatment (Russell *et al.*, 1981), but there is no consistent relationship between the patterns of increases in choline levels and the changes during tolerance development.

Finally, it is possible that the levels of the transmitter and its precursor could remain relatively constant, but there could be changes in the mechanisms of its release. Theoretically, one would predict that there would be a reduction in the release of ACh during the development of tolerance to OPs if this mechanism were involved in tolerance. Surprisingly, however, the available studies demonstrate just the opposite: There is an enhanced release of ACh in *in vitro* preparations taken from OP-treated animals (Raiteri *et al.*, 1981; Russell *et al.*, 1985). Such an increased release of ACh during chronic OP treatment would lead to a potentiation of their effects rather than a diminution. It is more likely that this finding is related to the downregulation of mAChRs reported in OP-treated rats (see next section), as it is known that presynaptic mAChRs regulate the release of ACh (Jenden, 1980). Support for this conclusion comes from the recent observation that anticholinergic drugs stimulate ACh release more in OP-treated rats than in controls (Lim *et al.*, 1987b).

4.3.3. Postsynaptic Mechanisms

The large majority of studies of OP tolerance have reported a downregulation or decrease in mAChRs in chronically treated animals (Churchill *et al.*, 1984a, 1984b; Ehlert *et al.*, 1980a, 1980b; Gazit *et al.*, 1979; McKinney and Coyle, 1982; Schallert *et al.*, 1980; Schiller, 1979; Sivam *et al.*, 1983b; Uchida *et al.*, 1979; Yamada *et al.*, 1983a, 1983b; Yang *et al.*, 1990).

These studies are supported by an extensive number of *in vivo* functional studies, in which it has been reported that animals treated chronically with OPs are less sensitive to directly acting muscarinic agonists (Clement, 1991; Overstreet *et al.*, 1973, 1974; Russell *et al.*, 1975). Under some circumstances OP-treated animals are supersensitive to the behavioral effects of directly acting muscarinic antagonists (Chippendale *et al.*, 1972; Raffaele *et al.*, 1990; Russell *et al.*, 1971). Thus, there is a wealth of data to support the model that a downregulation of the mAChR largely accounts for tolerance development to OPs. [See Overstreet and Yamamura (1979) for a general review of receptors and tolerance].

Studies of nicotinic receptor mechanisms in OP-treated animals have been much less common than those of muscarinic receptor mechanisms. In general, however, the studies mirror those for mAChRs. There is evidence both for a functional subsensitivity to nicotinic agonists in OP-treated rats (Overstreet *et al.*, 1974) and for downregulation of nicotinic receptors (Costa and Murphy, 1983; Schwartz and Keller, 1983). There is a need for further work in this area in order to determine the relative contribution of nicotinic and muscarinic receptor decreases to OP tolerance. The need for more work has been reinforced by a recent study demonstrating that continuous infusion of the carbamate physostigmine led to an *increase* in nicotinic receptors (Bhat *et al.*, 1990).

There have been relatively few reports on mAChR second-messenger responses in OP-treated animals and none at all on nicotinic second-messenger responses. The available reports would seem to be consistent with the frequently reported downregulation of mAChRs. For example, Olianas *et al.* (1983) reported subsensitivity of mAChR-induced inhibition of striatal adenylate cyclase in rats treated chronically with OPs, and Costa *et al.* (1986) reported a decrease in carbachol-stimulated phosphoinositide metabolism. In contrast, Cioffi and El-Fakahany (1988) did not find any change in a mAChR-mediated response in animals acutely treated with OPs. There is a great need for more studies of this type, because there is a growing concern that the mAChR downregulation cannot provide a complete answer to OP tolerance. This concern has come about because of several reports that tolerance to OPs or muscarinic agonists may develop prior to or in the absence of any changes in mAChRs (Dawson and Jarrott, 1981; Genovese *et al.*, 1988a, 1988b, 1990; Maayani *et al.*, 1977; Marks *et al.*, 1981; Overstreet and Dubas, 1978). Some of these studies have led to the suggestion of behaviorally augmented tolerance: the notion that animals required to perform a task while under the influence of the drug may develop tolerance more readily (see Russell and Overstreet, 1987).

4.3.4. Compensation by Other Systems

As discussed earlier, the cholinergic system interacts with multiple other systems in the regulation of particular behavioral and/or physiological functions (see Section 3.2.5). It is possible, therefore, that changes in some components of these other systems may contribute to the development of tolerance to OPs. Sivam *et al.* (1983b), for example, have reported evidence for time-dependent changes in GABA and dopamine receptors in rats chronically treated with DFP. Unfortunately, there were not any functional studies, so we cannot assess the significance of these receptor elevations. Others have focused on the levels of particular neurotransmitters (Fernando *et al.*, 1984b; Potter *et al.*, 1984), but the results of these studies are difficult to interpret without information on receptors and functional studies (i.e., have the OP treatments altered the sensitivity of the rats to drugs interacting with noncholinergic systems?).

Based on the observation that serotonin might contribute to the behavioral effects of OPs (Fernando *et al.*, 1984a), we decided to examine serotonergic function in DFP-treated rats. It was initially confirmed that FSL rats were more sensitive to serotonergic agonists. Upon chronic treatment with DFP, both FSL and FRL rats became subsensitive to muscarinic agonists, but they also became subsensitive to serotonergic agonists (Schiller and Overstreet, in preparation). Binding studies are in progress; if they support the *in vivo* functional studies, then conclusive evidence for the alteration in serotonergic function would be obtained. Whether this change contributes to the tolerance development to OPs could then be explored in subsequent studies.

5. LOW-DOSE OP TREATMENT

Because of the evidence that OPs and/or their residues may exist in foods or groundwater (see introduction), it is likely that a much greater proportion of the human population will be exposed to chronic low-level OPs than to the relatively large exposure rates described in most of these pages. The question then becomes, "Are there any hazards to such individuals?" In fact, there are a number of animal studies that relate to this topic and we will deal with them and their implications in this section.

Early in our studies of OP tolerance, we recognized that the rate of tolerance development was a function of dose (Chippendale *et al.*, 1972). However, we also discovered that virtually the same endpoint of adaptation or tolerance could be achieved by very low dose regimens of OPs because these compounds irreversibly inhibit AChE; thus, the concept of tolerance without acute behavioral change (Chippendale *et al.*, 1972). Using the *in vivo* challenge design, Overstreet (1974) determined that a low-dose OP regimen that did not alter operant behavior led to evidence for subsensitivity to muscarinic agonists within 5 days, with nearly complete changes by 9 days. The fact that rats treated chronically with doses of OPs that did not affect their behavior but altered their responses to cholinergic agonists and antagonists (Chippendale *et al.*, 1972; Overstreet, 1974) raised the possibility that humans so exposed might exhibit similar changes.

In more recent years other investigators have taken up this story. An important observation in this field was the recognition that the cholinergic system appeared to be involved in memory storage processes in both animals and humans (Bartus *et al.*, 1982; Coyle *et al.*, 1983) and that chronic OP administration might lead to changes in memory. Loullis *et al.* (1983) provided further impetus for this idea by demonstrating that rats withdrawn from chronic scopolamine treatment, expected to increase mAChR concentrations, exhibited improved memories, while rats withdrawn from chronic physostigmine treatment, expected to decrease mAChR concentrations, exhibited impaired memories. Subsequently, Gardner *et al.* (1984), using a typical high-dose chronic DFP regimen, demonstrated that rats withdrawn from this treatment also exhibited impaired memory. Recent work in mice suggests that genetic factors may contribute to this OP-induced memory deficit (Upchurch and Wehner, 1988). Thus, it is possible that the cognitive deficits exhibited by the humans in recent studies may be in part a consequence of downregulated mAChRs.

The studies mentioned above contained several flaws that make them difficult to relate to the human situation. These include the relatively high dose of administration and the relatively unsophisticated behavioral task (passive avoidance). Very recently new studies have appeared that have used chronic low-dose regimens and more sophisticated operant behavioral tasks. In the first of these, Raslear *et al.* (1988) reported that relatively low doses of DFP altered time perception in rats. In the second paper, Raffaele *et al.* (1990) reported no evidence for an effect of the chronic regimen on the performance of the task, but the memory-disruptive effects of muscarinic antagonists were increased in the OP-treated rats. In the final paper, Bushnell *et al.* (1991) found that the OP treatment, while producing no acute effects, led to impaired memory-related performance in 10 days, about the time when a subsensitivity to muscarinic agonists was observed (Overstreet, 1974). They could not replicate the observation (Raffaele *et al.*, 1990) of increased sensitivity to antagonists in their paradigm. Nevertheless, these reports taken together suggest that chronic OP treatment can have negative consequences for cognitive behavior in rats, even though there are not any apparent acute effects. Therefore, it is possible that humans could be at risk for cognitive deficits if their exposure to low-level OPs is long enough. In the animal studies brain AChE has been measured and needs to be below 40% before these effects are seen. What are needed are studies of blood AChE as well, so that some measure of human exposure can be obtained. It is likely that red blood cell AChE will provide a more useful measure of long-term human exposure to OPs than serum ChE because of its slow recovery rate (like brain AChE).

6. CONCLUSIONS

The present chapter has summarized the evidence for the involvement of various mechanisms underlying sensitivity and tolerance development to OPs. Changes in AChE and other enzymes may partially account for the resistance to OPs exhibited by many insect species, but cannot account for the increased sensitivity of FSL rats to DFP. Instead, FSL rats may be supersensitive to OPs because they have greater numbers of mAChRs, although coupling of receptors to second messengers needs to be further explored. Changes in mAChRs, in particular, a downregulation, also appear to be a key mechanism underlying tolerance development to OPs. However, this adaptive or plastic response may have maladaptive consequences under some circumstances. Blockade of mAChRs by anticholinergic agents is well known to disrupt memory, and several reports have shown that low-level exposure to OPs can also result in disrupted memory.

The literature referred to in the introduction suggests that a large number of humans may be at risk for exposure to low levels of OPs, because of the contamination of groundwater and/or foods. It is extremely difficult to say whether these levels are "safe" because it is well documented that OPs irreversibly inhibit AChE and may have long-term consequences through the progressive inhibition of this enzyme, even though no apparent acute effects were seen. It is important, therefore, to (1) keep pesticide residues as low as possible in everything likely to be ingested by humans, and (2) develop procedures for detecting long-term, subsymptomatic OP exposure in humans.

Finally, the fact that rats that are supersensitive to OPs can be selectively bred (Overstreet *et al.*, 1988) raises the possibility that there may be a certain number of human individuals who are also supersensitive to OPs. Rosenthal and Cameron (1991) have recently called attention to just such an individual, who exhibited symptoms of OP intoxication up to several months after his house was sprayed with an OP. One group of such people could be those who have had a history of depression because there is evidence that these individuals are supersensitive to the carbamate physostigmine (see Overstreet *et al.*, 1988). Such individuals probably should avoid exposure to agricultural pesticides. Procedures for detecting other individuals who may be more sensitive to the effects of OPs also need to be developed.

ACKNOWLEDGMENTS.   This chapter was supported, in part, by research funds granted by the Australian National Health and Medical Research Council and the Flinders University Research Budget. We acknowledge the support of the following collaborators: Roger Russell, Lyn Daws, Joe Orbach, and Ann Crocker. The comments of Philip Bushnell on an earlier version of this chapter is greatly appreciated.

REFERENCES

Andersen, R.A., Aaraas, I., Vaare, G., and Fonnum, F., 1977, Inhibition of acetylcholinesterase from different species by organophosphorus compounds, carbamates and methysulphonylfluoride, *Gen. Pharmacol.* 8:331–334.

Bartus, R.T., Dean, R.L., Beer, B., and Lippa, A.S., 1982, The cholinergic hypothesis of geriatric memory dysfunction, *Science* 217:408–417.

Bellet, E.M., and Casida, J.E., 1976, Bicyclic phosphorus esters, high toxicity without cholinesterase inhibition, *Science* 182:1135–1136.

Bhat, R.V., Turner, S.L., Marks, M.J., and Collins, A.C., 1991, Selective changes in sensitivity to cholinergic agonists and receptor changes elicited by continuous physostigmine infusion, *J. Pharmacol. Exp. Ther.* 255:187–196.

Bushnell, P.J., Padilla, S.S., Ward, T., Pope, C.N., and Olszyk, V.B., 1991, Behavioral and neurochemical changes in rats dosed repeatedly with diisopropylfluorophosphate (DFP), *J. Pharmacol. Exp. Ther.* 256:741–750.

Chippendale, T.J., Zawolkow, G.A., Russell, R.W., and Overstreet, D.H., 1972, Tolerance to low acetylcholinesterase levels: Modification of behavior without acute behavioral changes, *Psychopharmacologia* 26:127–139.

Churchill, L., Pazdernik, T.L., Samson, F., and Nelson, S.R., 1984a, Topographical distribution of down-regulating muscarinic receptors in rat brains after repeated exposure to diisopropylfluorophosphate, *Neuroscience* 11:463–472.

Churchill, L., Pazdernik, T.L., Jackson, J.L., Nelson, S.R., Samson, F.E., and McDonough, J.E., 1984b, Topographical distribution of decrements and recovery in muscarinic receptors from rat brains repeatedly exposed to sublethal doses of soman, *J. Neurosci.* 4:2069–2079.

Churchill, L., Pazdernik, T.L., Samson, F., Nelson, S.R., Samson, R.E., McDonough, J.E., and McLeod, C.G., 1985, Soman-induced brain lesions demonstrated by muscarinic receptor autoradiography, *Neurotoxicology* 6:61–70.

Cioffi, C.L., and El-Fakahany, E.E., 1988, Lack of alterations in muscarinic receptor subtypes and phosphoinositide hydrolysis upon acute DFP treatment, *Eur. J. Pharmacol.* 156:35–45.

Clement, J.G., 1984, Role of aliesterase in organophosphate poisoning, *Fundam. Appl. Toxicol.* 4:S96–S105.

Clement, J.G., 1991, Hypothermia: Limited tolerance to repeated soman administration and cross-tolerance to oxotremorine, *Pharmacol. Biochem. Behav.* 39:305–312.

Coats, J.R., 1987, Toxicology of pesticide residues in foods, in: *Nutritional Toxicology, Vol. II* (J.N. Hathcock, ed.), Academic Press, New York, pp. 249–279.

Cohen, S.D., 1984, Mechanisms of toxicological interactions involving organophosphate insecticides, *Fundam. Appl. Toxicol.* 4:315–324.

Costa, L.G., and Murphy, S.D., 1983, [^{3}H] nicotine binding in rat brain: Alteration after chronic acetylcholinesterase inhibition, *J. Pharmacol. Exper. Ther.* 226:392–397.

Costa, L.G., Schwab, B.W., and Murphy, S.D., 1982, Tolerance to anticholinesterase compounds in mammals, *Toxicology* 25:79–97.

Costa, L.G., Kaylor, G., and Murphy, S.D., 1986, Carbachol- and norepinephrine-stimulated phosphoinositide metabolism in rat brain: Effect of chronic cholinesterase inhibition, *J. Pharmacol. Exper. Ther.* 239:32–37.

Coyle, J.T., Price, D.L., and DeLong, M.R., 1983, Alzheimer's disease: A disorder of cortical cholinergic innervation, *Science* 219:1184–1190.

Crocker, A.D., and Overstreet, D.H., 1991, Changes in dopamine sensitivity in rats selectively bred for differences in cholinergic function, *Pharmacol. Biochem. Behav.* 38:105–108.

Dawson, R.M., and Jarrot, B., 1981, Response of muscarinic cholinoreceptors of guinea pig brain and ileum to chronic administration of carbamate or organophosphate cholinesterase inhibitors, *Biochem. Pharmacol.* 30:2365–2368.

DeRoeth, A., Dettbarn, W.D., Rosenberg, P., Wilensky, J.G., and Wong, A., 1965, Effect of phospholine iodide on blood cholinesterase levels of normal and glaucoma subjects, *Am. J. Ophthalmol.* 59:586–592.

Ehlert, F.J., Kokka, N., and Fairhurst, D.S., 1980a, Altered [^{3}H] quinuclidinyl benzilate binding in the striatum of rats following chronic cholinesterase inhibition with diisopropylfluorophosphate, *Molec. Pharmacol.* 17:24–30.

Ehlert, F.J., Kokka, N., and Fairhurst, D.S., 1980b, Altered [^{3}H] quinuclidinyl benzilate binding in the longitudinal muscle of the rat ileum following chronic anticholinesterase treatment with diisopropylfluorophosphate, *Biochem. Pharmacol.* 29:1391–1397.

Fernando, J.C.R., Hoskins, B.H., and Ho, I.K., 1984a, A striatal serotonergic involvement in the behavioral effects of anticholinesterase organophosphates, *Eur. J. Pharmacol.* 98:129–132.

Fernando, J.C.R., Hoskins, B., and Ho, I.K., 1984b, Effects on striatal dopamine metabolism and differential motor behavioral tolerance following chronic anticholinesterase treatment with diisopropyl fluorophosphate, *Pharmacol. Biochem. Behav.* 20:951–957.

Gardner, R., Ray, R., Frankenheim, J., Wallace, K., Loss, M., and Robichaud, R., 1984, A possible mechanism for diisopropyl fluorophosphate-induced memory loss in rats, *Pharmacol. Biochem. Behav.* 21:43–46.

Gazit, H., Silman, I., and Dudai, Y., 1979, Administration of an organophosphate causes a decrease in muscarinic receptor levels in rat brain, *Brain Res.* 174:351–356.

Genovese, R.F., 1990, Effects of azaprophen, scopolamine and trihexyphenidyl on schedule-controlled behavior before and after chronic physostigmine, *Eur. J. Pharmacol.* 176:271–279.

Genovese, R.F., Elsmore, T.F., and King, L.R., 1988a, Tolerance to oxotremorine's effects on schedule-controlled behavior in physostigmine-tolerant rats, *Life Sci.* 43:571–576.

Genovese, R.F., Elsmore, T.F., and Witkin, J.M., 1988b, Environmental influences on the development of tolerance to the effects of physostigmine on schedule-controlled behavior, *Psychopharmacology* 9:462–467.

Glisson, S.N., Karczmar, A.G., and Barnes, L., 1974, Effects of DFP on acetylcholine, cholinesterase and catecholamines of several parts of rabbit brain, *Neuropharmacology* 13:623–631.

Hama, H., and Hosoda, A., 1983, High aliesterase activity and low acetylcholinesterase sensitivity involved in organophosphate and carbamate resistance in the brown planthopper, *Nilaparvata-Lugena stas* (Homoptera, Delphacidae), *Appl. Ent. Zool.* 18:475–485.

Jenden, D.J., 1980, Regulation of acetylcholine synthesis and release, in: *Psychopharmacology and Biochemistry of Neurotransmitter Receptors* (H.I. Yamamura, R.W. Olsen, and E. Usdin, eds.), Elsevier, New York, pp. 3–15.

Jope, R.S., 1979, High affinity choline transport and acetyl CoA production in brain and their roles in the regulation of acetylcholine synthesis, *Brain Res. Rev.* 1:313–344.

Kar, P.P., and Matin, M.A.J., 1972, Possible role of gamma-aminobutyric acid in paraoxon-induced convulsions, *J. Pharmac. Pharmacol.* 24:996–997.

Karczmar, A.G., 1984, Acute and long-lasting central actions of organophosphorus agents, *Fundam. Appl. Pharmacol.* 4:S1–S17.

Katz, L.S., and Marquis, J.K., 1989, Modulation of central muscarinic binding *in vitro* by ultralow levels of the organophosphate paraoxon, *Toxicol. Appl. Pharmacol.* 101:114–123.

Koehn, G.L., Henderson, G., and Karczmar, A.G., 1982, Diisopropyl phosphofluoridate-induced antinociception: Possible role of endogenous opiates, *Eur. J. Pharmacol.* 61:161–173.

LeMercier, G., Carpentier, Q., Senteac-Roumanou, H., and Morelis, P., 1983, Histological and histochemical changes in the central nervous system of the rat poisoned by an irreversible anticholinesterase organophosphorus compound, *Acta Neurophatol., Berlin* 61:123–129.

Lim, D.K., Hoskins, B., and Ho, I.K., 1987a, Evidence for the involvement of presynaptic cholinergic functions in tolerance to DFP, *Toxicol. Appl. Pharmacol.* 90:465–476.

Lim, D.K., Porter, A.B., Hoskins, B., and Ho, I.K., 1987, Changes in acetylcholine levels in the rat brain during subacute administration of DFP, *Toxicol. Appl. Pharmacol.* 90:477–489.

Lipp, J.A., 1973, Effect of benzodiazepine derivative on soman-induced seizure activity and convulsions in the monkey, *Arch. Int. Pharmacodyn. Ther.* 220:244–251.

Loullis, C.C., Dean, R.L., Lippa, L.S., Meyerson, L.R., Beer, B., and Bartus, R.T., 1983, Chronic administration of cholinergic agents: Effects of behavior and calmodulin, *Pharmacol. Biochem. Behav.* 18:601–604.

Lundy, P.R., and Magor, G.F., 1977, Cyclic GMP concentrations in cerebellum following organophosphate administration, *J. Pharmac. Pharmacol.* 30:251–252.

Lundy, P.M., Magor, G.F., and Shaw, R.K., 1978, Gamma aminobutyric acid metabolism in different areas of rat brain at the onset of soman-induced convulsions, *Arch. Int. Pharmacodyn. Ther.* 234:64–73.

Maayani, S., Egozi, Y., Pinchasi, I., and Sokolovsky, M., 1977, On the interaction of drugs with the cholinergic nervous system. IV. Tolerance to oxotremorine in mice. *In vivo* and *in vitro* studies, *Biochem. Pharmacol.* 26:1681–1687.

Marks, R.J., Artman, L.D., Patinkin, D.M., and Collins, A.C., 1981, Cholinergic adaptations to chronic oxotremorine infusion, *J. Pharmacol. Exper. Ther.* 218:337–343.

Mays, M.Z., McDonough, J.H., Modrow, H.E., Smith, C.D., and McLeod, C.G., 1984, Behavioral correlates of neuropathology produced by soman intoxication, *Pharmacol. Biochem. Behav.* 20:994–995.

McKinney, M., and Coyle, J.T., 1982, Regulation of neocortical muscarinic receptors: Effects of drug treatment and lesions, *J. Neurosci.* 2:97–106.

McKinney, M., and Richelson, E., 1984, The coupling of neuronal muscarinic receptor to responses, *Annu. Rev. Pharmacol. Toxicol.* 24:121–146.

McLeod, C.G., Singer, A.W., and Harrington, D.C:, 1984, Acute neuropathy in soman-poisoned rats, *Neurotoxicology* 5, 53–58.

Meneguz, A., Bisso, G.M., and Michalek, H., 1981, Regional difference in brain-soluble acetylcholinesterase and its molecular forms after acute poisoning by isofluorophate in rats, *Clin. Toxicol.* 18:1443–1445.

Michalek, H., Meneguz, A., and Bisso, O.M., 1981a, Molecular forms of rat brain acetylcholinesterase in diisopropyl fluorophosphate intoxication and subsequent recovery, *Neurobehav. Toxicol. Teratol.* 3:303–312.

Michalek, H., Bisso, G.M., and Meneguz, S., 1981b, Comparative studies or rat brain soluble acetylcholinesterase and its molecular forms during intoxication by DFP and paraoxon, in: *Cholinergic Mechanisms* (G. Pepeu, and H. Ladinsky, eds.) Plenum, New York, pp. 847–852.

Olianas, M.C., Onali, P., Schwartz, J.P., Neff, N.H., and Costa, E., 1984, The muscarinic receptor adenylate cyclase complex of the rat striatum: Desensitization following chronic inhibition of acetylcholinesterase activity, *J. Neurochem.* 42:1439–1443.

Oppenorth, F.J., and Welling, W., 1976, Biochemistry and physiology of resistance, in: *Insecticide Biochemistry and Physiology* (C.F. Wilkinson, ed.), Plenum, New York, pp. 507–551.

Overstreet, D.H., 1974, Reduced behavioral effects of pilocarpine during chronic treatment with DFP, *Behav. Biol.* 11:49–58.

Overstreet, D.H., 1984, Behavioural plasticity and the cholinergic system, *Prog. Neuro-Psychopharmacol. Biol. Psychiatry* 8:133–151.

Overstreet, D.H., 1986, Selective breeding for increased cholinergic function: Development of a new animal model of depression, *Biol. Psychiatry* 21:49–58.

Overstreet, D.H., 1989, Correlations of ethanol-induced hypothermia in FSL and FRL rats with hypothermia induced by other drugs, Paper presented at 13th Annual Symposium of the North Carolina Alcoholism Research Authority, Raleigh, NC.

Overstreet, D.H., and Crocker, A.D., 1991, Genetic aspects of cholinergic sensitivity in inbred and selectively bred rats, Paper presented at meeting of Behavioral Genetics Association, St. Louis, MO, June, 1991.

Overstreet, D.H., and Dubas, G., 1978, Tolerance to the behavioural effects of physostigmine in rats: Lack of behavioural compensation, *Commun. Psychopharmacol.* 2:93–98.

Overstreet, D.H., and Russell, R.W., 1982, Selective breeding for sensitivity to diisopropyl fluorophosphate. Effects of cholinergic agonists and antagonists, *Psychopharmacology* 78:150–154.

Overstreet, D.H., and Schiller, G.D., 1979, Behavioural compensation, muscarinic receptors and tolerance development to physostigmine, *Soc. Neurosci.* 6:658.

Overstreet, D.H., and Yamamura, H.I., 1979, Receptor alterations and drug tolerance, *Life Sci.* 25:1865–1878.

Overstreet, D.H., Kozar, M.D., and Lynch, G.S., 1973, Reduced hypothermic effects of cholinomimetic agents following chronic anticholinesterase treatment, *Neuropharmacology* 12:1017–1032.

Overstreet, D.H., Russell, R.W., Vazquez, B.J., and Dalglish, F.W., 1974, Involvement of muscarinic and nicotinic receptors in behavioural tolerance to DFP, *Pharmacol. Biochem. Behav.* 2:45–54.

Overstreet, D.H., Russell, R.W., Helps, S.C., Runge, P., and Prescott, A.M., 1979a, Sex differences following manipulation of the cholinergic system by DFP and pilocarpine, *Psychopharmacology* 61:49–58.

Overstreet, D.H., Russell, R.W., Helps, S.C., and Messenger, M., 1979b, Selective breeding for sensitivity to the anticholinesterase, DFP, *Psychopharmacology* 65:15–20.

Overstreet, D.H., Russell, R.W., Kerni, W., and Netherton, R.W., 1981, The influence of ovariectomy on the sex-dependent effects of the anticholinesterase, DFP, *Psychopharmacology* 74:393–394.

Overstreet, D.H., Russell, R.W., Crocker, A.D., and Schiller, G.D., 1984, Selective breeding for differences in cholinergic function: Pre- and post-synaptic mechanisms involved in sensitivity to the anticholinesterase, DFP, *Brain Res.* 294:327–332.

Overstreet, D.H., Booth, R.A., Dana, R., Risch, S.C., and Janowsky, D.S., 1986a, Enhanced elevation of corticosterone following arecoline administration to rats selectively bred for increased cholinergic function, *Psychopharmacology* 88:129–130.

Overstreet, D.H., Janowsky, D.S., Gillin, J.C., Shiromani, P.S., and Sutin, E.L., 1986b, Stress-induced immobility in rats with cholinergic supersensitivity, *Biol. Psychiatry* 21:657–664.

Overstreet, D.H., Russell, R.W., Crocker, A.D., Gillin, J.C., and Janowsky, D.S., 1988, Genetic and pharmacological models of cholinergic supersensitivity and affective disorders, *Experientia* 44:465–472.

Overstreet, D.H., Clement, J.G., Schiller, G.D., Bruzzone, A.D., and Kovaliski, J., 1990, Differences in plasma carboxylesterase activity: Relevance to anticholinesterase sensitivity, *Biochem. Pharmacol.* 39:2063–2064.

Pedigo, N.W. Jr., 1988, Pharmacological adaptations and muscarinic receptor plasticity in hypothalamus of senescent rats treated chronically with cholinergic drugs, *Psychopharmacology* 95:497–501.

Pepe, S., Overstreet, D.H., and Crocker, A.D., 1988, Enhanced benzodiazepine responsiveness in rats with increased cholinergic function, *Pharmacol. Biochem. Behav.* 31:15–19.

Pintor, A., Fortuna, S., Volpe, M.T., and Michalek, H., 1988, Muscarinic receptor plasticity in the brain of senescent rats—down-regulation after repeated administration of diisopropylfluorophosphate, *Life Sci.* 42:2113–2121.

Pintor, A., Fortuna, S., DeAngells, and Michalek, H., 1990, Recovery of brain muscarinic receptor sites following an adaptive down-regulation induced by repeated administration of DFP in aged rats, *Life Sci.* 46:1027–1036.

Potter, P.E., Hadji-Constantinou, M., Rubinstein, J.S., and Neff, N.H., 1984, Chronic treatment with DFP increases dopamine turnover in the striatum of the rat, *Eur. J. Pharmacol.* 106:607–612.

Raffaele, K., Olton, D., and Annau, Z., 1990, Repeated exposure to diisopropyl-fluorophosphate (DFP) produces increased sensitivity to cholinergic antagonists in discrimination retention and reversal, *Psychopharmacology* 100:267–274.

Raiteri, M., Marchi, M., and Paudice, P., 1981, Adaptation of presynaptic autoreceptors following long-term drug treatment, *Eur. J. Pharmacol.* 74:109–110.

Raslear, T.G., Shurtleff, D., and Simmons, L., 1988, The effects of diisopropyl fluorophosphate (DFP) on time perception in rats, *Physiol. Behav.* 43:805–813.

Ritter, W.F., 1990, Pesticide contamination of ground water in the United States—A review, *J. Environ. Sci. Health* B25:1–29.

Rosenthal, N.E., and Cameron, C.L., 1991, Exaggerated sensitivity to an organophosphate pesticide, *Am. J. Psychiatry* 148:270.

Rosenstock, L., Daniell, W., Barnhardt, S., Schwartz, D., and Demers, P.A., 1990, Chronic neuropsychological sequelae of occupational exposure to organophosphate insecticides, *Am. J. Ind. Med.* 18:321–325.

Russell, R.W., 1982, Cholinergic system in behaviour: The search for mechanisms of action, *Annu. Rev. Pharmacol. Toxicol.* 22:435–463.

Russell, R.W., and Overstreet, D.H., 1987, Mechanisms underlying sensitivity to organophosphorus anticholinesterase compounds, *Prog. Neurobiol.* 28:97–131.

Russell, R.W., Warburton, D.M., and Segal, D.S., 1969, Behavioral tolerance during chronic changes in the cholinergic system, *Commun. Behav. Biol.* 4:121–128.

Russell, R.W., Vasquez, B.J., Overstreet, D.H., and Dalglish, F.W., 1971a, Consummatory behavior during tolerance to and withdrawal from chronic depression of cholinesterase activity, *Physiol. Behav.* 7:523–528.

Russell, R.W., Vazquez, B.J., Overstreet, D.H., and Dalglish, F.W., 1971b, Effects of cholinolytic agents on behavior following development of tolerance to low cholinesterase activity, *Psychopharmacologia* 20:32–41.

Russell, R.W., Overstreet, D.H., Cotman, C.W., Carson, V.G., Doyle, L., Dalglish, F.W., and Vasquez, B.J., 1975, Experimental tests of hypotheses about neurochemical mechanisms underlying behavioral tolerance to the anticholinesterase, DFP, *J. Pharmacol. Exp. Ther.* 192:73–85.

Russell, R.W., Carson, V.G., Jope, R.S., Booth, R.A., and Macri, J., 1979, Development of behavioural tolerance: A search for subcellular mechanisms, *Psychopharmacology* 66:155–168.

Russell, R.W., Carson, V.G., Booth, R.A., and Jenden, D.J., 1981, Mechanisms of tolerance to the anticholinesterase, DFP: Acetylcholine levels and dynamics in the rat brain, *Neuropharmacology* 20:1197–1201.

Russell, R.W., Overstreet, D.H., Messenger, M., and Helps, S.C., 1982, Selective breeding for sensitivity to DFP. Generalization of effects beyond criterion variables, *Pharmacol. Biochem. Behav.* 17:885–891.

Russell, R.W., Overstreet, D.H., and Netherton, R.A., 1983, Sex-linked and other genetic factors in the development of tolerance to DFP, *Neuropharmacology* 22:75–81.

Russell, R.W., Booth, R.A., Jenden, D.J., Roch, M., and Rice, K.M., 1985, Changes in presynatpic release of acetylcholine during development of tolerance to the anticholinesterase, DFP, *J. Neurochem.* 45:293–299.

Russell, R.W., Booth, R.A., Smith, C.A., Jenden, D.J., Roch, M., Rice, K.M., and Lauretz, S.D., 1989, Roles of neurotransmitter receptors in behavior: Recovery of function following decreases in muscarinic receptor density induced by cholinesterase inhibition, *Behav. Neurosci.* 103:881–892.

Samson, F.E., Pazdernik, T.L., Cross, K.S., Giesler, M.P., Melles, K., Nelson, S.R., and McDonough, J.H., 1984, Soman-induced changes in brain regional glucose use, *Fundam. Appl. Toxicol.* 4:S173–S183.

Savage, E.P., Keefe, T.J., Mounce, L.M., Heaton, R.K., Lewis, J.A., and Burcar, P.J., 1988, Chronic neurological sequelae of acute organophosphate pesticide poisoning, *Arch. Environ. Health* 43:38–45.

Schallert, T., Overstreet, D.H., and Yamamura, H.I., 1980, Muscarinic receptor binding and behavioral effects of atropine following chronic catecholamine depletion or acetylcholinesterase inhibition in rats, *Pharmacol. Biochem. Behav.* 13:187–192.

Schiller, G.D., 1979, Reduced binding of ^{3}H-quinuclidinyl benzilate associated with chronically low acetylcholinesterase activity, *Life Sci.* 24:1149–1154.

Schiller, G.D., 1991, Altered behavioral sensitivity to serotonergic agonists in an animal model of depressive disorders: Receptor binding correlates and cholinergic-serotonergic systems interaction, Paper presented at 13th Biennial Meeting of the International Society for Neurochemistry, Sydney, Australia, July, 1991.

Schiller, G.D., Overstreet, D.H., and Orbach, J., 1988, Effects of intracerebroventricular administration of site selective muscarinic drugs in rats genetically selected for differing cholinergic sensitivity, Paper presented at meeting of Australasian Society for Clinical and Experimental Pharmacology, Adelaide, Australia, December, 1988.

Schwartz, R.D., and Keller, K.J., 1983, Nicotinic cholinergic receptor binding sites in the brain: Regulation *in vitro*, *Science* 220:214–216.

Shih, T.-M., 1982, Time course of soman on acetylcholine and choline levels in six discrete areas of the rat brain, *Psychopharmacologia* 78:170–175.

Sihotang, K., and Overstreet, D.H., 1983, Studies on the possible relationship of brain proteins to behavioral sensitivity to DFP, *Life Sci.* 32:413–420.

Sivam, S.P., Nabeshima, F., Lim, D.K., Hoskins, B., and Ho, I.K., 1983a, DFP and GABA synaptic function—effect on levels, enzymes, release and uptake in the striatum, *Res. Commun. Chem. Pathol. Pharmacol.* 42:51–60.

Sivam, S.P., Norris, J.C., Lim, D.K., Hoskins, B., and Ho, I.K., 1983b, Influence of acute and chronic cholinesterase inhibition with diisopropylfluorophosphate on muscarinic, dopamine and GABA receptors in the rat striatum, *J. Neurochem.* 40:1414–1422.

Sivam, S.P., Hoskins, B., and Ho, I.K., 1984, An assessment of comparative acute toxicity of diisopropyl fluorophosphate, tabun, sarin, and soman in relation to cholinergic and GABAergic enzyme activities in rats, *Fundam. Appl. Toxicol.* 4:531–538.

Smolen, A., Smolen, T.N., Wehner, J.M., and Collins, A.C., 1985, Genetically determined differences in acute responses to diisopropylfluorophosphate, *Pharmacol. Biochem. Behav.* 22:623–630.

Taylor, P., 1980, Anticholinesterase agents, in: *The Pharmacological Basis of Therapeutics* (A.G. Gilman, A.S. Goodman, and A. Gilman, eds.), Macmillan, New York, pp. 100–119.

Tucek, S., 1984, Problems in the organization and controls of acetylcholine synthesis in brain neurons, *Prog. Biophys. Molec. Biol.* 44:1–46.

Uchida, S., Takeyasu, K., Matsuda, T., and Yoshida, H., 1979, Changes in muscarinic acetylcholine receptors of mice by chronic administrations of diisopropylfluorophosphate and papaverine, *Life Sci.* 24:1805–1812.

Ugaki, M., Abe, T., Fukami, S., and Shono, T., 1983, Electrophoretic analysis of nonspecific esterases and acetylcholinesterase S from the housefly *Musca domestica L* (Diptera; muscidae) with reference to organophosphorus insecticide resistance, *Appl. Ent. Zool.* 18:447–455.

Upchurch, M., Pounder, J.I., and Wehner, J.M., 1988, Heterosis and resistance to DFP effects on spatial learning in C57BL × DBA hybrids, *Brain Res. Bull.* 21:499–503.

Vianna, G., Davis, L., and Kauffman, F.C., 1988, Effects of organophosphates and nerve growth factor on muscarinic receptor binding in rat pheochromocytoma PC12 cells, *Toxicol. Appl. Pharmacol.* 93:251–266.

Volpe, L., Biagini, T., and Marquis, J.K., 1985, *In vitro* modulation of bovine caudate muscarinic receptor number by organophosphates and carbamates, *Toxicol. Appl Pharmacol.* 78:226–234.

Wainer, B.H., Bolam, S.P., Freund, J.F., Henderson, Z., Tottendell, S., and Smith, A.D., 1984, Cholinergic synapses in the rat brain: A correlated light and electron microscopic immunohistochemical study employing a monoclonal antibody against choline acetyltransferase, *Brain Res.* 308:69–76.

Wallis, E., Overstreet, D.H., and Crocker, A.D., 1988, Selective breeding for increases in cholinergic function: Psychopharmacological evidence for increases in serotonergic sensitivity, *Pharmacol. Biochem. Behav.* 31:345–350.

Wang, C., and Murphy, S.D., 1982, The role of noncritical binding proteins in the sensitivity of acetylcholinesterases from different species to DFP, *in vitro, Life Sci.* 31:134–149.

Wecker, L., Mobley, P.L., and Dettbarn, W.D., 1977, Central cholinergic mechanisms underlying adaptation to reduced cholinesterase activity, *Biochem. Pharmacol.* 26:633–637.

Yamada, S., Isogai, M., Okudaira, H., and Hayashi, E., 1983, Regional adaptation of muscarinic receptors and choline uptake in brain following repeated administration of diisopropylfluorophosphate and atropine, *Brain Res.* 268:315–320.

Yamada, S., Isogai, M., Okudaira, H., and Hayashi, E., 1983, Correlation between cholinesterase inhibition and reduction in muscarinic receptors and choline uptake by repeated diisopropylfluorophosphate administration—Antagonism by physostigmine and atropine, *J. Pharmacol. Exper. Ther.* 226:519–525.

Yang, C.-M., Dwyer, T.M., Murali Mohan, P., Ho, I.K., and Farley, J.M., 1990, Down-regulation of muscarinic receptors in the striatum of OP-treated swine, *Toxicol. Appl. Pharmacol.* 104:375–385.

Zabik, M.E., 1987, Pesticides and other industrial chemicals, in: *Toxicological Aspects of Food* (K. Miller, ed.), Elsevier, New York, pp. 73–102.

Zahavi, M., Takori, A.S., and Klimer, F., 1971, Insensitivity of acetylcholinesterases to organophosphorus compounds as related to size of esteratic site, *Molec. Pharmacol.* 7:611–619.

Chapter 12

Silver Impregnation of Organophosphorus-Induced Delayed Neuropathy in the Central Nervous System

Duke Tanaka, Jr., Steven J. Bursian, and *Ellen J. Lehning*

1. INTRODUCTION

The use of organophosphorus compounds is widespread in industry, finding such diverse applications as insecticides, flame retardants, plasticizers, petroleum additives, and intermediates in the manufacture of pharmaceuticals (Davis and Richardson, 1980; U.S. Environmental Protection Agency, 1985). It has been well documented that exposure to certain of these compounds may result in organophosphorus-induced delayed neurotoxicity (OPIDN), a neurological condition characterized by progressively developing hindlimb ataxia and paralysis, inhibition of the enzyme neuropathy target esterase (NTE), and development of axonal degeneration in both the central (CNS) and peripheral (PNS) nervous systems (Abou-Donia, 1981; Abou-Donia and Lapadula, 1990; Baron, 1981; Davis and Richardson, 1980; Johnson, 1975, 1982, 1990).

Recently OPIDN has been divided into two categories, Type I and Type II, with each type possessing distinctive clinical and neuropathological characteristics (Abou-Donia and Lapadula, 1990). Type I is produced by exposure to organophosphorus compounds such as tri-*o*-tolyl phosphate or TOTP (also known as tri-*ortho*-cresyl phosphate or TOCP), *bis* (1-methylethyl) phosphoroflouridate (DFP), mipafox, or leptophos. It is char-

Duke Tanaka, Jr. • Department of Anatomy, Michigan State University, East Lansing, Michigan 48824. *Steven J. Bursian* and *Ellen J. Lehning* • Department of Animal Science, Michigan State University, East Lansing, Michigan 48824.
The Vulnerable Brain and Environmental Risks, Volume 2: Toxins in Food, edited by Robert L. Isaacson and Karl F. Jensen. Plenum Press, New York, 1992.

acterized by the presence of a relatively long delay period of 10–21 days before the onset of hindlimb ataxia and paralysis. The accompanying neuropathology is restricted to the peripheral nerves, brainstem, and spinal cord. In contrast, Type II OPIDN may be produced by exposure to triphenyl phosphite or tri-*ortho*-, tri-*meta*-, or tri-*para*-cresyl phosphite. In addition to a shortened delay period of 4–7 days before the onset of ataxia and hindlimb paralysis, affected rats may also exhibit bidirectional circling and tail kinking (Veronesi *et al.*, 1986; Veronesi and Dvergsten, 1987). Results of recent work in our lab also showed that Type II associated neuropathology involves not only structures in the spinal cord and brainstem, but in the midbrain and forebrain as well (Tanaka *et al.*, 1990b, 1991a).

The dangers associated with human exposure to organophosphorus compounds are best illustrated by the series of poisonings caused by ingestion of TOTP that occurred at intervals during the period from 1930 through the 1970s. In most of these cases, poisoning was the result of ingestion of Jamaica ginger extract, cooking oil, or food adulterated with TOTP (Morgan, 1982; Senanayake and Johnson, 1982). The victims displayed acute signs of vomiting and diarrhea followed by delayed onset of muscle pain, muscle weakness, and paresthesias. In chronic cases, individuals showed signs of persistent ataxia and spasticity. More recently, concern has been expressed over occupational exposure to organophosphorus pesticides (Windebank, 1987), particularly in underdeveloped countries (Forget, 1991). Several studies have shown that, in addition to the acute and delayed effects associated with OPIDN, higher order dysfunctions may be present as well, manifested as difficulties in concentration, nervousness, depression, and the presence of various forms of psychiatric disturbances (Amr, 1989; Tabershaw and Cooper, 1966).

Although the clinical signs associated with OPIDN have been well documented and the initial biochemical event has been assumed to involve phosphorylation and aging of NTE, the extent of the accompanying degeneration in the CNS has not been as well defined. This is because those who have studied the CNS have primarily confined their efforts to the spinal cord and medulla and, with few exceptions (Cavanagh and Patangia, 1965; Illis *et al.*, 1966), have used less sensitive myelin or axonal stains to determine the location and severity of neuronal damage (Abou-Donia and Pressig, 1976; Abou-Donia *et al.*, 1979; Barnes and Denz, 1953; Beresford and Glees, 1963; Carrington *et al.*, 1988; Cavanagh, 1954; Lotti *et al.*, 1987; Jortner and Ehrich, 1987; Prentice and Roberts, 1983; Sprague and Bickford, 1981; Veronesi and Dvergsten, 1987; Veronesi *et al.*, 1986). Of necessity, this has limited the amount of data collected, with the result that the most commonly reported neuropathological characteristic of OPIDN has been degeneration of long axons in the peripheral nerves, spinal cord, and medulla. These findings suggest that use of standard axon or myelin stains may be appropriate for studies on the effects of organophosphorus compounds in the PNS (Cavanagh, 1964; Glazer *et al.*, 1978; Prineas, 1969), where axons are of greater diameter and length, more heavily myelinated, and more discretely organized. However, these stains are less useful for identifying small-diameter unmyelinated degenerating axons and terminal fields spread over wide areas of the brain and spinal cord.

The present report reviews the results of a series of studies we initiated using the Fink–Heimer silver impregnation method to map the total extent of neuropathology following exposure to several organophosphorus compounds in the hen, rat, and ferret (Lehning *et al.*, 1990; Tanaka and Bursian, 1989; Tanaka *et al.*, 1990a, 1990b, 1991a, 1991b). In each study, the major objective was to identify the origin, course, and termination patterns of specific afferent and efferent axonal pathways affected by exposure to organophosphorus compounds. The hen and rat were chosen as subjects in order to compare the data obtained using the Fink–Heimer method with results obtained by other investigators using different techniques. Although the hen has been used most widely in studies of OPIDN, several recent studies have shown that the rat (Padilla and Veronesi, 1988; Veronesi, 1984; Veronesi and Dvergsten, 1987) and mouse (Lapadula et al., 1985; Veronesi et al., 1991) may also be appropriate mammalian models for OPIDN. The ferret was chosen as a subject since an initial study investigating the clinical, biochemical, and neuropathological effects of TOTP in this species showed that ferrets were susceptible to OPIDN (Stumpf et al., 1989), and further investigation of CNS degeneration characteristic of OPIDN seemed appropriate. We chose TOTP and TPP for our studies because each has been used as the prototypical compound for Type I and Type II OPIDN, respectively. DFP was used because we wished to compare the neuropathological effects of different Type I compounds and because DFP does not require metabolic activation for it to produce a neurotoxic effect, as does TOTP.

2. MAPPING CNS DEGENERATION CHARACTERISTIC OF OPIDN WITH THE FINK–HEIMER TECHNIQUE— ADVANTAGES AND DISADVANTAGES

The Fink–Heimer silver impregnation method (Fink and Heimer, 1967) has been used for decades to map axonal and terminal degeneration following mechanically or chemically induced lesions of the CNS. Indeed, much of the initial data on connectivity patterns in the CNS were obtained from carefully done Fink–Heimer silver impregnation studies. With the advent of newer autoradiographic, horseradish peroxidase, and lectin anterograde tracing techniques, the Fink–Heimer method fell out of favor for mapping CNS connections. However, this technique remains useful in studies in which the primary focus of investigation is to determine the location or extent of axonal or terminal degeneration resulting from CNS insult. Curiously, the Fink–Heimer method and its variants have not been used to any great extent in identifying regions of the nervous system affected in cases of OPIDN, even though those who have utilized silver-impregnation methods to examine the effect of neurotoxicants have reported much more extensive patterns of degeneration than those who have used the more traditional hematoxylin-eosin or toluidine blue methods (Cavanagh and Patangia, 1965; Illis et al., 1966; Scallet et al., 1988).

The advantages of the Fink–Heimer method are several. First, it is selective for degenerating axons and terminals, and thus is relatively easy to interpret. In well-processed tissue sections, degenerating axons and terminals will appear as black-impregnated linearly or randomly arranged fragments or punctate debris against a relatively light homogeneous background. The impregnation of degenerating terminals also allows degenerating axonal pathways to be traced to their nuclei or regions of termination and is of obvious importance in correlating loss of specific afferents or efferents with physiologically or clinically defined functional deficits. Second, the Fink–Heimer method is also capable of detecting the presence of degenerating cell bodies in both mature (Switzer, 1976; Tanaka, 1976; Tanaka and Chen, 1974) and immature (Yamamoto et al., 1986) brains, allowing the simultaneous demonstration of both axonal and somatic degeneration within a single CNS nucleus or area. This capability has been shown to be particularly useful in studying the neuropathological effects of TPP (Tanaka *et al.*, 1990b, 1991a), which had been previously shown by others to cause degeneration in both axons and neuronal somata (Carrington *et al.*, 1988; Veronesi and Dvergsten, 1987; Veronesi *et al.*, 1986). Finally, the ability of this method to stain tissue sections 40 μm thick and as large as 2–3 cm on a side allows degenerating pathways to be traced over relatively long distances. A more complete picture of resultant degeneration is presented, and involvement of multiple tracts and nuclei through several brain or spinal cord levels can be easily traced.

The disadvantages of this method are related primarily to the technical aspects of the procedure. It is a capricious method, as are most silver techniques, and consistent results are sometimes difficult to obtain. The central nervous system of the animal must be well perfused with fixative (usually a 10% formalin or buffered formalin solution), and the brain and spinal cord removed carefully. Frozen sectioning of the tissue is necessary for best results, and presoaking the tissue block in a 30% sucrose-formalin solution and careful freezing of the block are necessary to minimize cutting artifacts (knife marks, ragged cuts, or uneven section thicknesses). Since tissues are best processed individually through solutions as free-floating sections, the staining procedure itself can be time consuming and tedious. The glassware must be chemically clean and all solutions should be fresh. Interpretation of the results can be difficult if the impregnation is uneven, shows artifactual silver deposition, or excessively stains blood vessels. However, these potential artifacts have been documented as to appearance and particular areas of occurrence (Giolli and Karamanlidis, 1978; Heimer, 1970; de Olmos *et al.*, 1981), and with practice the observer can learn to differentiate degeneration from background artifact.

In summary, it is our opinion that the advantages of the Fink–Heimer method far outweigh any technical difficulties that might be encountered and that this method is the technique of choice for mapping the total and complete pattern of CNS somatic, axonal, and terminal degeneration resulting from exposure to organophosphorus delayed neurotoxicants.

3. NEUROPATHOLOGY CHARACTERISTIC OF OPIDN

3.1. Comparative Effects of TOTP, DFP, and TPP in the Hen

The purpose of this series of studies was to determine the location and severity of somatic and axonal degeneration resulting from exposure to three different organophosphorus neurotoxicants in the domestic hen (*Gallus domesticus*), the most frequently studied animal model for OPIDN. The results indicated that the effects of Type I delayed neurotoxicants TOTP and DFP were similar and were restricted to brainstem, cerebellar, and spinal cord regions (Tanaka and Bursian, 1989; Tanaka *et al.*, 1990a), whereas exposure to the Type II delayed neurotoxicant TPP resulted in widespread degeneration, also involving the midbrain and forebrain (Tanaka *et al.*, 1991a).

3.1.1. Effects of TOTP and DFP

In studies investigating the effects of TOTP or DFP, birds were administered a single oral dose of 500 mg TOTP/kg body weight or a single subcutaneous dose of 1 mg DFP/kg body weight, respectively, and killed after postexposure periods of 7, 14, 21, or 28 days. The densest and most widespread CNS degeneration was noted in hens exposed for 21 or 28 days.

Exposure to either compound resulted in moderate to dense amounts of axonal degeneration in the spinal cord. Degenerating axons were noted in the cervical parts of the fasciculus gracilis, and dorsal and ventral spinocerebellar tracts, and in the lumbar part of the medial pontine-spinal tract. Moderate amounts of terminal degeneration were also noted in the medial part of the ventral horn at lumbar cord levels (Fig. 1).

In the medulla, exposure to TOTP or DFP resulted in moderate amounts of terminal and preterminal degeneration appearing in the lateral vestibular, gracile-cuneate, external cuneate, and lateral cervical nuclei (Figs. 2, 3A,B). Lesser amounts of degeneration were noted in the solitary, inferior olivary, and raphae nuclei, in the medial and dorsal vestibular nuclei, and in the lateral paragigantocellular, gigantocellular, and lateral reticular nuclei. Fiber degeneration was also present in the medullary portions of the dorsal and ventral spinocerebellar tracts and in the spinal lemniscus. The dorsal spinocerebellar fibers passed dorsally and medially into the cerebellar peduncle, while spinal lemniscal fibers continued rostrally to terminate in the reticular formation. Axonal degeneration was also present in nerve fascicles making up the intramedullary portions of the glossopharyngeal and vagus nerves. In hens exposed to DFP, these fibers could be traced to their terminations within the mid-to-rostral portion of the nucleus tractus solitarius and a small portion of the adjacent dorsal motor nucleus of the vagus.

Within the cerebellum, exposure to TOTP or DFP resulted in mossy fiber degeneration in the granular layer of foliae I-Vb (Fig. 4), with the heaviest degeneration present in foliae IV and V. The degenerating fibers and preterminals were organized into alternating parasagittal bands of heavy and light degeneration. Small amounts of coarse fiber degeneration were also noted in the deep cerebellar nuclei of both TOTP- and DFP-exposed birds. In hens exposed to TOTP, moderate amounts of terminal degeneration were also noted in the deep cerebellar nuclei at 1 week postexposure. No degeneration was noted in the midbrain or forebrain of either TOTP- or DFP-exposed hens.

3.1.2. Effects of TPP

In this study, hens received a single subcutaneous injection of 1000 mg TPP/kg body weight and were killed 7, 14, and 21 days after exposure. The densest degeneration was noted 14 and 21 days after injection.

Axonal and terminal degeneration were noted throughout the length of the spinal cord and were thus more widespread than that seen after TOTP or DFP exposure. Small amounts of degeneration were seen in the fasciculus gracilis at cervical levels, while moderate to dense amounts of degeneration were noted in the spinocerebellar and medial pontine-spinal tracts at all cord levels. A scattered pattern of fine fiber degeneration was also present deep within the lateral and ventral funiculi. Dense degeneration was located in spinal laminae VII and VIII, extending into the lateral parts of the ventral horn at the

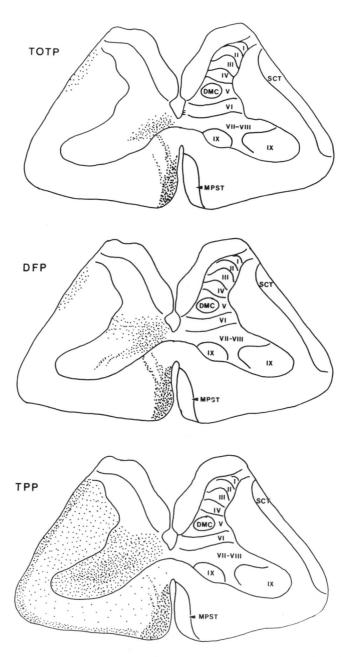

FIGURE 1. Line drawings illustrating cross sections through the lumbar spinal cord of hens 21 days after the administration of single doses of 500 mg TOTP/kg body weight, 1 mg DFP/kg body weight, and 1000 mg TPP/kg body weight. Roman numerals refer to spinal laminae and stippling indicates areas containing axonal and terminal degeneration. Note the extension of degeneration into the lateral part of the ventral horn in the TPP case.

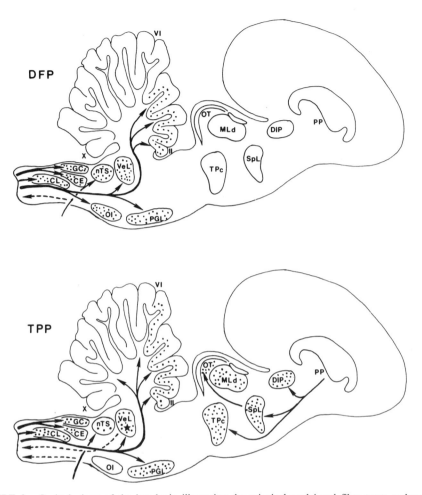

FIGURE 2. Sagittal views of the hen brain illustrating the principal nuclei and fiber tracts undergoing degeneration after exposure to 1 mg DFP/kg body weight and 1000 mg TPP/kg body weight. The solid arrows show the major degenerating pathways in the brain, while dashed arrows denote degenerating pathways descending into the spinal cord. Stippling indicates nuclei and areas containing terminal degeneration, and the star in VeL indicates the presence of degenerating cell somata. Note the additional forebrain degeneration present after exposure to TPP.

cervicothoracic and lumbosacral levels (Fig. 1). Light to moderate amounts of degeneration were also noted in laminae V, VI, and IX throughout the length of the spinal cord.

Axonal degeneration was extensive within the medulla and was present in the spinocerebellar tract, ventral part of the medial longitudinal fasciculus, spinal lemniscus, fascicles of cranial nerves IX and X, and reticular formation. Moderate to heavy terminal degeneration was also noted within the gracile-cuneate, lateral cervical, external cuneate, and lateral paragigantocellular reticular nuclei (Fig. 2). Lighter and more scattered terminal degeneration was noted within the parvocellular and gigantocellular reticular nuclei. The lateral vestibular nucleus contained degenerating cell bodies, as well as degenerating axons and terminals. Coarse degenerating spinocerebellar fibers could be traced into the

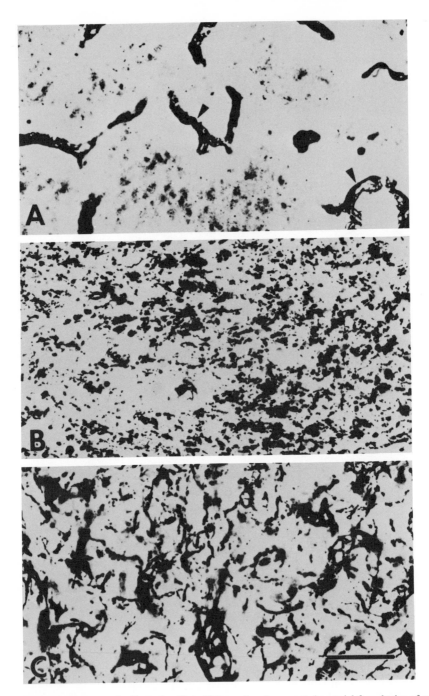

FIGURE 3. Photomicrographs illustrating Fink–Heimer silver-impregnated material from brains of control and treated hens. (A) Gracile-cuneate nucleus of a control hen. Note the absence of any fragmented or punctate degeneration. Small arrowheads indicate impregnated reticular fibers surrounding capillaries. (B) Terminal and axonal degeneration in the gracile-cuneate nucleus of a hen 21 days after the administration of 1 mg DFP/kg body weight. Note the presence of a large amount of punctate axonal and terminal debris. (C) Terminal and axonal degeneration in the lateral spiriform nucleus of a hen 21 days after exposure to 1000 mg TPP/kg body weight. In this nucleus the degeneration consists of longer fragments and little punctate debris is present. The scale bar is 50 μm and applies to all plates.

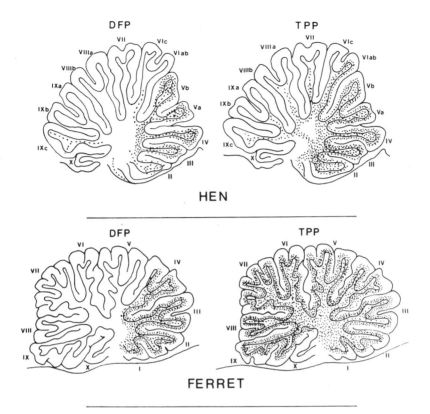

FIGURE 4. Sagittal views through the cerebella of DFP- and TPP-exposed hens and ferrets. In each view, rostral is to the right and caudal is to the left. Roman numerals refer to cerebellar foliae and stippling indicates axonal and terminal degeneration. Note that in both the hen and ferret, DFP exposure results in degeneration confined to the more rostral foliae of the anterior lobe. In contrast, TPP exposure results in more extensive cerebellar degeneration in both species, with the ferret showing the most widespread degeneration.

cerebellum, where light to moderate degeneration was noted in the deep nuclei and heavy mossy fiber degeneration was present in granule-cell layers of foliae I–VI (Fig. 4). Lighter fiber degeneration was also noted in the underlying white matter of foliae VII–IX.

Moderate to dense axonal and terminal degeneration were present in several nuclei of the midbrain and forebrain (Fig. 2). A band of degenerating axons originating in the paleostriatum primitivum passed caudally into the lateral forebrain bundle and ansa lenticularis. A small group of degenerating fibers branched off from these axons within the ansa lenticularis and coursed dorsally to terminate in the dorso-intermediate posterior thalamic nucleus. The majority of degenerating fibers continued caudally and terminated in the lateral spiriform and pedunculopontine tegmental nuclei (Figs. 2 and 3C). Smaller numbers of degenerating fibers, possibly originating from the lateral spiriform nucleus, passed dorsally and laterally into the deep layers of the optic tectum. The lateral mesencephalic nucleus, pars dorsalis also contained moderate numbers of degenerating terminals.

3.1.3. Summary and Synthesis

In the hen, exposure to the Type I delayed neurotoxicants TOTP and DFP results in axonal degeneration in major ascending fiber tracts in the spinal cord and medulla, as well as in the descending medial pontine-spinal tract. The presence of axonal degeneration in the spinocerebellar tracts and gracile fasciculus confirms data reported in previous studies using standard myelin and axonal stains. However, our results with the Fink–Heimer method extend these findings by identifying the brainstem nuclei and cerebellar areas receiving these degenerating inputs. Our data also show that, in addition to large heavily myelinated fiber tracts, smaller diameter fiber tracts, as well as visceral afferent fibers, may be affected by exposure to Type I delayed neurotoxicants.

The Fink–Heimer method was most useful in determining the total extent of degeneration arising from exposure to the Type II neurotoxicant, TPP. We found that our data verified the results of earlier TPP studies in the hen (Carrington and Abou-Donia, 1988; Carrington *et al.*, 1988) in that the brainstem contained both degenerating axons and cell somata. In general, fiber tracts and terminals underwent detectable degenerative changes somewhat sooner with TPP (heavy and extensive degeneration seen 14 days after exposure) than with either TOTP or DFP (heaviest degeneration seen at 21–28 days postexposure). As with hens exposed to TOTP or DFP, exposure to TPP resulted in heavy degeneration in the medulla, cerebellum, and spinal cord. However, in each of the TPP-exposed hens, the degeneration involved not only ascending fiber tracts and the medial pontine-spinal tract, but several additional descending brainstem-spinal pathways as well. For example, TPP-exposed hens also showed degeneration in the medial longitudinal fasciculus and vestibulospinal tract. In birds, the medial longitudinal fasciculus conveys projections from several brainstem nuclei to the spinal cord, while the vestibulospinal tract carries descending information from the lateral vestibular nucleus to both the cervical and lumbar spinal cord levels (Cabot *et al.*, 1982; Webster and Steeves, 1988).

In the spinal cord of TOTP- or DFP-exposed hens, the degeneration in the gray matter was more or less confined to the medial part of the ventral horn at lumbar cord levels. In contrast, in TPP-exposed hens, extensive degeneration was noted throughout the ventral horn at almost all levels of the cord, with dense degeneration noted around the ventral horn motoneurons located in the lateral part of lamina IX. Although we were not able to distinguish the presence of degenerating ventral horn motoneurons, others have reported degeneration of ventral horn cells after TPP exposure in both the hen and rat (Carrington *et al.*, 1988; Veronesi *et al.*, 1986; Veronesi and Dvergsten, 1987).

No signs of degeneration were noted in the midbrain or forebrain of the hen following the administration of TOTP or DFP. However, injections of TPP did result in large amounts of axonal and terminal degeneration in both midbrain and forebrain nuclei and tracts related to the avian basal ganglia system. The principal source of this degeneration appeared to be the paleostriatum primitivum—the avian homologue of the external segment of the globus pallidus in mammals (Karten and Dubbeldam, 1973). These fibers terminate principally in the dorso-intermediate posterior thalamic nucleus, pedunculopontine tegmental nucleus, and the lateral spiriform nucleus. The first two nuclei listed above are considered to be homologous to the mammalian ventral lateral thalamic nucleus and the substantia nigra, pars compacta, respectively (Karten and Dubbeldam, 1973; Reiner *et al.*, 1982). The lateral spiriform nucleus also receives direct input from the pedunculopontine tegmental nucleus and the nucleus of the ansa lenticularis (Reiner *et al.*, 1982). Since the only known efferent projection from the avian lateral spiriform nucleus is to the optic tectum (Reiner *et al.*, 1982), the convergence of these basal ganglia afferents onto this nucleus provides a pathway by which the basal ganglia may influence visuomotor activities.

In summary, exposure to Type I delayed neurotoxicants TOTP and DFP in the hen results in a delayed ataxia and paralysis, accompanied by axonal and terminal degeneration of several ascending brainstem fiber tracts. Degeneration is also present in the descending medial pontine-spinal tract, cerebellum, and medial part of the ventral horn. The clinical signs noted in these hens are probably related to the loss of proprioceptive afferents from the hindlimb to the cerebellum, along with loss of descending motor input to ventral horn motoneurons. In contrast, exposure to the Type II delayed neurotoxicant TPP results in a rapid and severe loss of motor control and activity. The involvement of higher order visuomotor and basal ganglia circuits, as well as additional descending fiber tracts, may account for the more rapid onset, severity, and complexity of the clinical signs seen after TPP exposure.

3.2. Comparative Effects of DFP and TPP in the Ferret and Rat

Recently, interest has developed in identifying new mammalian models of Type I OPIDN (Padilla and Veronesi, 1988; Veronesi, 1984; Veronesi and Dvergsten, 1987; Veronesi *et al.*, 1986, 1991). Although a number of mammalian species are susceptible to Type I compounds, the majority of laboratory mammals show few clinical signs (Baron, 1981; Johnson, 1975). Our studies in the ferret were prompted by the desire to determine whether the ferret might serve as an appropriate mammalian model for Type I OPIDN (Tanaka *et al.*, 1991b). An additional study using TPP as the delayed neurotoxicant was also performed in ferrets in order to assess Type II OPIDN degeneration patterns in this species (Tanaka *et al.*, 1990b).

Previous studies of OPIDN in the rat have shown that there is only a limited neuropathological response following the administration of TOTP or DFP, involving primarily the dorsal columns and spinocerebellar tracts, while exposure to TPP results in more widespread medullary and spinal cord degeneration (Padilla and Veronesi, 1988; Veronesi, 1984; Veronesi and Dvergsten, 1987). We used the Fink–Heimer method to examine more fully the extent and severity of neuropathology resulting from exposure to Type I and Type II delayed neurotoxicants in the rat (Lehning *et al.*, 1990, unpublished results). Based upon the results obtained in the hen and ferret, we anticipated that the more sensitive Fink–Heimer method might reveal a more extensive pattern of axonal and terminal degeneration.

3.2.1. Effects of DFP

Ferrets were injected subcutaneously with 2 or 4 mg DFP/kg body weight and were killed at postinjection intervals ranging from 6 hr to 28 days. Those animals exposed to 4 mg DFP and maintained for 21–28 days showed the greatest extent and severity of neuropathology.

In the spinal cord, dense axonal degeneration was present in the fasciculus gracilis and dorsal spinocerebellar tract at cervical levels and in the lateral corticospinal tract at lumbar levels (Fig. 5). Degenerating terminals were also noted in spinal cord laminae VI–

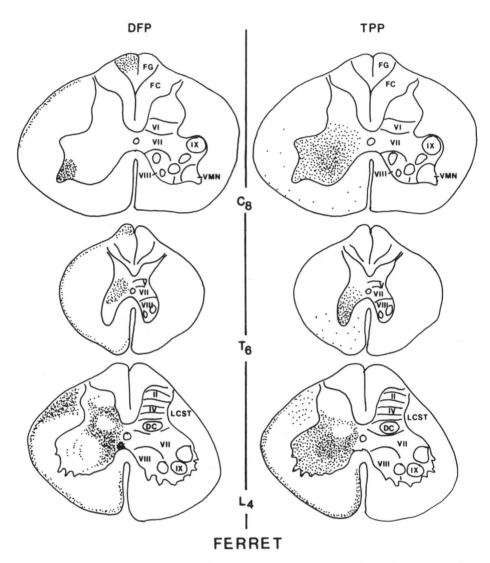

FIGURE 5. Line diagrams of cross sections through the spinal cords of ferrets 21 days after exposure to 4 mg DFP/kg body weight and 8 days after exposure to 1000 mg TPP/kg body weight. Roman numerals refer to spinal laminae and stippling indicates axonal and terminal degeneration. Note the more extensive degeneration seen in the ventral horns after exposure to TPP.

VII throughout most of the cord, with increased densities noted at lumbosacral levels. At C7–T1 spinal cord levels, dense degeneration was noted in the ventral motor nucleus of the cervical enlargement.

In the medulla, dense axonal and terminal degeneration were noted in the fasciculus and nucleus gracilis, medial and dorsal accessory nuclei of the inferior olive, inferior vestibular nucleus, and lateral reticular formation (Figs. 6, 7A, and 7B). Degenerating axons were also present in granule cell layers of cerebellar foliae I–IV (Fig. 4). The pattern of cerebellar mossy fiber degeneration was similar to that seen in the hen and consisted of alternating parasagittally oriented bands of dense and light degeneration.

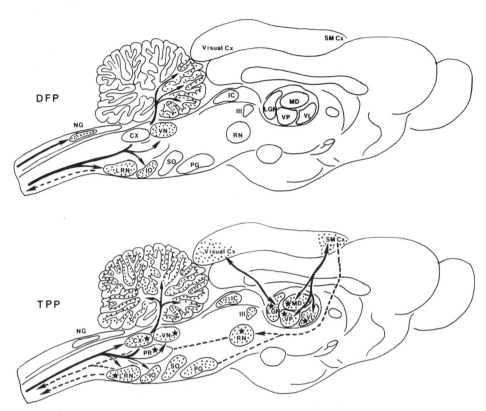

FIGURE 6. Sagittal views of the ferret brain illustrating the principal pathways and nuclei showing degeneration after exposure to 4 mg DFP/kg body weight and 1000 mg TPP/kg body weight. Solid arrows indicate major degenerating fiber pathways within the brain, while dashed arrows denote major degenerating pathways to the spinal cord. Stippling indicates nuclei and areas containing terminal degeneration and stars indicate nuclei containing degenerating cell somata. Note the additional involvement of thalamic and cortical regions in the TPP-exposed brain.

In contrast to our findings in the ferret, single subcutaneous injections of 4 mg DFP/kg body weight in rats resulted in quite restricted areas of degeneration, involving only the cervical portion of the fasciculus gracilis and the nucleus gracilis. No signs of degeneration were noted in any other spinal cord or brainstem nuclei. No degeneration was seen in the midbrain or forebrain of either species after exposure to DFP.

3.2.2. Effects of TPP

Ferrets received single subcutaneous injections of 500, 1000, or 2000 mg undiluted TPP/kg body weight and were killed 8–12 days after dosing. A large number of spinal cord and brainstem sensory and motor systems were affected in these animals. In the spinal cord, axonal and terminal degeneration were present throughout the medial-lateral extent of spinal laminae VI–IX at the cervical, thoracic, lumbar, and sacral levels (Fig. 5). Degenerating axons were also noted in the lateral and ventral funiculi throughout the length of the cord. Axonal and terminal debris were present in the external cuneate nucleus, pontine gray, nuclei of the reticular formation, and the red nucleus (Fig. 6).

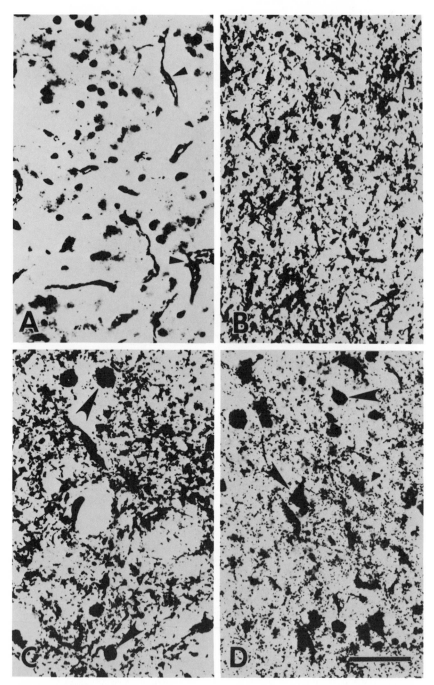

FIGURE 7. Photomicrographs illustrating Fink–Heimer silver-impregnated material from control and treated ferret brains. (A) Nucleus gracilis of a control ferret. Note the absence of fragmented degenerating axons and terminals. Small arrowheads indicate silver-impregnated reticular fibers surrounding blood vessels. (B) Nucleus gracilis 21 days after exposure to 4 mg DFP/kg body weight. Note the presence of dense fragmented and punctate degeneration. (C) Lateral reticular nucleus 8 days after exposure to 1000 mg TPP/kg body weight. Note the presence of degenerating axons, terminals, and neuronal somata (large arrowheads). (D) Lateral geniculate nucleus 8 days after exposure to 1000 mg TPP/kg body weight. Note the presence of fragmented axonal and terminal degeneration as well as somatic (large arrowheads) degeneration. Scale bar = 50 μm and applies to all plates.

Degeneration of neuronal somata, represented by black-impregnated cell bodies in the Fink–Heimer material, was also present in the external cuneate nucleus, nuclei of the reticular formation, red nucleus, and lateral vestibular nucleus (Figs. 6 and 7C). Dense axonal degeneration was present in the dorsal spinocerebellar tract, and mossy fiber degeneration was located in the granule cell layers of cerebellar foliae I–IX and crura I and II (Fig. 4).

Forebrain and brainstem nuclei and tracts associated with auditory, visual, and sensorimotor systems also showed signs of degeneration (Fig. 6). In the auditory system, degenerating axons and terminals were located in the superior olivary nucleus and inferior colliculus. In the visual system, the lateral geniculate nucleus contained dense and widespread axonal and somatic degeneration (Fig. 7D), while the visual cortex lying along the dorsomedial edge of the occipital lobe showed dense axonal and terminal degeneration within lamina IV. Likewise, extensive axonal, terminal, and somatic degeneration were present in the ventral posterior (somatosensory) and ventral lateral (motor) thalamic nuclei. Dense axonal and terminal degeneration were also present in laminae III and IV in the sensorimotor cortex surrounding the cruciate sulcus. It seems reasonable to assume that the degeneration seen in cortical laminae of the visual and sensorimotor cortices originated from thalamic neurons undergoing cellular degeneration.

In the rat, exposure to TPP (1184 mg/kg body weight administered via three subcutaneous injections at 3-day intervals) also resulted in widespread CNS degeneration. However, in contrast to the findings in the ferret, the spinal cord of the rat contained only minimal degeneration. Almost all of the degeneration was confined to the upper cervical cord and consisted of occasional scattered fibers within laminae V–IX. In the medulla, moderate amounts of axonal and terminal degeneration were found in the external cuneate, dorsal cochlear, prepositus hypoglossal, and parasolitary nuclei, dorsal motor nucleus of the vagus nerve, and the vestibular complex of nuclei, particularly within the spinal and medial vestibular nuclei. Widespread mossy fiber degeneration was also noted in the granule-cell layer of cerebellar lobules I–X, the flocculus and paraflocculus, and crura I and II. At midbrain levels, degeneration was located within the superior and inferior colliculi and in the nuclei making up the oculomotor complex. Several components of the basal ganglia, including the subthalamic nucleus, zona incerta, and substantia nigra, pars compacta, also contained moderate amounts of terminal degeneration.

Forebrain degeneration was also quite extensive in the rat. The hypothalamic mamillary nuclei contained terminal degeneration, as did the thalamic parafascicular, ventromedial, paracentral, central lateral, and central medial nuclei. Lighter degeneration was present in the medial geniculate nucleus and anterior nuclear group. Degeneration was also found in the presubiculum and diagonal band area, and in lamina IV of prefrontal, auditory, and sensorimotor cortices. Again, it is reasonable to assume that the majority of degenerating fibers and terminals in lamina IV arose from thalamic neurons. No signs of degenerating neuronal somata were noted in any area of the rat CNS.

3.2.3. Summary and Synthesis

These data indicate that exposure to the Type I compound DFP does result in different degeneration patterns in the ferret and rat. In the ferret, the location and extent of axonal and terminal degeneration are similar to those seen in the hen. In contrast, our data obtained from the rat indicate that DFP exposure results in only minimal degeneration, confined principally to the fasciculus and nucleus gracilis. Veronesi and her colleagues, however, have consistently reported degenerating myelinated axons in the lateral and ventral funiculi of the spinal cord in TOTP-injected rats (Padilla and Veronesi, 1988; Veronesi, 1984) and mice (Veronesi *et al.*, 1991). Despite this presence of degenerating axons within several ascending and descending spinal tracts, rats and mice nevertheless show remarkably little ataxia and hindlimb impairment, even after extended postexposure periods (Veronesi, 1984). To explain this finding, it has been proposed that rapid regeneration of peripheral nerves may allow a reestablishment of sensorimotor innervation and may prevent the appearance of signs of ataxia or paralysis (Veronesi, 1984; Veronesi *et al.*, 1991). An alternative possibility is that the severity and extent of CNS degeneration in rodents is initially less extensive than that seen in either the hen or ferret. Whether any particular CNS tract or combination of tracts has to be destroyed before specific Type I clinical signs become manifest is unknown. However, it might be expected that damage to cerebellar mossy fiber input from the spinal cord and brainstem might contribute to the appearance of ataxia and that preservation of this fiber system may result in the absence of detectable cerebellar signs. In support of this proposal, we found that in those DFP-exposed ferrets in which cerebellar mossy fiber degeneration was absent, no ataxia or hindlimb dysfunction was observable (Tanaka *et al.*, 1991b). A similar absence of degenerating mossy fibers in the rat may also account, at least in part, for the absence of the usual clinical signs of Type I agents noted in this species.

Injections of TPP result in widespread degeneration patterns in both the ferret and rat, with extensive axonal and somatic degeneration noted in the thalamus and cerebral cortex. Previous studies in the rat have reported TPP-induced degeneration in only the brainstem and spinal cord (Lillie and Smith, 1932; Veronesi and Dvergsten, 1987; Veronesi *et al.*, 1986), and our finding of extensive thalamic and cerebral cortical degeneration indicates that other CNS regions are susceptible to TPP as well. Although there were some individual differences with regard to the location of forebrain degeneration between the rat and ferret, in both species dense axonal and terminal degeneration were noted in the sensorimotor portions of the cerebral cortex and related thalamic nuclei. In the rat, degeneration was also noted in the auditory cortex and medial geniculate nucleus, while in the ferret, additional degeneration was present in the primary visual cortex and lateral geniculate nucleus. When these data are combined with the degeneration noted in the midbrain, brainstem, and spinal cord, it becomes evident that TPP may affect nuclei and fiber tracts associated with major sensorimotor, visual, and/or auditory systems at several levels of the CNS.

4. CONCLUSIONS AND FUTURE DIRECTIONS IN ASSESSING DEGENERATION RELATED TO OPIDN

Data derived from the studies described above and from those of other investigators (Cavanagh and Patangia, 1965; Illis *et al.*, 1966; Scallett *et al.*, 1988; Switzer *et al.*, 1988) indicate that the silver-impregnation method for degenerating axons and terminals is the technique of choice when the objective of the study is to map out the location, extent, and density of neurotoxicant-induced somatic, axonal, and terminal degeneration. Also, this method is required when the fiber system or terminal field under investigation cannot be differentially localized using traditional myelin or axonal stains. For example, our studies of the effects of organophosphorus compounds on the CNS of both mammalian and avian species revealed a much more extensive pattern of degeneration than that previously described; the explanation that only long spinal tracts are affected by organophosphorus compounds now appears invalid. Any future studies of neuropathological effects of neurotoxicants should at least consider using one of the many Fink–Heimer variants available if the goals of the study include assessing the density and distribution of somatic, axonal, or terminal degeneration in the CNS.

Our findings suggest that the central nervous systems of the hen and ferret react similarly to exposure to both Type I and Type II organophosphorus delayed neurotoxicants. Although it is difficult to assess whether the degeneration seen in the hen and ferret involves homologous CNS nuclei or tracts, the overall pattern of degeneration involving primarily ascending somatosensory, viscerosensory, and spinocerebellar pathways following DFP exposure and the additional involvement of higher order sensorimotor, auditory, and visual pathways after TPP exposure are similar in the two species. Thus, degeneration of neurons and tracts located in higher order regions of the CNS appears to be a critical factor in distinguishing Type II from Type I OPIDN. The rat also shows severe neuropathological sequelae following injections of TPP, but shows only minimal CNS degeneration following exposure to DFP. As such, it appears that the ferret would be the more appropriate mammalian model in which to assess the neuropathological and clinical effects of Type I OPIDN.

It should also be noted that not all fiber tracts and nuclei within an affected functional system show signs of degeneration. The data obtained from our studies and from those of other investigators (Carrington et al., 1988; Veronesi et al., 1986; Veronesi and Dvergsten, 1987) show that several degrees of TPP-related susceptibility exist in the CNS. For example, only certain populations of neurons appear to undergo axonal degeneration, while others may undergo both axonal and somatic degeneration. The question of why some neural systems or fiber tracts are susceptible to organophosphorus compounds and others are not has yet to be resolved. A closer look at the affected neural systems with respect to the time course of degeneration, the specific neuronal organelles affected, and the neurotransmitters utilized might be of use in determining possible mechanisms underlying the resultant neuropathology. It does appear that fiber tracts and systems susceptible to particular compounds are consistent among species, and that some of these degeneration patterns, for example, those seen with TOTP or DFP, are similar to those patterns seen in humans with Friedreich's ataxia (Lamarche et al., 1984; Oppenheimer, 1976) or in *Dystonia musculorum* mutant mice (Sotelo and Guenet, 1988).

Some recent unpublished data from our laboratory also suggest that susceptibility of neurons to TPP may be differentially acquired over time. Four-week-old ferrets exposed to TPP showed axonal and terminal degeneration in the brainstem and cerebellum 7 days after exposure. However, no degeneration was noted in the cerebral cortex, and only limited amounts of degeneration were present in the thalamus at this time period. In adult ferrets exposed to TPP, large amounts of degeneration are present in both the cerebral cortex and thalamus (Tanaka et al., 1990b). These data indicate that at 4 weeks of age, brainstem and cerebellar fiber tracts are vulnerable to TPP exposure, while those in the cerebral cortex and thalamus are not. It may be that some aspect of maturation associated with these nuclei and tracts accounts, at least in part, for these observed differences. It is well documented that immature animals show less severe clinical signs after exposure to Type I organophosphorus compounds than do adults (Abou-Donia et al., 1982; Johnson and Barnes, 1970; Olson and Bursian, 1988). However, the effects of Type II compounds on young animals is not as clear. Some investigators have reported that 1-week-old chicks may display severe clinical and neuropathological signs (Abou-Donia and Lapadula,

1990), while others have reported the absence of ataxia in 60-day-old or younger hens exposed to TPP (Katoh *et al.*, 1990). A closer examination of individual developing CNS systems and their susceptibility to organophosphorus compounds might contribute much toward defining the mechanisms underlying the effects of OPIDN.

Finally, it is clear from the above data that exposure to certain organophosphorus compounds may have a detrimental effect on human health. While ingestion of organophosphorus-contaminated foodstuffs is less of a problem now than it has been previously (Okumura *et al.*, 1991; Smart, 1987), these compounds may still pose a human health threat through occupational or environmental exposure (Forget, 1991; Senanayake and Johnson, 1982; Windebank, 1987). Their irreversible effects on the central nervous system are of particular concern, and appropriate protective measures should be utilized when there is potential for exposure to these compounds.

ACKNOWLEDGMENTS.   We thank Mary Craig, Gareth Dulai, Mary Oswald, B. Kay Trosko, and Barbara Wheaton for their excellent technical assistance in the Fink–Heimer studies and Judy James for typing the manuscript. We also thank Dr. Richard J. Aulerich for his assistance and advice during the course of the ferret studies. This work was supported by funds from the Michigan Agricultural Experiment Station and BRSG funds awarded to the College of Veterinary Medicine.

ABBREVIATIONS

CE, CX	external cuneate nucleus	OT	optic tectum
CL	lateral cervical nucleus	PG	pontine gray matter
DC	dorsal nucleus of Clarke	PGL	lateral paragigantocellular nucleus
DIP	dorso-intermediate posterior thalamic nucleus	PP	paleostriatum primitivum
		PR	paramedian reticular nucleus
DMC	dorsal magnocellular column	RN	red nucleus
FC	fasciculus cuneatus	SCT	spinocerebellar tract
FG	fasciculus gracilis	SM Cx	sensorimotor cortex
GC	gracile-cuneate nucleus	SO	superior olivary nucleus
IC	inferior colliculus	SP1	lateral spiriform nucleus
IO, OI	inferior olivary nucleus	TPc	pedunculopontine tegmental nucleus, pars compacta
LCST	lateral corticospinal tract		
LGN	lateral geniculate nucleus	VeL	lateral vestibular nucleus
LRN	lateral reticular nucleus	Visual Cx	primary visual cortex
MD	mediodorsal thalamic nucleus	VL	ventral lateral thalamic nucleus
MLd	lateral mesencephalic nucleus, pars dorsalis	VN	vestibular nuclear group
		VMN	ventral motor nucleus of the cervical enlargement
MPST	medial pontine-spinal tract		
NG	nucleus gracilis	VP	ventral posterior thalamic nucleus
nTS	nucleus of the tractus solitarius		

REFERENCES

Abou-Donia, M.B., 1981, Organophosphorus ester-induced delayed neurotoxicity, *Annu. Rev. Pharmacol. Toxicol.* 21:511–548.

Abou-Donia, M.B., and Lapadula, D.M., 1990, Mechanisms of organophosphorus ester-induced delayed neurotoxicity: Type I and Type II, *Annu. Rev. Pharmacol. Toxicol.* 30:405–440.

Abou-Donia, M.B., and Pressig, S.H., 1976, Delayed neurotoxicity of leptophos: Toxic effects on the nervous system of hens, *Toxicol. Appl. Pharmacol.* 35:269–282.

Abou-Donia, M.B., Graham, D.G., and Komeil, A.A., 1979, Delayed neurotoxicity of O-ethyl O-2,4-dichlorophenyl phenylphosphonothioate: Effects of a single oral dose on hens, *Toxicol. Appl. Pharmacol.* 49:293–303.

Abou-Donia, M.B., Makkaway, H.A., Salama, A.E., and Graham, D.G., 1982, Effect of ages of hens and their sensitivity to delayed neurotoxicity induced by a single oral dose of tri-o-tolyl phosphate, *Toxicologist* 2:178.

Amr, M.M., 1989, Pesticide intoxication in Egypt, in: *Abstracts of the Third-World Conference on Environmental and Health Hazards of Pesticides,* p. S-18.

Barnes, J.M., and Denz, F.A., 1953, Experimental demyelination with organophosphorus compounds, *J. Pathol. Bacteriol.* 65:597–605.

Baron, R.L., 1981, Delayed neurotoxicity and other consequences of organophosphate esters, *Annu. Rev. Entomol.* 26:29–48.

Beresford, W.A., and Glees, P., 1963, Degeneration in the long tracts of the cords of the chicken and cat after triorthocresyl phosphate poisoning, *Acta Neuropathol.* 3:108–118.

Cabot, J.B., Reiner, A., and Bogan, N., 1982, Avian bulbospinal pathways: Anterograde and retrograde studies of cells of origin, funicular trajectories and laminar terminations, in: *Progress in Brain Research. Anatomy of Descending Pathways to the Spinal Cord, Volume 57* (H.G.J.M. Kuypers, and G.F. Martin, eds.), Elsevier, New York, pp. 79–108.

Carrington, C.D., and Abou-Donia, M.B., 1988, Triphenyl phosphite neurotoxicity in the hen: Inhibition of neurotoxic esterase and lack of prophylaxis by phenylmethylsulfonyl fluoride, *Arch. Toxicol.* 62:375–380.

Carrington, C.D., Brown, H.R., and Abou-Donia, M.B., 1988, Histopathological assessment of triphenyl phosphite neurotoxicity in the hen, *Neurotoxicology* 9:223–234.

Cavanagh, J.B., 1954, The toxic effects of tri-ortho-cresyl phosphate on the nervous system. An experimental study in hens, *J. Neurol. Neurosurg. Psychiatry* 17:163–172.

Cavanagh, J.B., 1964, Peripheral nerve changes in ortho-cresyl phosphate poisoning in the cat, *J. Pathol. Bacteriol.* 87:365–383.

Cavanagh, J.B., and Patangia, G.N., 1965, Changes in the central nervous system in the cat as the result of tri-o-cresyl phosphate poisoning, *Brain* 88:165–182.

Davis, C.S., and Richardson, R.J., 1980, Organophosphorus compounds, in: *Experimental and Clinical Neurotoxicology* (H.H. Schaumberg, and P.S. Spencer, eds.), Williams and Wilkins, Baltimore, pp. 527–544.

de Olmos, J.S., Ebbesson, S.O.E., and Heimer, L., 1981, Silver methods for the impregnation of degenerating axoplasm, in: *Neuroanatomical Tract Tracing Methods* (L. Heimer and M.J. Robards, eds.), Plenum Press, New York, pp. 117–170.

Fink, R.P., and Heimer, L., 1967, Two methods for selective silver impregnation of degenerating axons and their synaptic endings in the central nervous system, *Brain Res.* 4:369–374.

Forget, G., 1991, Pesticides and the third world, *J. Toxicol. Environ. Health* 32:11–31.

Giolli, R.A., and Karamanlidis, A.N., 1978, The study of degenerating nerve fibers using silver-impregnation methods, in: *Neuroanatomical Research Techniques* (R.T. Robertson, ed.), Academic Press, New York, pp. 211–240.

Glazer, E.J., Baker, T., and Riker, Jr., W.F., 1978, The neuropathology of DFP at cat soleus neuromuscular junction, *J. Neurocytol.* 7:741–758.

Heimer, L., 1970, Selective silver-impregnation of degenerating axoplasm, in: *Contemporary Research Methods in Neuroanatomy* (W.J.H. Nauta and S.O.E. Ebbeson, eds.), Springer-Verlag, New York, pp. 106–131.

Illis, L., Patangia, G.N., and Cavanagh, J.B., 1966, Bouton terminaux and tri-ortho-cresyl phosphate neurotoxicity, *Exp. Neurol.* 14:160–174.

Johnson, M.K., 1975, Organophosphorus esters causing delayed neurotoxic effects: Mechanism of action and structure/activity studies, *Arch. Toxicol.* 34:259–288.

Johnson, M.K., 1982, The target for initiation of delayed neurotoxicity by organophosphorus esters: Biochemical studies and toxicological applications, in: *Reviews in Biochemical Toxicology 4* (E. Hodgson, J.R. Bend, and R.M. Philpot, eds.), Elsevier, New York, pp. 141–212.

Johnson, M.K., 1990, Organophosphates and delayed neuropathy—is NTE alive and well?, *Toxicol. Appl. Pharmacol.* 102:385–399.

Johnson, M.K., and Barnes, J.M., 1970, Age and the sensitivity of chicks to the delayed neurotoxic effects of some organophosphorus compounds, *Biochem. Pharmacol.* 19:3045–3047.

Jortner, B.S., and Ehrich, M., 1987, Neuropathological effects of phenyl saligenin phosphate in chickens, *Neurotoxicology* 8:303–314.

Karten, H.J., and Dubbeldam, J.L., 1973, The organization and projections of the paleostriatal complex in the pigeon (*Columbia livia*), *J. Comp. Neurol.* 148:61–90.

Katoh, K., Konno, N., Yamauchi, T., and Fukushima, M., 1990, Effects of age on susceptibility of chickens to delayed neurotoxicity due to triphenyl phosphite, *Pharmacol. Toxicol.* 66:387–392.

Lamarche, J.B., Lemieux, B., and Lieu, H.B., 1984, The neuropathology of "typical" Friedreich's ataxia in Quebec, *Can. J. Neurosci.* 11:592–600.

Lapadula, D.M., Patton, S.E., Campbell, G.A., and Abou-Donia, M.B., 1985, Characterization of delayed neurotoxicity in the mouse following chronic oral administration of tri-o-cresyl phosphate, *Toxicol. Appl. Pharmacol.* 79:83–90.

Lehning, E., Tanaka, Jr., D., and Bursian, S.J., 1990, Widespread axonal and terminal degeneration in the forebrain of the rat after exposure to triphenyl phosphite (TPP), *Toxicologist* 10:341.

Lillie, R.D., and Smith, M.I., 1932, The histopathology of some neurotoxic phenol esters, *Natl. Instit. Health Bull.* 160:54–62.

Lotti, M., Caroldi, S., Moretto, A., Johnson, M.K., Fish, C.J., Gopinath, C., and Roberts, N.L., 1987, Central-peripheral neuropathy caused by diisopropyl phosphorofluoridate (DFP): Segregation of peripheral nerve and spinal cord effects using biochemical, clinical, and morphological criteria, *Toxicol. Appl. Pharmacol.* 88:87–96.

Morgan, J.P., 1982, The Jamaica ginger paralysis, *JAMA* 248:1864–1867.

Okumura, D., Melnicoe, R., Jackson, T., Drefs, C., Maddy, K., and Wells, J., 1991, Pesticide residues in food crops analyzed by the California Department of Food and Agriculture in 1989, in: *Reviews of Environmental Contamination and Toxicology, Volume 118* (G.W. Ware, ed.), Springer-Verlag, New York, pp. 87–151.

Olson, B.A., and Bursian, S.J., 1988, Effect of route of administration on the development of organophosphate-induced delayed neurotoxicity in 4-week-old chicks, *J. Toxicol. Environ. Health* 23:499–505.

Oppenheimer, D.R., 1976, Diseases of the basal ganglia, cerebellum and motor neurons, in: *Greenfield's Neuropathology* (W. Blackwood and J.A.N. Corsellis, eds.), Edward Arnold, London, pp. 608–651.

Padilla, S., and Veronesi, B., 1988, Biochemical and morphological validation of a rodent model of organophosphorus-induced delayed neuropathy, *Toxicol. Indus. Health* 4:361–371.

Prentice, D.E., and Roberts, N.L., 1983, Acute delayed neurotoxicity in hens dosed with tri-*ortho*-cresyl phosphate (TOCP): Correlation between clinical ataxia and neuropathological findings, *Neurotoxicology* 4:271–276.

Prineas, J.P., 1969, The pathogenesis of dying-back polyneuropathies. Part I. An ultrastructural study of experimental tri-ortho-cresyl phosphate intoxication in the cat, *J. Neuropathol. Exp. Neurol.* 28:571–597.

Reiner, A., Brecha, N.C., and Karten, H.J., 1982, Basal ganglia pathways to the tectum: The afferent and efferent connections of the lateral spiriform nucleus of pigeon, *J. Comp. Neurol.* 208:16–36.

Scallet, A.C., Lipe, G.W., Ali, S.F., Holson, R.R., Frith, C.H., and Slikker, Jr., W., 1988, Neuropathological evaluation by combined immunohistochemistry and degeneration-specific methods: Application to methylenedioxymethamphetamine, *Neurotoxicology* 9:529–538.

Senanayake, N., and Johnson, M.K., 1982, Acute polyneuropathy after poisoning by a new organophosphate insecticide, *N. Engl. J. Med.* 306:155–157.

Smart, N.A., 1987, Organophosphorus pesticide residues in fruits and vegetables in the United Kingdom and some other countries of the European Community since 1976, in: *Reviews of Environmental Contamination and Toxicology, Volume 98* (G.W. Ware, ed.), Springer-Verlag, New York, pp. 99–160.

Sotelo, C., and Guenet, J.L., 1988, Pathological changes in the CNS of *Dystonia musculorum* mutant mouse: An animal model for human spinocerebellar ataxia, *Neuroscience* 27:403–424.

Sprague, G.L., and Bickford, A.A., 1981, Effect of multiple diisopropylfluorophosphate injections in hens: A behavioral, biochemical and histological investigation, *J. Toxicol. Environ. Health* 8:973–988.

Stumpf, A.M., Tanaka, Jr., D., Aulerich, R.J., and Bursian, S.J., 1989, Delayed neurotoxic effects of tri-*o*-tolyl phosphate in the European ferret, *J. Toxicol. Environ. Health* 26:61–73.

Switzer, R.C., 1976, Neural argyrophilia induced by puromycin: A directed Golgi-like method, *Neurosci. Lett.* 2:301–305.

Switzer, III, R.C., Murphy, M.R., Campbell, S.K., Kerenyi, S.Z., Miller, S.A., and Hartgraves, S.L., 1988, Soman in multiple low doses: Damage to selected populations of neurons in rat brain, *Soc. Neurosci. Abstr.* 14:774.

Tabershaw, I.R., and Cooper, W.C., 1966, Sequelae of acute organophosphorus poisoning, *J. Occup. Med.* 8:5–20.

Tanaka, Jr., D., 1976, Thalamic projections of the dorsomedial prefrontal cortex in the Rhesus monkey (*Macaca mulatta*), *Brain Res.* 110:21–38.

Tanaka, Jr., D., and Bursian, S.J., 1989, Degeneration patterns in the chicken central nervous system induced by ingestion of the organophosphorus delayed neurotoxin tri-*ortho*-tolyl phosphate. A silver impregnation study, *Brain Res.* 484:240–256.

Tanaka, Jr., D., and Chen, J.Y.C., 1974, Retrograde thalamic degeneration: Observations using a modification of the Fink–Heimer silver impregnation technique, *Brain Res.* 65:333–337.

Tanaka, Jr., D., Bursian, S.J., and Lehning, E., 1990a, Selective axonal and terminal degeneration in the chicken brainstem and cerebellum following exposure to *bis* (1-methylethyl) phosphorofluoridate (DFP), *Brain Res.* 519:200–208.

Tanaka, Jr., D., Bursian, S.J., Lehning, E.J., and Aulerich, R.J., 1990b, Exposure to triphenyl phosphite results in widespread degeneration in the mammalian central nervous system, *Brain Res.* 531:294–298.

Tanaka, Jr., D., Bursian, S.J., and Lehning, E., 1991a, Terminal degeneration in the central nervous system (CNS) of the hen after exposure to triphenyl phosphite (TPP), *Toxicologist* 11:76.

Tanaka, Jr., D., Bursian, S.J., Lehning, E.J., and Aulerich, R.J., 1991b, Delayed neurotoxic effects of *bis* (1-methylethyl) phosphorofluoridate (DFP) in the European ferret: A possible mammalian model for organophosphorus-induced delayed neurotoxicity, *Neurotoxicology* 12:209–224.

U.S. Environmental Protection Agency, 1985, Triphenyl phosphite, CAS No. 101-02-0, Washington, D.C.

Veronesi, B., 1984, A rodent model of organophosphorus-induced delayed neuropathy: Distribution of central (spinal cord) and peripheral nerve damage, *Neuropathol. Appl. Neurobiol.* 10:357–368.

Veronesi, B., and Dvergsten, C., 1987, Triphenyl phosphite neuropathy differs from organophosphorus-induced delayed neuropathy in rats, *Neuropathol. Appl. Neurobiol.* 13:193–208.

Veronesi, B., Padilla, S., and Newland, D., 1986, Biochemical and neuropathological assessment of triphenyl phosphite in rats, *Toxicol. Appl. Pharmacol.* 83:203–210.

Veronesi, B., Padilla, S., Blackmon, K., and Pope, C., 1991, Murine susceptibility to organophosphorus-induced delayed neuropathy (OPIDN), *Toxicol. Appl. Pharmacol.* 107:311–324.

Webster, D.M.S., and Steeves, J.D., 1988, Origins of brainstem-spinal projections in the duck and goose, *J. Comp. Neurol.* 273:573–583.

Windebank, A.J., 1987, Peripheral neuropathy due to chemical and industrial exposure, in: *Handbook of Clinical Neurology, Vol. 7 (51): Neuropathies* (W.B. Matthews, ed.), Elsevier, New York, pp. 263–292.

Yamamato, T., Iwasaki, Y., Konno, H., and Iizuka, H., 1986, Identification of cells undergoing physiological neuronal death in the neonatal rat brain by the Fink–Heimer method, *Brain Res.* 374:419–424.

Chapter 13

Neuroreceptor and Behavioral Effects of DDT and Pyrethroids in Immature and Adult Mammals

Per Eriksson

1. INTRODUCTION

1.1. DDT

DDT [1,1,1-trichloro-2,2-bis(p-chlorophenyl)ethane] is one of the best known of all insecticides. Though first synthesized by Zeidler as long ago as 1874, it was not until 1939 that its insecticidal properties were discovered by Paul Müller, who was awarded a Nobel Prize in recognition of the humanitarian significance of his work on the control of vector-borne diseases. In 1942 DDT was introduced as a broad-spectrum insecticide for the protection of public health from vector-borne diseases, and it soon gained widespread use in agricultural, soil, and structure control programs. However, the major drawback with the use of DDT is its resistance to breakdown under environmental conditions (persistence) and its solubility in fat. In the 1960s convincing evidence showed that DDT and its metabolites accumulate in food chains and are stored in living organisms (Dustman and Stickel, 1969; Edwards, 1970). Thus, though used for human benefit, DDT came into direct conflict with human well-being. It also poses a threat to animal life in the environment from which we derive both pleasure and food. This discovery, coupled with ecologi-

Per Eriksson • Department of Zoophysiology, Uppsala University, S-751 22 Uppsala, Sweden.
The Vulnerable Brain and Environmental Risks, Volume 2: Toxins in Food, edited by Robert L. Isaacson and Karl F. Jensen. Plenum Press, New York, 1992.

cal considerations, led during the 1970s and early 1980s to a ban on, or at least restrictions on, the use of DDT in the developed countries. In India and China, however, and in countries in South America and Africa, it is still widely used (Coulston, 1985). Depending on the use and persistence of DDT in the environment, it will long continue to constitute a subject for research work and risk evaluation.

DDT is a compound that has been researched over many years. Some of the major reviews are those contributed by Hayes (1959) regarding the pharmacological and toxicological significance of DDT, by Hrdina *et al.* (1975) on the effect of DDT on neurotransmitter systems, and by Woolley (1982) on the ways in which DDT exerts its neurotoxic effects. The reader is referred to all these key summaries. But despite these well-documented data on the toxicity of DDT, there is still one area that requires further exploration, exposure to DDT during perinatal life and its possible neonatal effects and consequences in adult life. Transfer of DDT via the milk from mother to offspring is well known and was first reported by Woodard *et al.* (1945), and the intoxication of nursing pups of rats fed a diet containing 1000 ppm DDT was described the same year by Telford and Guthrie (1945).

1.2. Pyrethroids

The pyrethroids are derivatives of natural pyrethrins. The development of pyrethrins and pyrethroids started with the discovery of insecticidal activity in the flowers of certain members of the *Chrysanthemum* genus. Though the pyrethrins are very potent insecticides, their photolability precluded wider application for agricultural purposes. Photostable pyrethroids were a later discovery of Elliott and coworkers (1973, 1974). Commercial production of this group of compounds started in 1976, and they have now achieved worldwide use, with widespread agricultural and environmental health applications and an important position in the world insecticide market. Due to their high insect/mammal toxicity ratio, rapid detoxication in mammals, and absence of cumulative toxicity (Aldridge, 1990; Casida *et al.*, 1983), they have replaced many of the earlier compounds.

Some recent reviews have summarized the neurotoxic effects of pyrethroids in mammals (Aldridge, 1990; Gray and Soderlund, 1985) and their mode of action (Vijverberg and van den Bercken, 1990). Pyrethroids are commonly divided into Type I compounds (or T-syndrome pyrethroids), which lack an α-cyano substituent, and Type II compounds (or CS-syndrome pyrethroids), which contain an α-cyanophenoxybenzyl substituent (Gammon *et al.*, 1981; Verschoyle and Aldridge, 1980). The main symptom of exposure to the former type is tremor, while choreoathetosis and salivation are the main symptoms of exposure to the latter. Observations made on nonmammalian nerve membrane preparations have shown that one of the basic mechanisms of pyrethroid action involves interference with the nerve-membrane sodium channels, leading to prolonged depolarization and induction of repetitive activity (Narahashi, 1985; van den Bercken and Vijverberg, 1988; Wouters and van den Bercken, 1978). This kind of neurotoxic action and the development of neurotoxic symptoms, seen especially after exposure to Type I pyrethroids, is also observed with DDT (Lund and Narahashi, 1983; Narahashi, 1982; van den Bercken *et al.*, 1973). Even though pyrethroids are considered to be nonpersistent insecticides, they are highly soluble in fat and can be transferred from mother to offspring via the milk (Gaughan *et al.*, 1978; Hunt and Gilbert, 1977; Kavlock *et al.*, 1979).

As was the case with DDT, early exposure to pyrethroids and their possible effects at adult age have attracted little attention. A comparative study on whether persistent and nonpersistent insecticides having similar neurotoxic action can induce the same functional changes in the whole organism would, therefore, be of interest. Since pyrethroids and DDT have certain similarities with respect to both neurotoxic action and neurotoxic syndromes, it would also be interesting to ascertain whether neonatal exposure to a physiologically relevant dose of DDT could potentiate and/or modify the reaction to an adult exposure to short-acting insecticides.

2. BRAIN GROWTH AND THE INCORPORATION OF DDT

2.1. Brain Growth Spurt

During the development of an organism, there are periods that can be critical for its normal maturation. Vulnerable periods during the ontogenesis of the central nervous system (CNS) can be divided into two main courses of events in the development of the brain. The first includes its early development, a period during which the general adult shape of the brain is acquired and the spongioblasts and neuroblasts, precursors to glia cells and neurons, respectively, multiply. Interference by xenobiotics during this period of time can cause malformation of the brain. The second period coincides with the rapid growth of the brain, the so-called brain growth spurt (Davison and Dobbing, 1968). This does not take place at the same time in the development of all mammalian species, but can vary somewhat (Fig. 1). This period includes the maturation of axonal and dendritic outgrowth, and the establishment of neural connections and synaptogenesis, together with the multiplication of glia cells and accompanying myelinization. This stage is also associated with a large number of biochemical changes that will transform the feto-neonatal

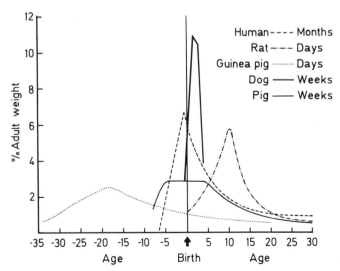

FIGURE 1. Rate curves of brain growth in relation to birth in different species. Values are calculated at different time intervals for each species. From Davison and Dobbing (1968), with permission.

brain into that of the mature adult. One of the major signal substances in the CNS is acetylcholine (ACh), which is the transmitter in the cholinergic pathways. The cholinergic system is involved in many behavioral phenomena, such as memory and learning, neurological syndromes, audition, vision, and aggression (Karczmar, 1975). In rodents, mice, and rats, the ontogenesis of various components of the cholinergic system, such as choline acetyltransferase, sodium-dependent choline uptake, acetylcholinesterase, and muscarinic and nicotinic receptors in the cerebral cortex, hippocampus, and cerebellum, takes place during the first 3–4 weeks after birth (Coyle and Yamamura, 1976; Falkeborn *et al.*, 1983; Höhmann and Ebner, 1985; Höhmann *et al.*, 1985; Marchi *et al.*, 1983). During this ontogenesis it can also be seen that the receptors precede the other aspects of the cholinergic system. It is during this period that spontaneous motor behavior peaks in the rodent (Bolles and Woods, 1964, Campbell *et al.*, 1969).

2.2. Incorporation of DDT into the Postnatal Brain

In many mammalian species, such as mouse, rat, dog, and human, the brain growth spurt coincides with lactation, when lipophilic chlorinated hydrocarbons are known to be transferred from the mother to her offspring via the milk. When [^{14}C]DDT was given as a single oral dose to mice at different ages, from newborn up to adult age, the most pronounced retention was measured in mice receiving DDT at the age of 10 days (Fig. 2). This coincides with a time in the development when the myelinization process peaks (Jacobsen, 1964). However, in an autoradiographic study the retention of DDT could not be correlated with incorporation into myelinated areas of the neonatal mouse brain; rather, DDT was found to be evenly distributed throughout the brain (Eriksson and Darnerud, 1985). This incorporation picture differs partly from that observed in the adult rodent

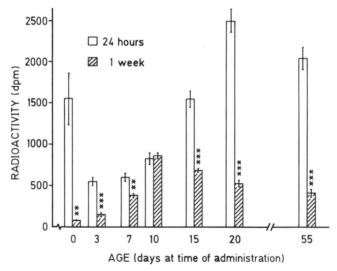

FIGURE 2. Radioactivity levels (dpm) in mouse brain 24 hr and 7 days after an oral administration of 1.48 MBq [^{14}C]DDT/kg body weight. The height of the bars represents the mean ± SD, and the statistical difference between 24 hr and 7 days is indicated by ** p ≤ 0.01; *** p ≤ 0.001. From Eriksson (1984), with permission.

brain, where initially there is a higher concentration of DDT in the gray matter (Bäckström *et al.*, 1965; Woolley and Runnells, 1967), but also a more rapid elimination from these areas than from the myelinated ones. The DDT retained in the brain may also be in metabolite form. One way in which environmentally toxic agents are retained in the body may be by conjugation to fatty acids, as has been reported with DDT, pentachlorphenol, and cannabinoids by Leighty and Fentiman (1981) and Leighty *et al.* (1976, 1980).

3. NEUROTOXIC EFFECTS AFTER NEONATAL EXPOSURE TO DDT AND PYRETHROIDS

Our research has been directed toward elucidating the consequences that exposure during the brain growth spurt can have on cholinergic and behavioral variables in neonatal and adult mammals. By administering substances during the 10–16 postnatal day period in the mouse there will be an exposure situation comparable to early postnatal life in many mammalian species, including humans (see Fig. 1). DDT and pyrethroids were given orally in a 20% fat emulsion vehicle in order to achieve a more physiological absorption, and hence a distribution of the substances throughout the organism, comparable to that occurring when agents are transferred via ingestion of mother's milk. In these experiments, the cholinergic muscarinic receptors (mAChR) were assayed in P2 fractions (Gray and Whittaker, 1962) from different brain regions, by measuring the binding of tritium-labelled quinuclidinyl benzilate ([³H]QNB) (Nordberg and Winblad, 1981; Yamamura and Snyder, 1974), which is a muscarinic antagonist to the transmitter ACh. The mAChR can be divided into subpopulations that can be analyzed in an antagonist ([³H]QNB)/agonist(carbachol) competition binding assay by using different concentrations of the agonist (Birdsall *et al.*, 1978; Nordberg and Wahlström, 1982). The behavioral testing of the animals was performed by measuring the spontaneous motor activities: locomotion, rearing, and total activity (Archer *et al.*, 1987). Details on the experimental procedure can be found in the original research papers.

3.1. Neuroreceptor Changes in the Neonatal Brain

Our experiments have shown that a single low peroral dose of DDT and its fatty acid conjugate DDOH-PA (a DDT metabolite, DDOH, conjugated to palmitic acid) (1.4 μmol/kg body weight; 0.5 mg and 0.7 mg, respectively), when given to suckling mice at the age of 10 days, affects the cholinergic system in the neonatal brain (Eriksson *et al.*, 1984; Eriksson and Nordberg, 1986). The dose used also caused regional differences within the brain, as the cerebral cortex was affected, but not the hippocampus. At the neonatal age of 17 days, the density of mAChR was increased (Table 1). The increased binding of the antagonist [³H]QNB in the cerebral cortex was also explored in an antagonist/agonist competition experiment, where a subdivision into sites with different affinities is obtained. The subpopulations of mAChR in the 17-day-old mouse were found to have changed, as the proportion of low-affinity (LA) binding sites (preferably postsynaptically located) was significantly increased, while that of high-affinity (HA) sites (preferably presynaptically located) was reduced (Table 2).

In the experiments in which the pyrethroids bioallethrin (Type I, non-cyano-contain-

TABLE 1. Muscarinic Receptor Density in Cerebral Cortex in 17-Day-Old and 4-Month-Old Mice Exposed to Low Doses of DDT, DDOH-PA, Bioallethrin, and Deltamethrin at Age 10 Days[a]

Exposure to mg/kg body wt.	DDT 0.5	DDOH-PA 0.7	Bioallethrin 0.7	Deltamethrin 0.7
Days	1	1	7	7
17 days old				
Treated	859 ± 58^e	850 ± 51^d	875 ± 47^e	868 ± 78^c
	(14)	(11)	(15)	(15)
Controls	773 ± 71	773 ± 71	805 ± 60	805 ± 60
	(13)	(13)	(17)	(17)
4 months old				
Treated	956 ± 47^d	1107 ± 64	1132 ± 188^c	1207 ± 89^b
	(16)	(15)	(15)	(18)
Controls	998 ± 30	1117 ± 82	1266 ± 82	1266 ± 82
	(15)	(14)	(12)	(12)

[a] Ten-day-old mice received either a single oral dose of DDT (0.5 mg), DDOH-PA (0.7 mg), or vehicle (10 ml/kg body weight) or one daily dose for 7 days of bioallethrin (0.7 mg), deltamethrin (0.7 mg), or vehicle (10 ml/kg body weight). The mice were killed when 17 days old or at 4 months. The density of mAChR (pmol/g protein, mean $\pm$ SD) was assessed by measuring the specific binding of [^{3}H]QNB in P2 fractions of cerebral cortex. [The data are taken from Eriksson and Nordberg (1986); Eriksson and Nordberg (1990); Eriksson and Fredriksson (1991); and Eriksson et al. (1990)].
[b] $0.1 \leq p \leq 0.05$; [c] $p \leq 0.05$; [d] $p \leq 0.01$; [e] $p \leq 0.001$, compared with respective controls.

ing pyrethroid) and deltamethrin (Type II, α-cyano-containing pyrethroid) were administered to 10-day-old mice, similar effects on the mAChR in the neonatal mouse brain were found (Eriksson and Nordberg, 1990) as had been observed earlier with DDT. As we have found that the pyrethroids are rapidly eliminated from the neonatal mouse brain (unpublished results), either bioallethrin or deltamethrin was given as a single oral dose (0.7 mg/kg body weight) for 7 days in order to simulate the exposure time effective for DDT (Eriksson, 1984; Eriksson and Nordberg, 1986). The mAChR in the cerebral cortex (but not in hippocampus) were affected by both bioallethrin and deltamethrin. An increased mAChR density was noticed (Table 1), and the data from the [^{3}H]QNB/carbachol competition binding assay showed further that in mice receiving bioallethrin, there was an increased proportion of LA sites, though no significant change in its affinity constant, whereas the affinity constant for the HA sites was significantly altered. The converse was observed in mice receiving deltamethrin; i.e., the proportion of HA sites increased and the affinity constant for HA sites was not significantly altered, whereas the affinity constant for the LA sites was significantly altered (Table 2).

The increases in both the specific [^{3}H]QNB binding sites and the proportion of LA binding sites in the cerebral cortex following exposure to DDT (0.5 mg/kg body weight) and bioallethrin (0.7 mg/kg body weight) might be due to changes within the neuronal membrane. A similar action has been observed in nerve membrane preparations for DDT and pyrethroids (Type I); both prolong the open time of the sodium channels on the axon, which leads to an increased neuronal activity and repetitive firing (Lund and Narahashi, 1983; Narahashi, 1982; van den Bercken et al., 1973; Vijverberg et al. 1982). Changes in receptors are usually reciprocal to the changes in stimulation, resulting in a pattern consistent with compensatory adaptation to the change in stimulation (Creese and Sibley, 1981). The pronounced retention of DDT in the neonatal mouse exposed on the 10th

TABLE 2.   Proportions of High- and Low-Affinity Muscarinic Binding Sites (%)
and Affinity Constants (k) in Cerebral Cortex of 17-Day-Old Mice Exposed to Low Doses
of DDT, DDOH-PA, Bioallethrin, and Deltamethrin at Age 10 Days[a]

Treatment	n	High-affinity site		Low-affinity site	
		%	k (μM)	%	k (μM)
Experiment 1					
Control	10	15.4 ± 2.9	0.57	80.6 ± 3.1	276
DDT					
0.5 mg/kg body wt.	9	11.4 ± 2.1[d]	1.22	84.4 ± 2.4[d]	298
DDOH-PA					
0.7 mg/kg body wt.	10	12.3 ± 3.5[c]	0.67	83.3 ± 3.4[b]	270
Experiment 2					
Control	9	23.1 ± 8.4	2.96	76.9 ± 8.4	349
Deltamethrin					
0.7 mg/kg body wt.	8	33.5 ± 10.7[c]	4.84	66.5 ± 10.7[c]	638[c]
Bioallethrin					
0.7 mg/kg body wt.	8	13.8 ± 6.2[c]	0.77[c]	86.2 ± 6.2[c]	314

[a] Experiment 1: Ten-day-old mice received a single oral dose of either DDT (0.5 mg), DDOH-PA (0.7 mg), or the vehicle (10 ml/kg body weight). [Data taken from Eriksson and Nordberg (1986).] Experiment 2: Ten-day old mice received either deltamethrin (0.7 mg), bioallethrin (0.7 mg), or the vehicle (10 ml/kg body weight) orally once daily for 7 days. [Data taken from Eriksson and Nordberg (1990).] The mice were killed at age 17 days. The binding parameters were estimated from [^{3}H]QNB/carbachol competition curves. The % values are means ± SD, and the affinity constants are geometric means.
[b] $0.1 \leq p \leq 0.05$; [c] $p \leq 0.05$; [d] $p \leq 0.01$ compared with respective controls.

postnatal day (see Fig. 2) and the repeated exposure to bioallethrin for 1 week may generate repetitive discharges of the neurons, leading to a reduction in the content of the transmitter ACh. The increased density of mAChR might therefore be a compensatory mechanism to cope with altered ACh turnover, such as is known to exist in adult rodents exposed to xenobiotics (Burgen, 1982; Nordberg and Wahlström, 1982). Regarding the development of the cholinergic system, there is an almost parallel increase in the amount of LA and HA sites between the ages of 5 and 20 days (Kuhar et al., 1980). Therefore the increased proportion of LA sites in DDT- and bioallethrin-treated mice, respectively, might have been due to the synthesis of these subpopulations of mAChR.

The increased proportion of HA sites in deltamethrin-treated mice seems more complex. The action of deltamethrin on nerve membrane sodium channels is basically the same as that of bioallethrin, but exposure to Type II pyrethroids can lead to a depolarization block, resulting in a nonexcitable nerve. Electrophysiological in vitro experiments on cholinergic synapse transmission in the CNS of the cockroach have shown that deltamethrin can block transmission in the synapse (Hue and Mony, 1987). In our experiments, deltamethrin was found to affect not only the mAChR, but also the nicotinic cholinergic receptors (nAChR); neonatal exposure to deltamethrin caused an increase in HA nicotinic binding sites (Eriksson and Nordberg, 1990). Since activation of nAChR in the brain can induce presynaptic release of ACh (Beani et al., 1985; Rowell and Winkler, 1984), there might be a parallel increase in the presynaptic HA sites of the mAChR to maintain homeostasis. In contrast to the mAChR (Hulme *et al.*, 1987), the nicotinic receptor is probably coupled to a receptor-ionophore complex belonging to the same family as the τ-aminobutyric acid (GABA) receptor (Schofield *et al.*, 1987). *In vitro* experiments on mammalian brain preparations have shown that Type II pyrethroids can interact with the GABA receptor (Crofton *et al.*, 1987; Lawrence and Casida, 1983; Lawrence *et al.*, 1985). Whether the effect of Type II pyrethroids constitutes a combined action on both sodium channels and cholinergic and GABAergic receptors is a question for further investigations.

3.2. Neuroreceptor Changes in the Adult Brain

Neonatal exposure to DDT was shown to lead to permanent changes in the cholinergic system in animals reaching adult age (Eriksson *et al.*, 1990b). The mAChR were still affected in the same brain region in 4-month-old mice as in 17-day-old mice, namely, the cerebral cortex (Table 1). In contrast to the increase in neonatal mice there was a significant decrease in the amount of mAChR in the adults, which was not accompanied by any significant change in subpopulations of mAChR (Erikkson *et al.*, 1991a), as was the case in the neonatal mouse. Further, in adult mice the ACh content was affected. Potassium-provoked release of ACh from cortical slices revealed a higher ACh content in the DDT-treated mice (Eriksson *et al.*, 1990b).

An interesting finding in the experiments on neonatal exposure to DDT was that the effect observed in the adult animal is partly in agreement with that observed in animals exposed to DDT as adults. As regards the mAChR, we have previously reported that a single oral dose of DDT (0.5 mg/kg body weight) given to adult mice reduced the density of mAChR in the cerebral cortex, measured 7 days after administration (Eriksson *et al.*, 1984). A decrease in mAChR density has also been found in the cerebellum of adult rats fed a diet containing 0.4 mg DDT/g food for 2 months (Fonseca *et al.*, 1986). The changes in ACh concentration are also evident in the acute effect of DDT in adult animals. St. Omer and Ecobichon (1971) reported that the total brain content of ACh in rat was increased between 5 and 60 min after an intracarotid administration of 50 mg DDT/kg body weight. A decrease in the ACh content in the cerebral cortex and striatum 5 hr after oral administration of 600 mg DDT/kg body weight in rat has been reported by Hrdina and coworkers (1971, 1973, 1975). These animals showed severe symptoms of poisoning, such as tremor and hyperthermia, and in rats death is known to occur between 5 and 8 hr after an oral dose of 600 mg/kg body weight (Henderson and Woolley, 1970). Other transmitters, or their metabolites, e.g., norepinephrine, serotonin, GABA, and glycine, are also known to be affected in adult animals exposed to a high dose of DDT (for references see Hrdina *et al.*, 1975 and Woolley, 1982; Hudson *et al.*, 1985; Tilson *et al.*, 1986). Whether these transmitter systems may also be permanently affected in animals exposed to a low dose of DDT during neonatal life remains to be established.

Neonatal exposure to pyrethroids also revealed that the cholinergic system was still affected in animals reaching an adult age of 4 months (Eriksson and Fredriksson, 1991). Here too the same brain region as in the 17-day-old mice was affected, namely, the cerebral cortex (Table 1). A definite decrease, and a tendency towards a decrease, in the density of mAChR following bioallethrin and deltamethrin treatment, respectively, were observed. Brain regions such as the hippocampus and striatum were not affected. As in the case of neonatal exposure to DDT, the decrease in mAChR density following pyrethroid exposure was not accompanied by any significant change in the proportions of HA and LA binding sites in the adult mouse brain (Eriksson and Fredriksson, 1991).

That pyrethroids can affect the cholinergic system in the CNS of the adult animal has been indicated in some reports. For example, a decreased brain ACh concentration was observed in rats exposed to high doses (50 mg/kg body weight) of deltamethrin (Aldridge *et al.*, 1978). Effects on the rat CNS observed after deltamethrin exposure include changes in the EEG pattern and glucose concentration, the latter of which can affect the ACh concentration (Cremer *et al.*, 1980; Ray, 1980).

3.3 Behavioral Changes in Adult Animals Exposed to DDT and Pyrethroids as Neonates

Exposure to the insecticides DDT and pyrethroids during neonatal life was further shown to lead to permanent functional changes in adult animals (Eriksson *et al.*, 1990a, 1990b; Eriksson and Fredriksson, 1991). The spontaneous behavior tests indicated disruption of a simple nonassociative learning process, i.e., habituation, in 4-month-old mice exposed to DDT, DDOH-PA, bioallethrin, and deltamethrin as neonates (Figs. 3 and 4). Habituation is defined here as a decrease in locomotion, rearing, and total activity variables in response to the diminishing novelty of the test chambers over the 60-min test period divided into three 20-min periods. The insecticide-treated animals showed an absence of or a delay in habituation to a novel environment. That a hyperactive condition was also observed in mice receiving the fatty acid conjugate of DDT, DDOH-PA, shows that the parent insecticide molecule is not the only one capable of inducing permanent functional changes.

In the neonatal mouse at an age of 17 days, the only spontaneous behavioral variable, locomotion, was also studied. It was particularly interesting to note that no behavior disparity was observed in neonatal mice 24 hr after the last dose of either bioallethrin or deltamethrin (Eriksson and Fredriksson, 1991). Whether the differing changes in receptors between neonatal and adult mice following neonatal exposure to the insecticides, which were not reflected in behavior, are an expression of receptor plasticity in the neonatal mouse, and hence of its ability to cope with challenges of an environmental nature, is of special interest. With advancing age, this alteration in homeostatic compensatory mechanisms seems to turn into a state in which the change in subpopulations of mAChR diminishes. A reduced ability to modify homeostatic compensatory mechanisms with advancing age could increase the sensitivity of the adult animal when exposed to environmental hazards as an adult. Recently we have observed that mice neonatally exposed to DDT (as described above) showed an increased sensitivity in spontaneous behavior and to cholinergic receptor changes when exposed to bioallethrin as adults (Eriksson *et al.*, 1991b).

Among the factors that can induce hyperactivity in adult animals are brain lesions in the cerebral cortex (McMahon *et al.*, 1989; Robinson *et al.*, 1975; Robinson, 1979) and the hippocampus (Douglas and Isaacson, 1964; Roberts *et al.*, 1962). The mAChR is the predominant cholinergic receptor of the CNS, where it is involved in both the excitation and inhibition of neurons. Since spontaneous behavior can be considered to involve the inhibition of responses, the changes observed in the cerebral cortex of mice reaching adult

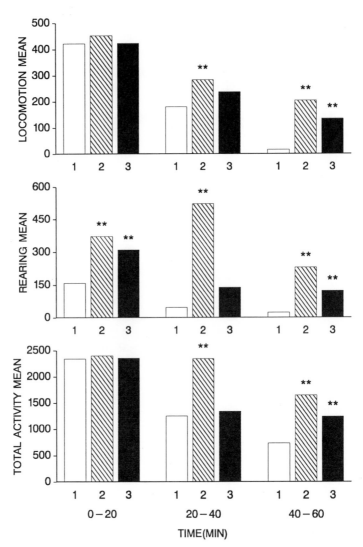

FIGURE 3. Spontaneous behavior (locomotion, rearing, and total activity) in 4-month-old NMRI male mice after a single oral dose of either DDT (0.5 mg), DDOH-PA (0.7 mg), or the vehicle (10 ml) per kilogram body weight at age 10 days. The treatment groups are indicated by 1, control; 2, DDT; 3, DDOH-PA, and the statistical difference vs. control is indicated by ** p ≤ 0.01. From Eriksson *et al.* (1990), with permission.

age may be the result of a lack of appropriate ability to inhibit responses, thereby allowing a hyperactive condition to develop in adult animals. Even the minor differences in potency between DDT and DDOH-PA, and between bioallethrin and deltamethrin, evident in behavior and mAChR in the adult mouse, and also observed on mAChR in the neonatal mouse brain (Table 1, Figs. 3 and 4), are of special interest. This indicates a dose-response relationship between early disturbances of the neonatal brain that can lead to permanent functional changes later in life. Recently we have observed that this might be the case, since neonatal exposure to bioallethrin (0.07–0.7 mg/kg body weight) caused a dose-

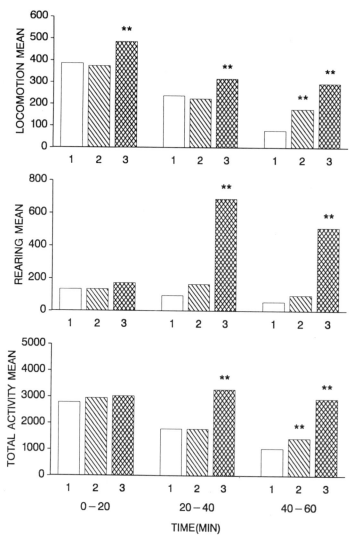

FIGURE 4. Spontaneous behavior (locomotion, rearing, and total activity) in 4-month-old NMRI male mice after repeated daily administration of either bioallethrin (0.7 mg), deltamethrin (0.7 mg), or the vehicle (10 ml) per kilogram of body weight per os to 10-day-old mice for 7 days. The treatment groups are indicated by 1, control; 2, deltamethrin; 3, bioallethrin, and the statistical difference vs. control is indicated by ** p ≤ 0.01. From Eriksson and Fredriksson (1991), with permission.

response change in mAChR in the cerebral cortex of 17-day-old mice and a dose-dependent increase in hyperactivity in 4-month-old mice (Ahlbom *et al.*, 1991).

In addition to similarities in the changes in the cholinergic system of adult animals following neonatal vs. adult exposure to DDT, there are also similarities in behavioral aberrations in adult animals exposed to DDT as neonates vs. as adults. Sobotka (1971) has reported an increased open-field activity in the adult rat 24 hr after an oral dose of 25 mg DDT/kg body weight, while lower doses of DDT had no significant effect on either exploration of or habituation to a novel environment. Sobotka concluded also that DDT affected passive avoidance in the adult rat. Recently several other workers have reported that DDT affects passive avoidance behavior (Tilson *et al.*, 1987), hyper-responsiveness (Tilson *et al.*, 1985), and tremor (Herr *et al.*, 1985, 1986; Herr and Tilson, 1987; Tilson *et al.*, 1985; 1986) in rats exposed as adults. The amount of DDT given to the adult animals to provoke changes in the neurotransmitter content and behavioral variables is between 50- and 1200-fold the dose used in our experiments. Hayes (1975) has reported that rats showing symptoms of, or dying from, DDT poisoning have a brain concentration of DDT ranging from 13 to 88 ppm. In the experiment concerning neonatal exposure to DDT, it can be calculated that the concentration of DDT and/or its metabolites in brain between the 11th and 17th postnatal day is far weaker, only about 15 ppt (Eriksson, 1984; Eriksson and Darnerud, 1985).

The same conformity between neonatal and adult exposure to pyrethroids and behavior in adult animals is not as clear as in the case of DDT, partly due to the different types of pyrethroids. Several reports have described a decrease in locomotor activity and operant or schedule responding in adult rodents exposed to Type I or II pyrethroids in acute experiments (Bloom *et al.*, 1983; Crofton and Reiter, 1984, 1987, 1988; Glowa, 1986; Mitchell *et al.*, 1988; Peele and Crofton, 1987; Stein *et al.*, 1987). Those studies showed a dose-dependent decrease in these behavioral variables. Crofton and Reiter (1984) have further reported that no significant cumulative effects could be observed on motor activity in the adult rat after a 30-day exposure to 2 mg/kg body weight/day of deltamethrin (Type II) or 6 mg/kg body weight/day of cismethrin (Type I). However, the disparity in the behavior variable, locomotor activity, might vary according to the length of the observation period. In our experiments we found that bioallethrin treatment of adult mice initially induced a hypoactive condition, but at the end of a 60-min observation period the animals had become hyperactive (Eriksson *et al.*, 1991b), a condition we observed in adult mice neonatally exposed to pyrethroids.

4. A DEFINED CRITICAL TIME IN POSTNATAL BRAIN DEVELOPMENT

The induction of these disturbances in the mouse seems to be limited to a short period of time during neonatal development (Fig. 5). When DDT (0.5 mg/kg body weight) was given to mice at different ages (3, 10, and 19 days), a significant increase in spontaneous motor behavior (locomotion) was only seen in mice receiving DDT at the age of 10 days. Furthermore, a significant decrease in the density of mAChR in the cerebral cortex was only seen in mice receiving DDT at this age (Eriksson *et al.*, 1991a). The induction of these disturbances coincides with the peak in the brain growth spurt (see Fig. 1), in spontaneous behavioral activity in the neonatal rodent (Campbell *et al.*, 1969), and during the rapid development of the cholinergic system.

As known from the earlier mentioned neurophysiological *in vitro* experiments, it has been concluded that one of the basic mechanisms of neurotoxic action that DDT and pyrethroids have in common is their interference with the sodium channels in nerve membrane. Such a mode of action might disturb the synaptic transmission. Disturbance of action potentials during the period of synaptogenesis could be critical for normal brain development (Kalil, 1989). The change in cholinergic receptors and behavior in the adult mouse following neonatal exposure to DDT or pyrethroids might therefore be the consequence of an early interference with the synaptic transmission in cholinergic nerve cells.

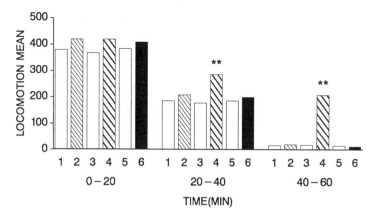

FIGURE 5. Spontaneous behavior (locomotion) in 4-month-old NMRI male mice after a single oral dose of DDT (0.5 mg/kg body weight) to either 3-day-old (bars 1 and 2), 10-day-old (bars 3 and 4), or 19-day-old (bars 5 and 6) mice. Plain bars denote controls, hatched bars denote DDT-treated mice; the statistical difference vs. control is indicated by ** $p \leq 0.01$.

However, it cannot be excluded that an interaction of the insecticides with the cholinergic receptors during their rapid development in the neonatal mouse may contribute to the changes.

In animals exposed to DDT as adults, the symptoms of poisoning are known to parallel the concentration of DDT in the gray matter (Woolley, 1982). A correlation between brain concentrations and poisoning symptoms is also seen with the pyrethroids (Gray *et al.*, 1980; Rickard and Brodie, 1985; Ruzo *et al.*, 1979). The symptom course of acutely DDT-poisoned mammals, such as rat, rabbit, cat, dog, and monkey, is similar, starting with hyperactivity and hyperexcitability, followed by tremors and convulsions, and finally ataxia and loss of equilibrium (Hrdina *et al.*, 1975; Woolley, 1982). The changes in cholinergic and behavioral variables that we have observed in the adult mouse, exposed on the 10th postnatal day to a single low oral dose of DDT, are not correlated with the presence of DDT or its metabolites in the adult mouse brain. Despite the pronounced retention of DDT in neonatal mouse brain, no DDT was detected in the brain 1 month after its administration to 10-day-old mice (Eriksson *et al.*, 1990b). This indicates that disturbances induced during the brain growth spurt can lead to irreversible changes in adult brain function, whereas disturbances caused by adult exposure seem more amenable to reversal.

5. CONCLUDING REMARKS

Our results demonstrate that interference with the cholinergic transmitter system during its rapid development phase from low doses of xenobiotics can lead to irreversible changes in adult brain function. It seems also that as long as the brain is undergoing rapid development, processes based on both positive and negative feedback between receptors and transmitters maintain homeostasis. During aging there is normally a decrease in many variables of different transmitter systems and a decline in brain function capacity. Aging and cholinergic dysfunction have long been mutually associated (Bartus *et al.*, 1982). It is therefore tempting to speculate whether a low-dose exposure to environmental pollutants, exemplified here by DDT and pyrethroids, during a critical time in animal development could contribute to an earlier onset of aging and/or degenerative processes in the brain. Another current area of interest is whether early exposure to toxicants can lead to an increased and/or modified reaction to xenobiotics in adult life, which might in turn accelerate a decline in brain functional capacity.

The amount of DDT given in our studies is of physiological significance and toxicological relevance, since it is of the same order of magnitude as that to which animals and humans can be exposed during lactation (Bevenue, 1976; Slorach and Vaz, 1983; WHO, 1979). Despite bans on and restrictions in the use of substances such as DDT that resist breakdown under environmental conditions, such agents will still be present in the environment for a long time to come. Whether the introduction of short-acting pesticides into an environment already contaminated with persistent environmental pollutants could lead to unexpected effects is therefore of special interest. Our studies have indicated that exposure to short-acting pesticides, such as pyrethroids, during a critical period of postnatal development can have the same effects as DDT. Short-acting pesticides might be of significance, since they can cause the same effects as long-lasting chemicals if they reach target organs in sufficient quantities.

REFERENCES

Ahlbom, J., Fredriksson, A., and Eriksson, P., 1992, Neonatal exposure to a Type I pyrethroid (bioallethrin) induces dose-response changes in brain muscarinic receptors and behavior in neonatal and adult mice (submitted).

Aldridge, W.N., 1990, An assessment of the toxicological properties of pyrethroids and their neurotoxicity *Crit. Rev. Toxicol.* 21(2):89–104.

Aldridge, W.N., Clothier, B., Forshaw, P., Johnson, M.K., Parker, V.H., Price, R.J., Skilleter, D.N., Verschoyle, R.D., and Stevens, C., 1978, The effect of DDT and the pyrethroids cismethrin and decamethrin on the acetylcholine and cyclic nucleotide content of rat brain, *Biochem. Pharmac.* 27:1703–1706.

Archer, T., Fredriksson, A., Lewander, T., and Söderberg, U., 1987, Marble burying and spontaneous motor activity in mice: Interactions over days and the effect of diazepam, *Scand. J. Psychol.* 28:242–249.

Bartus, R.T., Dean III, R.L., Beer, B., and Lippa, A.S., 1982, The cholinergic hypothesis of geriatric memory dysfunction, *Science* 217:408–417.

Beani, L., Bianchi, C., Nilsson, L., Nordberg, A., Romanelli, L., and Sivilotti, 1985, The effect of nicotine and cytisine on [^{3}H]-acetylcholine release from cortical slices of guinea pig brain, *Naunyn Schmiedbergs Arch. Pharmacol.* 331:293–296.

Bevenue, A., 1976, The "bioconcentration" aspects of DDT in the environment, *Residue Rev.* 61:37–112.

Birdsall, N.J.M., Burgen, A.S.V., and Hulme, E.C., 1978, The binding of agonists to brain muscarinic receptors, *Mol. Pharmacol.* 14:723–736.

Bloom, A.S., Staatz, C.G., and Dieringer, T., 1983, Pyrethroid effects on operant responding and feeding, *Neurobehav. Toxicol. Teratol.* 5:321–324.

Bolles, R.G., and Woods, P.J., 1964, The ontogeny of behaviour in the albino rat, *Anim. Behav.* 12:427–441.

Burgen, A.S.V., 1982, Regulation of acetylcholine receptors, in: *Advances in Pharmacology and Therapeutics. Neurotransmitters and Receptors*, Volume 2 (H. Yoshida, Y., Hagihara, and S. Ebashi, eds.), Pergamon Press, Oxford, pp. 51–55.

Bäckström, J., Hansson, E., and Ullberg, S., 1965, Distribution of ^{14}C-DDT and ^{14}C-dieldrin in pregnant mice determined by whole-body autoradiography, *Toxicol. Appl. Pharmacol.* 7:90–96.

Campbell, B.A., Lytle, L.D., and Fibiger, H.C., 1969, Ontogeny of adrenergic arousal and cholinergic inhibitory mechanisms in the rat, *Science* 166:635–637.

Casida, J.E., Gammon, D.W., Glickman, A.H., and Lawrence, L.J., 1983, Mechanisms of selective action of pyrethroid insecticides, *Annu. Rev. Pharmacol. Toxicol.* 23:413–438.

Coulston, F., 1985, Reconsideration of the dilemma of DDT for the establishment of an acceptable daily intake, *Reg. Toxicol. Pharm.* 5:332–383.

Coyle, J.T., and Yamamura, H.I., 1976, Neurochemical aspects of the ontogenesis of cholinergic neurons in the rat brain, *Brain Res.* 118:429–440.

Creese, I., and Sibley, D.R., 1981, Receptor adaptations to centrally acting drugs, *Annu. Rev. Pharmacol. Toxicol.* 21:357–391.

Cremer, J.E., Cunningham, V.J., Ray, D.E., and Sarna, G.S., 1980, Regional changes in brain glucose utilization in rats given a pyrethroid insecticide, *Brain Res.* 194:278–282.

Crofton, K.M., and Reiter, L.W., 1984, Effects of two pyrethroid insecticides on motor activity and the acoustic startle response in the rat, *Toxicol. Appl. Pharmacol.* 75:318–328.

Crofton, K.M., and Reiter, L.W., 1987, Pyrethroid insecticides and the τ-aminobutyric acid receptor complex: Motor activity and the acoustic startle response in the rat, *J. Pharmacol. Exp. Ther.* 243:946–954.

Crofton, K.M., and Reiter, L.W., 1988, The effects of type I and type II pyrethroids on motor activity and the acoustic startle response in the rat, *Fundam. Appl. Toxicol.* 10:624–634.

Crofton, K.M., Reiter, L.W., and Mailman, R.B., 1987, Pyrethroid insecticides and radioligand displacement from the GABA receptor chloride ionophore complex, *Toxicol. Lett.* 35:183–190.

Davison, A.N., and Dobbing, J., (eds), 1968, *Applied Neurochemistry*, Blackwell, Oxford, pp. 178–221, 253–316.

Douglas, R.J., and Isaacson, R.L., 1964, Hippocampal lesions and activity, *Psychon. Sci.* 1:187–188.

Dustman, E.H., and Stickel, L.F., 1969, The occurrence and significance of pesticide residues in wild animals, *Ann. N.Y. Acad. Sci.* 160:162–172.

Edwards, C.A., 1970, *Persistent Pesticides in the Environment*, CRC Monoscience Series, Chemical Rubber Co., Cleveland, OH.

Elliott, M., Farnham, A.W., Janes, N.F., Needham, P.H., Pulman, D.A., and Stevenson, J.H., 1973, A photostable pyrethroid, *Nature* 246:169–170.

Elliott, M., Farnham, A.W., Janes, N.F., Needham, P.H., and Pulman, D.A., 1974, Synthetic insecticide with a new order of activity, *Nature* 248:710–711.

Eriksson, P., 1984, Age-dependent retention of [¹⁴C]DDT in the brain of the postnatal mouse, *Toxicol. Lett.* 22:323–328.

Eriksson, P., and Darnerud, P.O., 1985, Distribution and retention of some chlorinated hydrocarbons and a phthalate in the mouse brain during the pre-weaning period, *Toxicology* 37:185–203.

Eriksson, P., and Fredrikkson, A., 1991, Neurotoxic effects of two different pyrethroids, bioallethrin and deltamethrin, on immature and adult mice: Changes in behavioral and muscarinic receptor variables, *Toxicol. Appl. Pharmacol.* 108:78–85.

Eriksson, P., and Nordberg, A., 1986, The effects of DDT, DDOH-palmitic acid, and a chlorinated paraffin on muscarinic receptors and the sodium-dependent choline uptake in the central nervous system of immature mice, *Toxicol. Appl. Pharmacol.* 85:121–127.

Eriksson, P., and Nordberg, A., 1990, Effects of two pyrethroids, bioallethrin and deltamethrin, on subpopulations of muscarinic and nicotinic receptors in the neonatal mouse brain, *Toxicol. Appl. Pharmacol.* 102:456–463.

Eriksson, P., Falkeborn, Y., Nordberg, A., and Slanina, P., 1984, Effects of DDT on muscarine- and nicotine-like binding sites in CNS of immature and adult mice, *Toxicol. Lett.* 22:329–334.

Eriksson, P., Archer, T., and Fredriksson, A., 1990a, Altered behaviour in adult mice exposed to a single low oral dose of DDT and its fatty acid conjugate as neonates, *Brain Res.* 514:141–142.

Eriksson, P., Nilsson-Håkansson, L., Nordberg, A., Aspberg, A., and Fredriksson, A., 1990b, Neonatal exposure to DDT and its fatty acid conjugate—Effects on cholinergic and behavioural variables in the adult mouse, *Neurotoxicology* 11:345–354.

Eriksson, P., Ahlbom, J., and Fredriksson, A., 1992, Exposure to DDT during a defined period in neonatal life induces permanent changes in brain muscarinic receptors and behavior in adult mice, *Brain Res.* 582:277–281.

Eriksson, P., Johansson, U., Ahlbom, J., and Fredriksson, A., 1992, Neonatal exposure to DDT induces increased susceptibility to pyrethroid (bioallethrin) at adult age: Changes in cholinergic muscarinic receptor and behavioral variables (submitted).

Falkeborn, Y., Larsson, C., Nordberg, A., and Slanina, P., 1983, A comparison of regional ontogenesis of nicotine- and muscarine-like binding sites in mouse brain, *Int. J. Dev. Neurochem.* 1:187–190.

Fonseca, M.I., Aguilar, J.S., López, C., García Fernández, J.C., and DeRobertis, E., 1986, Regional effect of organochlorine insecticides on cholinergic muscarinic receptors of rat brain, *Toxicol. Appl. Pharmacol.* 84:192–195.

Gammon, D.W., Brown, M.A., and Casida, J.E., 1981, Two classes of pyrethroid action in the cockroach, *Pestic. Biochem. Physiol.* 15:181–191.

Gaughan, L.C., Ackerman, M.E., Unai, T., and Casida, J.E., 1978, Distribution and metabolism of *trans-* and *cis*-permethrin in lactating Jersey cows, *J. Agric. Food Chem.* 26:613–618.

Glowa, J.R., 1986, Acute and sub-acute effects of deltamethrin and chlorodimeform on schedule-controlled responding in the mouse, *Neurobehav. Toxicol. Teratol.* 8:97–102.

Gray, A.J., and Soderlund, D.M., 1985, Mammalian toxicology of pyrethroids, in: *Insecticides—Progress in Pesticide Biochemistry and Toxicology*, Volume 5 (D.H. Hutson, and T.R. Roberts, eds.), John Wiley, Chichester, England, pp. 193–248.

Gray, A.J., Conners, T.A., Hoellinger, H., and Nguyen-Hoang-Nam, 1980, The relationship between the pharmacokinetics of intravenous cismethrin and bioresmethrin and their mammalian toxicity, *Pestic. Biochem. Physiol.* 13:281–293.

Gray, E.G., and Whittaker, V.P., 1962, The isolation of nerve endings from brain: An electron-microscopic study of cell fragments derived by homogenization and centrifugation, *J. Anat.* 96:79–87.

Hayes, W.J., Jr., 1959, The pharmacology and toxicology of DDT, in: *The Insecticide Dichlorodiphenyltrichloroethane and Its Significance*, Volume II (P. Müller, ed.) Basel, Birkhäuser, pp. 11–247.

Hayes, J.H., Jr., (ed.), 1975, *Toxicology of Pesticides*, Williams and Wilkins, Baltimore, pp. 166–167.

Henderson, G.L., and Woolley, D.E., 1970, Mechanisms of neurotoxic action of 1,1,1-trichloro-2,2-bis(p-chlorophenyl)ethane (DDT) in immature and adult rats, *J. Pharmacol. Exp. Ther.* 175:60–68.

Herr, D.W., and Tilson, H.A., 1987, Modulation of p,p'-DDT-induced tremor by catecholaminergic agents, *Toxicol. Appl. Pharmacol.* 91:149–158.

Herr, D.W., Hong, J.S., and Tilson, H.A., 1985, DDT-induced tremor in rats: Effects of pharmacological agents, *Psychophar-macology* 86:426–431.

Herr, D.W., Hong, J.S., Chen, P., Tilson, H.A., and Harry, G.J., 1986, Pharmacological modification of DDT-induced tremor and hyperthermia in rats: Distributional factors, *Psychopharmacology* 89:278–283.

Höhmann, C.C., and Ebner, F.F., 1985, Development of cholinergic markers in mouse forebrain. I. Choline acetyltransferase enzyme activity and acetylcholineesterase histochemistry, *Dev. Brain Res.* 23, 225–241.

Höhmann, C.C., Pert, C.C., and Ebner, F.F., 1985, Development of cholinergic markers in mouse forebrain. II. Muscarinic receptor binding in cortex, *Dev. Brain. Res.* 23:243–253.

Hrdina, P.D., Singhal, R.L., Peters, D.A.V., and Ling, G.M., 1971, Role of brain acetylcholine and dopamine in acute neurotoxic effects of DDT, *Eur. J. Pharmacol.* 15:379–382.

Hrdina, P.D., Singhal, R.L., Peters, D.A.V., and Ling, G.M., 1973, Some neurochemical alterations during acute DDT poisoning, *Toxicol. Appl. Pharmacol.* 25:276–288.

Hrdina, P.D., Singhal, R.L., and Ling, G.M., 1975, DDT and related chlorinated hydrocarbon insecticides: Pharmacological basis of their toxicity in mammals, *Adv. Pharmacol. Chemother.* 12:31–88.

Hudson, P.M., Chen, P.H., Tilson, H.A., and Hong, J.S., 1985, Effects of p,p'-DDT on the rat brain concentration of biogenic amine and amino acid neurotransmitters and their association with p,p'-DDT-induced tremor and hyperthermia, *J. Neurochem.* 45:1349–1355.

Hue, B., and Mony, L., 1987, Actions of deltamethrin and tralomethrin on cholinergic synaptic transmission in the central nervous system of the cockroach (*Periplaneta Americana*), *Comp. Biochem. Physiol.* 86C(2):349–352.

Hulme, E.C., Birdsall, N.J.M., Wheatly, M., Curtis, C., Pedder, E.K., Poyner, D., Stockton, J.M., and Eveleigh, P., 1987, Muscarinic acetylcholine receptors: Structure, function subtypes and therapeutic perspectives, *Postgrad. Med. J.* 63 (Suppl 1):5–12.

Hunt, L.M., and Gilbert, B.N., 1977, Distribution and excretion rates of ^{14}C-labeled permethrin isomers administered orally to four lactating goats for 10 days, *J. Agric. Food Chem.* 25:673–676.

Jacobson, S., 1963, Sequence of myelinization in the brain of the albino rat. A. Cerebral cortex, thalamus and related structures, *J. Comp. Neurol.* 121:5–29.

Kalil, R.E., 1989, Synapse formation in the developing brain, *Sci. Am.* 261:38–45.

Karczmar, A.G., 1975, Cholinergic influences on behavior, in: *Cholinergic Mechanisms* (P.G. Waser, ed.), Raven Press, New York, pp. 501–529.

Kavlock, R., Chernoff, N., Baron, R., Linder, R., Rogers, E., and Carver, B., 1979, Toxicity studies with decamethrin, a synthetic pyrethroid insecticide, *J. Environ. Pathol. Toxicol.* 2:751–765.

Kuhar, M.J., Birdsall, N.J.M., Burgen, A.S.V., and Hulme, E.C., 1980, Ontogeny of muscarinic receptors in rat brain, *Brain Res.* 184:375–383.

Lawrence, L.J., and Casida, J.E., 1983, Stereospecific action of pyrethroid insecticides on the τ-aminobuturic acid receptor-ionophore complex, *Science* 221:1399–1401.

Lawrence, L.J., Gee, K.W., and Yamamura, H.I., 1985, Interactions of pyrethroid insecticides with chloride ionophore-associated binding sites, *Neurotoxicology* 6:87–98.

Leighty, E.G., and Fentiman, A.F., Jr., 1981, Liver microsomal conjugation of pentachlorophenyl to fatty acids, *Fed. Proc. Fedn. Am. Socs. Exp. Biol.* 40:677.

Leighty, E.G., Fentiman, A.F., Jr., and Foltz, R.L., 1976, Long-retained metabolites of Δ^9 and Δ^8-tetrahydrocannabinols identified as novel fatty acid conjugates, *Res. Commun. Pathol. Pharmacol.* 14:13–28.

Leighty, E.G., Fentiman, A.F., Jr., and Thompson, R.M., 1980, Conjugation of fatty acids to DDT in the rat: Possible mechanism for retention, *Toxicology* 15:77–82.

Lund, A.E., and Narahashi, T., 1983, Kinetics of sodium channel modification as the basis for the variation in the nerve membrane effects of pyrethroids and DDT analogs, *Pestic. Biochem. Physiol.* 20:203–216.

Marchi, M., Caviglia, A., Paudice, P., and Raiteri, M., 1983, Calcium-dependent [^{3}H]acetylcholine release and muscarinic autoreceptors in rat cortical synaptosomes during development, *Neurochem. Res.* 8:621–628.

McMahon, F.J., Moran, T.H., and Robinson, R.G., 1989, Hyperactivity following posterior cortical injury is lateralized, sensitive to lesion size and independent of the nigrostriatal dopamine system, *Brain Res.* 503:185–190.

Mitchell, J.A., Wilson, M.C., and Kallman, M.J., 1988, Behavioral effects of pydrin and ambush in male mice, *Neurotoxicol. Teratol.* 10:113–119.

Narahashi, T., 1982, Cellular and molecular mechanisms of action of insecticides: Neurophysiological approach, *Neurobehav. Toxicol. Teratol.* 4:753–758.

Narahashi, T., 1985, Nerve membrane ionic channels as the primary target of pyrethroids, *Neurotoxicology* 6:3–22.

Nordberg, A., and Wahlström, G., 1982, Changes in populations of cholinergic binding sites in brain after chronic exposure to barbital in rats, *Brain Res.* 246:105–112.

Nordberg, A., and Winblad, B., 1981, Cholinergic receptors in human hippocampus—regional distribution and variance with age, *Life Sci.* 29:1937–1944.

Peele, D.B., and Crofton, K.M., 1987, Pyrethroid effects on schedule-controlled behavior: Time and dosage relationships. *Neurotoxicol. Teratol.* 9:387–394.

Ray, D.E., 1980, An EEG investigation of decamethrin-induced choreoathetosis in the rat, *Exp. Brain Res.* 38:221–227.

Rickard, J., and Brodie, M.E., 1985, Correlation of blood and brain levels of the neurotoxic pyrethroid deltamethrin with the onset of symptoms in rats, *Pestic. Biochem. Physiol.* 23:143–156.

Roberts, W.W., Dember, W.N., and Brodwick, M., 1962, Alternation and exploration in rats with hippocampal lesions, *J. Comp. Physiol. Psychol.* 55:695–700.

Robinson, R.G., 1979, Differential behavioral and biochemical effects of right and left hemispheric cerebral infarction in the rat, *Science* 205:707–710.

Robinson, R.G., Shoemaker, W.J., Schlumpf, M., Valk, T., and Bloom, F.E., 1975, Effect of experimental cerebral infarction in rat brain on catecholamines and behaviour, *Nature* 255:332–334.

Rowell, P.R., and Winkler, D.L., 1984, Nicotinic stimulation of^{3}H-acetylcholine release from mouse cerebral cortex synaptosomes, *J. Neurochem.* 43:1593–1598.

Ruzo, L.O., Engel, J.L., and Casida, J.E., 1979, Decamethrin metabolites from oxidative, hydrolytic, and conjugative reactions in mice, *J. Agric. Food Chem.* 27:725–731.

Schofield, P.R., Darlison, M.G., Fujita, N., Burt, D.R., Stephenson, F.A., Rodriguez, H., Rhee, L.M., Ramachandran, J., Reale, V., Glencorse, T.A., Seeburg, P.H., and Barnard, E.A., 1987, Sequence and functional expression of GABA$_A$ receptor shows a ligand-gated receptor super-family, *Nature* 328:221–227.

Slorach, S.A., and Vaz, R., 1983, Assessment of human exposure to selected organochlorine compounds through biological monitoring. Swedish National Food Administration, Uppsala, Sweden, pp. 1–134.

Sobotka, T.L., 1971, Behavioral effects of low doses of DDT, *Proc. Soc. Exp. Biol. Med.* 137:952–955.

Stein, E.A., Washburn, M., Walczak, C., and Bloom, A.S., 1987, Effects of pyrethroid insecticides on operant responding maintained by food, *Neurotoxicol. Teratol.* 9:27–31.

St. Omer, V.V., and Ecobichon, D.J., 1971, The acute effect of some chlorinated hydrocarbon insecticides on the acetylcholine content of rat brain, *Can. J. Physiol. Pharmacol.* 49:79–83.

Telford, H.S., and Guthrie, J.E., 1945, Transmission of the toxicity of DDT through the milk of white rats and goats, *Science* 102:647.

Tilson, H.A., Hong, J.S., and Mactutus, C.F., 1985, Effects of 5,5.diphenylhydantoin (phenytoin) on neurobehavioral toxicity of organochlorine insecticides and permethrin, *J. Pharmacol. Exp. Ther.* 233:285–289.

Tilson, H.A., Hudson, P.M., and Hong, J.S., 1986, 5,5-Diphenylhydantoin antagonizes neurochemical and behavioral effects of p,p′-DDT but not of chlordecone, *J. Neurochem.* 47:1870–1878.

Tilson, H.A., Shaw, S., and McLamb, R.L., 1987, The effects of lindane, DDT, and chlordecone on avoidance responding and seizure activity, *Toxicol. Appl. Pharmacol.* 88:57–65.

van den Bercken, J., Akkermans, L.M.A., and van der Zalm, J.M., 1973, DDT-like action of allethrin in the sensory nervous system of *Xenopus laevis, Eur. J. Pharmacol.* 21:95–106.

van den Bercken, and Vijverberg, H.P.M., 1988, Mode of action of pyrethroid insecticides, in: *Recent Advances in Nervous System Toxicology* (C.L. Galli, L. Manzo, and P.S. Spencer, eds.), Plenum Press, New York, pp. 91–105.

Verschoyle, R.D., and Aldridge, W.N., 1980, Structure-activity relationships of some pyrethroids in rats, *Arch. Toxicol.* 45:325–329.

WHO, 1979, DDT and its derivatives, *Environ. Health Crit.* 9:56–87.

Vijverberg, H.P.M., and van den Bercken, J., 1982, Action of pyrethroid insecticides on the vertebrate nervous system, *Neuropathol. Appl. Neurobiol.* 8:421–440.

Vijverberg, H.P.M., and van den Bercken, J., 1990, Neurotoxicological effects and the mode of action of pyrethroid insecticides, *Crit. Rev. Toxicol.* 21(2):105–126.

Woodard, G., Ofner, R.R., and Montgomery, C.M., 1945, Accumulation of DDT in the body fat and its appearance in the milk of dogs, *Science* 102:177–178.

Woolley, D.E., 1982, Neurotoxicity of DDT and possible mechanism of action, in: *Mechanism of Actions of Neurotoxic substances* (K.N. Prasad, and A. Vernadakis, eds.), Raven Press, New York, pp. 95–141.

Woolley, D.E., and Runnells, A.L., 1967, Distribution of DDT in brain and spinal cord of the rat, *Toxicol. Appl. Pharmacol.* 11:389–395.

Wouters, W., and van den Bercken, J., 1978, Action of pyrethroids, *Gen. Pharmacol.* 9:387–398.

Yamamura, H.I., and Snyder, S.H., 1974, Muscarinic cholinergic binding in rat brain, *Proc. Natl. Acad. Sci. USA* 71:1725–1729.

Part III

Selected
Mechanisms
of Action

Chapter 14

Formation of Excess Reactive Oxygen Species within the Brain

Stephen C. Bondy and *Carl P. LeBel*

1. INTRODUCTION

The terms *free radicals* or *oxygen radicals* have become commonly used in the past decade as a result of overwhelming data suggesting that oxygen radicals are involved in a variety of disease processes. The works of Freeman and Crapo (1982) and Halliwell and Gutteridge (1985, 1989) especially have addressed the ubiquitous role of free radicals in the biology of disease and tissue injury. Most of the issues considered to date have dealt with the role of free radicals in the mechanisms of carcinogenesis, ischemia, and aging. In the field of toxicology, free-radical research has primarily focused in the area of pulmonary, cardiac, and hepatic toxicity.

The liver and the lung have long been known to be organs vulnerable to oxidative stress. The brain, with its high lipid content, high rate of oxidative metabolism, and somewhat low levels of free-radical-eliminating enzymes, may also be a prime target of free-radical-mediated damage. The localization of antioxidant systems primarily to glia rather than neurons (Raps *et al.*, 1989, Savolainen, 1978), while providing a first line of defense, may render the neurons especially susceptible to toxicants successfully traversing this barrier.

It has been known for several decades that mammalian brain contains large amounts of substrates that are susceptible to free-radical attack, such as unsaturated lipids and catecholamines. However, Halliwell and Gutteridge (1985) were the first to discuss the potential role of oxygen radicals in the nervous system. The involvement of these reactive species in hyperoxia, ischemia, trauma, stroke, and transition metal-dependent reactions

---

Stephen C. Bondy • Department of Community and Environmental Medicine, University of California, Irvine, California 72717. *Carl P. LeBel* • Alkermes, Cambridge, Massachusetts 02139.
The Vulnerable Brain and Environmental Risks, Volume 2: Toxins in Food, edited by Robert L. Isaacson and Karl F. Jensen. Plenum Press, New York, 1992.

in the brain has since been a topic of considerable interest (Braughler and Hall, 1989; Floyd, 1990).

We are proposing here that several diverse neurotoxic and neuropathological events may lead to excess formation of free radicals. The idea that a variety of drug and chemical pathogeneses are associated with free-radical mechanisms has been previously proposed (Kehrer *et al.*, 1988). This may significantly contribute to the properties of many neurotoxic agents. Any imbalance of cellular redox status in favor of greater oxidative activity can lead to several kinds of macromolecular damage, such as disruption of genomic function by alterations to DNA, or impairment of membrane properties by attack on proteins or lipids. Lipid peroxidative events are especially hazardous, since lipoperoxy radicals can initiate oxidative chain reactions (Freeman and Crapo, 1982).

Neurotoxic compounds have characteristic and individual properties, and often cause distinctive morphological and biochemical lesions. However, some relatively nonspecific features also constitute part of the overall toxicity of a given agent. For example, many toxic agents induce a general organismic stress response. Such commonality may account for the finding that several unrelated neurotoxic agents can all cause similar endocrine changes, such as the elevation of circulating corticosterone and depression of testosterone levels. In addition, certain neurotransmitter-related changes, such as elevation of brain levels of 5-hydroxyindole acetic acid, are also frequently found following exposure of experimental animals to a wide range of neurotoxic agents (Bondy, 1986).

Recent attempts to unify the diffuse discipline of neurotoxicology have led to the concept of *final common pathways* that characterize frequently occurring cellular responses to disruption of homeostasis resulting from exposure to xenobiotic agents. Such final common pathways in neurotoxicology may include features such as elevation of intracellular levels of free ionic calcium (Bondy, 1990), disruption of membrane function (LeBel and Schatz, 1990), failure of oxidative phosphorylation (Hanstein, 1976), and induction of critical protooncogenes (Muma *et al.*, 1988). The present work considers the possibility that oxygen radicals may be mediators of a final common pathway in several mechanisms of neurotoxicity.

Neurotoxic insult is not an all-or-none event, since subtle and insidious gradations of damage can occur. Broad, low-level exposures to hazardous agents are common, and so the overall magnitude of the problem across the population is very difficult to estimate.

2. REGULATION OF OXYGEN RADICAL GENERATION RATES

Free radicals are defined as any species with one or more unpaired electrons. Since oxygen is ubiquitous in aerobic organisms, oxygen-centered free radicals have been implicated in several physiological, toxicological, and pathological phenomena. However, while superoxide anion and hydroxyl radical qualify as oxygen-centered radicals, hydrogen peroxide is a potent cellular toxicant that lacks unpaired electrons. The terms *reactive oxygen species* (ROS) or *oxygen radicals* have been used to describe all oxygen-centered radicals and nonradicals. Oxygen radical-induced damage is normally maintained at low levels due to the presence of a range of protective factors, which will be outlined in a later section.

The precise nature of oxygen radicals produced in the CNS is by no means clear. The difficulty of establishing this with certainty is due to the short half-life and rapid interconvertability of many of the putative key species (LeBel *et al.*, 1991). Relatively stable species, such as superoxide and hydrogen peroxide, give rise to less clearly defined, highly active, transient species that are the primary oxidants. Evaluation of free-radical-forming potential of neurotoxic agents and determination of whether oxygen radicals are common mediators of neurotoxicity should not be delayed until the identity of critical oxygen radicals is unequivocally clarified.

3. UNDERLYING CAUSES OF REACTIVE OXYGEN SPECIES FORMATION

3.1. Oxidative Phosphorylation

Around 2% of oxygen consumed by mitochondria is incompletely reduced and appears as oxygen radicals (Boveris and Chance, 1973). This proportion may be increased when the efficient functioning of mitochondrial electron transport systems is compromised. This could account for the increased lipid peroxidation found in the brains of mice exposed to nonlethal levels of cyanide (Johnson *et al.*, 1987).

3.2. Cytosolic Acidity

Lowered pH resulting from excess glycolytic activity may not only accelerate the process of liberating protein-bound iron in organisms, but it may also lead to an impairment of oxidative ATP generation and to the appearance of the prooxidant protonated superoxide (Siesjo, 1988). However, there is evidence that the reduction of pH during ATP depletion may be protective and may enhance cell survival (Kehrer *et al.*, 1990). Chlordecone, a neurotoxic insecticide, both elevates pH within synaptosomes and depresses oxygen radical synthesis (Bondy *et al.*, 1991).

3.3. Presence of Metal Ions with Multivalence Potential

Liberation of protein-bound iron can occur by enhanced degradation of important iron-binding proteins such as ferritin and transferrin. A small increase in levels of free iron within cells can dramatically accelerate rates of oxygen radical production (Minotti and Aust, 1989). A key feature in establishing the rate of production of oxygen radicals by tissue is the cytosolic concentration of free metal ions possessing the capacity to readily change their valence state. Iron is considered the most important of these, but levels of free manganese and copper may also be significant factors (Aust *et al.*, 1985).

3.4. Eicosanoid Production

Enhanced phospholipase activity can lead to the release of arachidonic acid. This polyunsaturated fatty acid contains four ethylenic bonds and is readily autooxidizable. In fact, impure preparations of this chemical may explode spontaneously on exposure to air

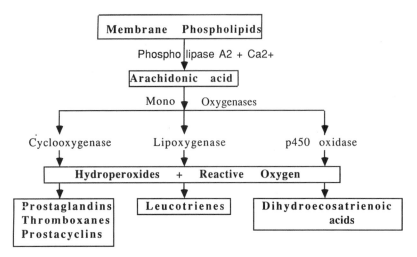

FIGURE 1. Eicosanoid formation: Pathways of phospholipid catabolism that involve enzymic degradation of arachidonic acid by molecular oxygen, and thereby lead to the generation of reactive oxygen species.

(Halliwell and Gutteridge, 1989). The enzymic conversion of this compound to many bioactive prostaglandins, leukotrienes, and thromboxanes by cyclooxygenases and lipoxygenases leads to considerable oxygen radical generation (Freeman and Crapo, 1982; Saunders and Horrocks, 1987). All major catabolic pathways of arachidonic acid involve the utilization of molecular oxygen and the formation of hydroperoxide or epoxide intermediates (Fig. 1). Subsequent metabolism by peroxidases and hydrolases can lead to further formation of free radicals. The physiological relevance of this is illustrated by the finding that antioxidants can protect against arachidonic acid-induced cerebral edema (Asano *et al.*, 1989).

Increased levels of cytosolic free calcium may result from either breakdown of the steep concentration gradient of calcium across the plasma membrane or from liberation of the large amounts of calcium bound intracellularly within mitochondria or endoplasmic reticulum. This elevation can activate phospholipases and thus stimulate oxygen radical production. In fact, the activation of phospholipase D has been functionally linked to superoxide anion production (Bonser *et al.*, 1989). A reciprocal relation exists, since free radicals can enhance phospholipase A_2 activity within cerebral capillaries (Au *et al.*, 1985). Conversely, phospholipase A_2 may selectively induce oxidative changes to the GABA-regulated chloride channel and thus increase cell excitability (Schwartz *et al.*, 1988). Evidence is accumulating for a messenger role for reactive oxygen species within cells. Endothelium-derived relaxing factor has been identified as nitric oxide, a free radical (Bruckdorfer *et al.*, 1990).

3.5. Oxidases

Chemical induction of cytochrome P_{450} containing mixed function monooxidases can increase the rate of detoxification reactions. The oxidative metabolism of many lipophilic compounds, while necessary for their conjugation and excretion, often involves the transient formation of highly reactive oxidative intermediates such as epoxides (Seva-nian *et al.*, 1990). While mixed-function oxidases predominate in the liver, they are also present in the nervous system, largely within neurons (Ravindranath *et al.*, 1989). At the intracellular level, most of these cerebral oxidases are mitochondrial rather than micro-somal, and like the corresponding hepatic enzymes, they are inducible (Perrin *et al.*, 1990).

Xanthine oxidase is a prime generator of superoxide and may be a significant exacer-bating factor in several pathological states (see later section).

3.6. Phagocytosis

Extracellular formation of superoxide anion by phagocytes has long been recognized as a bacteriocidal mechanism. Similar oxidative activity has been observed in cerebral microglia (Halliwell and Gutteridge, 1989). Astroglial activation is a common event following neural trauma, and reactive astrocytes are active in clearance of cell debris and, ultimately, in the formation of glial scar tissue. Although the phenomenon of reactive oxygen species generation has not been documented in the injured brain during neu-ronophagia, the ROS-enhancing potential of such events is worthy of further study.

4. FACTORS RELATING TO EXCESS GENERATION OF REACTIVE OXYGEN SPECIES WITHIN THE BRAIN

A large range of chemical agents and physiological processes can accelerate the production of ROS effected by the primary mechanisms described above.

4.1. Physiological Factors

4.1.1. Physical Trauma

One of the consequences of physical damage to brain tissue is vascular hemorrhage. The entry of blood into tissue leads to the breakdown of erythrocytes and consequent escape of hemoglobin into the extracellular compartment. Protein degradative events can lead to the liberation of iron from hemoglobin, and this is a primary initiator of ROS in the nervous system (Halliwell, 1989a; Sadrzadeh *et al.*, 1987).

4.1.2. Aging

Despite the numerous reports on the involvement of oxygen radicals with aging processes, the relation between these events is unresolved. Numerous aging-oxygen radi-cal studies exist regarding lipid peroxidation (Devasagayam, 1989; Sawada and Carlson, 1987), levels of antioxidant factors (Vanella *et al.*, 1989; Vitorica *et al.*, 1984), and membrane fluidity (Schmucker *et al.*, 1984). Many of these reports have conflicting data, and this has confounded understanding of the aging process.

Contributing to this problem is the fact that conclusions regarding the relation between oxygen radicals and aging are generally based on data obtained from events secondary (i.e., lipid peroxidation) to the formation of oxygen radicals.

A recent methodology allows the utilization of a fluorescent probe, dichlorofluorescein, to directly measure the rate of formation of several oxygen radicals (LeBel and Bondy, 1990). This procedure can provide an indication of the sum total of several oxygen radical species formed in a system. Using this approach, we have found that there is a significant age-dependant *decrease* in the velocity of oxygen radical generation. However, there is also evidence of protein damage and an increased rate of intracellular proteolysis in aged animals (LeBel and Bondy, 1991). The accumulation of damaged proteins in the aging brain may be compatible with a concurrent decrease in levels of ROS, since the former event represents a cumulative process, while the latter assay reflects only current activity. Increased proteolytic activity in the aging brain may reflect an adaptation to deal with an elevated amount of nonfunctional denatured proteins (Davies, 1987). Such damaged proteins appear abnormally early in diseases of premature aging, such as progeria and Werner's disease (Stadtman, 1990). Vitamin E deficiency in both experimental animals and humans also leads to an excessive accumulation of lipofuchsin (Sokol, 1989).

The lipofuchsin content of neurons increases with senescence, and this pigment consists of a proteinaceous complex that is resistant to breakdown (Porta, 1988). The accumulation of lipofuchsin with age appears to be a consistent parameter that holds true over a wide range of species (Floyd *et al.,* 1984). Such proteins may be crosslinked products produced by oxidative events, which are no longer substrates for proteolytic breakdown and thus accumulate within the cell (Gutteridge *et al.,* 1983). By this means, altered protein structure and function may be a contributing factor to senescence.

Levels of cerebral superoxide dismutase are found to increase with aging (Le Bel and Bondy, 1991; Scarpa *et al.,* 1987). This enzyme has been reported to be induced by oxidative stressors. Another antioxidant enzyme, glutathione peroxidase, also increases with age in the rat (Scarpa *et al.,* 1987; Vitorica *et al.,* 1984). These elevated levels of protective enzymes suggest that adaptation of the aged brain involves induction of enzymes that oppose adverse oxidative processes. Such an adaptation can be sufficiently successful so as to actually *decrease* oxidative events in affected cells (Bose *et al.,* 1990).

4.1.3. Stroke and Ischemia

Stroke leads to cerebral ischemia, which can be of varying duration, as the capillary supply may be restored. In addition to hemorrhage caused by the extravasating type of stroke, all transient interruptions of vascularity have the potential to lead to severe postischemic damage.

The pathological changes consequent to restoration of the normal blood supply may be initially related to excessively high levels of cytosolic calcium (Siesjo, 1986), but this appears to lead to excess levels of ROS (Dykens *et al.,* 1987; Murphy *et al.,* 1989; Oleson, 1986). It has been reported that the high metabolic rates associated with reperfusion injury can lead to excess oxygen radical production (Vlessis *et al.,* 1990). At the onset of ischemia there is an accumulation of hypoxanthine due to the breakdown of adenine nucleotides. Upon reperfusion, a combination of oxidative and proteolytic events coverts xanthine dehydrogenase to the direct oxygen acceptor, xanthine oxidase. The final combination of elevated enzyme and substrate leads to superoxide production and consequent oxidative stress.

The complex relation between oxygen-induced events and anoxia is illustrated by the finding that damage to the penumbra region around an ischemic region is generally more severe than at the core (Choi, 1990). The presence of oxygen free radicals in postischemic tissue has been directly demonstrated (Cao et al., 1988). Even a brief period of ischemia can lead to free radical generation and thence to delayed neuronal death (Kitagawa et al., 1990).

4.1.4. Edema

A deficiency of neuronal energy generating systems can result in intracellular accumulation of excess sodium and accompanying water. The subsequent expulsion of sodium must then be effected by the Na/H exchanger, since the sodium pump (Na,K ATPase) cannot function without ATP. By this means, cell swelling can be attenuated, but the cost involves a reduction of pH (Asano et al., 1989). A lower cytosolic pH can accelerate the formation of the intensely prooxidant protonated superoxide radical (Essman and Wollman, 1989) and can increase the reactivity of the hydroxyl radical (Tadolini and Cabrini, 1990). In the absence of optimal rates of oxidative phosphorylation, this drop in pH can be exacerbated by the increasing dependence on glycolysis and consequent accumulation of lactate. Finally, the sodium pump may be initially activated but ultimately specifically inhibited by ROS (Asano et al., 1989; Malis and Bonventre, 1986).

4.1.5. Seizures and Excitotoxicity

Seizure activity can elevate the content of ROS in the brain (Armstead et al., 1989). Excessive neuronal activity may lead to an influx of calcium that is sufficient to overwhelm the sequestering and pumping processes by which calcium homeostasis is maintained. There is an increasingly clear relation between excitotoxic events and oxidative damage (Kontos, 1989). Cerebral superoxide generation is elevated during seizures (Armstead et al., 1989; Essman and Wollman, 1989). We have found that a brief (1 sec) electroconvulsive shock is sufficient to cause elevated rates of cortical oxygen radical formation (LeBel and Bondy, unpublished data). In addition to calcium mediating this interrelation, the NMDA receptor may be in part regulated by ROS (Tauck and Ashbeck, 1990), but there are conflicting reports concerning the directionality of this regulation (Levy et al., 1990; Pellegrini-Gampeitro et al., 1990). For example, a mechanism by which free-radical generation can induce seizure activity is by the direct oxidative inactivation of glutamine synthetase, thereby permitting an abnormal buildup of the excitatory transmitter, glutamic acid (Oliver et al., 1990). In this manner neuronal hyperactivity and active oxygen induction may cooperate in the genesis of ischemia-induced neuronal damage (Pellegrini-Giampeitro et al., 1990).

4.2. Chemical Agents

While many neurotoxic agents can stimulate ROS production within the nervous system, this does not imply that such stimulation represents their primary mechanism of toxic action. Prooxidant properties of a chemical may (1) be the main source of its neurotoxicity, (2) contribute to its overall harmfulness, or (3) be an epiphenomenon, only secondarily relating to tissue damage.

4.2.1. Metals

Metals can catalyze the formation of excess ROS by several independent mechanisms that may act in concert, although initiated by a single metal.

The ability of a metal ion to exist in several valence states, and thus transfer single electrons, is found in many metals, including iron, manganese, and mercury. The neurotoxicity of manganese is thought to be specifically due to its capacity to catalyze the autooxidation of catecholamines (Donaldson et al., 1981).

Methyl mercury is able to increase cerebellar rates of ROS generation (LeBel et al., 1990). This may reflect both the valence ambiguity of mercury and also the deleterious effect of this heavy metal upon anabolic processes such as oxidative phosphorylation and protein synthesis (Verity et al., 1975). These latter events may be related to the powerful affinity of mercury for the sulfhydryl groups of proteins and glutathione. The capacity of methyl mercury to elevate cytosolic calcium (Komulainen and Bondy, 1987) may also be relevant to its oxidant properties.

Thallium owes some of its neurotoxicity to the fact that it can partially substitute for potassium and may interfere with critical functions of potassium. However, the ability of this element to exist in both mono- and trivalent states may account for its enhancement of lipid peroxidation in the striatum (Hasan and Ali, 1981).

Both organic and inorganic lead have been shown to enhance the rates of lipid peroxidation or ROS formation (Ali and Bondy, 1989; LeBel et al., 1990; Ramstoek et al., 1980; Rehman, 1984). Lead neither has a major affinity for sulfhydryl groups nor does its readily undergo valence flux under physiological conditions. However, calcium flux is deranged in cases of severe lead poisoning (Tonge et al., 1977), and this may form the basis of its oxidant properties.

The induction of hyperactivity by a toxic chemical may be sufficient to lead to enhanced ROS production, probably by way of increasing cytosolic levels of free calcium. This may account for the excess oxidant activity described in the brains of animals treated with organometals such as trimethyl tin and triethyl lead (Ali and Bondy, 1989; LeBel et al., 1990). In these studies, as with the methylmercury results, the regional distribution of the excess oxidative activity paralleled the sites of known neuropathological changes. This implies that induced oxidative events are likely to be a significant component of the neurotoxicity of these metals, rather than an irrelevant epiphenomenon.

4.2.2. Solvents

The ability of various organic solvents to effect excess ROS synthesis has been described for several tissues (Ahmad et al., 1987; Cojocel et al., 1989), but the brain has received little attention in this context. The neurotoxicity of two solvents of environmental significance has, however, been described. Ethanol has been reported to enhance cerebral ROS production (Nordmann, 1987; Rouach et al., 1987), and this has been ascribed to the liberation of iron from its sequestration sites within proteins (Rouach et al., 1990).

Whether ethanol-provoked oxidative events are also mediated by acetaldehyde (Frido-vitch, 1989; Phillips, 1987) or increased intracellular calcium (Daniell *et al.*, 1988; Dildy and Leslie, 1989) is unresolved.

An aromatic neurotoxic solvent, toluene, has recently been shown capable of induction of excess ROS in the CNS, both *in vitro* and *in vivo* (Mattia *et al.*, 1990). Since toluene has anesthetic properties, this is unlikely to be due to neuronal hyperactivity. In a recent study, phospholipase activity was significantly stimulated in synaptosomes isolated from rats exposed to toluene (LeBel and Schatz, 1990). This may underlie the observed enhancement of cerebral ROS. Toluene alters synaptosomal phospholipid methyltransferase activity, an event that has also been shown to be affected by oxygen radicals (Kaneko *et al.*, 1990).

The oxygen radical stimulatory effect of toluene can be blocked by pretreatment of rats with an inhibitor of mixed-function oxidases, namely, metyrapone (Mattia *et al.*, 1991). Therefore, the products of toluene catabolism were also examined for their oxygen radical-enhancing potential. Both benzyl alcohol and benzoic acid has free-radical quenching properties; however, benzaldehyde was a potent agent in enhancing oxygen radical formation. This suggests that benzaldehyde is the active metabolite responsible for the prooxidant properties of administered toluene. Benzene is not able to induce oxygen radical formation in a manner parallel to that of toluene, either *in vitro* or *in vivo* (Mattia *et al.*, 1991). It may be that the lack of activity of benzene in this regard is related to the absence of an attached methyl group available for oxidation. However, *trans,trans*-muconaldehyde, a minor, potentially toxic, metabolite of benzene, has been suggested to play a role in benzene-induced free-radical events (Witz *et al.*, 1985). Other aromatic solvents, including various isomers of xylene (dimethylbenzene), and styrene, also have ROS-induced properties similar to that of toluene (Mattia and Bondy, unpublished data).

The free-radical component of solvent effects may not enhance the acute toxicity of solvents but has been proposed to affect more subtle processes, such as an acceleration of normal aging processes (Ahmad *et al.*, 1987).

4.2.3. Specific Agents Acting on Dopaminergic Neurons

Dopaminergic circuitry is especially vulnerable to neurotoxic damage, and this is at least in part due to the readiness with which dopamine is autooxidized in the presence of trace amounts of metals with multivalence potential. In addition, dopamine can be enzymically oxidized by monoamine oxidases to 3,4 dihydroxyphenyl acetaldehyde and H_2O_2.

A role for oxidative stress in the processes underlying 1-methyl-4-phenyl-1,2,3,6-tetrahydropyridine (MPTP) neurotoxicity has been proposed in recent years. This compound, a contaminant of an illicitly manufactured meperidine analogue, has been the subject of much interest, since the neurological damage that it can cause closely resembles Parkinson's disease. MPTP is a very specific dopaminergic neurotoxin. (See Chapter 16). There is considerable support for the *mitochondrial theory* of MPTP toxicity, which postulates that 1-methyl-4-phenylpyridinium (MPP$^+$), the ultimate oxidation product of MPTP, blocks the reoxidation of NADH dehydrogenase by coenzyme Q_{10} and eventually leads to ATP depletion in a rotenone-like fashion (Heikilla *et al.*, 1989). However, there are also several studies that suggest oxygen radicals may play a role in the MPTP-induced neuronal damage (Odunze *et al.*, 1990; Rios and Tapia, 1987). These concepts may be reconciled by the finding that the metabolic inhibitors rotenone and antimycin can increase the generation rate of oxygen radicals in crude rat synaptosomes and mitochondria (Cino and Del Maestro, 1989; LeBel and Bondy, 1991).

Emerging information concerning MPTP has led to several new ideas concerning a very prevalent neurological disorder, Parkinson's disease. These concepts include both the possibility of an environmental agent being contributory to the pathogenesis of Parkinsonism (Tanner and Langston, 1990) and of the potential for antioxidant therapy of this disorder (Parkinson's Study Group, 1989). Parkinson's disease has been associated with abnormally high levels of superoxide dismutase within the substantia nigra (Saggu *et al.*, 1989), implying an induced response to oxidative stress. A contribution of environmentally prevalent agents, such as pyridines, to the incidence of this disorder has been proposed. In addition, the potential utility of several antioxidant therapies is currently under investigation (McCrodden *et al.*, 1990; Shoulson, 1989). There is evidence that n-hexane may specifically damage dopaminergic neurons and precipitate Parkinsonian symptoms in both humans and experimental animals (Pezzoli *et al.*, 1990). The environmental relevance of this is enhanced by the detection of the neurotoxic metabolite of n-hexane, 2,5 hexanedione, in the urine of persons not known to have been exposed to organic solvents (Fedtke and Bolt, 1986).

The neurotoxicity of another abused drug, metamphetamine, may in part be due to oxidative stress relating to dopaminergic and serotonergic circuitry (De Vito and Wagner, 1989). This was inferred by the attenuation of metamphetamine-induced neuropathologic changes by pretreatment with a variety of antioxidants. Neuronal destruction induced by levo-DOPA and 6-hydroxydopamine is also thought to occur via free-radical mechanisms (Olney *et al.*, 1990), and the administration of hydroxyl radical scavengers, such as phenylthiazolythiourea and methimazole, is protective against such induced damage (Cohen, 1988).

There are several reports that neuroleptics may elevate lipid peroxidation in the CNS, and it has been proposed that this is a cause of tardive dyskinesia and a result of increased catecholamine metabolism (Lohr *et al.*, 1990).

4.2.4. Other Agents

Cerebral lipid peroxidation can be stimulated by cyanide (Johnson *et al.*, 1987). This illustrates that interruption of the respiratory chain can lead to excess free-radical production. While acute cyanide exposure is rapidly lethal, more chronic exposures as a result of excess cyanogenic glycosides in the diet of some less developed countries (e.g., found in *Cassava*) can result in ataxic neuropathy (Montgomery, 1979). This may be related to the high levels of unsaturated fatty acids in myelin that form a clear target for ROS-induced lipid peroxidation (Halliwell, 1989).

Several antioxidant agents can protect against hexachlorophene-induced cerebral edema and myelin damage (Hanig *et al.*, 1984). The neurotoxicity of this chemical is thus likely to involve its catalysis of free-radical formation. A wide range of drugs and carcinogens can be involved in one-electron reduction and redox cycling (reviewed by Byczkowski and Gessner, 1988). These are generally not primarily neurotoxic because of their broad systemic toxicity and because of the blood–brain barrier.

5. MITIGATION OF CEREBRAL OXIDATIVE STRESS

Protection against excess levels of oxygen-reactive species is effected by several antioxidant mechanisms intrinsic to the cell. Oxygen-radical-induced damage is thus normally maintained at low levels. In addition, many forms of dietary additions and pharmacological interventions may enhance the protection of tissues from ROS. Such treatments may involve elevating the content of naturally occurring chemicals or the introduction of novel xenobiotic agents.

5.1. Endogenous Protectants

5.1.1. Enzymes and Proteins

Enzymes such as superoxide dismutase, catalase, and peroxidase are able to destroy the superoxide radical and hydrogen peroxide. While these oxidant species are not in themselves very active, they are able to interact in the presence of trace amounts of iron, and by the Haber–Weiss reaction give rise to the highly reactive, short-lived hydroxyl radical:

$$O_2' + H_2O_2 \rightarrow O_2 + OH' + OH^{\cdot}$$

Thus, superoxide dismutase, if induced in the absence of a similar induction of H_2O_2 degrading enzymes, may have a prooxidant effect (Seto et al., 1990). In addition, hydrogen peroxide, in the presence of iron, can be converted to the hydroxyl radical by the Fenton reaction:

$$H_2O_2 + Fe^{2+} \rightarrow OH^{\cdot} + OH' + Fe^{3+}$$

Iron-sequestering proteins, such as ferritin and transferrin, are important means of ensuring extremely low levels of cytosolic free iron. Some serum proteins, notably albumin, can act as free-radical scavengers (Halliwell, 1988). The low protein content of cerebrospinal fluid makes both albumin and ferritin largely unavailable to the CNS (Halliwell, 1989a). Lower antioxidant activity in Parkinson's disease has been related to decreased levels of ferritin in the brain (Dexter et al., 1990). Levels of protective enzymes are also somewhat low in brain (Savolainen, 1978). Much of this antioxidant capacity lies within cerebral capillaries and glial cells (Tayarani et al., 1987). This may prevent the diffusion of prooxidants into neurons, since the cerebral microvasculature is also a major site of lipid peroxidative activity (Hall and Braughler, 1989) and mixed-function oxidase activity (Ghersi-Egea, 1988).

Treatment of neurons with nerve growth factor is able to confer resistance to oxidative damage, apparently by induction of antioxidant enzymes (Jackson et al., 1990). This factor is known to promote the survival of those neurons taking it up from target tissues. Many protective enzymes are relatively concentrated in cerebral microvessels (Tayarani et al., 1987), where mixed-function oxidase activity is also high (Ghersi-Egea, 1988).

5.1.2. Low Molecular Weight Constituents

The presence of diffusible antioxidant vitamins and provitamins provides protection against oxygen radicals. Such molecules may be predominantly lipophilic (β-carotene, α-tocopherol, retinoic acid) or water soluble (ascorbic acid). β-carotene is distinguished by its effectiveness at the low partial pressures of oxygen found in tissues under physiological conditions (Burton and Ingold, 1984). In addition to its antioxidant properties, α-tocopherol may have other membrane-stabilizing properties (reviewed by Clement and Bourre, 1990). There is a close correlation between the cerebral content of α-tocopherol and polyunsaturated fatty acids during development (Clement and Bourre, 1990). While lipid-soluble vitamins are essential for the retardation of lipid membrane constituents, their reducing power needs continual replenishment by water-soluble reserves. Ascorbic acid, which may be a source of reducing power, also has powerful prooxidant potential when low concentrations of iron are present. This constitutes yet another mechanism by which iron acts as an ROS inducer.

Cellular glutathione is normally maintained at high concentrations intracellularly (1–5 mM). It is maintained very largely in the reduced form by glutathione reductase, acting in conjunction with NADPH, and this constitutes the major reducing capacity of the cytoplasm (Halliwell and Gutteridge, 1985). Thus the cell's reducing powers ultimately depend largely on the production of NADPH by the glycolytic pentose phosphate shunt. Glutathione reserves can be depleted by oxidative stress (Maellaro et al., 1990), and such depletion in the brain can cause neurological deficits (Calvin et al., 1986).

The brainstem has a rather low glutathione content and a high mixed-function oxidase content. It has been proposed that this combination may render the region especially vulnerable to oxidative damage and that this is relevant to nigral damage in Parkinson's disease (Perry et al., 1982; Ravindranath et al., 1989).

5.2. Pharmacological Reduction of Oxidant Status

The reversal of neurological deficits by antioxidants is further evidence of the relevance of oxidative stress to many disturbances of brain function.

5.2.1. Vitamins

α-Tocopherol supplementation of patients with impaired capacity for absorption of this vitamin has significantly improved their neurological deficits (Sokol, 1990). Animal studies have shown that pretreatment with α-tocopherol reduces the edema and ischemia that follows compression injury to the brain (Busto et al., 1984; Saunders and Horrocks, 1987). Vitamin E is protective against methylmercury and cadmium-induced neurotoxicity (Chang et al., 1978; Shukla et al., 1988) and can reduce the incidence of intraventricular hemorrhage in premature infants (Sinha et al., 1987). Vitamin E has also been shown to protect against neural oxidative stress induced by triethyl lead and MPTP (Odunze et al., 1990; Ramstoek et al., 1980). Antioxidative therapy of parkinsonism is currently under trial (Shoulson, 1989). The beneficial effects of vitamin E may be due to its membrane-stabilizing properties, as well as its antioxidant capacity, since fatty acid release following reperfusion of ischemic tissue is inhibited by this vitamin (Yoshida *et al.*, 1985).

Marginal deficiencies of antioxidant vitamins over extended periods may increase vulnerability to chronic exposure to low levels of free-radical-promoting environmental contaminants. The effect of this may be expressed as subclinical events that are very difficult to quantitate but may relate to the overall well-being of an individual.

5.2.2. Chelators

Deferoxamine, a potent iron chelator, can protect against cold-induced cerebral edema (Ikeda *et al.*, 1989). The specificity of this chelator toward iron is, however, not complete (Wahba *et al.*, 1990), and its precise mode of action remains uncertain (Halliwell, 1989). Disadvantages of deferoxamine are that it cannot be administered orally but requires injection, and that its penetrance across the blood–brain barrier is partial (Halliwell, 1989). However, deferoxamine pretreatment can block methylmercury-induced elevation of ROS within the brain (LeBel *et al.*, 1991).

5.2.3. Steroids

Glucocorticoids are antiinflammatory and are protective against lipid peroxidation (Hall and Braughler, 1989), and dexamethasone can attenuate ischemia-induced hippocampal damage (Dun *et al.*, 1990). The mode of action of dexamethasone may involve stimulation of the polypeptide factor, lipotropin, which inhibits phospholipase-stimulated liberation of arachidonic acid (Blackwell *et al.*, 1980). Some recently developed drugs, such as the 21-aminosteroid, U74006F (lazaroids), may combine the potential benefits of both a limited steroidal effect and chelation capacity (Hall and Yonkers, 1988). However, some estrogens, by redox cycling, can exacerbate ROS production (Liehr and Roy, 1990), and chronic exposure to glucocorticoids can damage the hippocampus (Sapolsky *et al.*, 1990).

5.2.4. Other Agents

Several other classes of chemicals have been reported to be protective against neural damage associated with excess oxidative activity. These include chloroquine, mepacrine, and dibucaine, which can inhibit phospholipases (Au *et al.*, 1985, Malis and Bonventre, 1986), and indomethacin, an inhibitor of cyclooxygenases (Kontos and Povlishock, 1986).

Ganglioside GM1, a membrane-stabilizing agent effective within the CNS, may also mitigate some components of oxidative damage to neural tissue. This ganglioside has been reported to be protective against MPTP (Hadjiconstantinou *et al.*, 1989), ischemia (Mahadik *et al.*, 1989), edema (Skaper *et al.*, 1989), and direct oxidative activity (Bondy and McKee, 1990).

The therapeutic application of macromolecular proteins as a means of reducing ROS production is obviously somewhat limited. However, superoxide dismutase linked to albumin has been reported to prevent cold-induced brain edema (Ando *et al.*, 1989).

6. FUTURE DIRECTIONS

The kinds of metabolic change effected by many agents deleterious to nerve tissue often have the potential for inducing excess oxygen radical production. The resulting oxidative damage may constitute a varying proportion of the total toxicity of a wide range of chemicals. Any chemical disrupting membrane structure or mitochondrial function, by any means, has the potential for induction of oxygen radicals. This is especially true of the broad range of agents causing hyperexcitation. Recently, heightened activation of the NMDA receptor has been correlated with many harmful excitatory events (Olney et al., 1989). Such excitotoxicity may have an oxygen-radical-related component. The application of glutamate to a neuronal cell line can·deplete levels of reduced glutathione and thus provoke oxidative stress (Murphy et al., 1989). Conversely, ROS have the potential to stimulate the release of excitatory amino acids (Pellegrini-Giampietro et al., 1990). Thus the relation between excitatory states and oxygen radicals may be bidirectional, but the major direction of such interactions is uncertain.

Many of these phenomena may be accounted for in terms of massive calcium entry leading to lipolysis and mitochondrial lipid peroxidation, and may also derange the function of the mitochondrial respiratory chain, which can increase rates of free-radical production. Conversely, free-radical-initiated damage may decrease the effectiveness of energy-dependent calcium pumps and impair the ability of the plasma membrane to exclude extracellular calcium. An important area for future work is the delineation of the extent of overlap between excitotoxic and "oxidotoxic" events. Little study has been carried out to date on the use of calcium-channel blockers in the treatment of neurological disorders thought to have an oxidative component. In addition to Parkinsonism, such disorders may include Alzheimer's disease (Halliwell, 1989b), genetic lipofuchsinoses (Gutteridge et al., 1983), and schizophrenia and Huntingdon's disease (Lohr et al., 1990; Zemlan et al., 1990). Conversely, the therapeutic potential of antioxidants in the treatment of diseases such as epilepsy, where excessive neuronal activity is involved, has not been extensively studied.

Another fruitful area for study is improved understanding of the role of ROS as cytosolic messengers. The effect of ROS upon protooncogenic activation is unclear. However, conditions such as seizures, eliciting increased ROS levels, can rapidly induce expression of the mRNA for c-fos (Zawia and Bondy, 1990).

ACKNOWLEDGMENTS.   This work was supported by grants from the National Institutes of Health and the Lancaster Foundation.

REFERENCES

Ahmad, F.F., Cowan, D.L., and Sun, A.Y., 1987, Detection of free radical formation various tissues after acute carbon tetrachloride administration in the gerbil, Life Sci.41:2469–2475.

Ali, S.F., and Bondy, S.C., 1989, Triethyl lead-induced damage in various regions of the rat brain, J. Toxicol. Environ. Health 26:235–242.

Ando, A., Inoue, M., Hirota, M., Morino, Y., and Arakai, S., 1989, Effect of a superoxide dismutase derivative on cold-induced brain edema, Brain Res. 477:286–291.

Armstead, W.M., Mirro, R., Leffler, C.W., and Busija, D.W., 1989, Cerebral superoxide anion generation during seizures in newborn pigs, J. Cereb. Blood Flow Metab. 9:175–179.

Asano, T., Koide, T., Gotch, O., Joshita, H., Hanamura, T., Shigeno, T., and Tokakura, K., 1989, The role of free radicals and eicosanoids in the pathogenic mechanism underlying ischemic brain edema, Mol. Chem. Neuropathol. 10:101–133.

Au, A.M., Chan, P.H., and Fishman, R.A., 1985, Stimulation of phospholipase A_2 activity by oxygen-derived free radicals in isolated brain capillaries, J. Cell Biochem. 27:449–459.

Aust, S.D., Morehouse, L.A., and Thomas, C.E., 1985, Role of metals in oxygen radical reactions, *J. Free Rad. Biol. Med.* 1:3–25.

Banik, N.L., Hogan, E.L., and Hsu, C.Y., 1987, The multimolecular cascade of spinal cord injury, *Neurochem. Pathol.* 7:57–77.

Blackwell, G.J., Carnuccio, R., Di Rosa, M., Flower, R.J., Parente, L., and Perisco, P., 1980, Macrocortin: A polypeptide causing the antiphospholipase effect of glucocorticoids, *Nature* 287:147–149.

Bondy, S.C., 1986, The biochemical evaluation of neurotoxic damage, *Fundam. Appl. Toxicol.* 6:208–216.

Bondy, S.C., 1990, Intracellular calcium and neurotoxic events, *Neurotoxicol. Teratol.* 11:527–531.

Bondy, S.C., and McKee, M., 1990, Prevention of chemically induced synaptosomal changes, *J. Neurosci. Res.* 25:229–235.

Bondy, S.C., McKee, M., and LeBel, C.P., 1991, Changes in synaptosomal pH and rates of oxygen radical formation induced by chlordecone, *Molec. Chem. Neuropathol.* 13:95–106.

Bonser, R.W., Thompson, N.T., Randall, R.W., and Garland, L.G., 1989, Phospholipase D activation is functionally linked to superoxide generation in the human neutrophil, *Biochem. J.* 264:617–620.

Bose, R., Sutherland, G.R., and Pinsky, C., 1990, Excitotoxins and free radicals: Accomplices in post-ischemic and other neurodegeneration, *Eur. J. Pharmacol.* 183:1170–1171.

Boveris, A., and Chance, B., 1973, The mitochondrial generation of hydrogen peroxide: General properties and the effect of hyperbaric oxygen, *Biochem. J.* 134:707–716.

Braughler, J.M., and Hall, E.D., 1989, Central nervous system trauma and stroke. I. Biochemical and considerations for oxygen radical formation and lipid peroxidation, *Free Rad. Biol. Med.* 6:289–301.

Bruckdorfer, K.R., Jacobs, M., and Rice-Evans, C., 1990, Endothelium-derived relaxing factor (nitric oxide), lipoprotein oxidation, and atherosclerosis, *Biochem. Soc. Trans.* 18:1061–1063.

Burton, G.W., and Ingolo, K.V., 1984, β carotene: An unusual type of lipid antioxidant, *Science* 224:569–573.

Busto, R., Yoshida, S., Ginsheng, M.D., Alonso, O., Smith, D.W., and Goldberg, W.J., 1984, Regional blood flow in compression-induced edema in rats: Effects of dietary vitamin E, *Ann. Neurol.* 15:441–448.

Byczkowski, J.Z., and Gessner, T., 1988, Biological role of the superoxide radical, *Int. J. Biochem.* 20:569–580.

Cadet, J.L., 1990, Chronic treatment with prolixin causes oxidative stress in rat brain, *Biol. Psychiat.* 28:738–740.

Calvin, H.I., Medvedovsky, C., and Worgul, B., 1986, Near-total glutathione depletion and age-specific cataracts induced by buthionine sulfoximine in mice, *Science* 233:553–555.

Cao, W., Carney, J.M., Duchon, A., Floyd, R.A., and Chevion, M., 1988, Oxygen free radical involvement in ischemia and superfusion injury to brain, *Neurosci. Lett.* 88:233–238.

Chan, P.K., 1988, in: *Cellular Antioxidant Defense Mechanisms, Vol. III* (C.K. Chow, ed.), CRC Press, Boca Raton, FL, pp. 89–109.

Chang, L.W., Gilbert, M., and Sprecher, J., 1978, Modification of methylmercury neurotoxicity by vitamin E, *Environ. Res.* 17:356–366.

Choi, D.W., 1990, Cerebral hypoxia: New approaches and unanswered questions, *J. Neurosci.* 10:2493–2501.

Cino, M., and Del Maestro, R.F., 1989, Generation of hydrogen peroxide by brain mitochondria: The effect of reoxygenation following postdecapatative ischemia, *Arch. Biochem. Biophys.* 269:623–638.

Clement, M., and Bourre, J.M., 1990, Alteration of α-tocopherol content in the developing and aging peripheral nervous system: Persistence of high correlations with total and specific (n-6) polyunsaturated fatty acids, *J. Neurochem.* 54:2110–2117.

Cohen, G., 1988, Oxygen radicals and Parkinson's disease, in: *Oxygen Radicals and Tissue Injury* (B. Halliwell, ed.), Clarendon Press, Oxford, pp. 130–135.

Cojocel, C., Beuter, W., Muller, W., and Mayer, D., 1989, Lipid peroxidation: A possible mechanism of trichloroethylene nephrotoxicity, *Toxicology* 55:131–141.

Daniell, L.C., Brass, E.P., and Harris, R.A., 1988, Effect of ethanol on intracellular ionized calcium concentrations in synaptosomes and hepatocytes, *Mol. Pharmacol.* 32:831–837.

De Vito, M.J., and Wagner, G.C., 1989, Metamphetamine induced neuronal damage: A possible role for free radicals, *Neuropharmacology* 28:1145–1150.

Devasagayam, T.P.A., 1989, Decreased peroxidative potential in rat brain microsomal fractions during aging, *Neurosci. Lett.* 103:92–96.

Dexter, D.T., Carayon, A., Vidarlhet, M., Ruberg, M., Agid, F., Agid, Y., Lees, A.J., Wells, F.R., Jenner, P., and Marsden, C.D., 1990, Decreased ferritin levels in brain in Parkinson's disease, *J. Neurochem.* 55:16–20.

Dildy, J.E., and Leslie, S.W., 1989, Ethanol inhibits NMDA-induced increase of free intracellular Ca^{2+} in dissociated brain cells, *Brain Res.* 499:383–387.

Donaldson, J., Labella, F.S., and Gessa, D., 1981, Enhanced autooxidation of dopamine as a possible basis of manganese neurotoxicity, *Neurotoxicology* 2:53–64.

Dreosti, I.E., 1987, Micronutrients, superoxide and the fetus, *Neurotoxicology* 8:445–450.

Dun, E., Ismail, M., Szerdahelyi, P., Joo, F., Dun, L., Koltai, M., and Draskoczy, M., 1990, Dexamethasone treatment attenuates the development of ischemic brain edema in gerbils, *Neuroscience* 34:203–207.

Dykens, J.A., Stern, A., and Trenkner, E., 1987, Mechanism of kainate toxicity to cerebellar neurons *in vitro* is analogous to reperfusion tissue injury, *J. Neurochem.* 49:1222–1228.

Essman, W.B., and Wollman, S.B., 1989, Free radicals, central nervous system processes and brain functions, in: *Oxygen Radicals: Systemic Events and Disease Processes* (D.K. Das and W.B. Essman, eds.), Karger, Basel, pp. 172–191.

Fedtke, N., and Bolt, H.M., 1986, Detection of 2,5 hexanedione in the urine of persons not exposed to n-hexane, *Int. Arch. Occup. Health* 57:143–148.

Floyd, R.A., 1990, Role of oxygen free radicals in carcinogenesis and brain ischemia, *FASEB J.* 4:2587–2597.

Freeman, B., and Crapo, J.D., 1982, Biology of disease: Free radicals and tissue injury, *Lab. Invest.* 47:412–426.

Fridovich, I., 1989, Oxygen radicals from acetaldehyde, *Free Rad. Biol. Med.* 7:557–558.

Ghersi-Egea, J.F., Mim, A., and Siest, G., 1988, A new aspect of the protective functions of the blood-brain barrier: Activities of four drug metabolizing enzymes in isolated rat brain microvessels, *Life Sci.* 42:2515–2523.

Graham, W.C., Robertson, R.G., Sambrook, M.A., and Crossman, A.R., 1990, Injection of excitatory amino acid antagonists into the medial pallidal segment of a 1-methyl-4-phenyl-1,2,3,6-tetrahydropyridine (MPTP) treated primate, reverses motor symptoms of Parkinsonism, *Life Sci.* 47:PL91–PL97.

Gutteridge, J.M., Westermarck, T., and Santavvori, P., 1983, Iron and oxygen radicals in tissue damage: Implications for neuronal ceroid lipofuchsinoses, *Acta. Neurol. Scand.* 68:365–370.

Hadjiconstantinou, M., Mariani, A.P., and Neff, N.H., 1989, GM_1 ganglioside-induced recovery of nigrostriatal dopaminergic neurons after MPTP: An immunohistochemical study, *Brain Res.* 484:297–303.

Hall, E.D., and Braughler, J.M., 1989, Central nervous system trauma and stroke. II Physiological and pharmacological evidence for involvement of oxygen radicals and lipid peroxidation, *Free Rad. Biol. Med.* 6:303–313.

Hall, E.D., Yonkey, P.A., McCall, J.M., and Braughler, J.M., 1988, Effects of the 21-aminosteroid V74006F on experimental head injuries in mice, *J. Neurosurg.* 68:462–465.

Halliwell, B., 1988, Albumin—an important extracellular antioxidant?, *Biochem. Pharmacol.* 37:569–571.

Halliwell, B., 1989a, Protection against tissue damage *in vivo* by desferrioxamine: What is its mechanism of action?, *Free Rad. Biol. Med.* 7:645–651.

Halliwell, B., 1989b, Oxidants and the central nervous system: Some fundamental questions. Is oxidant damage relevant to Parkinson's disease, Alzheimer's disease, traumatic injury or stroke?, *Acta. Neurol. Scand.* 126:23–33.

Halliwell, B., and Gutteridge, J.M.C., 1984, Oxygen toxicity, oxygen radicals, transition metals and disease, *Biochem. J* 219:1–14.

Halliwell, B., and Gutteridge, J.M.C., 1985, Oxygen radicals and the nervous system. *Trends Neurosci.* 8:22–26.

Halliwell, B., and Gutteridge, J.M.C., 1986, Oxygen free radicals and iron in relation to biology and medicine: Some problems and concepts, *Arch. Biochem. Biophys.* 246:501–514.

Halliwell, B., and Gutteridge, J.M.C., 1989, *Free Radicals in Biology and Medicine,* Clarendon Press, Oxford, p. 266.

Hanig, J.P., Yoder, P.D., and Krop, S., 1984, Protection with butylated hydroxytoluene and other compounds against intoxication and mortality caused by hexachlorophene, *Food Chem. Toxic.* 22:185–189.

Hanstein, W.G., 1976, Uncoupling of oxidative phosphorylation, *Biochem. Biophys. Acta.* 456:129–148.

Hasan, M., and Ali, S.F., 1981, Effects of thallium, nickel and cobalt administration on the lipid peroxidation in different regions of the rat brain, *Toxicol. Appl. Pharmacol.* 57:8–13.

Heikkila, R.E., Sieber, B.A., Mansino, L., and Sonsalla, P.K., 1989, Some features of the nigrostriatal dopaminergic neurotoxin 1-methyl-4-phenyl-1,2,3,6-tetrahydropyridine (MPTP) in the mouse, *Molec. Chem. Neuropathol.* 10:171–183.

Ikeda, Y., Ikeda, K., and Long, D.M., 1989, Protective effect of the iron chelator deferoxamine on cold-induced brain edema, *J. Neurosurg.* 71:233–238.

Jackson, G.R., Apffel, L., Werrbach-Perez, K., and Perez-Polo, J.R., 1990, Role of nerve growth factor in oxidant-antioxidant balance and neuronal injury. I Stimulation of hydrogen peroxide resistance, *J. Neurosci. Res.* 25:360–368.

Johnson, J.D., Conroy, W.G., Buxis, K.D., and Isom, G.E., 1987, Peroxidation of brain lipids following cyanide intoxication in mice, *Toxicology* 46:21–28.

Kaneko, M., Panagia, V., Paolillo, G., Majumder, S., Ou, C., and Challa, N.S., 1990, Inhibition of cardiac phosphatidylethanolamine N-methylation by oxygen free radicals, *Biochem. Biophys. Acta* 1021:33–38.

Kehrer, J.P., Mossman, B.T., Sevanian, A., Trush, M.A., and Smith, M.T., 1988, Free radical mechanisms in chemical pathogenesis, *Toxicol. Appl. Pharmacol.* 95:349–362.

Kehrer, J.P., Jones, D.P., LeMasters, J.J., Farber, J.L., and Jaeschke, H., 1990, Mechanisms of hypoxic cell injury, *Toxicol. Appl. Pharmacol.* 106:165–178.

Kitagawa, K., Matsumoto, M., Oda, T., Nunobe, M., Hoto, R., Handa, N., Fukunaga, R., Isaka, Y., Kimura, K., Maeda, H., Mikoshiba, K., and Kamado, T., 1990, Free radical generation during brief period of cerebral ischemia may trigger delayed neuronal death, *Neurosciences* 35:551–558.

Komulainen, H., and Bondy, S.C., 1987, Increased free intrasynaptosomal Ca^{2+} by neurotoxic organometals: Distinctive mechanisms, *Toxicol. Appl. Pharmacol.* 88:77–86.

Kontos, H.A, 1989, Oxygen radicals in CNS damage, *Chem.-Biol. Interact.* 72:229–255.

Kontos, H.A., and Povlishock, J.T., 1986, Oxygen radicals in brain injury, *CNS Trauma* 3:257–302.

LeBel, C.P., and Bondy, S.C., 1990, Sensitive and rapid quantitation of oxygen reactive species in rat synaptosomes, *Neurochem. Int.* 17:435–440.

LeBel, C.P., and Bondy, S.C., 1991, Persistent protein damage despite reduced oxygen radical formation in the aging rat brain, *Int. J. Dev. Neurosci.* 9:139–146.

LeBel, C.P., and Schatz, R.A., 1990, Altered synaptosomal phospholipid metabolism after toluene: Possible relationship with membrane fluidity, Na^+, K^+-adenosine triphosphatase and phospholipid methylation, *J. Pharmacol. Exp. Therap.* 253:1189–1197.

LeBel, C.P., Ali, S.F., McKee, and Bondy, S.C., 1990, Organometal-induced increases in oxygen radical activity: The potential of 2',7'-dichlorofluorescin diacetate as an index of neurotoxic damage, *Toxicol. Appl. Pharmacol.* 104:17–24.

LeBel, C.P., Ischiropoulos, H., and Bondy, S.C., 1992, Evaluation of the probe 2',7'-dichlorofluorescein as an indicator of reactive oxygen species formation and oxidative stress, *Res. Chem. Toxicol.* 5:227–231.

Levy, D.I., Sucher, N.J., and Lipton, S.A., 1990, Redox modulation of NMDA receptor-mediated toxicity in mammalian central nervous neurons, *Neurosci. Lett.* 110:291–296.

Lewin, R., 1987, Drug trial for Parkinson's, *Science* 236:1420.

Liehr, J.G., and Roy, D., 1990, Free radical generation by redox cycling of estrogens, *Free Rad. Biol. Med.* 8:415–423.

Lohr, J.B., Kuczenski, R., Bracha, H.S., Moir, M., and Jeste, D.V., 1990, Increased indices of free radical activity in the cerebrospinal fluid of patients with tardive dyskinesia, *Biol. Psychiatry* 28:535–539.

Maellaro, E., Cassini, A.F., Del Bello, B., and Comporti, M., 1990, Lipid peroxidation and antioxidant systems in the liver injury produced by glutathione depleting agents, *Biochem. Pharmacol.* 39:1513–1521.

Mahadik, S.P., Hawver, D.B., Hungund, B.L., Li, Y.S., and Kanpiak, S.E., 1989, GM$_1$ ganglioside treatment after global ischemia protects changes in membrane fatty acids and properties of Na$^+$, K$^+$ ATP ase and Mg^{2+} ATPase, *J. Neurosci. Res.* 24:402–412.

Malis, C.D., and Bonventre, J.V., 1986, Mechanism of calcium potentiation of oxygen free radical injury to renal mitochondria, *J. Biol. Chem.* 261:14201–14208.

Mattia, C., LeBel, C.P., and Bondy, S.C., 1991, Effect of toluene and its metabolites on cerebral oxygen radical formation, *Biochem. Pharmacol.* 42:879–882.

McCrodden, J.M., Tipton, K.F., and Sullivan, J.P., 1990, The neurotoxicity of MPTP and the relevance to Parkinson's disease, *Pharmacol. Toxicol.* 67:8–13.

Minotti, G., and Aust, S.D., 1989, The role of iron in oxygen radical mediated lipid peroxidation, *Chem. Biol. Interact.* 71:1–19.

Montgomery, R.D., 1979, In: *Handbook of Clinical Neurology, Intoxications of the Nervous System*, Vol. 32, Part I (P.J. Viwken and G.W. Bruyn, eds.), North Holland Publishing, Amsterdam, p. 515.

Muma, N.A., Troncoso, J.C., Hoffman, P.N., Koo, E.H., and Price, D.L., 1988, Aluminum neurotoxicity: Altered expression of cytoskeletal genes, *Mol. Brain Res.* 3:115–122.

Murphy, T.H., Myramato, M., Sastre, A., Schaar, R.L., and Coyle, J.T., 1989, Glutamate toxicity in a neuronal cell line involves inhibition of cystine transport leading to oxidative stress, *Neuron.* 2:1547–1558.

Nebert, D.W., Petersen, D.D., and Fornace, A.J., 1990, Cellular responses to oxidative stress: The [Ah] gene battery as a paradigm, *Environ. Health Perspect.* 88:13–25.

Nordmann, R., 1987, Oxidative stress from alcohol in the brain, *Alcohol* Suppl. 1:75–82.

Odunze, I.N., Klaidman, L.K., and Adams, J.D., 1990, MPTP toxicity in the mouse brain and vitamin E, *Neurosci. Lett.* 108:346–349.

Olesen, S.P., 1986, Rapid increase in blood-brain barrier permeability during severe hypoxia and metabolic inhibition, *Brain Res.* 368:24–29.

Oliver, C.N., Starke-Reed, P.E., Stadtman, E.R., Lin, G.J., Correy, J.M., and Floyd, R.A., 1990, Oxidative damage to brain proteins, loss of glutamine synthetase activity and production of free radicals during ischemia/reperfusion-induced injury to gerbil brain, *Proc. Natl. Acad. Sci. USA* 87:5144–5147.

Olney, J.W., Ikonomidou, C., Mosinger, J.L., and Friedrich, G., 1989, MK-801 prevents hypobaric-ischemic neuronal degeneration in the infant rat brain, *J. Neurosci.* 9:1701–1704.

Olney, J.W., Zorumski, C.F., Stewart, G.R., Price, M.T., Wong, G., and Labruyere, J., 1990, Excitotoxicity of l-DOPA and 6-OH-DOPA: Implications for Parkinson's and Huntington's diseases, *Exp. Neurol.* 108:269–272.

Parkinson's Study Group, 1989, DATATOP: A multicenter clinical trial in early Parkinson's disease, *Arch. Neurol.* 46:1052–1060.

Pellegini-Giampietro, D.E., Cherici, G., Alesiani, M., Carla, V., and Moroni, F., 1990, Excitatory amino acid release and free radical formation may cooperate in the genesis of ischemia-induced neuronal damage, *Neuroscience* 10:1035–1041.

Perrin, R., Minn, A., Ghersi-Egea, J.F., Grasshot, M.C., and Siest, G., 1990, Distribution of cytochrome p450 activities towards alkoxyresorufin derivatives in rat brain regions, subcellular fractions and isolated cerebral microvessels, *Biochem. Pharmacol.* 40:2145–2151.

Perry, T.L., Godin, D.V., and Hansen, S., 1982, Parkinson's disease: A disorder due to nigral glutathione deficiency?, *Neurosci. Lett.* 33:305–310.

Pezzoli, G., Ricciardi, S., Masotto, C., Mariani, C.B., and Cerenzi, A., 1990, N-hexane induces Parkinsonism in rats, *Brain Res.* 531:355–357.

Phillips, S.C., 1987, Can brain lesions occur in experimental animals by administration of ethanol or acetaldehyde?, *Acta. Med. Scand. [Suppl.]* 717:67–72.

Porta, E.A., 1988, Role of oxidative damage in the aging process, in: *Cellular Antioxoidant Defense Mechanisms*, Vol. III (C.K. Chow, ed.) CRC Press, New York, pp. 1–52.

Ramstoek, E.R., Hoekstra, W.G., and Ganther, H.E., 1980, Trialkyl lead metabolism and lipid peroxidation *in vivo* in Vitamin E—and selenium-deficient rats as measured by ethane production, *Toxicol. Appl. Pharmacol.* 54:251–257.

Raps, S.P., Lai, J.C.K., Hertz, L., and Cooper, A.J.L., 1989, Glutathione is present in high concentrations in cultured astrocytes, but not in cultured neurons, *Brain Res.* 493:398–401.

Ravindranath, V., Shivakumar, R., and Anandatheerthavarada, H.K., 1989, Low glutathione levels in aged rats, *Neurosci. Lett.* 101:187–190.

Rehman, S.V., 1984, Lead-induced regional lipid peroxidation in brain, *Toxicol. Lett.* 21:333–337.

Rios, C., and Tapia, R., 1987, Changes in lipid peroxidation induced by 1-methyl-4-phenyl-1,2,3,6-tetrahydropyridine and 1-methyl-4-phenylpyridinium in mouse brain homogenates, *Neurosci. Lett.* 77:321–326.

Rouach, H., Park, M.K., Orfanelli, M.T., Janvier, B., and Nordmann, R., 1987, Ethanol-induced oxidative stress in the rat cerebellum, *Alcohol [Suppl]* 1:207–211.

Rouach, H., Houye, P., Orfanelli, M.T., Gentil, M., Bourdon, R., and Nordmann, R., 1990, Effect of acute ethanol administration on the subcellular distribution of iron in rat liver and cerebellum, *Biochem. Pharmacol.* 39:1095–1100.

Sadrzadeh, S.M., Anderson, D.K., Panter, S.S., Hallaway, P.E., and Easton, J.W., 1987, Hemoglobin potentiates nervous system damage, *J. Clin. Invest.* 79:662–664.

Saggu, H., Cooksey, J., Dexter, D., Wells, F.R., Lees, A., Jenner, P., and Marsden, C.D., 1989, A selective increase in particulate superoxide dismutase activity in Parkinsonian substantia nigra, *J. Neurochem.* 53:692–697.

Sapolsky, C., Uno, H., and Rebert, C.S., 1990, Hippocampal damage associated with prolonged glucocorticoid exposure in primates, *J. Neurosci.* 10:2897–2902.

Saunders, R., and Horrocks, L.P., 1987, Eicosanoids, plasma membranes, and molecular mechanisms of spinal cord injury, *Neurochem. Pathol.* 7:1–22.

Savolainen, H., 1978, Superoxide dismutase and glutathione peroxidase activities in rat brain, *Res. Commun. Chem. Pathol. Pharmacol.* 21:173–175.

Sawada, M., and Carlson, J.C., 1987, Changes in superoxide radical and lipid peroxide formation in the brain, heart and liver during the lifetime of the rat, *Mech. Aging Dev.* 41:125–137.

Schmucker, D.L., Vessey, D.A., Wang, R.K., James, J.L., and Maloney, A., 1984, Age-dependent alterations in the physicochemical properties of rat liver membranes, *Mech. Aging Dev.* 27:207–217.

Schwartz, R., Skolnick, P., and Paul, S.M., 1988, Regulation of γ-aminobutyric acid/barbiturate receptor-gated chloride ion flux in brain vesicles by phospholipase A$_2$: Possible role of oxygen radicals, *J. Neurochem.* 50:565–571.

Seto, N.O., Hyashi, S., and Tener, G.M., 1990, Overexpression of Cu-Zn superoxide dismutase in Drosophila does not affect life-span, *Proc. Natl. Acad. Sci.* 87:4270–4274.

Sevanian, A., Nordenbrank, K., Kim, E., Ernster, L., and Hochstein, P., 1990, Microsomal lipid peroxidation: The role of NADPH-cytochrome P450 reductase and cytochrome P450, *Free Rad. Biol. Med.* 8:145–152.

Shoulson, I., 1989, Deprenyl and α-tocopherol antioxidative therapy of Parkinsonism (DATATOP), *Acta Neurol. Scand.* 126:171–175.

Shukla, G.S., Srivastava, R.S., and Chandra, S.V., 1988, Prevention of cadmium-induced effects on regional glutathione status of rat brain by vitamine E, *J. Appl. Toxicol.* 8:355–358.

Siesjo, B.K., 1986, Calcium and ischemic brain damage, *Exp. Neurol. 25* [Suppl. 1]:45–56.

Siesjo, B.K., 1988, Acidosis and ischemic brain damage, *Neurochem. Pathol.* 9:31–88.

Sinha, S., Toner, N., Chisuick, M., Davies, J., and Bogle, S., 1987, Vitamin E supplementation reduces frequency of periventricular hemorrhage in very preterm babies, *Cancer* 1:466–468.

Skaper, S.D., Facci, L., Milani, D., and Leon, A., 1989, Monosialioganglioside GM$_1$ protects against anoxia-induced neuronal death *in vitro*, *Exp. Neurol.* 106:297–305.

Sokol, R.J., 1989, Vitamin E and neurologic function in man, *Free Rad. Biol. Med.* 6:189–207.

Stadtman, E.R., 1990, Metal ion catalyzed oxidation of proteins: Biochemical mechanism and biological consequences, *Free Rad. Biol. Med.* 9:315–325.

Tadolini, B., and Cabrini, L., 1990, The influence of pH on OH-scavenger inhibition of damage to deoxyribose by Fenton reaction, *Mol. Cell. Biochem.* 94:97–104.

Tanner, C.M., and Langston, J.W., 1990, Do environmental toxins cause Parkinson's disease? A critical review, *Neurology* 40:17–30 [Suppl. 3].

Tauck, D.L., and Ashbeck, G.A., 1990, Glycine synergistically potentiates the enhancement of LTP induced by a sulfhydryl reducing agent, *Brain Res.* 519:129–132.

Tayarani, I., Chaudiere, J., Lefauconnier, J.M., and Bourre, J.M., 1987, Enzymatic protection against peroxidative damage in isolated brain capillaries, *J. Neurochem.* 48:1399–1410.

Tonge, J.I., Burry, A.F., and Saal, J.R., 1977, Cerebellar calcification: A possible marker of lead poisoning, *Pathology* 9:289–300.

Vanella, A., Villa, R.F., Gorini, A., Campisi, A., and Giuffrida-Stella, A.M., 1989, Superoxide dismutase and cytochrome oxidase activities in light and heavy synaptic mitochondria from rat cerebral cortex during aging, *J. Neurosci. Res.* 22:351–355.

Verity, M.A., Brown, W.J., and Cheung, M., 1975, Organic mercurial encephalopathy: *In vivo* and *in vitro* effects of methyl mercury on synaptosomal respiration, *J. Neurochem.* 25:759–765.

Vitorica, J., Machado, A., and Satrustegui, J., 1984, Age-dependent variations in peroxide-utilizing enzymes from rat brain mitochondria and cytoplasm, *J. Neurochem.* 42:351–356.

Vlessis, A.A., Widener, L.L., and Bartos, D., 1990, Effect of peroxide, sodium, and calcium on brain mitochondrial respiration potential role in cerebral ischemia and reperfusion, *J. Neurochem.* 54:1412–1418.

Wahba, Z.Z., Murray, W.J., and Stohs, S.J., 1990, Desferrioxamine-induced alterations in hepatic iron distribution, DNA damage and lipid peroxidation in control and 2,3,7,8-tetrachlorodibenzo-p-dioxin-treated rats, *J. Appl. Toxicol.* 10:119–124.

Witz, G., Rao, G.S., and Goldstein, B.D., 1985, Short-term toxicity of *trans, trans*-muconaldehyde, *Toxicol. Appl. Pharmacol.* 80:511–516.

Yoshida, S., Busto, R., Watson, B.D., Sanitso, M., and Ginsberg, M.D., 1985, Postischemic cerebral lipid peroxidation in vitro: Modification by dietary vitamin E, *J. Neurochem.* 44:1593–1600.

Zawia, N.H., and Bondy, S.C., 1990, Electrically stimulated rapid gene expression in the brain: Ornithine decarboxylase and c-fos, *Brain Res.* 7:243–247.

Zemlan, F.P., Thienhaus, O.J., and Bosmann, H.B., 1989, Superoxide disimutase activity in Alzheimer's disease: Possible mechanisms for paired helical filament formation, *Brain Res.* 476:160–162.

Chapter 15

Acute and Chronic Neurodegenerative Disorders Produced by Dietary Excitotoxins

Charles F. Zorumski and *John W. Olney*

1. INTRODUCTION

In recent years, glutamate (Glu) and aspartate (Asp) have become recognized as Jekyll–Hyde molecules of the central nervous system (CNS). These common acidic amino acids are abundantly present in the environment, and are synthesized and maintained in high concentration within the CNS, where they serve vitally important metabolic, neurotrophic, and neurotransmitter roles, but also harbor treacherous neurotoxic potential. Significant progress has been made recently in understanding the neurotoxic (excitotoxic) properties of Glu and related excitatory amino acids (EAA). Three EAA receptor subtypes—N-methyl-D-aspartate (NMDA), kainate, and quisqualate—have been linked to excitotoxicity, drugs with antiexcitotoxic actions have been discovered, and evidence for the complicity of both endogenous and exogenous excitotoxins in human neurodegenerative disorders, in both youth and old age, has begun to unfold. Here we will review the current information pertaining to EAA receptors, how these receptors are thought to be involved in neurodegeneration, and evidence suggesting that dietary exposure to EAA can lead to specific neuropsychiatric syndromes.

Charles F. Zorumski and *John W. Olney* • Department of Psychiatry, Washington University Medical School, St. Louis, Missouri 63110.

The Vulnerable Brain and Environmental Risks, Volume 2: Toxins in Food, edited by Robert L. Isaacson and Karl F. Jensen. Plenum Press, New York, 1992.

2. EXCITATORY AMINO ACID RECEPTORS

EAA interact with at least three classes of ion-channel linked (ionotropic) postsynaptic receptors in the vertebrate CNS (Collingridge and Lester, 1989; Mayer and Westbrook, 1987a). These receptors are named according to exogenous ligands that interact with each class. The NMDA, quisqualate, and kainate receptors represent "classical" EAA receptor types that are thought to mediate fast excitatory synaptic transmission. When activated these receptors gate cation-selective channels that allow the flow of Na^+, Ca^{2+}, and K^+ ions into and out of neurons, depending on transmembrane ion concentrations and neuronal membrane potential. Under normal conditions, this produces a net influx of positive charge and a depolarization of the membrane, bringing the neuron closer to its threshold for firing action potentials.

NMDA receptors have several properties that distinguish them from other EAA receptor subtypes. In addition to selective activation by the exogenous agent NMDA, these receptors are also activated relatively selectively by the endogenous amino acid, Asp (Collingridge and Lester, 1989). NMDA receptors are competitively inhibited by 2-amino-5-phosphonovalerate (APV) and other ω-substituted amino acids, and are noncompetitively inhibited by a variety of agents, including the street drug phencyclidine (PCP) and its analogues ketamine and MK-801 (Anis et al., 1982; Wong et al., 1986). It is postulated that the NMDA blocking actions of PCP may account for both its dissociative anesthetic and its psychotomimetic effects (Olney, 1989, 1990). NMDA receptors are also noncompetitively inhibited by several divalent cations, which appear to act at two separate sites within the NMDA complex to impede the flow of ions through the channel. Mg^{2+}, at physiological concentrations, produces a voltage-dependent block of NMDA responses, imparting a marked nonlinearity to NMDA current-voltage (IV) curves (Mayer et al., 1984; Nowak et al., 1984). This Mg^{2+}-induced voltage dependence accounts for observations that NMDA receptors contribute little to synaptic responses at membrane potentials near rest (~ -70mV). When the membrane is depolarized and the Mg^{2+} block is relieved, NMDA receptors contribute significantly to synaptic responses (Forsythe and Westbrook, 1988). In contrast to Mg^{2+}, Zn^{2+} blocks macroscopic NMDA currents in a voltage-independent fashion (Peters et al., 1987; Westbrook and Mayer, 1987). Single channel studies suggest that Zn^{2+} exerts two actions on NMDA channels. At low concentrations (1–10 μM), the ion produces a voltage-independent decrease in the channel opening frequency. At higher concentrations, Zn^{2+} also produces a voltage-dependent fast flickering open channel block (Christine and Choi, 1990; Legendre and Westbrook, 1990). These results suggest that Zn^{2+} may act at two separate sites within the NMDA ion channel. As Zn^{2+} is present in synaptic regions and is released during CNS stimulation, the actions of this divalent cation are likely to be of physiological importance (Assaf and Chung, 1984; Howell et al., 1984).

NMDA responses are potentiated by the amino acids glycine (Johnson and Ascher, 1987) and D-serine. Glycine appears to be a required cofactor for activation of NMDA ion channels (Kleckner and Dingledine, 1988) and may act by inhibiting a rapid form of desensitization (Mayer et al., 1989), thus increasing the probability of channel opening (Johnson and Ascher, 1987). Recently, a polyamine-binding regulatory site has been described as a possible component of the NMDA receptor complex (Williams et al., 1991). Although polyamines appear to augment NMDA responses, the physiological significance of this site remains uncertain at present (Sprosen and Woodruff, 1990).

Another distinguishing feature of NMDA-gated ion channels is their high permeability to Ca^{2+}. Biophysical studies indicate that NMDA channels may have the highest Ca^{2+} permeability of any ligand gated receptor-channel complex in the vertebrate CNS (MacDermott et al., 1986; Mayer and Westbrook, 1987b), being perhaps as much as 10 times more permeable to Ca^{2+} than non-NMDA (kainate/quisqualate) channels (Mayer and Westbrook, 1987b). The high Ca^{2+} permeability is likely to contribute to the role that NMDA receptors play in both synaptic plasticity and excitotoxicity (Choi, 1988; Kuba and Kumomoto, 1990). Ca^{2+} also appears to play a role in regulating NMDA receptor-mediated responses by promoting a slow form of desensitization (Clark et al., 1990; Mayer and Westbrook, 1987b; Zorumski et al., 1989).

Ionotropic non-NMDA (kainate/quisqualate) receptors can be distinguished from NMDA receptors in binding and physiological studies (Foster and Fagg, 1984; Mayer and Westbrook, 1984). Recent evidence suggests that α-amino-3-hydroxy-5-methyl-4-isoxazole-propionic acid (AMPA) is more selective than quisqualate as a ligand at ionotropic quisqualate receptors, and some investigators have recommended that these sites be termed *AMPA receptors* (Watkins et al., 1990). Whether kainate and AMPA receptors are distinct entities remains uncertain. In many systems, including cloned receptors expressed in heterologous cells (Boulter et al., 1990; Keinanen et al., 1990; Sommer et al., 1990), kainate, quisqualate and AMPA show considerable crossensitivity for each other's receptors. Non-NMDA receptors are activated nonselectively by Glu, which also acts at NMDA sites (Mayer and Westbrook, 1984). To date a selective endogenous ligand for non-NMDA receptors has not been found. Non-NMDA receptors can be inhibited competitively by the quinoxalinedione compounds 6,7 dinitroquinoxaline-dione (DNQX), 6-cyano-7 nitro-quinoxaline-dione (CNQX), and 2,3-dihydro-6-nitro-7-sulfamoyl-benzo(F)quinoxaline (NBQX) (Honore et al., 1988; Sheardon et al., 1990). Although these quinoxalinediones also antagonize glycine sites linked to NMDA receptors, this action is relatively weak; thus currently these agents are the most selective antagonists available for non-NMDA receptors.

Currents gated by kainate and quisqualate receptors are carried primarily by Na^+ and K^+ and exhibit little voltage dependency. In CNS neurons, one feature distinguishing kainate and quisqualate-gated responses is the pattern of desensitization that occurs in response to repeated or prolonged agonist administration (Kiskin et al., 1986; Trussell et al., 1988). Quisqualate responses exhibit very rapid desensitization with a time course on the order of 10 msec. This desensitizing phase is followed by a smaller sustained response (~10% of the peak response), which persists for the duration of agonist exposure. In contrast, kainate responses show no desensitization, even during prolonged administration. This difference in desensitization may account for the more profound neuronal swelling and acute toxicity produced by kainate (Zorumski et al., 1990).

Two other classes of EAA receptors have been described in the CNS but have no documented relationship to excitotoxicity. One class is linked by a guanine nucleotide binding protein (G-protein) to the phosphoinositide (PI) second messenger system. This receptor is activated by ibotenate, quisqualate, and *trans*-amino-1,3-cyclopentanedicarboxylic acid (ACPD), and is referred to as a *metabotropic receptor* (Desai and Conn, 1990; Sladeczek et al., 1985). This receptor class may regulate developmental plasticity in the visual system (Bear et al., 1987; Dudek et al., 1989). Although the toxicological significance of metabotropic receptors is uncertain, activation of the PI cycle leads to the release of intracellular calcium (Berridge, 1987), which could contribute to delayed phases of EAA toxicity (Choi, 1988). A fifth class of EAA receptors exists in the retina and serves as the synaptic receptor for depolarizing-bipolar cells (Miller and Slaughter 1986). The receptor class is activated by 2-amino-4-phosphonobutyrate (APB) and appears to act by closing ion channels (Slaughter and Miller, 1981). In other brain regions, APB-sensitive receptors may mediate presynaptic inhibitory effects (Cotman *et al.*, 1986; Forsythe and Clements, 1990). An involvement of APB receptors in the toxic effects of EAA has not been reported.

3. EXCITOTOXICITY

Three decades ago, Lucas and Newhouse (1957) reported that subcutaneous administration of Glu to infant mice produces acute degeneration of neurons in the inner layer of the retina. This finding was extended by Olney and colleagues, who observed that either oral (Olney and Ho, 1970) or systemic (Olney, 1969a, 1969b, 1971) administration of Glu to a variety of animal species, including monkeys (Olney *et al.*, 1972b), produces acute damage in brain regions lacking blood–brain barriers (known as circumventricular organs, CVO). In addition, it was shown (Olney *et al.*, 1971) that specific Glu analogues known to share the neuroexcitatory (depolarizing) properties of Glu (Curtis and Watkins, 1960) mimic its neurotoxic effects, that these analogs have a parallel order of potencies for their excitatory and toxic actions, and that analogs lacking excitatory activity also lack neurotoxicity. Moreover, ultrastructural studies (Olney 1969a, 1971) localized the apparent site of toxic action to postsynaptic dendrosomal membranes, where Glu excitatory synaptic receptors were presumed to be located. These and related observations gave rise to the excitotoxic concept (Olney *et al.*, 1971, 1975) that Glu destroys neurons by excessive activation of excitatory receptors on the dendrosomal surfaces of neurons. It was assumed that the persistent depolarizing stimulus caused pathological increases in membrane permeability and disruption of transmembrane ion homeostasis, but evidence available at the time provided no basis for formulating a more detailed hypothesis regarding which ions or related cofactors might contribute to the toxic process.

The electron microscopic observation that the retinal and CVO lesions characteristically produced by Glu and its analogs selectively involve dendrites and neuronal somata while sparing axons of passage (Olney, 1971; Olney *et al.*, 1971, 1972b) was of interest for several reasons. In addition to providing a clue to the involvement of EAA receptors in the toxic process, it suggested the strategy of using excitotoxin agonists as lesioning tools for removing neuronal cell bodies from a given brain region without destroying axonal pathways afferent to or passing through the region (Olney *et al.*, 1975). This strategy has been applied subsequently in numerous studies concerned with elucidating structure-function relations in the CNS, and for developing animal models for studying human neurodegenerative diseases (Coyle and Schwartz, 1976; Coyle *et al.*, 1978; McGeer and McGeer, 1976). Finally, it has been observed that several types of acute brain injury, including brain damage associated with status epilepticus (Collins and Olney, 1982; Olney *et al.*, 1983), hypoxia/ischemia (Ikonomidou *et al.*, 1989b; Rothman, 1984), and hypoglycemia (Wieloch, 1985), which are putatively caused by abnormal accumulations of endogenous Glu at EAA receptors, feature the same acute dendrosomal, axon-sparing type of cytopathology that is typically seen in CVO brain regions following subcutaneous administration of exogenous Glu.

In recent years the use of *in vitro* preparations has allowed the cellular mechanisms underlying excitotoxicity to be studied with greater precision. It now appears that there are at least two forms of neurodegeneration produced by EAA. An acute process characterized by marked neuronal swelling occurs in the isolated chick embryo retina (Olney *et al.*, 1986) or cultured rat hippocampal neurons (Rothman, 1985) during exposures to EAA for prolonged periods (30 min or longer). This form of acute neuronal damage is abolished by the removal of Na^+ or Cl^- from the incubation media but not by removal of Ca^{2+}. This suggests that the damage results from the influx of Na^+ into neurons through EAA-gated ion channels and the passive redistribution of Cl^- and fluid. Both NMDA and non-NMDA ionotropic receptors mediate this form of toxicity. Interestingly, among non-NMDA agonists, it has been found that kainate, an agent that produces large nondesensitizing responses, is a more effective acute toxin than quisqualate, an agonist that activates rapidly desensitizing responses (Zorumski *et al.*, 1990). This supports the hypothesis that it is the continuous flow of ions and fluid across neuronal membranes that accounts for the greater acute toxicity of kainate.

The Garthwaites (1986, 1989a, 1989b), using tissue slices from the cerebellum and hippocampus of immature rats, have confirmed that exposure to EAA for 30 min causes neurons to undergo acute edematous swelling, but they found that recovery can occur if EAA are removed and the incubation is continued for 90 min in Ca^{2+}-free medium, whereas recovery does not occur if the medium contains Ca^{2+}. In hippocampal slices, Ellren and Lehmann (1989) reported that Ca^{2+} either was or was not important, depending on the type of hippocampal neuron involved and on the EAA agonist used. Thus, the role of Ca^{2+} in acute EAA-induced neuronal death requires further clarification.

Choi and colleagues (1987) have described a slower neurodegenerative process that is triggered by brief (5 min) exposure of cultured cortical neurons to Glu. This damage takes 24 hr to develop and is facilitated by the presence of Ca^{2+} in the incubation media (Choi, 1987). This Ca^{2+}-dependent delayed toxicity occurs following exposure to both NMDA and non-NMDA agonists, despite the fact that non-NMDA channels do not have a high permeability to Ca^{2+} (Koh *et al.*, 1990). Subsequent experiments have suggested that activation of voltage-gated calcium channels may be critical in producing the delayed non-NMDA toxicity, as calcium channel blockers reduce this damage (Weiss *et al.*, 1990). How Ca^{2+} plays a role in delayed toxicity is uncertain, but activation of Ca^{2+}-dependent enzymes and second-messenger systems are likely possibilities (Choi, 1988). Better definition of the mechanisms underlying delayed toxicity is needed because many human neurodegenerative disorders involve the subacute or chronic degeneration of neurons.

4. EXCITOTOXINS AND NEURODEGENERATIVE DISORDERS

The excitotoxic properties of EAA have prompted several lines of investigation attempting to link these agents to human illnesses. The first human condition to receive specific attention as a possible excitotoxic disorder was sulfite oxidase deficiency. This rare disorder results from an inherited inborn error of metabolism in which cysteine-S-sulfate (CSS) accumulates in various tissues (Mudd *et al.*, 1967). This leads to neuronal degeneration, resulting in blindness, spastic quadriplegia, and death early in infancy. CSS has been found to display excitotoxic activity when systemically administered to infant rats or when injected into the brains of adult rats (Olney *et al.*, 1975). CSS excitotoxicity is mediated by NMDA receptors and is effectively blocked by NMDA antagonists.

Adult-onset olivopontocerebellar degeneration (OPCD) is a neurological syndrome characterized by ataxia and motor incoordination. Plaitakis *et al.*, (1984) have shown that patients with this disorder have a deficiency in Glu dehydrogenase that impairs the ability to metabolize Glu. Ingestion of Glu causes abnormally high levels of the amino acid in the blood. It is postulated that a similar accumulation of Glu occurs in the CNS and causes a slow degeneration of neurons.

In amyotrophic lateral sclerosis (ALS), a disorder characterized by muscle wasting, fasciculations, and spastic paraparesis, Plaitakis and Coroscio (1987) have also found that ingestion of Glu leads to abnormally high blood Glu levels. These individuals, unlike patients with OPCD, do not have a defect in Glu dehydrogenase, and the mechanisms responsible for the elevated Glu levels are uncertain. Recently, Rothstein *et al.* (1990) have found two- to threefold elevations of Glu, Asp, and N-acetyl-aspartyl-glutamate (NAAG) in the spinal fluid of patients with ALS supporting the possible involvement of excitotoxins. Whether the elevated EAA levels in this disorder are of primary pathological importance is uncertain at present.

Several lines of evidence suggest that disorders involving the basal ganglia, Huntington's disease (HD), and Parkinson's disease (PD) could result from an excitotoxic process. It has been known for some time that injection of kainate into the rat striatum produces pathological and biochemical changes characteristic of HD, leading to the use of kainate injections as an animal model for the disease (Coyle *et al.*, 1978). Intrastriatal injection of Glu, in sufficiently high dosage, produces similar damage, prompting the hypothesis that a local defect affecting the Glu system may be responsible for the loss of striatal neurons in HD (Olney, 1979). An alternative hypothesis is that quinolinate, an excitotoxin found naturally in the brain, may be the causative agent (Beal *et al.*, 1986). Quinolinate is more potent in destroying striatal neurons than other CNS neurons and spares a population of aspiny cells that are also spared in HD (Schwarcz and Kohler, 1983). However, arguing against a role for quinolinate is evidence that levels of this agent are not elevated in the striatum of HD patients (Reynolds *et al.*, 1988).

Recently Olney *et al.* (1990b) reported observations that may be relevant to the pathophysiology of both HD and PD. These authors found that L-dihydroxyphenylalanine (L-DOPA), the natural precursor of dopamine, is a weak excitotoxin and that its ortho-hydroxylated derivative 6-hydroxy-DOPA is a powerful excitotoxin. Both agents exert excitotoxic activity primarily through effects on non-NMDA receptors. The neurons that selectively degenerate in PD contain DOPA, while those that degenerate in HD receive input from DOPA-containing neurons (Albin *et al.*, 1989). It is possible that DOPA or 6-hydroxy-DOPA could be generated in excessive amounts in the cell bodies of DOPA-containing neurons. If these toxins leaked from dopaminergic neurons in the substantia nigra into the extracellular space or from dopaminergic terminals in the striatum, they could promote the excitotoxic degeneration of neurons.

An alternate possibility is that L-cysteine, which is both an exogenous and endogenous excitotoxin, could play a role in PD. This agent has been shown to exert excitotoxic activity primarily at NMDA receptors (Olney *et al.*, 1990a). Interestingly, recent evidence suggests a metabolic disturbance in patients with PD leading to elevated L-cysteine levels (Heafield *et al.*, 1990). A role for the NMDA receptor in parkinsonism is also supported by recent studies focusing on the methamphetamine and MPTP animal models of the disease. In these studies it was found that the NMDA antagonist, MK-801, prevents the neurotoxic effects of methamphetamine (Sonsalla *et al.*, 1989) or MPTP (Turski *et al.*, 1991) on nigrostriatal neurons.

Indirect evidence has been presented linking an excitotoxic mechanism to Alzheimer's disease (AD) (Maragos *et al.*, 1987). A striking feature of AD is the loss of cholinergic neurons in the basal forebrain that project to the hippocampus, amygdala, and cerebral cortex (Bartus *et al.*, 1982). Acute degeneration of these cholinergic neurons can be reproduced in animals by the injection of excitotoxins into the basal forebrain regions (Coyle *et al.*, 1983). This implies that these neurons possess receptors through which they could be killed by an excitotoxic process. Additionally, focal applications of excitotoxins to the cerebral cortex cause a retrograde degeneration of forebrain cholinergic neurons, suggesting that either by a direct or indirect mechanism excitotoxins could play a role in the pathology of AD (Sofroniew and Pearson, 1985). Although controversial (Thal *et al.*, 1990), pathological changes resembling neuritic plaques and neurofibrillary tangles, hallmarks of AD, have been found in rat brains about 1 year after cholinergic neurons were destroyed by excitotoxic injections (Arendash *et al.*, 1987). In addition, cultures of human spinal neurons develop paired helical filaments of the type that comprise neurofibrillary tangles after exposure to Glu, suggesting that the pathological changes of AD could be a delayed manifestation or secondary reaction to an excitotoxic process (DeBoni and McLachlan, 1985). Other evidence indicates that the β-amyloid protein, postulated to be involved in AD, renders cultured cortical neurons more sensitive to excitotoxic damage (Koh *et al.*, 1990). In biopsy specimens obtained from AD brains early in the disease process, there is a loss of Glu uptake sites, a possible consequence of which would be an excitotoxic accumulation of Glu at EAA receptors (Procter *et al.*, 1988). Since this would be expected to cause elevated levels of Glu in cerebrospinal fluid in AD, it is noteworthy that Pomara *et al.*, (1990) have reported such elevations. It is also possible that other agents acting at EAA receptors could promote neuronal damage in AD. One such agent is the endogenous phosphomonoester, L-phosphoserine, an agent that acts at multiple EAA receptor types and that has been found in elevated levels in AD patients (Klunk *et al.*, 1991). Alternatively, based on the recent finding of abnormalities in sulphur metabolism in AD patients, it is possible that the sulphur-containing amino acid L-cysteine could serve as a causative agent in the disorder (Heafield *et al.*, 1990).

5. DIETARY EXCITOTOXINS

The above discussion, although pertaining to the potential role of endogenous excitotoxins in neurodegenerative disorders, does not rule out a possible combined action of exogenous and endogenous excitotoxins in the pathophysiology of such conditions. Over the past 20 years, evidence has accumulated to suggest that dietary ingestion of certain excitotoxins can have profound neurotoxic consequences, leading to the development of specific neurodegenerative disorders (Olney, 1984). In fact, each of the ionotropic EAA receptor types has been tentatively linked to a different human neurodegenerative disorder through the action of a dietary excitotoxin—NMDA receptors via β-N-methylamino-L-alanine (BMAA) in the Guamanian Parkinson-ALS-dementia syndrome, quisqualate receptors via β-N-oxalylamino-L-alanine (BOAA) in neurolathyrism, and kainate receptors via domoate in toxic mussel poisoning. Based on experimental data in animals, it is also possible that dietary ingestion of Glu, Asp, and L-cysteine can produce neurodegeneration in humans.

5.1. BMAA and the ALS-Parkinsonism-Dementia Complex of Guam

In the 1950s it was found that the prevalence of ALS among the Chamorro population of Guam and the Mariana islands was 50–100 times that in the United States (Garruto and Yase, 1986). The syndrome is characterized by progressive limb weakness with spasticity, bulbar dysfunction, muscular fasciculations, and atrophy. Some subjects manifest signs of parkinsonism, with the slowed movements, tremor, and rigidity characteristic of that disorder. A smaller percentage of cases develop the cognitive changes typical of a dementing illness. The decline in this syndrome after 1955, coupled with the absence of inheritable or transmissible factors, led to a search for environmental causes. Epidemiological studies demonstrated that during World War II the false sago palm (*Cycas circinalis*) became one of the mainstays of the Chamorro diet. This plant contains a number of potential neurotoxins, including cycasin, a derivative of the alkylating agent methylazoxymethanol, and BMAA, an agent with weak excitotoxic properties (Spencer *et al.*, 1990).

Spencer and colleagues (1987) have examined the toxic effects of BMAA by gavage-feeding the agent to macaque monkeys. After 2–12 weeks of daily feeding, animals exhibit tremor, weakness involving the forelimbs, and disinterest in their surroundings. These symptoms progress over several months to include irritability, blank staring, and a slowed, shuffling gait. These animals develop neuronal damage involving the motor cortex and spinal cord, with less conspicuous damage in the substantia nigra. The basal ganglia, hippocampus, and cerebellum are unaffected. These behavioral and pathological features have similarities to the human syndrome. Recently, Seawright *et al.* (1990) demonstrated the acute degeneration of cerebellar neurons in mice treated with BMAA. Importantly, these cerebellar lesions have the pathological appearance of Glu-type damage, further supporting the concept that BMAA functions as an excitotoxin. Implicit in these findings is the conclusion that either BMAA or a neurotoxic derivative of this agent can penetrate blood–brain barriers.

The toxic actions of BMAA have also been investigated in several *in vitro* preparations. In motor cortex explants, antagonists of NMDA receptors partially prevent the postsynaptic vacuolization caused by BMAA, suggesting that this agent may act by an excitotoxic mechanism (Spencer *et al.*, 1987). More complete inhibition of BMAA-induced toxicity requires the combined use of antagonists acting at both NMDA and non-NMDA receptors. Thus BMAA is likely to be a mixed agonist acting at more than one ionotropic EAA receptor (Olney, unpublished observations). Additionally, BMAA is reported to have potent effects at metabotropic EAA receptors, activating PI turnover at concentrations that are one-sixth those required to activate NMDA receptors (Copani *et al.*, 1990). This raises the possibility that activation of the PI second messenger system and the release of intracellular Ca^{2+} may be important in the toxic effects of this agent.

A puzzling feature of BMAA is that the molecule lacks the dicarboxylic acid structure that is a critical basis for the neurotoxic activity of other EAA. Weiss and Choi (1988) observed that the excitatory and toxic properties of BMAA are dependent on the presence of bicarbonate ions and have suggested that bicarbonate may transform BMAA into a molecule with much greater excitotoxic potency. Consistent with this, Nunn and colleagues (1991) have recently presented evidence demonstrating that BMAA is transformed by bicarbonate into an α-amino-carbamate that stereochemically resembles the NMDA molecule. Thus, BMAA has a native chemical structure unlike other excitotoxins, a factor that may facilitate penetration of blood–brain barriers, and, once inside the brain, it may undergo a structural change rendering the molecule capable of destroying CNS neurons by a complex excitotoxic mechanism.

5.2. BOAA and Neurolathyrism

Neurolathyrism is a crippling upper motor-neuron disorder endemic to certain parts of Africa and Asia, particularly Ethiopia, Bangladesh, and India (Spencer et al., 1986). The disorder is characterized by muscle weakness (usually involving the legs), cramps, tremulousness, and coarse movements of the upper extremities. Associated features include paresthesias, numbness, and gastrointestinal and genitourinary symptoms. Autopsies performed on victims of the disease reveal damage to Betz cells in the motor cortex, with less conspicuous damage in the spinal cord (Spencer et al., 1986). The disorder cannot be attributed to genetic or infectious causes but has been noted to become more prevalent during periods of famine. Epidemiological studies suggest that the causative agent is contained in the seeds of the chickling pea (Lathyrus sativus), which becomes a major dietary staple during periods of famine in regions where the disorder is endemic (Spencer et al., 1986). The seeds of the chickling pea contain BOAA, an agent that has the structural features of an EAA and that was shown 15 years ago to produce excitotoxic brain lesions when administered to immature rodents (Olney et al., 1976b).

More recently, Spencer and colleagues (1986) have demonstrated that macaque monkeys develop features of neurolathyrism when maintained chronically on a diet containing chick-pea pellets or BOAA. Signs of the disorder appear months after the start of the chick-pea diet and within 1 month after starting a BOAA-enriched diet. The macaque disorder, like the human syndrome, appears to be self-limiting, with stabilization of symptoms after discontinuation of the toxin (Spencer et al., 1990).

Weiss et al. (1989) have examined the actions of BOAA in cortical cell cultures. This agent is a relatively slow-acting toxin in this preparation, taking days of exposure at moderate concentrations to produce toxic effects. Recent observations suggest that the slowness of toxic effect may result from two features of BOAA action. First, BOAA is a fairly selective quisqualate receptor agonist (Bridges et al., 1989; Olney et al., unpublished) and, like other quisqualate receptor agonists, BOAA induces rapid desensitization of electrophysiological responses (Zorumski et al., 1990). This desensitization occurs on the time scale of 10–50 msec and is followed by a small sustained phase of response, which persists for the duration of BOAA exposure. When this rapid desensitization is blocked by lectins, BOAA and other desensitizing quisqualate agonists become more effective acute excitotoxins (Zorumski et al., 1990). Thus a hypothetical mechanism to explain how BOAA might cause degeneration of motor neurons in neurolathyrism would be the presence of a lectin-like substance in chick peas that partially blocks desensitization of the quisqualate receptor, thereby increasing the likelihood that chronic BOAA exposure will eventually cause excitotoxic degeneration of motor neurons. Secondly, Weiss et al. (1990) have observed that the slow toxicity produced by non-NMDA agonists is at least partially inhibited by L-type voltage-gated calcium-channel blockers. As non-NMDA agonists are not known to gate L-type calcium channels directly, this implies that the slow action of these toxins occurs through an indirect mechanism, which may require chronic exposure. Other studies (Ross et al., 1989) showing that BOAA displays greater preference for cerebrocortical than spinal-cord quisqualate receptors suggest a basis for the regional selectivity (cerebral cortex > spinal cord) of neuropathological changes in neurolathyrism.

5.3. Domoate Encephalopathy

In 1987 an outbreak of food poisoning affected more than 100 individuals in eastern Canada. This poisoning produced a disorder characterized by the acute onset of gastrointestinal symptoms and neurological abnormalities (Perl *et al.,* 1990; Teitelbaum *et al.,* 1990). Acute neurological symptoms included altered levels of consciousness, with confusion, combativeness, memory impairment, and seizures. Three patients died as a result of the poisoning, and a number of the survivors were left with severe deficits in anterograde memory. Elderly males were found to be at highest risk for developing memory impairments, and among cases examined pathologically neuronal loss was found primarily in the hippocampus and amygdala. The syndrome was traced to the ingestion of cultured blue mussels harvested from estuaries in Prince Edward Island. These mussels were found to contain high concentrations of the kainate analogue, domoate, a potent neuroexcitant and neurotoxin. The source of the domoate was a specie of plankton, *Nitzschia pungens,* which was found in the water of the island at the time. When *Nitzschia pungens* is in full bloom, it synthesizes large amounts of domoate, which becomes concentrated in the flesh of mussels that filter feed upon the plankton.

The neurological symptoms seen in the poisoning victims are reminiscent of symptoms produced by kainate in experimental animals (Lothman and Collins, 1981). After systemic injection, kainate-treated animals experience recurring limbic seizures, animal equivalents of human partial complex seizures, and brain damage involving the hippocampus and amygdala, among other areas. Stewart *et al.* (1990) have observed that systemic injections of domoate produce similar seizures and brain damage in rats, suggesting that recurring seizures play an important role in the neurodegenerative process. Receptor binding and physiological studies have shown that domoate is likely to exert its effects through actions on kainate receptors (Slevin *et al.,* 1983; Stewart *et al.,* 1990). These receptors are heavily concentrated in the CA3 region of the hippocampus (Monaghan and Cotman, 1982), which may explain the propensity of domoate to produce limbic seizures and hippocampal damage. Like its structural analogue kainate, domoate activates large nondesensitizing physiological responses in CNS neurons (Patneau and Mayer, 1990) and produces dramatic acute neuronal swelling and damage during a 20- to 30-min exposure *in vitro* (Stewart *et al.,* 1990). These physiological features may, in part, account for the rapid onset and progression of the human syndrome. However, based on analogy to the kainate syndrome in animals, it is likely that much of the CNS damage in regions outside the hippocampus results from the recurring seizures and concomitant release of excessive Glu at NMDA receptors. This conclusion is based on evidence that NMDA receptor antagonists prevent seizure-mediated brain damage, including that associated with kainate-induced seizures (Clifford *et al.,* 1989, 1990). Thus available evidence supports the conclusion that both kainate and NMDA receptors are sensitive mediators of excitotoxic pathology in the aged human brain.

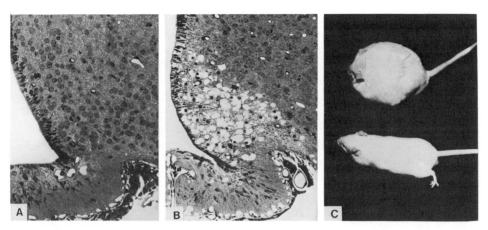

FIGURE 1.   (A) The normal appearance of the arcuate hypothalamic nucleus from a control mouse that did not receive glutamate. (B) The light micrograph depicts acutely necrotic neurons (bull's-eye profiles) in the arcuate hypothalamic nucleus of a 21-day-old mouse 4 hr following voluntary ingestion of drinking water containing 10% (w/v) glutamate. Glutamate treatment in infancy gives rise to a neuroendocrine deficiency syndrome characterized by an abnormal body habitus (short and fat) and stunting of the pituitary and gonads. (C) A glutamate-treated mouse manifesting this syndrome (top) is shown for comparison with a normal litter mate control (bottom). These illustrations are reproduced in part from Olney *et al.* (1980) and Olney (1969b), with permission.

5.4. Glutamate-Induced Neuroendocrinopathies

Historically, the first demonstration that an environmental excitotoxin produces a brain-damage syndrome was provided by Olney (1969a, 1969b), who observed that oral or subcutaneous administration of Glu to rodents damaged neurons in brain regions lacking blood–brain barriers. One of the areas affected, the arcuate nucleus of the hypothalamus (AH), is a known neuroendocrine regulatory center. Consistent with the neuroendocrine role of the AH, when infant mice treated with Glu grew to adulthood they exhibited a syndrome that included obesity, skeletal shortening, and reproductive failure (Olney, 1969a, 1969b) (Fig. 1). These animals also had low levels of luteinizing hormone (LH), growth hormone (GH), and prolactin (Prl). Although Glu treatment in infancy did not directly damage the pituitary, in adulthood the anterior lobe of the gland was smaller than controls, suggesting the absence of an important trophic influence during development (Olney and Price, 1980). Asp was as effective as Glu in producing this syndrome (Olney *et al.*, 1971).

Subsequent studies showed that doses of Glu that were subtoxic to AH neurons produced changes in the neuroendocrine status of weanling and adult male rats (Olney *et al.*, 1976a). These subtoxic doses induced elevations of LH and a depression of the pulsatile release of GH. More recently it has been shown that administration of Glu (150 mg/kg) intravenously to prepubescent monkeys causes an acute plasma elevation of both LH and GH (Medhamurthy *et al.*, 1990). The LH-releasing action of Glu is mimicked by other EAA. In female monkeys N-methyl-aspartate (NMA) induces a similar increase in the release of LH, Prl, and follicle stimulating hormone (FSH) (Gay and Plant, 1987). The LH-releasing effect of NMA is dependent on AH neurons and is inhibited by NMDA antagonists (Price *et al.*, 1979). In both primates and lower species, semichronic administration of NMA during the prepubescent period accelerates the onset of puberty, whereas NMDA antagonists, when similarly administered, retard the onset of puberty (Plant *et al.*, 1989; Urbansky and Ojeda, 1990). These studies indicate that the administration of excitotoxins can have profound effects on neuroendocrine status and that even in subtoxic doses these agents produce acute disturbances in the release of hormones by presumably acting on neurons that regulate pituitary output. This raises the important question as to whether dietary exposure to Glu or other EAA can produce similar effects.

Although *in vivo* studies pertaining to Glu neurotoxicity have typically relied on either subcutaneous or feeding tube administration, Olney *et al.*, (1980) have demonstrated that when weanling mice (comparable in developmental age to an adolescent human) are water deprived overnight, the next morning they voluntarily ingest sufficient quantities of Glu or Asp in drinking water to produce hypothalamic damage. This suggests that the sensitivity of the developing hypothalamus to either the excitatory or neurotoxic effects of Glu following oral intake extends well beyond the neonatal period. It is noteworthy, therefore, that immature humans are currently being fed multiple excitotoxins, including Asp contained in aspartame (Nutrasweet®); Glu, Asp, and cysteine contained in protein hydrolysates (added heavily to foods); and exceedingly large amounts of Glu in the form of its sodium salt (monosodium glutamate, MSG). For example, certain commonly marketed soups contain 1300 mg of added Glu per 6 oz serving (Olney, 1984), which provides an immature human weighing 10 kg with 130 mg Glu/kg body weight. The oral dose of Glu required to destroy neurons in the immature mouse hypothalamus is in the range of 250–500 mg/kg (Olney, 1984). Of singular importance in evaluating human risk is the fact that ingestion of a given amount of Glu causes a much higher and much more sustained blood Glu elevation in adult humans than in either adult mice or monkeys (Himwich *et al.*, 1954; Stegink *et al.*, 1979), and a much higher blood Glu elevation in infant than in adult mice or monkeys (Bizzi *et al.*, 1977; Himwich *et al.*, 1954). Although comparable studies have not been conducted on immature humans, these findings suggest that immature humans, on the basis of both species and age, may be exceedingly vulnerable to Glu-induced brain damage (Fig. 2). An additional critical determinant of vulnerability is suggested by two lines of recent evidence, one showing that hypothalamic damage induced by Glu in the immature brain is mediated exclusively by NMDA receptors, and the other showing that NMDA receptors in the immature brain are hypersensitive to excitotoxic stimulation (Ikonomidou *et al.*, 1989a; MacDonald *et al.*, 1988; Wang *et al.*, 1990). This provides an explanation for the long-recognized fact that in rodents the infant hypothalamus is much more sensitive than the adult hypothalamus to Glu-induced damage. Moreover, it warrants the inference that in humans it might not require very high blood levels of excitotoxins that act at NMDA receptors (such as Glu and Asp) to excite and/or kill neurons in the immature hypothalamus. Finally, it is important to recognize that when a neurotoxic dose of Glu or Asp is administered to immature animals, they do not display any outward signs of distress or dysfunction during the acute period when hypothalamic neurons are being destroyed.

5.5. L-Cysteine Neurotoxicity

L-cysteine (Cys) is a sulfur-containing, nonessential, amino acid present normally in the CNS and environment. Initial studies demonstrated that this agent produces neu-

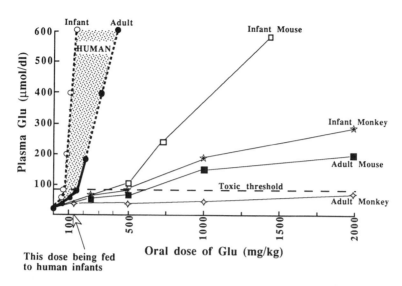

FIGURE 2. The graph displays a composite of data from several literature sources depicting oral glutamate dose-response data for infant and adult monkeys or mice, and adult humans, with hypothetical data points (connected by dashed lines) inserted for human infants and for higher doses than have been tested on human adults. The data for mice and monkeys are from Stegink *et al.* (1979). The data for adult humans at 60 mg/kg are from Bizzi *et al.* (1977), at 100 and 150 mg/kg from Stegink *et al.* (1979), and at 200 mg/kg are from Himwich *et al.* (1954). Hypothetical data points are entered for human infants, and the area between the curves for human infants and adults is stippled to indicate the zone in which data points for human children presumably would fall if adequate test data for human young were available. It should be noted that the data points given for adult humans are means and that there were striking individual differences noted in each human study. Thus, the curve for some individual humans would be steeper than is shown here. The oral dose (500 mg/kg) and plasma glutamate concentration (60–100 μmol/dl) at which infant mice begin to sustain brain damage is indicated as the toxic threshold (horizontal dashed line).

rodegeneration following systemic administration to infant rats (Olney *et al.*, 1972a). Additionally, Cys crosses the placenta and produces neuronal damage in rodent fetal brain when administered to the pregnant mother. The lesions produced by Cys resemble those produced by Glu, but differ in one important way. Whereas systemic Glu damages only CNS regions lacking blood–brain barriers, Cys produces a generalized pattern of damage throughout the forebrain, suggesting that this agent readily penetrates blood–brain barriers. Damage typically involves the neocortex, hippocampus, septum, caudate, and thalamus. Interestingly, the distribution and pattern of lesions produced by Cys resemble those produced by perinatal hypoxia/ischemia, suggesting that this agent may function pathologically as a hypoxia/ischemia equivalent. In addition, L-Cys can serve in research as a valuable tool for studying mechanisms underlying developmental neuropathology syndromes. *In vitro* studies have shown that Cys exerts its effects primarily through actions at NMDA receptors, although quisqualate receptors also contribute to toxicity at higher concentrations (Olney *et al.*, 1990a). Additionally, the physiological and toxic effects of Cys are augmented greatly by the presence of bicarbonate ions. In the absence of bicarbonate, Cys is a relatively weak excitotoxin. Like BMAA, Cys lacks the dicarbox-ylic acid structure typical of EAA. However, Nunn and colleagues (1991) have found that in the presence of bicarbonate the Cys molecule, like BMAA, is converted to an α-aminocarbamate with a structure resembling other excitotoxins. Other evidence indicates that Cys may, in part, exert its effects by chelating Zn^{2+}, thus removing one of the inhibitory influences that keeps the NMDA system in check.

Clinical interest in Cys is likely to be stimulated by the recent report that patients with ALS, parkinsonism, and Alzheimer's dementia have altered sulphur metabolism (Heafield *et al.*, 1990), resulting in elevated Cys/sulfate ratios in blood. Interestingly, these are the same neurodegenerative disorders with which BMAA exposure is associated. These findings, coupled with the ability of Cys and BMAA to penetrate blood–brain barriers, make it important to consider whether an occult metabolic disturbance in Cys pathways might contribute both to the endemic occurrence of these three disorders in Guam, where both Cys and BMAA are environmentally present, and their sporadic occurrence throughout the world, where Cys itself, being both exogenously and endogenously present, might be sufficient to induce the disease process. If corroborated this would serve as an instructive example of a synergistic action between a metabolic defect and excitotoxins of both endogenous and exogenous origin.

6. DISCUSSION

Evidence has been slowly accumulating for a role of both endogenous and exogenous EAA in human neurodegenerative disorders. Evidence for involvement of endogenous EAA has been most compelling for CNS injury associated with acute conditions such as stroke, status epilepticus, and physical CNS trauma. It has been more difficult to establish a link between excitotoxic mechanisms and chronic neurodegenerative processes, and to determine whether it is primarily endogenous or exogenous factors, or both acting in concert, that may be responsible for the more chronic human neurodegenerative disorders, such as motor neuron disease, parkinsonism, and Alzheimer's disease. This is partly due to the lack of adequate animal models for studying these chronic disease processes. However, progress is being made toward resolving these issues, and a primary strategy permitting new insights has been to focus on specific neurodegenerative processes that occur in humans in association with exposure to specific environmental excitotoxins.

The domoate food poisoning incident provides an instructive example of brain injury being triggered by exposure to an exogenous excitotoxin, with cooperative input from an endogenous excitotoxin (probably Glu), and involvement of at least two EAA receptor systems (NMDA and kainate) in the expression of relatively acute brain injury that results finally in a chronic organic brain syndrome. While this helps clarify one mechanism by which exogenous and endogenous excitotoxins can act in concert to produce relatively acute brain damage, it does not shed light on the possible role of excitotoxins in slowly evolving neurodegenerative disorders.

Recent evidence strongly implicating another food excitotoxin, BOAA, in neurolathyrism provides an example of a more slowly evolving neurodegenerative process triggered by an exogenous excitotoxin. Whereas the EAA receptor subtypes primarily implicated in the acutely evolving domoate syndrome are kainate and NMDA receptors, BOAA acts exclusively at quisqualate receptors. Therefore, it will be important to continue studying how BOAA or related molecules can interact pathologically with quisqualate receptors to cause slowly evolving degeneration of motor neuron systems and paralytic symptoms, in that this could lead not only to a better understanding of neurolathyrism but of other more chronically progressive motor-neuron disorders such as ALS.

A role for the environmental excitotoxin, BMAA, in the ALS-parkinsonism-dementia complex of Guam remains tentative at present. However, certain parallels between BMAA and Cys, and a recent study (Heafield *et al.*, 1990) linking Cys with the same three disease entities in Britain that BMAA is linked to in Guam, suggest the interesting possibility that an occult metabolic disturbance in Cys pathways might underlie both the sporadic occurrence of these three diseases throughout the world and their endemic occurrence as a disease triad in Guam. If this were corroborated, it would represent an example of a cooperative action between an endogenous excitotoxin (Cys) accumulating in the CNS due to a metabolic block and two environmental excitotoxins (BMAA and Cys) passing via the gastrointestinal tract and blood into the brain to augment the excitotoxic consequences of the endogenous metabolic disturbance. This is potentially an important line of research for the light it may shed on chronically progressive disease processes. For example, the Guamanian syndrome is known to have onset in victims after they have migrated from Guam to other parts of the world and are no longer in contact with the environmental toxins indigenous to Guam. Once onset of the disease occurs, the course is progressively downhill. Therefore, either an environmental toxin in Guam can induce a pathological process that is expressed on a delayed basis and becomes progressive, even without further exposure to the toxin, or a pathogenic principle (such as a Cys metabolic defect) is intrinsic to the host while on Guam and travels with the host to other parts of the world. It is noteworthy that BMAA and Cys have the same dual receptor specificities, each molecule being able to activate both NMDA and quisqualate receptors. This suggests the possibility that chronic exposure to agents capable of simultaneously activating these two receptor systems may be a formula for inducing slowly progressive neurodegenerative processes.

Unlike the above situations in which neuroscientists are working fervently to understand how accidental exposure to excitotoxic substances in the environment might be responsible for well-recognized crippling human disease processes is the scenario in which excitotoxins are intentionally being added to foods in large amounts worldwide because they impart flavor, which is considered advantageous for purposes of marketing the food. The intentional addition of Glu and substances containing high concentrations of Glu, Asp, or other excitotoxins to foods in amounts potentially hazardous to the developing human brain was first identified as a public health problem 20 years ago. In the ensuing years, food regulatory authorities, instead of taking steps to reduce the hazard, have been instrumental in increasing it (by approving aspartame for children's foods and beverages, in addition to the large amount of Glu being fed to children). Currently Glu, which may be the most widely and heavily used food additive in the world, is sanctioned by the Food and Drug Administration (FDA) as a GRAS (generally regarded as safe) substance that can be added in any amount to any food without informative labeling or meaningful scrutiny because, by definition, GRAS items are exempt from regulation. In the authors' opinion, Glu poses a public health problem that is long overdue for correction. The following corrective measures could easily be taken: (1) Glu could be removed from the GRAS list and subjected to regulation. (2) The amounts of Glu added to foods could be regulated at a level that poses no significant risk to the developing nervous system. (3) The fact that Glu is added and the amounts that are added to specific foods could be honestly stated on the label. (4) Instead of representing Glu as a totally safe and innocuous substance, the food and Glu industries and regulatory authorities could begin educating the public regarding the toxic potential of Glu for the developing CNS.

In parts of the world where BOAA poisoning results in neurolathyrism, measures are being taken to discourage ingestion of the offending legume, *Lathyrus sativus,* and/or to develop processing methods that would remove its BOAA content, thereby making this abundant foodstuff safe for human consumption. There is basis for believing that domoate poisoning poses an ongoing threat to seafood lovers in both Canada and the United States. Food safety authorities in Canada have begun monitoring the domoate concentration in mussels marketed in that country, but authorities in the United States have not, to the best of our knowledge, developed a comparable consumer-protection program.

There is a large and growing number of adults who have come to associate the ingestion of Glu with a variety of adverse effects, ranging from a burning sensation over the face and neck (Chinese restaurant syndrome) and severe headaches, to vaso-vagal reactions, prostration, and life-threatening asthmatic attacks. While we believe that regulatory authorities should be more attentive to the voiced concerns of these consumers, we have intentionally focused primary attention in this chapter on practices that are potentially hazardous to the developing brain and that annually place at risk the health of millions of infants and children who are not in a position to speak for themselves. It should be noted that if regulatory authorities would follow the simple measures outlined above, it would markedly reduce the potential hazards for both of these large consumer groups without interfering with any identifiable consumer benefits.

ACKNOWLEDGMENTS.   This work was supported in part by Physician Scientist Award MH00630 (CFZ) and Research Scientist Award MH38894 (JWO) and grants AG05681 and MH45493.

REFERENCES

Albin, R.L., Young, A.B., and Penney, J.B., 1989, The functional anatomy of basal ganglia disorders, *Trends Neurosci.* 12:366–375.

Anis, N.A., Burton, N.R., Berry, S.C., and Lodge, D., 1983, The dissociative anesthetics, ketamine and phencyclidine, selectively reduce excitation of spinal neurones by N-methylaspartate. *Br. J. Pharmacol.* 79:565–575.

Arendash, G.W., Millard, W.J., Dunn, A.J., and Meyer, E.M., 1987, Long-term neuropathological and neurochemical effects of nucleus basalis lesions in the rat, *Science* 238:952–956.

Assaf, S.Y., and Chung, S.H., 1984, Release of endogenous zinc from brain tissue during activity, *Nature* 308:734–736.

Bartus, R.T., Dean, R.C., Beer, B., and Lippa, A.S., 1982, Cholinergic hypothesis of geriatric memory dysfunction, *Science* 217:408–417.

Beal, M.F., Kowall, N.W., Ellison, D.W., Mazurek, M.F., and Swartz, K.J., 1986, Replication of the neurochemical characteristics of Huntington's disease by quinolinic acid, *Nature* 321:168–171.

Bear, M.F., Cooper, L.N., and Ebner, F.F., 1987, A physiological basis for a theory of synapse modification, *Science* 237:42–48.

Berridge, M.J., 1987, Inositol trisphosphate and diacyglycerol: Two interacting second messengers, *Ann. Rev. Biochem.* 56:159–193.

Bizzi, A.E., Veneroni, E., Salmona, M., and Garatinnni, S., 1977, Kinetics of monosodium glutamate in relation to its neurotoxicity, *Toxicol. Lett.* 1:123–130.

Boulter, J., Hollmann, M., O'Shea-Greenfield, A., Hartley, M., Deneris, E., Maron, C., and Heinemann, S., 1990, Molecular cloning and functional expression of glutamate receptor subunit genes, *Science* 249:1033–1037.

Bridges, R.J., Stevens, D.R., Kahle, J.S., Nunn, P.B., Kadri, M., and Cotman, C.W., 1989, Structure-function studies on N-oxalyl-diamino-dicarboxylic acids and excitatory amino acid receptors: Evidence that β-L-ODAP is a selective non-NMDA agonist, *J. Neurosci.* 9:2073–2079.

Choi, D.W., 1987, Ionic dependence of glutamate neurotoxicity, *J. Neurosci.* 7:357–368.

Choi, D.W., 1988, Glutamate neurotoxicity and diseases of the nervous system, *Neuron* 1:623–634.

Choi, D.W., Maulucci-Gedde, M., and Kriegstein, A.R., 1987, Glutamate neurotoxicity in cortical cell culture, *J. Neurosci.* 7:357–368.

Christine, C.W., and Choi, D.W., 1990, Effect of zinc on NMDA receptor-mediated channel currents in cortical neurons, *J. Neurosci.* 10:108–116.

Clark, G.D., Clifford, D.B., and Zorumski, C.F., 1990, The effect of agonist concentration, membrane voltage and calcium on N-methyl-D-aspartate receptor desensitization, *Neuroscience* 39:787–797.

Clifford, D.B., Zorumski, C.F., and Olney, J.W., 1989, Ketamine and MK-801 prevent degeneration of thalamic neurons induced by focal cortical seizures, *Exp. Neurol.* 105:272–279.

Clifford, D.B., Olney, J.W., Benz, A.M., Fuller, T.A., and Zorumski, C.F., 1990, Ketamine, phencyclidine and MK-801 protect against kainic acid induced seizure-related brain damage, *Epilepsia* 31:382–390.

Collingridge, G.L., and Lester, R.A.J., 1989, Excitatory amino acid receptors in the vertebrate central nervous system, *Pharm. Rev.* 40:143–210.

Collins, R.C., and Olney, J.W., 1982, Focal cortical seizures cause distant thalamic lesions, *Science* 218:177–179.

Copani, A., Canonico, P.L., and Nicoletti, F., 1990, β-N-methylamino-L-alanine (L-BMAA) is a potent agonist of metabolotropic glutamate receptors, *Eur. J. Pharmacol.* 181:327–328.

Cotman, C.W., Flatman, J.A., Ganong, A.H., and Perkins, M.N., 1986, Effects of excitatory amino acid antagonists on evoked and spontaneous excitatory potentials in guinea pig hippocampus, *J. Physiol. (London)* 378:403–415.

Coyle, J.T., and Schwarcz, R., 1976, Lesions of striatal neurons with kainic acid provides a model for Huntington's chorea, *Nature* 263:244–246.

Coyle, J.T., McGeer, E.F., McGeer, P.L., and Schwarcz, R., 1978, Neostriatal injections: A model for Huntington's chorea, in: *Kainic Acid as a Tool in Neurobiology* (E. McGeer, J.W. Olney, and P. McGeer, eds.), Raven Press, New York, pp. 139–159.

Coyle, J.T., Price, D.L., and DeLong, M.A., 1983, Alzheimer's disease: A disorder of cortical cholinergic innervation, *Science* 219:1184–1190.

Curtis, D.R., and Watkins, J.C., 1960, The excitation and depression of spinal neurons by structurally related amino acids, *J. Neurochem.* 6:117–141.

DeBoni, U., and McLachlan, D.R.C., 1985, Controlled induction of paired helical filaments of the Alzheimer type in cultured human neurons by glutamate and aspartate, *J. Neurol. Sci.* 68:105–118.

Desai, M.A., and Conn, J.P., 1990, Selective activation of phosphoinositide hydrolysis by a rigid analogue of glutamate, *Neurosci. Lett.* 109:157–162.

Dudek, S.M., Bowen, W.D., and Bear, M.F., 1989, Postnatal changes in glutamate stimulated phosphoinositide turnover in rat neocortical synaptoneurosomes, *Dev. Brain Res.* 47:123–128.

Ellren, K., and Lehmann, A., 1989, Calcium dependency of N-methyl-D-aspartate toxicity in slices from the immature rat hippocampus, *Neuroscience* 32:371–379.

Forsythe, I.D., and Clements, J.D., 1990, Presynaptic glutamate receptors depress excitatory monosynaptic transmission between mouse hippocampal neurones, *J. Physiol. (London)* 429:1–16.

Forsythe, I.D., and Westbrook, G.L., 1988, Slow excitatory postsynaptic currents mediated by N-methyl-D-aspartate receptors on cultured mouse central neurones, *J. Physiol. (London)* 396:515–533.

Foster, A.C., and Fagg, G.E., 1984, Acidic amino acid binding sites in mammalian neuronal membranes: Their chracteristics and rtnp to synaptic receptors, *Brain Res. Rev.* 7:103–164.

Garruto, R.M., and Yase, Y., 1986, Neurodegenerative disorders of the western Pacific: The search for mechanisms of pathogenesis, *Trends Neurosci.* 9:368–374.

Garthwaite, G., and Garthwaite, J., 1986, Neurotoxicity of excitatory amino acid receptor agonists in rat cerebellar slices: Dependence on extracellular calcium concentration, *Neurosci. Lett.* 66:193–198.

Garthwaite, G., and Garthwaite, J., 1989a, Neurotoxicity of excitatory amino acid agonists in young rat hippocampal slices, *J. Neurosci. Methods* 29:33–42.

Garthwaite, G., and Garthwaite, J., 1989b, Differential dependence on Ca^{2+} of N-methyl-D-aspartate and quisqualate neurotoxicity in young rat hippocampal slices, *Neurosci. Lett.* 97:316–322.

Gay, V.L., and Plant, T.M., 1987, N-Methyl-D-aspartate elicits hypothalamic gonadotropin-releasing hormone release in prepubertal male rhesus monkeys (*Macaca mulatta*), *Endocrinology* 120:2289–2296.

Heafield, M.T., Fearn, S., Steventon, G.B., Waring, R.H., Williams, A.D., and Sturman, S.G., 1990, Plasma cysteine and sulfate levels in patients with motor neurone, Parkinson's and Alzheimer's disease, *Neurosci. Lett.* 110:216–220.

Himwich, W.A., Peterson, I.M., and Graves, I.P., 1954, Ingested glutamate and plasma levels of glutamic acid, *J. Appl. Physiol.* 7:196–201.

Honore, T., Davies, S.N., Drejer, J., Fletcher, E.J., Jacobsen, P., Lodge, D., and Nielsen, F.E., 1988, Quinoxalinediones: Potent competitive non-NMDA glutamate receptor antagonists, *Science* 241:701–703.

Howell, G.A., Welch, M.G., and Frederickson, C.J., 1984, Stimulation-induced uptake and release of zinc in hippocampal slices, *Nature* 308:734–736.

Ikonomidou, C., Mosinger, J.L., Salles, K., Labruyere, J., and Olney, J.W., 1989a, Sensitivity of the developing rat brain to hypobaric/ischemic damage parallels sensitivity to N-methyl-D-aspartate neurotoxicity, *J. Neurosci.* 9:2809–2818.

Ikonomidou, C., Price, M.T., Mosinger, J.L., Friedrich, G., Labruyere, J., Salles, K.S., and Olney, J.W., 1989b, Hypobaric-ischemic conditions produce glutamate like cytopathology in infant rat brain, *J. Neurosci.* 9:1693–1700.

Johnson, J.W., and Ascher, P., 1987, Glycine potentiates the NMDA response in cultured mouse brain neurons, *Nature* 325:529–531.

Keinanen, K., Wisden, W., Sommer, B., Werner, P., Herb, A., Verdoorn, T.A., Sakmann, B., and Seeburg, P.H., 1990, A family of AMPA-selective glutamate receptors, *Science* 249:556–560.

Kiskin, N.I., Krishtal, O.A., and Tsyndrenko, A.Y., 1986, Excitatory amino acid receptors in hippocampal neurons: Kainate fails to desensitize them, *Neurosci. Lett.* 63:225–230.

Kleckner, N.W., and Dingledine, R., 1988, Requirement for glycine in activation of NMDA receptors expressed in Xenopus oocytes, *Science* 241:835–837.

Klunk, W.E., McClure, R.J., and Pettegrew, J.W., 1991, L-phosphoserine, a metabolite elevated in Alzheimer's disease interacts with specific L-glutamate receptor subtypes, *J. Neurochem.* 56:1997–2003.

Koh, J.Y., Goldberg, M.P., Hartley, D.M., and Choi, D.W., 1990, Non-NMDA receptor-mediated neurotoxicity in cortical culture, *J. Neurosci.* 10:693–705.

Koh, J.Y., Yang, L.L., and Cotman, C.W., 1990, β-amyloid protein increases the vulnerability of cultured cortical neurons to excitotoxic damage, *Brain Res.* 533:315–320.

Kuba, K., and Kumamoto, E., 1990, Long-term potentiation in vertebrate synapses: A variety of cascades with common subprocesses, *Prog. Neurobiol.* 34:197–269.

Legendre, P., and Westbrook, G.L., 1990, The inhibition of single N-methyl-D-aspartate activated channels by zinc ions on cultured rat neurones, *J. Physiol. (London)* 429:429–449.

Lothman, E.W., and Collins, R.C., 1981, Kainic acid induced limbic seizures: Metabolic, behavioral, electroencephalographic and neuropathological correlates, *Brain Res.* 218:299–318.

Lucas, D.R., and Newhouse, J.P., 1957, The toxic effect of sodium L-glutamate on the inner layers of the retina, *AMA Arch. Ophthalmol.* 58:193–201.

MacDermott, A.B., Mayer, M.L., Westbrook, G.L., Smith, S.J., and Barker, J.L., 1986, NMDA receptor activation increases cytoplasmic calcium concentration in cultured spinal cord neurons, *Nature* 321:519–522.

MacDonald, J.W., Silverstein, F.S., and Johnston, M.V., 1988, Neurotoxicity of N-methyl-D-aspartate is markedly enhanced in developing rat central nervous system, *Brain Res.* 459:200–203.

Maragos, W.F., Greenamyre, J.T., Penney, J.B., and Young, A.B., 1987, Glutamate dysfunction in Alzheimer's disease: An hypothesis, *Trends Neurosci.* 10:65–68.

Mayer, M.L., and Westbrook, G.L., 1984, Mixed agonist action on excitatory amino acids on mouse spinal cord neurons under voltage-clamp, *J. Physiol. (London)* 354:29–53.

Mayer, M.L., and Westbrook, G.L., 1987a, The physiology of excitatory amino acids in the vertebrate central nervous system, *Prog. Neurobiol.* 28:197–276.

Mayer, M.L., and Westbrook, G.L., 1987b, Permeation and block of N-methyl-D-aspartic acid receptor channels by divalent cations in mouse cultured central neurones, *J. Physiol. (London)* 394:501–527.

Mayer, M.L., Westbrook, G.L., and Guthrie, P.B., 1984, Voltage-dependent block by $Mg++$ of NMDA responses in spinal cord neurons, *Nature* 309:261–263.

Mayer, M.L., Vyklicky Jr., L., and Clements, J., 1989, Regulation of NMDA receptor desensitization in mouse hippocampal neurons by glycine, *Nature* 338:425–427.

McGeer, E.G., and McGeer, P.L., 1976, Duplication of biochemical changes of Huntington's chorea by intrastriatal injections of glutamic and kainic acids, *Nature* 263:517–519.

Medhamurthy, R., Dichek, H.L., Plant, T.M., Bernardini, I., and Cutler, G.B., 1990, Stimulation of gonadotropin secretion in prepubertal monkeys after hypothalamic excitation with aspartate and glutamate, *J. Clin. Endocrinol. Metab.* 71:1390–1392.

Miller, R., and Slaughter, M., 1986, Excitatory amino acid receptors of the retina: Diversity of subtypes and conductance mechanisms, *Trends Neurosci.* 9:211–218.

Monaghan, D.T., and Cotman, C.W., 1982, The distribution of [³H]-kainic acid binding sites in rat CNS as determined by autoradiography, *Brain Res.* 252:91–100.

Mudd, S.H., Irreverre, F., and Laster, L., 1967, Sulfite oxidase deficiency in man: Demonstration of the enzyme defect, *Science* 156:1599–1602.

Nowak, L., Bregestovski, P., Ascher, P., Herbert, A., and Prochiantz, A., 1984, Magnesium gates glutamate-activated channels in mouse central neurons, *Nature* 307:462–465.

Nunn, P.B., Davis, A.J., and O'Brien, P., 1991, On carbamate formation and the neurotoxicity of L-α-amino acids, *Science* 251:1619.

Olney, J.W., 1969a, Glutamate-induced retinal degeneration in neonatal mice. Electron microscopy of the acutely evolving lesion, *J. Neuropathol. Exp. Neurol.* 28:455–474.

Olney, J.W., 1969b, Brain lesions, obesity and other disturbances in mice treated with monosodium glutamate, *Science* 164:719–721.

Olney, J.W., 1971, Glutamate-induced neuronal necrosis in the infant mouse hypothalamus: An electron microscopic study, *J. Neuropathol. Exp. Neurol.* 30:75–90.

Olney, J.W., 1979, Excitotoxic amino acids and Huntington's disease, in: *Advances of Neurology*, Vol. 23, *Huntington's Disease* (T.N. Chase, A. Wexler, and A. Barbeau, eds.), Raven Press, New York, pp. 609–624.

Olney, J.W., 1984, Excitotoxic food additives—relevence of animal studies to human safety, *Neurobehav. Toxicol. Teratol.* 6:455–462.

Olney, J.W., 1989, Excitatory amino acids and neuropsychiatric disorders, *Biol. Psychiatry* 26:505–526.

Olney, J.W., 1990, Excitotoxic amino acids and neuropsychiatric disorders, *Ann. Rev. Pharmacol. Toxicol.* 30:47–71.

Olney, J.W., and Ho, O.L., Brain damage in infant mice following oral intake of glutamate, aspartate or cysteine, *Nature* 227:609–610.

Olney, J.W., and Price, M.T., 1980, Neuroendocrine interactions of excitatory and inhibitory amino acids, *Brain Res. Bull.* 5 (Suppl 2):361–368.

Olney, J.W., Ho, O.L., and Rhee, V., 1971, Cytotoxic effects of acidic and sulphur-containing amino acids on the infant mouse central nervous system, *Exp. Brain Res.* 14:61–76.

Olney, J.W., Ho, O.L., Rhee, V., and Schainker, B., 1972a, Cysteine induced brain damage in infant and fetal rodents, *Brain Res.* 45:309–313.

Olney, J.W., Sharpe, L.G., and Feigin, R.D., 1972b, Glutamate induced brain damage in infant primates, *J. Neuropathol. Exp. Neurol.* 31:464–488.

Olney, J.W., Misra, C.H., and DeGubareff, T., 1975, Cysteine-S-sulfate: A brain damaging metabolite in sulfite oxidase deficiency, *J. Neuropathol. Exp. Neurol.* 34:167–176.

Olney, J.W., Cicero, T.J., Meyer, E.F., and DeGubareff, T., 1976a, Acute glutamate induced elevations in serum testosterone and leutenizing hormone, *Brain Res.* 112:420–424.

Olney, J.W., Misra, C.H., and Rhee, V., 1976b, Brain and retinal damage from the lathyrus excitotoxin, β-N-oxalyl-L-α,β-diaminopropionic acid (ODAP), *Nature* 264:659–661.

Olney, J.W., Labruyere, J., and DeGubareff, T., 1980, Brain damage in mice from voluntary ingestion of glutamate and aspartate, *Neurobehav. Toxicol.* 2:135–129.

Olney, J.W., DeGubareff, T., and Sloviter, R.S., 1983, Epileptic brain damage in rats induced by sustained electrical stimulation of the perforant path. II. Ultrastructural analysis of acute hippocampal pathology, *Brain Res. Bull.* 10:699–712.

Olney, J.W., Price, M.T., Samson, L., and Labruyere, J., 1986, The role of specific ions in glutamate neurotoxicity, *Neurosci Lett.* 65:65–71.

Olney, J.W., Zorumski, C., Price, M.T., and Labruyere, J., 1990a, L-cysteine, a bicarbonate sensitive endogenous excitotoxin, *Science* 248:596–599.

Olney, J.W., Zorumski, C.F., Stewart, G.R., Price, M.T., Wang, G., and Labruyere, J., 1990b, Excitotoxicity of L-DOPA and 6-OH-DOPA: Implications for Parkinson's and Huntington's diseases, *Exp. Neurol.* 108:269–272.

Patneau, D.K., and Mayer, M.L., 1990, Structure-activity relationships for amino acid transmitter candidates acting at N-methyl-D-aspartate and quisqualate receptors, *J. Neurosci.* 10:2385–2399.

Perl, T.M., Bedard, L., Kosatsky, T., Hockin, J.C., Todd, E.C.D., and Remis, R.S., 1990, An outbreak of toxic encephalopathy caused by eating mussels contaminated with domoic acid, *N. Engl. J. Med.* 322:1775–1780.

Peters, S., Koh, J., and Choi, D.W., 1987, Zinc selectively blocks the action of N-methyl-D-aspartate on cortical neurons, *Science* 236:589–593.

Plaitakis, A., and Caroscio, J.T., 1987, Abnormal glutamate metabolism in amyotrophic lateral sclerosis, *Ann. Neurol.* 22:575–579.

Plaitakis, A., Berl, S., and Yahr, M., 1984, Neurological disorders associated with deficiency of glutamate dehydrogenase, *Ann. Neurol.* 15:144–153.

Plant, T.M., Gay, V.L., Marshall, G.R., and Arslan, M., 1989, Puberty in monkeys is triggered by chemical stimulation of the hypothalamus, *Proc. Natl. Acad. Sci. USA* 86:2506–2510.

Pomara, N., Deptula, D., Singh, R., LeWitt, P.A., and Banay-Schwartz, M., 1990, Excitatory amino acid concentrations in CSF of patients with Alzheimer's disease, *Biol. Psychiatry* 27:97a.

Price, M.T., Olney, J.W., Anglim, M., and Buchsbaum, S., 1979, Reversible action of N-methyl aspartate on gonadotropin neuroregulation, *Brain Res.* 176:165–168.

Procter, A.W., Palmer, A.M., Frances, P.T., Lowe, S.L., Neary, D., Murphy, E., Doshi, R., and Bowen, D.M., 1988, Evidence of glutamatergic denervation and possible abnormal metabolism in Alzheimer's disease, *J. Neurochem.* 50:790–802.

Reynolds, G.P., Pearson, S.J., Halket, J., and Sandler, M., 1988, Brain quinolinic acid in Huntington's disease, *J. Neurochem.* 50:1959–1960.

Ross, S.M., Roy, D.N., and Spencer, P.S., 1989, β-N-oxalylamino-L-alanine action on glutamate receptors, *J. Neurochem.* 53:710–715.

Rothman, S.M., 1984, Synaptic release of excitatory amino acid neurotransmitter mediates anoxic neuronal death, *J. Neurosci.* 4:1884–1891.

Rothman, S.M., 1985, The neurotoxicity of excitatory amino acids is by passive chloride influx, *J. Neurosci.* 5:1483–1489.

Rothstein, J.D., Tsai, G., Kuncl, R.W., Clawson, L., Cornblath, D.R., Drachman, D.B., Pestronk, A., Stauch, B.L., and Coyle, J.T., 1990, Abnormal excitatory amino acid metabolism in amyotrophic lateral sclerosis, *Ann. Neurol.* 28:18–25.

Schwarcz, R., and Kohler, C., 1983, Differential vulnerability of central neurons of the rat to quinolinic acid, *Neurosci. Lett.* 38:84–90.

Seawright, A.D., Brown, A.W., Nolan, C.C., and Cavanagh, J.B., 1990, Selective degeneration of cerebellar cortical neurons caused by cycad neurotoxin β-methylaminoalanine (L-BMAA) in rats, *Neuropath. Appl. Neurobiol.* 16:153–169.

Sheardon, M.J., Nielson, E.O., Hansen, A.J., Jacobsen, P., and Honore, T., 1990, 2,3-dihydroxy-6-nitro-7-sulfamoyl-benzo(F)quinoxaline: A neuroprotectant for cerebral ischemia, *Science* 247:531–574.

Sladeczek, F., Pin, J.P., Recasens, M., Bockaert, J., and Weiss, S., 1985, Glutamate stimulates inositol phosphate formation in striatal neurons, *Nature* 317:717–719.

Slaughter, M.M., and Miller, R.F., 1981, 2-amino-4-phosphonobutyrate: A new pharmacological tool for retina research, *Nature* 211:182–185.

Slevin, J.T., Collins, J.F., and Coyle, J.T., 1983, Analogue interactions with the brain receptor labeled by [^{3}H]kainic acid, *Brain Res.* 265:169–172.

Sofroniew, M.V., and Pearson, R.C.A., 1985, Degeneration of cholinergic neurons in the basal nucleus following kainic or N-methyl-D-aspartic acid application to the cerebral cortex in the rat, *Brain Res.* 339:186–190.

Sommer, B., Keinanen, K., Verdoorn, T.A., Wisden, W., Burnashev, N., Herb, A., Kohler, M., Takagi, T., Sakmann, B., and

Seeburg, P.H., 1990, Flip and flop. A cell specific functional switch in glutamate operated channels of the CNS, *Science* 249:1580–1585.

Sonsalla, P.K., Niklas, W.J., and Heikkila, R.E., 1989, Role for excitatory amino acids in methamphetamine-induced nigrostriatal dopaminergic toxicity, *Science* 243:398–400.

Spencer, P.S., Ludolph, A., Dwivedi, M.P., Roy, D.N., Hugon, J., and Schaumbure, H.H., 1986, Lathyrism: Evidence for a role of the neuroexcitatory amino acid BOAA, *Lancet* 2:1066–1067.

Spencer, P.S., Nunn, P.B., Hugon, J., Ludolph, A.C., Ross, S.M., Roy, D.N., and Robertson, R.C., 1987, Guam amyotrophic lateral sclerosis-Parkinsonism-dementia linked to a plant excitant neurotoxin, *Science* 237:517–522.

Spencer, P.S., Allen, R.G., Kisby, G.E., and Ludolph, A.C., 1990, Excitotoxic disorders, *Science* 248:144.

Sprosen, T.S., and Woodruff, G.N., 1990, Polyamines potentiate NMDA induced whole cell currents in cultured striatal neurons, *Eur. J. Pharmacol.* 179:477–478.

Stegink, L.D., Reynolds, W.A., Filer, L.J., Baker, G.L., Daabees, T.T., and Pitkin, R.M., 1979, Comparative metabolism of glutamate in the mouse, monkey and man, in: *Glutamic Acid: Advances in Biochemistry and Physiology* (L.J. Filer Jr., M.R. Kare, S. Garattini, and W.A. Reynolds, eds.), Raven Press, New York, pp. 85–102.

Stewart, G.R., Zorumski, C.F., Price, M.T., and Olney, J.W., 1990, Domoic acid: A dementia-inducing excitotoxic food poison with kainic acid receptor specificity, *Exp. Neurol.* 110:127–138.

Teitelbaum, J.S., Zatorre, R.J., Carpenter, S., Gendron, D., Evans, A.C., Gjedde, A., and Cashman, N.R., 1990, Neurologic sequelae of domoic acid intoxication due to the ingestion of contaminated mussels, *N. Engl. J. Med.* 322:1781–1787.

Thal, L.J., Mandel, R.J., Terry, R.D., Buzsaki, G., and Gage, F.H., 1990, Nucleus basalis lesions fail to induce senile plaques in the rat, *Exp. Neurol.* 108:88–90.

Trussell, L.O., Thio, L.L., Zorumski, C.F., and Fischbach, G.D., 1988, Rapid desensitization of glutamate receptors in vertebrate central neurons, *Proc. Natl. Acad. Sci. USA* 85:2834–2838.

Turski, L., Bressler, K., Rettig, K-J., Loschmann, P-A., and Wachtel, H., 1991, Protection of substantia nigra from MPP+ neurotoxicity by N-methyl-D-aspartate antagonists, *Nature* 349:414–418.

Urbanski, H.F., and Ojeda, S.R., 1990, A role for N-methyl-D-aspartate (NMDA) receptors in the control of LH secretion and initiation of female puberty, *Endocrinology* 126:1774–1776.

Wang, G.J., Labruyere, J., Price, M.T., and Olney, J.W., 1990, Extreme sensitivity of infant animals to glutamate toxicity: Role of NMDA receptors, *Soc. Neurosci. Abstr.* 16:198.

Watkins, J.C., Krogsgaard-Larsen, P., and Honore, T., 1990, Structure-activity relationships in the development of excitatory amino acid receptor agonists and competitive antagonists, *Trends Pharm. Sci.* 11:25–33.

Weiss, J.H., and Choi, D.W., 1988, Beta-N-methylamino-L-alanine neurotoxicity: Requirement for bicarbonate as a cofactor, *Science* 241:973–975.

Weiss, J.H., Koh, J.Y., and Choi, D.W., 1989, Neurotoxicity of β-N-methylamino-L-alanine (BMAA) and β-N-oxalylamino-L-alanine (BOAA) on cultured cortical neurons, *Brain Res.* 497:64–71.

Weiss, J.H., Hartley, D.M., Koh, J., and Choi, D.W., 1990, The calcium channel blocker nifedipine attenuates slow excitatory amino acid neurotoxicity, *Science* 247:1474–1477.

Westbrook, G.L., and Mayer, M.L., 1987, Micromolar concentrations of Zn^{++} antagonize NMDA and GABA responses of hippocampal neurons, *Nature* 328:640–643.

Wieloch, T., 1985, Hypoglycemia induced neuronal damage prevented by an N-methyl-D-aspartate antagonist, *Science* 230:681–683.

Williams, K., Romano, C., Dichter, M.A., and Molinoff, P.B., 1991, Modulation of the NMDA receptor by polyamines, *Life Sci.* 48:469–498.

Wong, E.H.F., Kemp, J.A., Priestley, T., Knight, A.R., Woodruff, G.N., and Iversen, L.L., 1986, The anticonvulsant MK-801 is a potent N-methyl-D-aspartate antagonist, *Proc. Natl. Acad. Sci. USA* 83:7104–7108.

Zorumski, C.F., Yang, J., and Fischbach, G.D., 1989, Calcium-dependent, slow desensitization distinguishes different types of glutamate receptors, *Cell. Mol. Neurobiol.* 9:95–104.

Zorumski, C.F., Thio, L.L., Clark, G.D., and Clifford, D.B., 1990, Blockade of desensitization augments quisqualate excitotoxicity in hippocampal neurons, *Neuron* 5:61–66.

Chapter 16

Behavioral and Neuropathological Consequences of Chronic Exposure to Low Doses of the Dopaminergic Neurotoxin MPTP

J. S. Schneider

1. INTRODUCTION

This chapter will discuss the consequences of exposure to the neurotoxin MPTP in non-human primates, and particularly the consequences of chronic exposure to low doses of this toxin. Before such a discussion can proceed, some background material about MPTP, its effects on the central nervous system, and the clinical manifestations of these effects needs to be presented.

The chemical 1-methyl-4-phenyl-1,2,3,6-tetrahydropyridine (MPTP) was produced as a byproduct of the uncontrolled synthesis of a new synthetic form of heroin. This synthetic heroin, inadvertently contaminated with MPTP, was made available to intravenous drug users in Northern California in the early 1980s. A number of individuals who self-administered this compound developed a clinical syndrome that was remarkably similar to idiopathic Parkinson's disease (PD) (Ballard *et al.*, 1985; Langston *et al.*, 1983). Parkinson's disease is a well-defined clinical entity characterized by the presence

J. S. Schneider • Center for Neurological Research of the Department of Neurology, Hahnemann University School of Medicine, Philadelphia, Pennsylvania 19102.
The Vulnerable Brain and Environmental Risks, Volume 2: Toxins in Food, edited by Robert L. Isaacson and Karl F. Jensen. Plenum Press, New York, 1992.

of akinesia (difficulty initiating movements), rigidity, loss of postural reflexes, and a resting tremor. Neuropathologically, PD is characterized by loss of pigmented substantia nigra pars compacta (SNc) dopamine-producing neurons (Forno, 1982), as well as loss of pigmented neurons in the locus coeruleus and dorsal vagal nucleus (Jellinger, 1986), and the presence of Lewy bodies (round, eosinophilic intraneuronal inclusions) (Forno, 1982, 1986). Neurochemically, PD is defined by a massive loss of dopamine, particularly within the nigrostriatal system, although a number of other neurochemical systems are also compromised (Hornykiewicz and Kish, 1986). The primary neurochemical defect in patients with MPTP-induced parkinsonism is presumed to be similar to that in PD (i.e., loss of nigrostriatal dopamine), since patients with MPTP-induced parkinsonism respond well to traditional anti-Parkinson pharmacotherapies (i.e., dopamine replacement and dopamine agonist therapies) and develop treatment-related side effects (such as peak-dose L-dopa dyskinesias), as do patients with PD (Ballard *et al.*, 1985). Postmortem examination of the brain of a 23-year-old male with parkinsonism and with probable MPTP exposure showed selective destruction of SNc neurons (Davis *et al.*, 1979). While PD is a well-defined clinical entity, the term *parkinsonism* can refer to any condition in which physical signs similar to those observed in PD are exhibited (Langston *et al.*, 1987). The term *parkinsonism* then does not refer to a singular disease entity but describes clinical syndromes that might be caused by a variety of factors, which most probably lead to massive destruction of the nigrostriatal dopamine system.

While MPTP has neurotoxic effects in a number of animal species, it produces a clinical syndrome similar to parkinsonism only in cats, dogs, and nonhuman primates (Burns *et al.*, 1983; Schneider *et al.*, 1986; Wilson *et al.*, 1987). The parkinsonism in the macaque monkey produced by MPTP exposure closely resembles human parkinsonism (Burns *et al.*, 1983). These animals typically present with stooped, flexed posture; akinesia; bradykinesia (slowing of movement); and rigidity. They respond to traditional anti-Parkinson drug therapies and also develop treatment-related side effects as seen in humans (Clarke *et al.*, 1987). Neurochemically, the nigrostriatal dopamine system is most severely disrupted in this model, although some alterations have been described in other neurochemical systems as well (Zamir *et al.*, 1984). Neuropathologically, MPTP produces in the nonhuman primate brain a pattern of neuronal destruction remarkably similar to that seen in humans with PD (German *et al.*, 1989; Schneider *et al.*, 1987); that is, dopaminergic neurons in the central and ventral regions of the SNc are most affected, while there is some sparing of dopaminergic rostral dorsal tier neurons, ventral tegmental area neurons, and retrorubral and SN pars lateralis neurons. Thus, in both human PD and MPTP-induced parkinsonism in the monkey, certain subpopulations of ventral mesencephalic dopaminergic neurons are more susceptible to degeneration than are others.

2. MPTP-INDUCED PARKINSONISM IN NONHUMAN PRIMATES: EVALUATION OF THE MODEL

The discovery of MPTP certainly provided the research community with a new way to model PD and stimulated a tremendous amount of interest in Parkinson's disease. The MPTP model in the nonhuman primate provides the best available tool for assessing the efficacy and potential side effects of anti-Parkinson pharmacotherapies. A greater understanding of the physiology of the dopamine system, the mechanisms that might play a role in the degeneration of the nigrostriatal dopamine system, and factors contributing to its plasticity and response to injury will form the basis for developing of new improved therapeutic strategies for the human disorder.

Despite some very positive aspects of the MPTP model of parkinsonism in the monkey, there are some potential shortcomings that need to be kept in mind when working with this model. First, in the nonhuman primate, MPTP produces parkinsonism and not Parkinson's disease. This is not merely a semantics problem. MPTP administered to monkeys can result in a well-defined and highly reproducible motor disorder and loss of nigrostriatal dopamine neurons, but it does not reliably result in widespread destruction of locus coerulus or dorsal vagal pigmented neurons, or in the presence of Lewy bodies or cytoplasmic inclusions, except in very old animals (Forno *et al.*, 1986). Also, while human PD is characterized by extensive loss of the dopamine innervation of the putamen and somewhat less severe loss of caudate dopamine, the MPTP model in the monkey presents in the opposite manner (Pifl *et al.*, 1988); that is, most studies to date have shown a more severe dopamine depletion in the caudate nucleus in the MPTP monkey than in the putamen. PD is considered to be a slowly progressing degenerative disorder with what is believed to be an extended preclinical phase, during which time there is extensive depletion of nigrostriatal dopamine but adequate neurochemical compensatory mechanisms that enable the motor system to function normally. MPTP-induced parkinsonism as produced in monkeys does not model this disease process, since the damage to the CNS and the ensuing motor deficits develop over the course of days rather than months or years.

Parkinson's disease is also known to have a definite cognitive component. Due to severe motor disability, cognitive deficits are not easily observed in monkeys with MPTP-induced parkinsonism. Patients with PD can present with a number of mental status changes over the course of their disease (Levin *et al.*, 1989). While dementia has been described in PD patients, deficits in cognitive functioning can be more subtle than and independent of a generalized dementing disorder. Patients with early PD (less than 2 years duration) and with minimal motor symptomatology have been shown to perform worse than normal age-matched controls on selected frontal lobe tasks, such as the Wisconsin Card Sort (Levin *et al.*, 1989). Early PD patients have also been reported to experience difficulty in extracting relevant information from complex embedded material, suggesting that such patients cannot focus on salient stimuli and ignore irrelevant or competing information (Levin *et al.*, 1989). This concept of a disorder of attention or switching of attention is further supported by a recent study of early PD patients in which it was shown that such patients were more prone to producing task performance errors in the presence of a distractor than were normal controls (Sharpe, 1990). Increased distractibility was independent of mood and intellectual status, and did not reflect a significant short-term memory deficit. Therefore, there may be a selective attention deficit in early PD patients that involves a defect in striatal mechanisms that allow the selection of relevant from irrelevant stimuli for processing and use in appropriate responses (Levin *et al.*, 1989; Sharpe, 1990). Other recent neuropsychological studies of PD patients also suggest that cognitive functions dependent upon the integrity of the frontal association cortex or frontal-striatal circuits are disrupted, whereas cognitive functions dependent upon the integrity of visual, parietal, and temporal association cortices are mostly intact (Taylor *et al.*, 1986).

3. CAN EXPOSURE TO MPTP REPRODUCE OTHER THAN MOTOR ASPECTS OF PARKINSONISM?

Since PD involves cognitive as well as motor disturbances, we were interested to see if cognitive aspects of the disorder could be reproduced with the MPTP model. This posed a significant problem because development of a parkinsonian movement disorder would make it impossible to study any potential cognitive disturbance in these animals.

In our first effort to attack this problem (Schneider et al., 1988), we trained monkeys to perform a relatively simple operant behavior in which they were required to hold down a bar for 1–3 sec to cause one of three buttons located above the bar to become illuminated. The monkey then had to release the bar and press the illuminated button within a specified time (1–2 sec) to receive the juice reward. All animals were overtrained on this task and performed in excess of the 90% criterion level. We then began to administer MPTP to these animals (0.15–0.33 mg/kg) while continuing to assess their task performance.

Interestingly, all animals in this study developed similar disruptions in task performance after receiving up to three MPTP injections but prior to the appearance of any gross motor deficits. Upon being placed in the testing chamber, animals would typically begin to perform the task in a normal fashion, but after only a few trials performance would cease. If the experimenter guided the monkey through the task for a few trials, responding could be reestablished for a few trials but performance would again cease. In the original publication describing this phenomenon, we suggested that perhaps the MPTP-induced lesion caused a generalized attention deficit in these animals prior to the appearance of motor deficits. In the early post-MPTP period, these monkeys appeared more distractible than they had been prior to MPTP exposure, and this may have contributed to their failure to maintain task performance. More recently, we have discussed the similarities between the type of task impersistence described in these monkeys and motor or cognitive impersistence observed in children with attention deficit disorder (ADD) (Roeltgen and Schneider, 1991).

The distractibility and the restlessness of monkeys during task performance may be analogous to deficits in the sustaining of attention due to distracting hyperactive behaviors in ADD children. Increased distractibility and a disorder of attention, or in switching of attention, have also been described in early Parkinson's patients (Sharpe, 1990), as mentioned earlier. Perhaps the performance deficits in the MPTP-treated monkeys and cognitive deficits in Parkinson's patients may be explained by a dopamine-dependent defect in sensory information filtering, perhaps centered in the caudate nucleus.

Might there be a relationship between striatal dopamine depletion and certain types of cognitive disorders? Recently, Stern and colleagues (1990) have reported that people exposed to MPTP but asymptomatic for a parkinsonian movement disorder showed similar cognitive deficits as had been shown previously in PD patients and patients with MPTP-induced parkinsonism (Stern and Langston, 1985). Interestingly, all of the MPTP-asymptomatic patients had significantly reduced striatal dopaminergic function, as demonstrated by 6-fluorodopa PET scans (Stern et al., 1990). These results support the concept of a specific role of the nigrostriatal dopamine system in certain cognitive functions.

One problem with the prior monkey study performed in our laboratory (Schneider et al., 1988) was that all except one monkey went on to develop a parkinsonian motor disorder. Because of this, it was difficult to provide any possible link between specific neurochemical or neuropathological defects to the observed cognitive changes. Also, because of the nature of the task that was used in that study, it was difficult to assess whether the monkeys had specific "cognitive" disturbances in addition to the obvious impersistence or response maintenance problems.

4. COGNITIVE DEFICITS IN MOTOR ASYMPTOMATIC MONKEYS: THE CHRONIC LOW-DOSE MPTP MODEL

In response to the above-mentioned problems, a new set of primate studies have been performed (Schneider and Kovelowski, 1990). Since monkeys in the original study showed behavioral changes prior to the appearance of parkinsonian motor problems, it was felt that perhaps cognitive deficits in monkeys could be demonstrated if the MPTP-induced dopamine depletion could be kept subthreshold for the appearance of motor deficits. We have since developed a method of chronic low-dose MPTP administration in monkeys that produces specific cognitive impairments but does not produce gross motor impairment (Schneider and Kovelowski, 1990). This chronic low-dose MPTP model may serve as a model for "early" or preclinical parkinsonism. Since early PD patients seem to have difficulty in performing frontal-lobe-mediated tasks, since MPTP disrupts the nigrostriatal dopamine system (and particularly the dopamine innervation of the caudate nucleus), and since the frontal cortex sends a large projection to the caudate nucleus, we hypothesized that monkeys trained to perform both frontal and nonfrontal tasks would have specific impairments in the performance of the frontal-mediated tasks. The tasks that were chosen as tests of the integrity of the frontal-caudate axis were delayed response, delayed alternation, object retrieval, and discrimination reversal (Battig et al., 1960). Visual pattern discrimination was used as a task that is not disturbed by the disruption of frontal-striatal circuits (Divac et al., 1967). For example, delayed response and delayed alternation tasks are disrupted in monkeys and humans with frontal lobe lesions, as well as caudate nucleus lesions, and in Parkinson's disease and Alzheimer's disease patients (Battig et al., 1960; Freedman and Oscar-Berman, 1986). Object retrieval performance is impaired in monkeys with dorsolateral prefrontal cortex lesions, as well as in normal infant monkeys and humans (Diamond, 1990). Visual pattern discrimination, in contrast, is disturbed by lesions of the inferior temporal cortex or the tail of the caudate nucleus (Divac et al., 1967).

Four adult Macaca nemistrina monkeys were trained to perform the above-mentioned behavioral tasks in a modified Wisconsin General Test Apparatus. All animals were trained to a 90% criterion level on all tasks. Once the criterion level was reached, MPTP administration began. Immediately after a testing session, animals were administered MPTP (as the hydrochloride salt) intravenously two to three times per week, in doses beginning at 0.010 mg/kg and ranging up to 0.175 mg/kg. Cognitive testing continued daily and MPTP injections continued until cognitive deficits were observed, or in some animals continued even after the initial onset of performance deficits. Data referred to as "post-MPTP data" were obtained following the first appearance of cognitive decline, defined as two consecutive testing days with at least a 15% reduction in the number of correct responses as compared with pre-MPTP baseline performance. Motor behavior in the home cage and while seated in the restraining chair was observed and rated daily for all monkeys.

The number of MPTP injections and the total amount of MPTP administered varied

TABLE 1. Appearance of Deficits in Delayed Response and Delayed Alternation in Relation
to Duration and Amount of MPTP Administered

Monkey	Task disrupted	No. of MPTP injections	Dose (mg)	Period (days)
No. 8724	DA	18	4.70	38
	DR	20	5.79	45
No. 8727	DA	15	8.04	40
	DR	15	8.04	40
No. 8740	DA	14	8.13	37
	DR	20	13.89	51
No. 8742	DA	32	15.20	175
	DR	32	15.20	175

DA = delayed alteration; DR = delayed response.

from animal to animal but ranged from 4.7 mg administered over 38 days to 15.2 mg
administered over 175 days (Table 1). All monkeys tested eventually developed delayed
response and delayed alternation deficits, while visual pattern discrimination performance
remained intact in all animals (Fig. 1). Specifically, the four animals performed delayed
response, delayed alternation, and visual discrimination at 93.9%, 88.8%, and 93.9%
levels in the pre-MPTP period. Following chronic low-dose exposure to MPTP, delayed
response, delayed alternation, and visual discrimination performance were 69.7%,
67.2%, and 94.9%, respectively. Thus, the specific cognitive deficit was in the performance of frontal-mediated tasks and not the nonfrontal visual discrimination task.

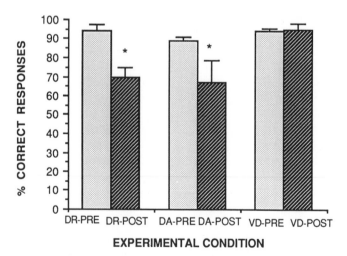

FIGURE 1. Cognitive performance deficit in monkeys following MPTP exposure. Graphs represent means
and standard deviations for four monkeys tested on delayed response (DR), delayed alternation (DA), and visual
discrimination (VD) task performance. The graphs show that, while all animals performed these tasks well in the
pre-MPTP condition, DR and DA task performance was significantly impaired in the post-MPTP condition. The
asterisk denotes significance at the 0.001 level on a one-factor repeated measures ANOVA. No impairment in
VD performance was apparent at any time in the post-MPTP condition.

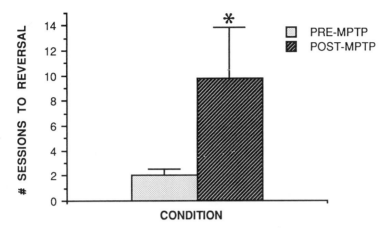

FIGURE 2. Performance of discrimination reversal by monkeys when normal (Pre) and following chronic exposure to low doses of MPTP (Post). Note that animals took significantly longer to learn the reversal after chronic MPTP exposure (Student's t test, $p < 0.001$).

In addition to the above-mentioned cognitive deficits, animals exposed to low doses of MPTP over an extended period of time displayed other behavioral alterations. Overall, these animals showed an increased irritability, increased restlessness (particularly during task performance), decreased attention to tasks (particularly to frontal lobe tasks), increased distractibility during task performance, increased hesitation to respond (particularly to delayed response or delayed alternation trials), and an increased frustration at their inability to correctly perform delayed response and delayed alternation tasks. While animals all showed relatively normal performance on visual discrimination trials, when tested on a discrimination reversal task they performed significantly worse than they had prior to chronic MPTP exposure. In discrimination reversal, the animals are trained to respond to a positive stimulus regardless of position. Once that response is performed at a 90% criterion level, the positive stimulus is switched so that a previously unreinforced stimulus is now the positive stimulus for the discrimination. The number of test sessions required for the animal to again reach a 90% criterion level following the reversal is recorded. Prior to MPTP exposure, animals successfully performed the reversal in approximately two test sessions. However, following chronic MPTP exposure, it took the same animals an average of 10 sessions in order to successfully complete the discrimination reversal (Fig. 2). Deficits on such discrimination reversal tasks are also considered to reflect a disruption of prefrontal cortex function or again, the frontal-striatal axis (Goldman and Rosvold, 1972).

Some of the animals exposed to low doses of MPTP have also been tested on their ability to perform an object retrieval task. Object retrieval has been shown by others to be a sensitive task for detecting frontal-lobe dysfunction (Diamond, 1990). Briefly, animals were trained to reach into a transparent box, open only on one side, to retrieve a food reward (a raisin). The position of the food within the box (front, center, or back) and the location of the open side of the box (front, left, right, or back) were varied throughout the testing session. Normal animals quickly learned to reach into the open side of the box, regardless of its position, and had no difficulty in retrieving the food, again regardless of its position within the box. However, after chronic exposure to low doses of MPTP, monkeys had a great deal of difficulty reaching into the box and successfully retrieving the

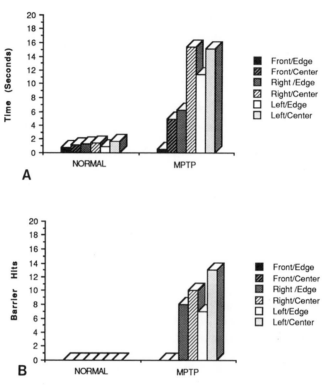

FIGURE 3. Object retrieval performance by chronic MPTP-treated monkeys. (A) Normal monkey could retrieve reward (raisin) quickly regardless of the position of the opening of the box or of the location of the raisin within the box. After MPTP exposure, the monkey retrieved the reward quickly only when the open side of the box was facing him and the raisin was at the edge of the box. The long retrieval times obtained when the opening of the box was facing left or right were due a combination of hesitation on the part of the monkey and the performance of numerous "barrier hits." (B) A "barrier hit" is when the monkey reaches for the closed side of the box (facing him) when the open side of the box is either facing left or right. After the task was learned, normal monkeys made no "barrier hits." In contrast, the chronic MPTP monkey made numerous "barrier hits." Legend: ex. Front/edge refers to the position of open side of box/position of reward inside the box.

food if the opening of the box was not placed directly in front of them. The animals could clearly see the reward in the box and in fact could see the experimenter placing the reward in the box, yet if the open side of the box was facing left, right, or back, they would hit their hand against the closed side of the box facing them. This type of error in task performance was called a "barrier hit" (Fig. 3). In many instances, after making these "barrier hits," the monkeys were unable to make a detour movement to get their hand into the open side of the box that was facing away from them. A peculiar response pattern of monkeys with chronic MPTP exposure was to approach the box, make some "barrier hits," not make a detour movement and collect the reward, and then give up and walk to the back of the cage. On successive trials, the amount of task persistence would generally decrease. From their position at the back of the cage, the monkeys would observe the presentation of the task and after several trials would no longer venture to the front of the cage to attempt a response if they could not clearly see the open side of the box facing them. Similar dysfunctions in object retrieval performance have been reported in infant monkeys and humans, and in frontal-lobe-lesioned adult monkeys (Diamond, 1990). Object retrieval deficits have also recently been reported in monkeys treated 8–12 months earlier with MPTP, but that were asymptomatic for a parkinsonian motor disorder at the time of cognitive testing (Taylor et al., 1990). The deficits on object retrieval performance, particularly in our animals that were exposed to low doses of MPTP over an extended period of time, may be analogous to deficits in planning, organizing, and switching response strategies suggested in certain frontal lobe patients and in children with attention deficit disorder (Roeltgen and Schneider, 1991).

During the course of object retrieval testing in the chronic MPTP monkeys, we noticed that task impersistence was a considerable problem for these animals. The impersistence and lack of interest in pursuing a difficult task was a behavior that we had seen previously while testing animals on an operant behavior (Schneider et al., 1988) and on frontal-lobe tasks (Schneider and Kovelowski, 1990). As described earlier, animals exposed to MPTP but not yet parkinsonian showed a distinct problem in response maintenance during operant task performance. Animals with chronic low-dose MPTP treatment often showed a lack of interest in pursuing delayed response and delayed alternation trials, particularly after they had made a number of response errors on these tasks. Cognitive and motor impersistence has also been described in children with attention deficit disorder (Voeller et al., 1989) and in patients with striatal lesions (Roeltgen et al., 1989). In view of the striking impersistence displayed by these animals in a number of different situations, we decided to directly assess and measure task persistence.

The apparatus used to test task persistence was similar to that used for object retrieval. Monkeys were presented with a clear lucite box in which a raisin was placed by the experimenter. On some trials, the monkey would be presented with the box, with an open side facing him, and he would be able to easily reach into the box and retrieve the raisin. These are referred to as reinforced trials. Other trials, which randomly occurred between the previously described reinforced trials, were unreinforced trials, in which a lucite block was attached to the opening of the box so that it was impossible for the monkey to retrieve the raisin. The amount of time spent on the task and the number of reaches or attempts made for the raisin were recorded on both reinforced and unreinforced trials. Analysis of the data has shown that on performance of unreinforced trials, monkeys that had received chronic low-dose MPTP exposure spent significantly less time on the task than did normal monkeys and made significantly fewer attempts at obtaining the raisin than did normal monkeys. The chronic low-dose MPTP monkeys were not significantly different from normal monkeys in the number of attempts they made to retrieve the reward on reinforced trials but were slower than normal monkeys in performing these trials (Fig. 4).

A number of pharmacological studies have been begun with monkeys exposed to chronic low-dose MPTP in an effort to provide additional information concerning the physiological bases of their specific behavioral problems. The dopamine D2 receptor agonist LY-171555 was used in doses of 0.01–0.25 mg/kg. At higher doses, the monkeys became hyperactive and appeared to have increased difficulty attending to and performing any of the tasks. However, at lower doses, the D2 agonist appeared to increase attention to the tasks, to reduce irritability and aggressiveness, and to dramatically improve the animals' task persistance; that is, at times when animals showed a large number of "no response errors," due to impersistence on the delayed response task, we found that these animals were able to complete this task after D2 agonist administration (Fig. 5). Interestingly, when impersistence was apparently overcome by administration of the D2

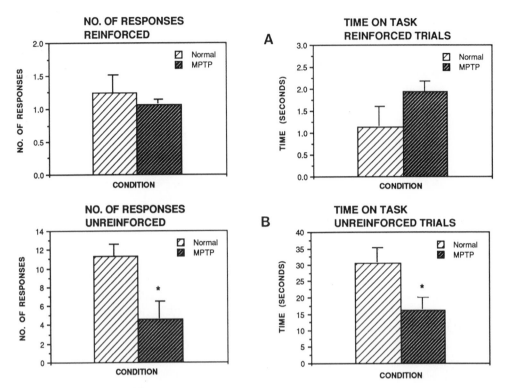

FIGURE 4. On our specific test of impersistence, chronic MPTP animals were no different from normals in the number of responses made on (A) reinforced trials (where the monkey had access to the reward) but had significantly decreased responses to (B) unreinforced trials (where monkey could not get the reward). MPTP monkeys also took slightly longer than normals to retrieve the reward on reinforced trials and spent significantly less time attempting to get the reward on unreinforced trials.

agonist, performance on the delayed response task was still disturbed (i.e., animals completed the task but still made many errors). Interestingly, a similar phenomenon has been observed in children with attention deficit disorder (a cognitive disorder that may be due to alterations in striatal neurochemistry) (Lau *et al.,* 1984) when given stimulant medication. Although the children showed an increase in on-task performance, their accuracy on difficult school-related tasks did not usually show improvement. This might imply that there may be a dissociation between task persistence and the ability to correctly perform different cognitive tasks and that these functions may be mediated by different neurochemical systems.

The D1 receptor agonist SKF-38393 has been tested in chronic low-dose MPTP monkeys in doses ranging from 0.05 to 10.0 mg/kg. This drug has thus far had no beneficial effects on any of the behaviors and, in fact, tended to decrease performance slightly on all tasks assessed. It is interesting to note that in at least one study in primates, SKF-38393 has been suggested to act as a D1 receptor antagonist rather than an agonist (Boyce *et al.,* 1990). Clonidine, an alpha-2 adrenergic agonist, has also been tested in doses ranging from 0.01 to 0.03 mg/kg. Clonidine appeared to have no effect on reversing task impersistence, but if the animals were persistent, clonidine increased delayed response performance by an average of 23% in two animals tested. These preliminary

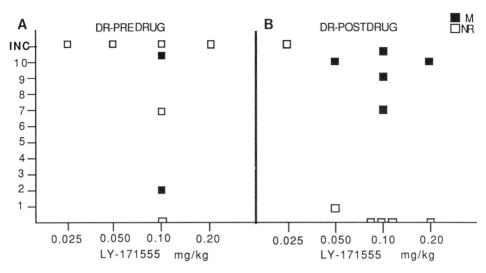

FIGURE 5. Delayed response performance by a monkey treated with chronic low-dose MPTP before and after different doses of D2 agonist (LY-171555). In the predrug condition (A), the monkey made many no-response (NR) errors and often could not complete all trials in a session. After performance of the predrug session, the monkey was administered a dose of LY-171555 (i.m.) and retested (B). At doses of 0.05–0.20 mg/kg, the D2 agonist decreased the number of no-response errors made and allowed the animal to complete the session. However, now that the animal was able to complete the session, more mistakes (M) were made. Thus, the D2 agonist improved task persistence but did not correct the underlying cognitive deficit.

results suggest that the behavioral disorder produced by chronic MPTP treatment may be reversed to some extent by pharmacological treatments. What is interesting is that drugs acting on different receptors at different brain sites had different effects on the behavior. The dopamine D2 agonist, which had beneficial effects on motor persistence, might have been acting at the striatal level, where there is an abundance of D2 receptors. The effects of specific and partial D1 agonists and antagonists need to be more carefully assessed. On the other hand, activation of alpha-2 receptors, predominently in the cortex (Arnsten and Goldman-Rakic, 1985), may be important, at least for the correct expression of delayed response-type behaviors. The combination of behavioral and pharmacological data may eventually give important clues as to the anatomical localization of certain behaviors and insights into pharmacological therapies that may be effective in correcting certain aspects of catecholamine-dependent behavioral disorders.

Preliminary pharmacological studies have also been performed on chronic low-dose MPTP-treated animals and normal animals during performance of the persistence task. After administration of a D2 agonist (LY-171555, 0.10 mg/kg), the chronic MPTP animals spent significantly more time on tasks and emitted significantly more responses on unreinforced trials than they did prior to drug administration (Fig. 6). After administration of the D2 agonist, the performance of the MPTP monkeys was not significantly different from the performance of nondrugged normal monkeys. Interestingly, normal monkeys given the D2 agonist performed poorer on unreinforced trials than they did prior to drug administration. In contrast to the changes observed with the D2 agonist, one MPTP animal treated with the alpha-2 agonist clonidine showed no change in persistence.

The responses to the D2 agonists in both the chronic MPTP and normal control

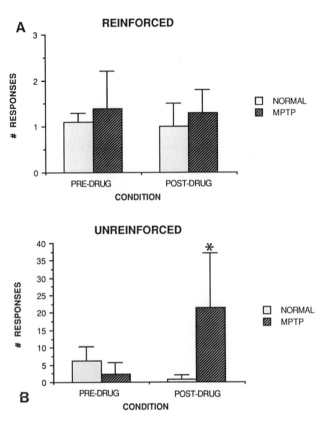

FIGURE 6. Impersistence testing in normal and chronic MPTP monkeys, with and without LY-171555 (D2 agonist, 0.10 mg/kg, i.m.). (A) On reinforced trials (i.e., monkey can get reward), there was no difference between normal and MPTP monkeys in terms of the number of responses (i.e., reaches) made to obtain a reward. The D2 agonist also had no effect on this parameter. (B) On unreinforced trials (i.e., monkey cannot get reward), normal animals were more persistent (i.e., made more reaches) than MPTP monkeys ($p < 0.001$). The D2 agonist made normal monkeys less persistent than they had been without the drug and made the MPTP monkeys more persistent.

animals are of considerable interest. It would appear from most studies, although it is controversial, that normal human subjects do not show increased on-task performance or improved performance when given stimulant medication (Johnston, 1986; Mesulam, 1985). The chronic MPTP monkeys appear to respond to the D2 agonist by increased attention to the task. Normal subjects are most probably already performing at their maximum level, and stimulant medications cannot improve their performance (and may actually impair performance). Similarly the normal monkey used in the pilot experiment had already performed six previous sets of trials (over a 3 week period) on the persistence task, and may have had an opportunity to learn that there would be no reinforcement on "unreinforced trials." Consequently, the D2 agonist, which may have some stimulant effect and positive effects on attention and persistence when there is a dopamine defect, had no positive effect on performance.

5. THE NEUROCHEMISTRY OF CHRONIC LOW-DOSE MPTP EXPOSURE

The monkeys used in the study of the effects of chronic low-dose MPTP exposure have been sacrificed and neurochemical analyses have been performed on selected cortical and subcortical brain regions (Schneider, 1990). Levels of dopamine, norepinephrine, serotonin, and their major metabolites were assessed in the frontal pole, dorsal lateral prefrontal cortex, orbitofrontal cortex, arcuate cortex, and inferotemporal cortex. Despite the behavioral deficts that suggested frontal-lobe disturbance, dopamine levels were not significantly altered in the dorsal lateral prefrontal cortex or other frontal cortical regions in these animals. This was somewhat surprising, since it had been previously shown that cognitive deficits similar to those observed in our study (particularly the delayed response deficit) had been caused by regional depletion of dopamine in the prefrontal cortex in rhesus monkeys (Brozoski *et al.*, 1979). While cortical dopamine depletions were unremarkable, cortical norepinephrine (NE) levels were decreased somewhat in some regions sampled in three of four monkeys studied. Frontal pole and dorsolateral prefrontal cortex NE was decreased by 14–69% and 36–76%, respectively, in some animals. Orbital and arcuate cortices had NE decreases of 25–74% and 9–73%, respectively. Cortical serotonin levels were within normal ranges in all areas in all monkeys.

Compared with mean values obtained from normal control animals, all four of the chronic low-dose MPTP animals had a profound loss of dopamine in the caudate and putamen regions sampled. Within the striatum, there appeared to be greatest loss of dopamine in the dorsal lateral caudate, slightly less loss in the dorsal medial caudate, and a relatively small loss of dopamine in the nucleus accumbens. The mean percent decrease in dopamine level in the dorsal lateral caudate was 97.9% (±2.0), with a range between 95.3% and 99.7%. Dopamine had a mean 93.7% (±6.5) decrease in the dorsal medial caudate, with a range between 84% and 97.9%. In comparison, the loss of dopamine in the putamen was less severe, with a mean decrease of 89.1% (±6.5) and a range of 81–96.8%. In the nucleus accumbens, the dopamine loss was not as severe as in the dorsal striatum (mean 41% decrease (±11.1), range 29.7–54.5%). Norepinephrine levels were also reduced in the dorsal medial caudate (mean 93% decrease, ±6) and the dorsal lateral caudate (mean 79% decrease, ±21), but not in the putamen or nucleus accumbens.

Levels of the dopamine metabolites DOPAC and HVA were also markedly reduced in the dorsal striatum, and reductions in levels of these metabolites broadly followed the pattern of DPM loss. DOPAC levels in the dorsal lateral caudate, dorsal medial caudate, and putamen were reduced a mean 95.1% (±3.7), 88.2% (±4.9), and 80.8% (±9.9), respectively, while mean DOPAC levels in the nucleus accumbens were only reduced 61% (±11). HVA levels in the dorsal lateral caudate, dorsal medial caudate, and putamen were decreased an average of 93.6% (±2.7), 91.6% (±1.6), and 80.6% (±11.4), respectively. Again, HVA levels in the nucleus accumbens were less markedly reduced (mean 74.2%, ±6.0) than those in dorsal striatal structures.

In contrast to the severe depletions of dopamine in the dorsal striatum, the levels of serotonin (5-HT) were increased above normal values to some extent in all striatal regions. Serotonin in the dorsal medial caudate was increased an average 271% (±136, range: 129–399%), while the dorsal lateral caudate showed a mean increase of 292% (±86, range: 239–420%). Three out of four animals had a mean putamen 5-HT increase of 238% (±8), while one monkey had an excessively large 1441% increase. Even nucleus accumbens 5-HT levels were slightly increased above normal (mean 171%, ±19). The possible functional significance of this increased serotonin is presently unclear.

The most severe and consistent neurochemical changes observed in these animals occurred within the striatum, and particularly within the caudate nucleus. It seems likely then that the cognitive difficulties experienced by these animals may have been due, at least in part, to the severe depletion of striatal dopamine, particularly within the dorsal lateral region of the caudate nucleus. The dorsal lateral caudate nucleus of the monkey receives inputs primarily from dorsal lateral prefrontal cortex, posterior parietal cortex, and the arcuate premotor area, and sends its output back to the dorsal lateral prefrontal cortex, via the medial dorsal thalamus (Alexander *et al.*, 1986). Dysfunction of this corticostriatothalamocortical system due to the massive loss of dopamine within the dorsal lateral caudate could have disrupted functions that rely upon the integrity of this particular segment of the basal ganglia thalamocortical circuit. Thus, while the behavioral deficit was phenomenologically similar to that seen in monkeys with frontal-lobe damage or with frontal-lobe catecholamine depletion, the major neurochemical deficit, and perhaps the locus of the disrupted function, was in the striatum rather than in the cortex. Thus, neurochemical inactivation of the dorsal lateral caudate might have resulted in disruption of tasks mediated via prefrontal cortex-dorsal lateral caudate circuits. The possible disturbance of noradrenergic systems in both the striatum and the cortex may have also contributed to the overall syndrome.

The neuropathology of chronic low-dose MPTP exposure was found to be remarkably similar to the neuropathology observed in monkeys made overtly parkinsonian from MPTP exposure (Schneider, 1990). All animals had extensive loss of substantia nigra pars compacta (SNc) neurons, particularly in the central and ventral regions of the nucleus, and partial sparing of dopaminergic neurons in the dorsal tier of the SN rostrally, and in the retrorubral area and SN pars lateralis caudally. There was also partial sparing of dopaminergic neurons in the ventral tegmental area and in the most ventral medial aspects of the SN.

6. SUMMARY

Administration of MPTP to nonhuman primates can result in a parkinsonian movement disorder that bears striking resemblance to human PD. However, by administering MPTP in low doses (subthreshold for producing motor effects) over an extended period of time, it is possible to produce an animal that motorically appears normal but that has distinct cognitive and behavioral disturbances. The tremendous plasticity within the dopamine system and its capacity to compensate for large losses of transmitter may lead to the mistaken conclusion that if the animal moves normally then it is a normal animal. This conclusion does not stand true in the nonhuman primate or in the human with dopamine-depleting lesions. People with known subthreshold MPTP exposure have distinct cognitive problems and massive loss of striatal dopamine despite apparently normal motor function. Whether these people will develop motor symptoms of parkinsonism with advancing age and continued loss of the nigrostriatal dopamine system remains to be seen. Whether monkeys exposed to low doses of MPTP would develop motor problems with advanced age also remains an unanswered question. Exposure to low doses of MPTP or other neurotoxins like it may result in subtle behavioral deficits that may eventually progress to more global functional problems. The prevalence and consequences of such toxin exposures are certainly topics for further study.

REFERENCES

Alexander, G.E., DeLong, M.R., and Strick, P.L., 1986, Parallel organization of functionally segregated circuits linking basal ganglia and cortex, *Ann. Rev. Neurosci.* 9:357–381.

Arnsten, A.F.T., and Goldman-Rakic, P.S., 1985, Alpha-2 adrenergic mechanisms in prefrontal cortex associated with cognitive decline in aged non-human primates, *Science* 230:1273–1276.

Ballard, P.A., Tetrud, J.W., and Langston, J.W., 1985, Permanent human parkinsonism due to 1-methyl-4-phenyl-1,2,3,6-tetrahydropyridine (MPTP): Seven cases, *Neurology* 35:949–956.

Battig, K., Rosvold, H.E., and Mishkin, M., 1960, Comparison of the effects of frontal and caudate lesions on delayed response and alternation in monkeys, *J. Comp. Psychol.* 53:400–404.

Boyce, S., Rupniak, N.M.J., Steventon, M.J., and Iversen, S.D., 1990, Differential effects of D1 and D2 agonists in MPTP-treated primates: Functional implications for Parkinson's disease, *Neurology* 40:927–933.

Brozoski, T., Brown, R.M., Rosvold, H.E., and Goldman, P.S., 1979, Cognitive deficit caused by regional depletion of dopamine in prefrontal cortex of rhesus monkey, *Science* 205:929–931.

Burns, R.S., Chiueh, C., Markey, S.P., Ebert, M.H., Jacobowitz, D.M., and Kopin, I.J., 1983, A primate model of parkinsonism: Selective destruction of dopaminergic neurons in the pars compacta substantia nigra by MPTP, *Proc. Natl. Acad. Sci USA* 80:4546–4550.

Clarke, C.E., Sandbrook, M.A., Mitchell, I.J., and Crossman, A.R., 1987, Levodopa-induced dyskinesia and response fluctuations in primates rendered parkinsonian with 1-methyl-4-phenyl,1,2,3,6-tetrahydropyridine (MPTP), *J. Neurol. Sci.,* 78:273–280.

Davis, G.C., Williams, A.C., Markey, S.P., Ebert, M.H., Caine, E.D., Reichert, C.M., and Kopin, I.J., 1979, Chronic parkinsonism secondary to intravenous injection of meperidine analogues, *Psychiat. Res.* 1:249–254.

Diamond, A., 1990, Developmental time course in human and infant monkeys, and the neural bases of, inhibitory control in reaching, in: *The Development and Neurol Bases of Higher Cognitive Functions* Volume 608, Annals of the New York Academy of Sciences (A. Diamond, ed.), The New York Academy of Sciences, New York, pp. 637–677.

Divac, I., Rosvold, H.E., and Szarcbart, M.K., 1967, Behavioral effects of selective ablation of the caudate nucleus, *J. Comp. Physiol. Psychol.* 63:184–190.

Forno, L.S., 1982, Pathology of Parkinson's disease, in: *Movements Disorders* (C.D. Marsden and S. Fahn, eds.), Butterworth, London, pp. 25–40.

Forno, L.S., 1986, The Lewy body in Parkinson's disease, in: *Advances in Neurology,* Volume 45 (M.D. Yahr and K.J. Bergmann, eds.), Raven Press, New York, pp. 35–50.

Forno, L.S., Langston, J.W., DeLanney, L.E., Irwin, I., and Ricaurte, G.A., 1986, Locus ceruleus lesions and eospinophilic inclusions in MPTP-treated monkeys, *Ann. Neurol.* 20:449–455.

Freedman, M., and Oscar-Berman, M., 1986, Selective delayed response deficits in Parkinson's and Alzheimer's disease, *Arch. Neurol.* 43:886–890.

German, D.C., Manaye, K., Smith, W.K., Woodward, D.J., and Saper, C.B., 1989, Midbrain dopaminergic cell loss in Parkinson's disease: Computer visualization, *Ann. Neurol.* 26:507–514.

Goldman, P.S., and Rosvold, H.E., 1972, The effects of selective caudate lesions in juvenile rhesus monkeys, *Brain Res.* 43:53–66.

Hornykiewicz, O., and Kish, S.J., 1986, Biochemical pathophysiology of Parkinson's disease, in: *Advances in Neurology,* Volume 45 (M.D. Yahr, and K.J. Bergmann, eds.), Raven Press, New York, pp. 19–34.

Jellinger, K., 1986, Overview of morphological changes in Parkinson's disease, in: *Advances in Neurology,* Volume 45 (M.D. Yahr, and K.J. Bergmann, eds.), Raven Press, New York, pp. 1–18.

Johnston, C.W., 1986, The neuropsychological evaluation of attention deficit disorder, *Psychiatr. Ann.* 16:47–51.

Langston, J.W., Ballard, P., Tetrud, J.W., and Irwin, I., 1983, Chronic parkinsonism in humans due a product of medperidine-analogue synthesis, *Science* 219:979–980.

Langston, J.W., Irwin, I., and Ricaurte, G.A., 1987, Neurotoxins, parkinsonism and Parkinson's disease, *Pharmac. Ther.* 32:19–49.

Lau, H.C., Henricksen, L., and Bruhn, P., 1984, Focal cerebral hypoperfusion in children with dysphasia and/or attention deficit disorder, *Arch. Neurol.* 41:825–829.

Levin, B.E., Llabre, N.M., and Weiner, W.J., 1989, Cognitive impairments associated with early Parkinson's disease, *Neurology* 39:557–561.

Mesulam, M.M., 1985, *Principles of Behavioral Neurology,* F.A. Davis, Philadelphia, p. 29.

Pifl, Ch., Schingnitz, G., and Hornykiewicz, O., 1988, The neurotoxin MPTP does not produce in the rhesus monkey, the interregional pattern of striatal dopamine loss typical of human idiopathic Parkinson's disease, *Neurosci. Lett.* 92:228–233.

Roeltgen, M.G., Roeltgen, D.P., and Heilman, K.M., 1989, Unilateral motor impersistence and hemispatial neglect from a right striatal lesion, *Neuropsychol. Neuropsychiatry Behav. Neurol.* 2:125–135.

Roeltgen, D.P., and Schneider, J.S., 1991, Chronic low-dose MPTP in non-human primates: A possible model for attention deficit disorder, *J. Child Neurol.* 6:582–589.

Schneider, J.S., 1990, Chronic exposure to low doses of MPTP. II. Neurochemical and pathological consequences in cognitively-impaired, motor asymptomatic monkeys, *Brain Res.* 534:25–36.

Schneider, J.S., and Kovelowski, C.J., 1990, Chronic exposure to low doses of MPTP. I. Cognitive deficits in motor asymptomatic monkeys, *Brain Res.* 519:122–128.

Schneider, J.S., Yuwiler, A., and Markham, C.H., 1986, Production of a Parkinson-like syndrome in the cat with N-methyl-4-phenyl-1,2,3,6-tetrahydropyridine (MPTP): Behavior, histology, and biochemistry, *Exp. Neurol.* 91:293–307.

Schneider, J.S., Yuwiler, A., and Markham, C.H., 1987, Selective loss of subpopulations of ventral metencephalic dopaminergic neurons in the monkey following exposure to MPTP, *Brain Res.* 411:144–150.

Schneider, J.S., Unguez, G., Yuwiler, A., Berg, S.C., and Markham, C.H., 1988, Deficits in operant behavior in monkeys treated with N-methyl-4-phenyl-1,2,3,6-tetrahydropyridine (MPTP), *Brain* 111:1265–1285.

Sharpe, M.H., 1990, Distractibility in early Parkinson's disease, *Cortex* 26:239–246.

Stern, Y., and Langston, J.W., 1985, Intellectual changes in patients with MPTP-induced parkinsonism, *Neurology* 35:1506–1509.

Stern, Y., Tetrud, J.W., Martin, W.R.W., Kutner, S.J., and Langston, J.W., 1990, Cognitive change following MPTP exposure, *Neurology* 40:261–264.

Taylor, A.E., Saint-Cyr, J.A., and Lang, A.E., 1986, Frontal lobe dysfunction in Parkinson's disease, *Brain* 109:345–383.

Voeller, K.K.S., Alexander, A.W., Carter, R.L., and Heilman, K.M., 1989, Motor impersistence in children with attention deficit hyperactivity disorder decreases in response to treatment with methylphenidate, *Neurology* 39 (Suppl 1): 276.

Wilson, J.S., and Wilson, J.A. 1986, Intracellular recordings in the caudate nucleus of normal and MPTP treated dogs, in: *MPTP: A Neurotoxin Producing a Parkinsonian Syndrome* (S.P. Markey, N. Castagnoli, A.J. Trevor, and I.J. Kopin, eds.), Academic Press, Orlando, pp. 695–699.

Zamir, N., Skofitsch, G., Bannen, N.J., Helke, C.J., Kopin, I.J., and Jacobowitz, D.M., 1984, Primate model of Parkinson's disease: Alterations in multiple opiod systems in the basal ganglia, *Brain Res.* 322:356–360.

Part IV

Legal Issues

Chapter 17

Courts, Agencies, and Social Risk Assessment*

Clayton P. Gillette and *James E. Krier*

1. INTRODUCTION

The recent development of new technologies in the health and medical areas has not occurred without cost. Progressive technologies to treat or prevent disease or discomfort may create new risks, even as they reduce risks attributed to "natural" conditions. Selective aversion to the manmade risks of advanced technologies can be counterproductive. A world with vaccines or pharmaceuticals is not perfectly safe, for example, but might be safer than a world without. The objective should not be to eliminate risk, but to reduce it to the minimum *overall* level by employing new technologies only when they promise to displace a greater amount of risk than they create.

Given the ubiquity of risk, the objective of risk minimization seems noncontroversial. The problem arises in choosing a structure of governance to decide which risks are worth taking or avoiding. Our current strategy is to integrate judicial decision making and regulatory procedures. The one permits parties injured or threatened by new technologies to obtain judicial redress if they were subjected to a risk deemed inappropriate under a legal standard of liability. The other requires potential risk producers to seek administrative approval prior to engaging in risky activity or to make production decisions constrained by government fiat. Recently, though, there have been attacks on the capacity of the judicial system to make accurate determinations of comparative risk. The argument is that the judicial system imposes too much liability on technologies and the humans who utilize them—physicians and entrepreneurs. The judicial system is said to cater to the

*This is a modified version of a longer essay by the authors, Risk, Courts, and Agencies, 138 U. Penn. L. Rev. 1027 (1990).

Clayton P. Gillette • University of Virginia School of Law, Charlottesville, Virginia 22908. *James E. Krier* • University of Michigan Law School, Ann Arbor, Michigan 48109.
The Vulnerable Brain and Environmental Risks, Volume 2: Toxins in Food, edited by Robert L. Isaacson and Karl F. Jensen. Plenum Press, New York, 1992.

misperceptions of lay juries, to irrational preferences for a larger amount of familiar risk over a lesser amount of unfamiliar risk, to sympathy for injured victims, and to the venality of plaintiffs' attorneys—the result being that the social quantum of risk is greater than it ought to be. The proposed remedy is often to deny courts a role in the process of risk assessment and management, and to defer instead to the expertise of administrative agencies. In this essay, we seek to examine the propriety of both the attack and the suggested solution. Our conclusion is that the case against the courts is hardly as clear as the advocates of agencies suggest. They have not carried the burden that we imagine must be satisfied before embarking on radical institutional change.

2. RISK AND MARKETS

Selecting among potential risk-management systems assumes that some regulatory mechanism is necessary, that we would encounter an unacceptable level of risk if we simply left risk creators unfettered. It is worthwhile to consider why we begin with that assumption, since the circumstances that render regulation necessary may also tell us something about the best regulatory mechanism.

Risk producers, generally firms presumed to act in rational, profit-maximizing ways, are likely to improve the safety of their technologies only when it is in their self-interest to do so. While altruistic decisions to reduce risk are theoretically possible, we do not think of them as the norm. That altruism would be necessary is clear from the observation that risk reduction typically imposes costs on the risk producer; unless that cost is offset by some greater liability that the producer will incur should it fail to take risk-reduction measures, risk production will remain unnecessarily high. The reason is simple: If risk producers would have to expend resources to minimize risk, but can escape legal liability for failure to reduce risks, one would expect that risk-reduction measures will not be taken.

In some situations, concern for the profitability of the firm, coupled with the market for managers, might be sufficient to induce optimal investment in safety, even in the absence of legal inducements. Firms with a reputation for safety might enjoy a marketing advantage over their competition. But the characteristics of new technologies suggest that concern for reputation and profitability alone cannot be expected to reduce substantially the risks they create. These technologies often produce hazards that are latent (so their adverse effects do not materialize for long periods after exposure) and diffuse (so that large numbers of persons may suffer adverse effects that are individually small but are substantial in the aggregate). These characteristics, in turn, may skew decision making by risk producers. Risk producers may be unaware of the latent risks they pose; even if informed, they may discount the risky effects not only by the probability of their occur-rence, but also by the fact that any risks that materialize will do so only in the distant future. Thus, the firm's current reputation and profits are unlikely to be implicated by the materialization of risk. Consumers are similarly unlikely to decrease consumption of products whose adverse effects are perceived as minimal or are offset by immediate benefits. Where latency periods exceed 10–15 years, discounting effectively means ignor-ing the risk totally. Where liability is not a factor, so that even future earnings will not be affected by the present creation of risks, even omniscient investors and managers attentive to long-term prices of a firm's shares will have few incentives to investigate or consider adverse effects visited primarily on the public at large.

Internal decision-making processes of risk producers may further exacerbate the effects of latency. Decisions to address even known long-term risks usually require the risk producer to incur short-run costs. The benefits of the decision, however, usually will materialize only in the future, if at all. Managers acting out of self-interest are likely systematically to resolve this uncertainty against attending to potential risk. A self-interested concern with short-term profits makes it unlikely that managers will dedicate corporate resources to discover (much less avoid) risks whose costs will only be reflected on a long-term balance sheet. If managers expose their companies to no liability when they fail to protect against risks that are unforeseeable, they have little incentive to overcome self-interested motivations towards underinvestment in remote risks. The problem is particularly acute where the benefits of risk avoidance by a firm would simply result in the nonappearance of a problem, and there is no assurance that the problem would otherwise have materialized. Assume, for instance, a manager who has sufficient resources to invest in either of two ventures, but not in both. The first bears a .1 probability of increasing profits from sales of the company's product by $10 million. The second is expected (with the same probability) to avoid losses from injuries by $10 million. A desire for tangible indicia of success suggests that a self-interested manager would pursue the former venture. It is difficult for a manager who is looking to demonstrate the wisdom of his decisions to prove that he has generated a corporate benefit where the ultimate result is that nothing bad happened. The incentive to pursue tangible gains rather than to avoid ethereal losses may become greater as the relative certainty of the former increases, notwithstanding that the expected value of the two is the same. Assume in the above example, for instance, that if losses materialize they will approximate $100 million, but that there is only a 0.01 probability that they will occur at all. The manager now faces an even greater incentive to pursue the first strategy, because relatively certain demonstrable gains are more likely to enhance his reputation than is avoidance of less certain harms.

The corporate incentives associated with diffusion and latency would not be too great an obstacle to optimal risk avoidance where they not so closely linked to irreversibility once the risk materialized. Yet one of the most poignant characteristics of technological risks is the permanence of their effects. Irreversibility becomes a particular obstacle in the case, again linked to modern technology, of zero-infinity problems—those with a small probability (approaching zero) of ever materializing, but that generate catastrophic effects (approaching infinity) should they come to pass (Page, 1978). Yet, these features also engender systematic biases in favor of too little investment in safety. Accurate assessment of the probability of a risk and the expected harm it will cause may require investment of substantially greater resources than firms are willing to incur where indeterminate values (zero or infinity) are involved. These investments are difficult to justify given the common—if inappropriate—reaction that small chances are to be ignored, notwithstanding the magnitude of losses that would be generated by materialization. Further, risk producers, being optimistic and potentially reluctant to admit the adverse effects of their products, can be expected to underestimate both the probability and severity of those effects (Buchanan and Faith, 1981), particularly if they do not anticipate liability for the materialization of remote risks.

Thus, inducements for firms to invest in risk reduction must emerge from external sources that render potential losses more salient to risk producers. These inducements may take a variety of forms. In a market composed of informed purchasers who possess substantial choice and are willing to pay producers to incorporate cost-effective risk reduction, recalcitrant sellers would suffer a loss of profitable sales. In a perfect market for labor, employers who impose inefficient risks on knowledgeable employees would lose their best workers to more rational competitors or would pay excessive compensation to maintain the workforce. These markets, however, remain largely fictional baselines against which to measure the existing level of consumer and worker ignorance. Government regulation could impose substantial fines where regulators possessed sufficient information to devise standards for safety and to monitor their implementation. Indeed, regulation will be necessary where catastrophe looms large. No firm can be expected to protect against accidents with an expected cost that exceeds the value of the firm. Yet regulation cannot be relied on to address technological risks perfectly, since the same characteristics of latency and diffusion that reduce private incentives for risk reduction also cause an undersupply of interest groups to demand government regulation (Krier and Gillette, 1985).

3. RISK AND COURTS

Given the frailty of market correctives, legal liability has become largely a story of an alternative means for encouraging risk producers to employ risk-optimizing measures. Judicially imposed liability makes particular sense where those at risk do not reach informed, bargained relationships with risk producers. By requiring risk producers to internalize the costs of the risks they create, the adjudicative system seeks to make the self-interest of the producer coincide with the interest of society at large.

Complaints about legal liability stem primarily from claims about specific doctrines that threaten to impose substantial costs on risk producers whose activities, all would agree, generate net benefits, notwithstanding the harms they occasionally cause. Doctrines such as liability for unforeseeable injury, joint and several liability, relaxed burdens of proof regarding injury or causation, and damages for pain and suffering are considered by some to permit too much liability to be imposed too easily on manufacturers of vaccines, pesticides, or drugs, the absence of which would detract from the quality of life. Let us assume, for the moment, that these allegations are true, that legal doctrine imposes liability too readily and hence overdeters technological advances that, though they produce risk, are nevertheless risk reducing on balance. Might it still be the case that the liability system underdeters risk, that it fails to avoid losses worth avoiding?

That possibility would exist if an insufficient number of cases were actually brought to court. The biases of legal doctrine can only come into play once a case has been filed. If there are countervailing biases that prevent cases from reaching litigation in the first place, then the judicial system as a whole might well underdeter, rather than overdeter, risk. At first glance, the notion that individuals would fail to seek legal redress for injuries seems counterintuitive, and certainly contrary to the assumption with which we began above, that individuals seek to maximize their own utility. On reflection, however, it becomes apparent that even (especially) self-interested actors will frequently fail to pursue any recourse for injuries, especially where those injuries are of the type and arise from the behavior associated with new technologies.

Litigation is itself a scarce, and hence costly, commodity. Proceeding through the judicial system requires both time and financial resources. Obviously, even among the injured, only those who expect to reap judgments in excess of litigation costs will enter the adjudicative process. Where injuries are discrete, immediate, and readily cognizable, obstacles to recovery, such as proof of causation or defendant's negligence, may be relatively low. In these situations, those who suffer such injuries can be expected to bring actions. But expectations of recovery may be insufficient to induce an optimal level of litigation. Even where commenced to redress harm from a readily identifiable source, litigation creates public goods. Others who either use or produce the product that is the subject of litigation will benefit from the judgment and information that emerges during the first litigation, even though they made no contribution to that process. Thus litigants, even those who favor the same outcome (all plaintiffs as opposed to defendants), find themselves in a strategic relationship. Each will benefit if someone else files the initial suit. The temptation to free ride on the efforts of others, of course, induces even those litigants with positive expected recoveries to hold back in order to maximize the recovery in any action they ultimately bring (Landes and Posner, 1979).

Litigants who suffer harms from private risks are likely to overcome the incentive to free ride for two reasons. First, the immediateness of the injury lowers the costs of identifying the injurer and thus reduces an obstacle to recovery that might otherwise generate the temptation to free ride. Second, the injury is likely to be sufficiently fact specific to limit the expected gains from free riding. Where the defendant's conduct places a limited number of people at risk (e.g., the standard slip-and-fall case) or the plaintiff's own conduct is a relevant datum in analyzing liability (e.g., users of power lawnmowers who suffer lacerations), the likelihood of finding others who suffered injuries in sufficiently similar circumstances to permit free riding is remote. Taken together, these characteristics of private risk litigation suggest that injured parties will anticipate that their expected recovery will not be increased by strategic delay while others litigate.

At the same time, defendants will be induced to save costs (avoid liability) by producing information that suggests alternative explanations for, or the reasonableness of, plaintiff's injuries. As all parties involved in the dispute have significant incentives to appear before the court and to explain what happened and the social consequences of the event, it is unlikely that parties affected by the outcome will be under-represented in the process. Because recoveries can be substantial, it is also unlikely that serious harms will go unredressed. Some accommodation of the public interest, therefore, is likely to be reflected by individual actors motivated by self-interest.

These features that elicit nearly optimal decisions in private risk litigation, however, function less forcefully in the case of the diffuse, uncertain harms that characterize technological risk. Indeed, here *both* disincentives to commence litigation—the uncertainty that the process will produce net benefits and the tendency to free ride—are large relative to the traditional, private risk counterpart. Uncertainty may initially affect the likelihood that a potential plaintiff will develop the injury, the risk of which gives rise to the claim. Unable to show a matured injury, individuals at risk cannot expect substantial recoveries. Even if they appear before sympathetic courts willing to permit recovery for injury suffered from the risk, damages may be discounted by the likelihood that the injury will materialize.* Consequently, the costs of litigation may be substantial enough to

---

*This has been the legal rule applied in some, but not all, relevant cases. Compare Ayers v. Township of Jackson, 189 N.J. 561, 461 A.2d 184 (Law Div. 1983), vacated on other grounds, 202 N.J. Super. 106, 493 A.2d 1314 (A.D. 1985); Jackson v. Johns-Manville Sales Corp., 727 F.2d 506 (5th Cir. 1984); Payton v. Abbott Laboratories, 386 Mass. 540, 437 N.E.2d 171 (1982) (no cause of action for being at risk); Herber v. Johns-Manville Sales Corp., 785 F.2d 79 (3d Cir. 1986); Adams v. Johns-Manville Sales Corp., 783 F.2d 589 (5th Cir. 1986). Cf. Metropolitan Edison Co. v. People Against Nuclear Energy, 460 U.S. 766 (1983) (Nuclear Regulatory Commission not required to consider psychological injury to residents from operation of nuclear power plant).

make prosecution inefficient from the victim's self-interested perspective, even if it would be socially desirable. Uncertainty may also reduce expected recoveries by increasing the costs of litigation. If courts require identification of a particular defendant whose activities placed the plaintiff at risk, litigation costs will escalate in cases that involve multiple defendants, only one of whom actually caused the injury to the plaintiff.

Simultaneously, incentives to free ride increase. Diffusion of an equivalent risk among large numbers of persons diminishes the incentive that any of them has to initiate the litigation. Since the risks are largely involuntary or passive, the conduct of individual plaintiffs may be irrelevant, so that the spillover effects of one decision into subsequent cases would be more substantial than in private risk litigation. The latency of numerous technological risks reduces the anticipated adverse effects of delay, as the potential victim may see little harm (and may anticipate a larger net recovery) in waiting to see if adverse effects actually become manifest.

Victims might overcome these effects if they could form a coalition, with each victim contributing to the collective effort. But the broad geographic dispersion of new technological risks means that communication among victims will be hampered. The fact that one victim who seeks redress from risk producers assists all those who have not contributed to the effort (for instance, by making discoveries of negligence in manufacture that other victims can subsequently utilize) means that there is less incentive to overcome the obstacles to coalition. Psychological factors further reduce the likelihood. Phenomena such as dissonance (Akerlof and Dickens, 1982) could push mightily against activities that would require us to recognize that we should regret our prior conduct. Failure to litigate, on the other hand, may be consistent with a self-perceived, if erroneous, low risk of injury in prior behavior. Only when confronted with the materialization of serious risk might potential litigants desire the cathartic effect of seeking "justice" through a legal forum.

Procedural devices, class actions in particular, may help to overcome these obstacles by giving one entrepreneur—the class-action attorney financed by a contingent-fee contract—enough expectation of personal gain to justify efforts to consolidate the diffuse group. Since the active assistance of class members would not be essential to prosecution, individual disincentives to participate—whether emerging from insufficiency of harm, dissonance, or a desire to free ride—would not preclude socially optimal levels of litigation. Indeed, if class-action attorneys can garner both large fees and personal publicity by prosecuting technological risk cases, their incentives to litigate may dramatically exceed the social optimum.

Yet, even if attorneys are motivated by avarice, the social consequences of their activity remain uncertain. Avarice means that class attorneys are likely to accept only those cases that return expected personal benefits in excess of personal costs (including opportunity costs); thus they will fail to litigate cases that would produce net social benefits, but inadequate personal rewards (Coffee, 1986). While expected damages for the class may be high in technological risk cases, the costs of prosecution are also likely to be great. The uncertainties of the substantive law concerning causation, standard of liability, defendant identification, and allocation among multiple defendants necessarily requires substantial discount of the likelihood of success. Unlike the readily identifiable product that causes injury in typical private-risk litigation, risks of new technologies tend to have sources whose identities remain mysterious—in that no one is sure who is producing the risk—or multifarious—in that so many risk producers create the same risk that no one can identify the producer of a particular injury.

Demonstrating the unreasonableness of the risk—a threshold to liability—is similarly likely to be expensive to establish, especially where defendants are exonerated for the "unforeseen consequences" of their conduct. Latency suggests that currently exposed harms do not represent the full range of compensable injuries. Thus, attorneys may be reluctant to bring cases for fear that subsequent discoveries will lead them to regret early attempts to litigate issues frustrated by problems of proof or low damages. While this disincentive may be somewhat mitigated by the desire to "stake a claim" in an early stage of a litigation campaign, its effects cannot be eliminated entirely. Even where success is assured, the attorney will weigh the result against personal, not social, benefits of recovery. Since the attorney is receiving only a percentage of damages as a fee, he will be unwilling to bring the action unless his expected fee exceeds personal costs. The discrepancy between personal and social break points may be quite dramatic. Thus, an attorney who expects to incur personal costs (including opportunity costs) of $500,000 will not take a case with an expected contingent fee award of 25% of recovery unless expected damages (i.e., damages alleged, discounted by the probability of success) exceed $2,000,000 (Coffee, 1986). Barring alternative mechanisms for overcoming the inertia that forestalls collective action by victims, the threat of litigation will fail to deter risk producers from creating undue technological risks unless the expected loss is sufficiently high to justify an attorney's involvement. The fee incentive even more dramatically reduces the possibility of obtaining injunctive or administrative relief for which contingent fees or statutory attorney fees will generally be unavailable.

Even an attorney who accepts a class action may engage in behavior that undersupplies litigation about technological risk. Since the class members are unlikely to possess the technical information or daily contact with the case necessary to monitor the attorney's conduct, the attorney faces few disincentives to skew results in favor of self-interest. Most obviously, an attorney may bring a claim in order to establish a stake in the litigation, but fail to prosecute vigorously, either because opportunity costs rise or because the attorney expects damages to increase in the interim. Alternatively, the attorney may settle the case for an amount that is artificially low, i.e., one that compensates the attorney's investment, but that is below the amount required fully to vindicate clients' interests. Since only the latter amount would induce risk producers to internalize the costs of the injuries they cause, litigation that generates smaller payments can be expected to reduce producer incentives to avoid excess risk.

Ironically, then, the judiciary's ineptitude in properly assessing the optimal level of risk is not necessarily rooted in excessive zeal to restrict risk producers. Indeed, if we are correct, the underdeterrence of risk litigation—born of biases that limit access to courts—is equally problematic (although it is conceivable that courts are too harsh on those risks that they *do* address).* The appropriate concern, therefore, is institutional incapacity to impose sufficient constraints on the creation of technological risks. The characteristics of these risks—latency, diffusion, irreversibility, low probability of catastrophe—that render judicial assessment suspect are endemic to the problem, not to the adjudicative solution. The inadequacy of courts to address these issues does not lie solely in biases between old and new risks, or in a ruthless plaintiffs' bar. Rather, the difficulty lies in judicial inability to overcome structural biases. If judicial failure is due to institutional incapacity rather

---

*The imposition of a stringent penalty on producers of risks that courts do address is not necessarily evidence that courts are too harsh. If courts are aware that litigation emerging from risks is undersupplied, they might increase the penalties for risks that are addressed in order to keep the expected costs faced by risk producers (costs imposed discounted by the probability of being found liable) closer to the optimal level.

than to idiosyncratic biases, then a mere shift in forum will not necessarily produce more appropriate risk decisions. Any alternative forum must also be examined for similar disabilities. That being the case, the more difficult issue becomes how, in the technological risk context, any forum can provide appropriate incentives for risk reduction.

The relationship between social risk and the litigation system is thus less clear than might have been anticipated. The producers of technological risks will be inclined to overindulge, absent signals that align their self-interest with the larger social interest. Where markets fail to create proper incentives, the judicial system may act as a curative by imposing liability on those who create unreasonable risks. Viewed in isolation, the doctrines that underlie liability may look too harsh. Recognition that injured parties may fail to seek redress, however, creates just the opposite conclusion. The question that remains is how these two biases work on balance. It may be that the systematic bias against seeking access to the courts outweighs the doctrinal, or process, bias that affects those few cases that reach the litigation stage. Or it may be that inflating the liability imposed on *any* risk producer brought to judgment increases the expected liability that must be anticipated by *all,* so that the expected loss from unreasonable conduct approaches the social optimum. If this is the case, then there is less reason for complaint about those cases in which substantial damages are imposed, as they do not indicate a general overdeterrent for risk producers as a class.

At this stage, however, we are unable to conclude which of these possible effects dominates. Our claim, therefore, is not that the judicial system systematically underdeters social risk. Rather, our more modest claim is that those who contend that the judicial system systematically overdeters risk and therefore hampers technological advances that are risky, but risk reducing, have not carried the burden of persuasion. But even if courts do not perfectly balance risk-producing and risk-reducing technologies, the investigation cannot end there. Just as existing and proposed technologies must be compared, so must risk-assessing institutions. The imperfections of courts must be compared to the imperfections of alternatives, primarily regulatory agencies. While *ex ante* risk regulation has been the target of criticism, similar to that addressed to *ex post* litigation, a number of commentators nevertheless believe that the expertise of administrative agencies makes them superior risk assessors. Hence, proposals abound to replace or reduce judicial intervention in the risk-assessment process with a more professional administrative technocracy. These recommendations, however, are typically made without attention to the possible defects of and biases in the administrative decision-making process. It is to the possibility that biases in the administrative process might exceed, exacerbate, or balance those in the judicial process that we now turn.

4. RISK AND AGENCIES

Enthusiasts of agency risk assessment begin from an idealized conception of the administrative process: staffed by publicly interested experts who are capable of rationally formulating hypotheses about risk-creating technologies, testing through scientific method, and exercising objective judgment in the interpretation of data and resolution of conflicts. It is doubtful, we contend, whether even the most well-intentioned agencies can perform these tasks with anything close to the comprehensive rationality implicit in the argument for agency displacement of judicial risk assessment.

The first challenge to this idealized model comes from the same assumption that we applied in the market and litigation contexts: that individuals tend to act in their rational self-interest. Certainly there is little reason to believe that altruists are over-represented among those who enter government service. Within the judicial context, we argued that self-interest might lead to an undersupply of litigation because potential plaintiffs (and their attorneys) would have insufficient incentives to seek redress. Agencies might initially seem different, since they need not await victim claims to begin regulatory efforts. Nevertheless, agencies must have *some* reason to select the risks they do for investigation. If self-interest skews selection, there is no reason to believe that the resulting decisions will be any more free of bias than those produced by the judicial process.

The possibility that self-interest could affect agency decisions about what and how to investigate and regulate is well documented in a literature that comes under the broad heading of "capture." Capture theory proceeds from the notion that the behavior of private citizens and public officials in public or "political" markets is similar to the behavior of producers and consumers in ordinary economic markets. Citizens (both risk producers and risk consumers) and officials (potential risk regulators) are assumed to act in ways that may have little in common with what would serve the larger public interest. For officials, this might include conduct that seeks to maximize their personal leisure time, their reputation with a particular group, their advancement within government, their employment possibilities in the private sector, or their personal wealth. Depending on the objective selected, the public official may act in a manner that enhances personal reputation with agency heads, legislative leaders, a particular subgroup of citizens, or potential employers, but not necessarily with the public at large.

The willingness of public officials to serve their self-interest unfortunately coincides with the capacity of citizens to take advantage of it. Citizens can offer public officials information, political support, employment, and dollars. To some extent, citizen participation in the political process to influence public officials is exactly what a democratic conception of the "public interest" anticipates. That conception, however, anticipates that all sides of a public issue will have roughly equal access to officials and that the ultimate decision will subsequently be made only after balancing the expressed views of all those affected. We saw in our discussion of adjudicative responses to risk, however, that access to the courts by risk victims is constrained by the costs imposed on potential litigants. Similarly, victim groups will commonly lack sufficient incentives to attain the administrative ear. The same characteristics of latency, diffusion, low probability, and nonexclusivity at work in the judicial setting also discourage mobilization efforts by potential victims who might otherwise seek administrative relief from risk creation.

The capacity of risk producers to mobilize effective interest groups, on the other hand, appears to be substantial. Their organizational burdens will generally be lighter because there are fewer potential group members; each member (within an industry) will usually know the identity of others; each member is likely to have a relatively large, concentrated, and immediate stake in agency decisions; each has greater assets to tap than any similar number of victims; and communication among them will likely be facilitated by their membership in preexisting associations. Taken together, these considerations permit producers to enjoy a considerable advantage in mobilizing interest groups and exercising influence. While public interest organizations may act as a palliative, they are by no means a panacea. Because they serve diffuse interests that confer benefits on noncontributors, they are likely to suffer from the same underfunding and deviations that affect class action litigation in the adjudicative setting. The result is that asymmetric access is likely to infect the agency process, just as it does the adjudicative. Indeed, what was originally considered a strength of the administrative process—an agency's capacity to anticipate and to resolve issues without the need for intervention by members of the public—turns out to be a (potential) weakness, because risk producers with superior access can initiate favorable regulations well in advance of focused public concerns. In both courts and agencies, then, the same group—potential victims—is likely to be under-represented. Looking at access alone, one might conclude that neither courts nor agencies are disposed to regulate risk in a manner that approximates the public interest.

Even if agencies were equally receptive to all affected parties, however, it does not follow that their decisions would similarly reflect public preferences about risk. This is not to say that public officials should simply embody public perceptions. The public at large may occasionally be so uninformed in their views as to be irrational. The fact is, however, that public perceptions of what is risky differ significantly, but not irrationally, from that of public officials who have developed a particular occupational conception of risk. Hence, even a selfless agency, determined to assess and manage risk in accord with its own best view of that term, might end up regulating differently from what is called for from the public's view.

To understand this argument, consider what risk means. To some, risk entails what-ever threatens mortality and morbidity. When technical experts are asked to rank the risks of various activities and technologies, "their responses correlate highly with technical estimates of annual fatalities" (Slovic et al., 1985). Technical calculations of risk that consider fatalities are also likely to treat all lives as equal, such that the same value is attributed to an expectation that 1000 lives will be lost annually regardless of whether they are lost through a single anticipated annual catastrophe, or through fewer lives lost per accident but with many accidents expected every year, or through 10,000 lives lost only once every decade on average. Further, the value of lives lost remains the same without regard to their concentration in a single community or their dispersal across the country.

The lay population is likely to have a very different, and in some ways more complex, conception of risk. Lay individuals are likely to consider characteristics not easily incorporated into the expected value calculations of the technical experts: involun-tariness of exposure, irreversibility of consequences, delayed or catastrophic effects may all add up to public "dread" of particular risks that is difficult to classify as "irrational" but that does not coincide with expected deaths standing alone. This is very different from asserting that public estimation of risks is simply uninformed, a traditional basis for deferring to experts on the regulation of risk. Much of the work done on public vs. expert risk perception supports this view. Paul Slovic and his colleagues (Slovic et al., 1980) measured "riskiness" of activities and technologies as perceived by experts and nonex-perts. As might be expected, the expert rankings were relatively consistent with statistical or calculated frequencies of death. Lay rankings deviated from these measures. The lay rankings, however, did not differ from those of the experts simply because the lay subjects made inaccurate fatality estimates. To the contrary, when the investigators asked lay subjects to estimate annual fatalities, they found "only a low to moderate agreement" between lay fatality estimates and lay riskiness judgments. Quite clearly, something other than mortality rates was motivating the nonexperts. That "something," concluded Slovic and his associates, comprised the characteristics of catastrophe, involuntariness, un-familiarity, and severity of the risk.

Consider the association of dread with particular distributions of risk. Risks that might result in death or disease are often considered worth taking because they confer significant benefits not otherwise available. This risk burden may be regarded as equitably distributed only if borne by those who simultaneously enjoy the benefits. Alternatively, risks concentrated in time and space might be regarded as inequitable or otherwise unacceptable because concentration can result in losses to valued objects other than life and limb that can be avoided by broader distributions. Imagine, for instance, a decision maker who is forced to choose between two actions. The first action poses a 1 in 1000 chance of causing 100,000 deaths spread randomly across the country; the second has a 1 in 1200 chance of causing the near obliteration of a city of 100,000. A rational decision maker could obviously select the first alternative, notwithstanding its larger expected mortality loss. The second choice, unlike the first, would additionally provoke the collective trauma of disasters that wipe out neighborhoods and entire networks of relationships. That costs other than loss of life are visited on victims helps to explain the public aversion to catastrophe and the willingness to incur a larger number of (expected) deaths to protect against it. The experts' insistence on pure body counting is not necessarily senseless. It may be defended by reference to an ideological position, to administrative ease in comparing otherwise incomparable risks, or by the rationality of a common denominator. Thus, our argument is not that experts are necessarily wrongheaded. Rather, our argument is that the public response has its own legitimacy and rationality. Admit this and it follows that the choice of approach is an ethical or political one to which the experts have neither special knowledge nor special authority.

The different, if equally rational, approaches to risk taken by experts and lay people suggest that agency decision making cannot capture the very characteristics that account for the differences between them. Even if experts, those who reside in agencies and give them credibility, were to accept the characteristics of risk endorsed by lay people, the regulatory processes of agencies would be incapable of incorporating these characteristics into decision making. Regulation is typically *ex ante,* that is, prior to exposure, and thus is incapable of considering the position of the particular individuals on whom the risk has been visited. Litigation, on the other hand, is predominantly *ex post,* that is, after exposure, so that the victims on whom the statistical probability of harm has actually been visited appear in all their trauma. For some, this fact is a defect of the litigation process insofar as it introduces emotional elements into the risk allocation decision. But why should not the fact that lay persons care to take certain characteristics into account suggest that distribution of risk is as important as its probability?

An example may be useful here. Few would argue, for instance, that polio vaccine should be eliminated because some inoculations lead tragically to contracting the disease. Yet once the individuals on whom these costs are visited emerge from the nebulous world of statistical probabilities and appear before us with all their suffering, it becomes more difficult to deny them any recompense. If we knew that providing compensation would cause the rest of us to bear an increased cost for vaccine or to incur additional difficulty in obtaining vaccine, few might object. The same phenomenon leads us to dedicate substantial resources to save identifiable injured persons, e.g., earthquake victims, who, on a cost basis alone, should be left to their demise rather than risking additional resources (including the lives of rescuers). This is not to suggest that the decision to rescue is mistaken; to the contrary, it is to suggest that the social decision to compensate identifiable victims, even where the harm was incurred in the service of the greater good, even where compensation may deter production of further public benefits, is one that we expect to see reflected in institutional decisions.

If we extrapolate from the individual case to a widespread class of victims, the argument for compensation becomes stronger still. Those who suffer the latent effects of advancing technology constitute the victims of Albert Hirschman's Principle of the Hiding Hand (1982): Once the adverse effects are known, amelioratives may prevent their repetition, "but this whole process implies that the first generations of users serve as guinea pigs for the subsequent ones without first being asked whether they are willing to play that role." While the underlying technology may produce intergenerational net social benefits, the disproportionate imposition of costs on the first generation may give rise to some restitutionary claim against those later users who benefit from the earlier misfortune. Since the "public" nature of the risk suggests that all within the first generation were similarly at risk, there seems little justification for visiting the full costs of the hazard on the unlucky few as to whom the risk materialized.

If we wish to address our concern for identifiable victims, however, risk-balancing decisions made by agencies will be unsatisfactory. The *ex ante* valuation placed on lives in general and factored into a bureaucratic decision concerning total social risks and benefits may fail to recognize the quite different *ex post* value placed on identifiable victims. The latter calculations can only be made on a case-by-case basis as the individual victims emerge with their injuries, a function typically performed through judicial intervention. Agencies engaged in *ex ante* rulemaking will provide a forum only for those previously injured to appear and will rescue others still at risk. If courts alone can vindicate our sympathy for individual victims or provide for them a forum in which to express concerns or to have their misfortune explained, it is unclear what rational concept precludes us from employing courts for that purpose.

We are left, then, with an imperfect scheme for regulating risk. Neither courts nor agencies promise the ability to reduce risk to a socially optimal level. But the story does not end there, for we can imagine that certain tendencies prevail. Our investigation of biases in the judicial system indicated that the biases related to process, or doctrinal law, might tend to impose too much liability on those cases that actually reach litigation. This tendency, however, might be countered by access biases that suggest too few cases actually reach the litigation stage. What is unclear is whether these countervailing tendencies cancel each other out. On the agency side, the mix looks quite different. The access bias in the agency setting suggests that agency personnel can fall under the spell of interest groups dominated by risk producers who favor under-regulation. The process bias at this level similarly suggests under-regulation from the public perspective, because risks measured only in terms of mortality exclude characteristics dreaded by the public at large. Thus, all tendencies in the administrative process point to regulation that permits too much risky activity. We do not want to condemn agencies on this basis. After all, there may be some countervailing tendencies, such as the willingness of agency personnel to over-regulate in order to avoid blame for the materialization of risks or the possibility that risks that are regulated suffer such substantial regulation as to induce socially appropriate behavior by industries that fear mistakes will cause them to fall within the administrative net. But these speculations do not constitute proof of the assertion that our current mix of judicial and agency regulation would be improved by deferring to the experts who occupy administrative offices.

Our concerns in this regard are exacerbated by the nature of the "expertise" required for the regulation of novel risks. Risks associated with new technologies require the exercise of judgment. Where technologies are new and probabilities are small, as is typically the case in the risks with which we are concerned, risk assessments must be based on complex mathematical models, extrapolations from related but different research, and subjective judgments rather than empirical observation. Here even experts are operating under conditions of uncertainty in which the wisdom of judgments is threatened not by any malevolence inherent in administrative decision making but by the constraints burdening all humans. Recent literature in cognitive psychology, for instance, illuminates how individuals employ heuristics to cope with the sorts of uncertainties involved in questions of risk. These heuristics may reduce complex tasks of prediction to simpler judgments (Tversky and Kahneman, 1982) but can also generate "severe and systematic errors." Someone employing the *representative* heuristic, for example, may consider anecdotal information about risks to be representative of his own situation and measure the probability of facing a similar risk accordingly. If the background information is not, in fact, representative of the actor's situation, the assumed probability may bear no relationship to actual risks. Similarly, the *availability* heuristic will lead individuals to assess frequencies and probabilities in terms of the ease with which instances of the phenomenon come to mind, so that recent reports of materialized risks are likely to increase the estimated probabilities of their occurrence. *Anchoring* suggests that initial estimates about probabilities will bias predictions so that investigators have difficulty making adjustments for contrary, but subsequently obtained, information. Finally, the *framing* heuristic suggests that normatively inconsequential changes in the way a decision problem is formulated can affect the problem's resolution. For instance, proposing two programs, one in terms of saving lives and the other in terms of allowing people to die, may lead to radically different recommendations, even though the number of expected lives saved or lost is exactly the same under each proposal.

Little reason exists to expect experts working under uncertainty to be less susceptible to heuristic biases than laypersons. Commonly recalled disasters, from Bhopal to thalidomide to Chernobyl to Challenger, suggest how expert designs may be flawed when dealing with technologies that require the use of intuition and value judgments rather than historical data. Indeed, one set of researchers concluded that "experts, once they are forced to go beyond their data and rely on judgment, may be as prone to overconfidence as lay people" (Slovic *et al.*, 1982). This is not to say, of course, that experts are any worse at estimating probabilities under uncertainty than are laypersons. It is only to suggest that expert assessments in these circumstances are not necessarily better. Nor does the presence of bias require that risk assessments by experts using heuristics will necessarily generate too much risk. It is also possible that experts will overestimate the riskiness of new technologies, and thus abandon efforts that would, on balance, be risk reducing. Our conclusion is only that because the issues in question are not and cannot be objectively grounded, they cannot be resolved on purely objective grounds. Much less should these nontechnical issues be consigned entirely to experts whose competence lies in the technical arts.

To this point, our discussion assumes that risk-assessment decisions must be made by either courts or agencies, and has asked which is better suited to the task. Our response, however, has been that neither is particularly well suited to calculating or addressing the risks inherent in new technologies that threaten widespread injury to large numbers of people. Institutional failures, we have argued, result in part from structural defects and in part from attitudes towards risk. On the question whether judicial intervention deters risk-reducing technologies, we said that the interplay of access and process bias makes any conclusion speculative. On the matter of agencies, we suggested why access and process biases might generate too little regulation of risk, although it might be buffered by the remainder of a system that includes both courts and agencies. Finally, we suggested that the appropriate level and type of risk regulation might depend on what counts as risk, an issue of attitudes on which agencies have no advantage.

If we take this last point seriously, it raises substantial questions about the desirability of deference to agencies. If expert attitudes toward risk are not consonant with those of the population at large, then a purported liability of judges and juries—that they are *not* experts—turns out to be an asset. Indeed, if lay determinations of risk are (on a series of assumptions about democratic governance) essential to the issue of appropriate risk regulation, then the real issue may be how to increase popular participation in the risk assessment process.

A growing body of literature advances just this view. Its authors argue that the appropriate response to different conceptions of risk is to democratize the management process by encouraging public participation in decisions about which risks are worth avoiding. Given the intractable problems and tradeoffs of defining and balancing risks, the idea behind participation is not necessarily to improve the technical accuracy of risk decisions. Rather the objective is to enhance the legitimacy of the decision-making process.

The difficulty is that direct democratic participation poses special problems in the case of risk. Sensible risk regulation depends on an equally sensible grasp of technical matters that cannot be expected of the general public. There is little reason to suppose that participatory processes provide good means for filtering out cognitive errors and some reason to believe they might aggravate them. Logistical problems pose additional obstacles. Effective participation requires a considerable degree of decentralized decision making and locally accessible decision forums. Many of the risks of new technologies, however, typically call for highly centralized management. Modern technologies can impose costs and benefits, effects and side effects, that have consequences for broad geographical areas or that make discrimination among potential victims unwieldy.

Finally, democratic process are inherently unsuitable for many of the characteristics that make the risks of which we have been speaking salient in popular discourse. Recall that those characteristics include latency, involuntariness, and catastrophic potential. In dealing with uncertainty, a chief virtue of democracy is its reliance on trial and error to promote incremental learning. In the case of modern risk, however, this process of "muddling through" (Lindblom, 1959) is also fraught with vices. The reactive technique of trial and error is useful only to the extent that information generated by one experiment can be considered and exploited in a subsequent one. With too many risks associated with new technologies, the potential to learn from error is also the potential to bring about irreversible catastrophe. Especially where errors have latent effects, too much may be learned too late.

There are reasons, then, to prefer a holistic, systematic, "synoptic" method of expert analysis to a participatory, incremental one. Certainly this view reverts back to a preference for centralized agency risk assessment and management over participatory or judicial institutions. But the shortcomings of these familiar decision-making structures suggest that we should be skeptical about limiting our choices to institutions—courts and agencies—that were created to solve issues very different from those that occupy the landscape of technological risk. The challenge is instead to devise solutions as powerful as the problems they confront. We need to imagine institutional breakthroughs that match our technological ones.

REFERENCES

Akerlof, G.A., and Dickens, W.T., 1982, The economic consequences of cognitive dissonance, *Am. Econ. Rev.* 72:307.

Buchanan, J.M., and Faith, R.L., 1981, Entrepreneurship and the internalization of externalities, *J. Law Econ.* 24:95.

Calabresi, G., and Bobbitt, P., 1978, *Tragic Choices,* Norton, New York.

Coffee, J., 1986, Understanding the plaintiff's attorney: The implications of economic theory for private enforcement of law through class and derivative actions, *Colum. L. Rev.* 86:669.

Coffee, J., 1987, The regulation of entrepreneurial litigation: Balancing fairness and efficiency in the large class action, *U. Chi. L. Rev.* 54:877.

Dam, K., 1975, Class actions: Efficiency, compensation, deterrence and conflict of interest, *J. Legal Stud.* 4:47.

Gillette, C.P., and Krier, J.E., 1990, Risk, courts, and agencies, *U. Penn. L. Rev.* 138:1027.

Hampton, J., 1987, Free-rider problems in the production of collective goods, *Econ. Phil.* 3:245.

Henderson, J.A., 1983, Product liability and the passage of time: The imprisonment of corporate rationality, *N.Y.U. L. Rev.* 58:765.

Henderson, J.A., Jr., and Eisenberg, T., 1990, The quiet revolution in products liability: An empirical study of legal change, *U.C.L.A. L. Rev.* 37:479.

Hirschman, A.O., 1982, *Shifting Involvements,* Princeton University Press, Princeton.

Huber, P., 1985, Safety and the second best: The hazards of public risk management in the courts, *Colum. L. Rev.* 85:277.

Kahneman, D., and Tversky, A., 1979, Prospect theory: An analysis of decisions under risk, *Econometrica* 47:262.

Kahneman, D., Slovic, P., and Tversky, A., (eds.), 1982, *Judgment Under Uncertainty: Heuristics and Biases,* Cambridge University Press, Cambridge.

Krier, J.E., 1971, The pollution problem and legal institutions: A conceptual overview, *U.C.L.A. L. Rev.* 18:429.

Krier, J.E., and Gillette, C.P., 1985, The un-easy case for technological optimism, *Mich. L. Rev.* 84:405.

Krier, J.E., and Ursin, E., 1977, *Pollution and Policy,* University of California Press, Berkeley.

Landes, W., and Posner, R.A., 1979, Adjudication as a private good, *J. Legal Stud.* 8:235.

Lindblom, C., 1959, The science of muddling through, *Pub. Admin. Rev.* 19:79.

Nelkin, D., and Brown, M.S., 1984, *Workers at Risk: Voices from the Workplace,* University of Chicago Press, Chicago.

Page, T., 1978, A generic view of toxic chemicals and similar risks, *Ecol. L. O.* 7:207.

Robinson, G.O., 1982, Multiple Causation in Tort Law: Reflections on the DES cases, *Va. L. Rev.* 68:713.

Schelling, T.C., 1984, The life you save may be your own, in: *Choice and Consequence* (T.C. Schelling, ed.), Harvard University Press, Cambridge, pp. 113–146.

Shavell, S., 1986, The judgment proof problem, *Intl. Rev. L. Econ.* 6:45.

Slovic, P., Fischhoff, B., and Lichtenstein, S., 1980, Facts and fears: Understanding perceived risk, in: *Societal Risk Assessment: How Safe is Safe Enough?* (R. Schwing, and W. Albers, Jr., eds.), Plenum Press, New York, pp. 181–216.

Slovic, P., Fischhoff, B., and Lichtenstein, S., 1985, Regulation of risk: A psychological perspective, in: *Regulatory Policy and the Social Sciences* (R. Noll, ed.), University of California Press, Berkeley, pp. 241–278.

Tversky, A., and Kahneman, D., 1986, Rational choice and the framing of decisions, in: *Rational Choice: The Contrast between Economics and Psychology* (R. Hogarth, and M. Reder, eds.), University of Chicago Press, Chicago, pp. 67–94.

Williams, S., 1978, Running out: the problem of exhaustible resources, *J. Legal Stud.* 7:165.

Epilogue

Despite the length of Volumes 1 and 2, we realize that much more could have been said about food-related toxins and pollutants. However, there are practical limits, and we have probably exceeded the usual reader's attention span as it is. We believe that the authors have provided a good sampling of the effects of inadequate nutrition, a number of the toxins and toxicants that may reach us through our diet, some of the mechanisms by which these toxins act, and some of the issues that must be faced in connection with the regulation of production and processing of food.

We have a number of regrets, not only about the errors of commission or omission we may have made in editing Volumes 1 and 2, but also about the significance of the content for humankind. Obviously, we regret the malnutrition that exists in the world.

To say that "we regret" the fact that 35,000 people starve to death every day is far too mild a statement and does not present the intensity of our sadness and mourning. To further recognize that this is occurring when there are agricultural surpluses in many countries and no global shortage of food makes us angry about the state of world economic policies. This knowledge weighs heavily on us.

Among our other regrets are the facts presented in this book about contaminated foods, dangerous consequences in food production and processing, and the ineffectiveness of the governments of the world to ameliorate a growing number of problems associated with food-related hazards. We feel that many millions of people are concerned, but the translation of this concern often fails to produce political or economic actions. We regret that comprehensive surveys for the presence of toxins and pollutants in our food supply still remain inadequate. In the chapter by McLachlan and Massiah, the need for including assays for aluminum in such surveys is clearly spelled out, yet we doubt such testing will be undertaken in the foreseeable future. The same thing can be said about testing for the presence of many of the agents mentioned by other authors in this book.

We regret that pollution-related decisions made by courts, agencies, officials, committees, and the "body politic" throughout the world are sometimes more easily influenced by economic considerations and special interests than by a knowledge of, or a concern for, world health. Possibilities are numerous and alarming. While the use of a hazardous substance may be strictly regulated in the country where it is manufactured, it may be exported to other countries where its use may not be regulated. Banning the agricultural use of a pesticide in the country where it is manufactured does not prevent it

---

The Vulnerable Brain and Environmental Risks, Volume 2: Toxins in Food, edited by Robert L. Isaacson and Karl F. Jensen. Plenum Press, New York, 1992.

from being exported for use in other countries. More appalling is the possibility that when produce is identified as having excess levels of pesticide residues, it can be transported to another country where regulation or enforcement may be lax. While Third World countries undoubtedly fare worse by such exchanges, fruits and vegetables at groceries stores in countries such as the United States can also be imported from countries with few regulations or lax enforcement. Monitoring of such imported produce is limited, and the consumer is rarely provided information as to what pesticides and herbicides have been applied to fruits and vegetables. Clearly the need exists for greater awareness of chemicals in food.

We regret that there are no easy answers to the question of what agents, minerals, metals, or chemicals have neurotoxic properties. There are no simple tests for neurotoxicants, and the only way they can be identified is through comprehensive multidisciplinary approaches. It is hard to emphasize this enough. No one technique will provide a magical touchstone for determining human neurotoxicity. The toxic consequences are too varied, often subtle, sometimes delayed in appearance, and always compounded with other changes in the body associated with the exposure to the agent. In the human, such confounding is worse, being influenced by social, economic, and genetic variables. We hope that people become convinced of the importance and urgency of this and related work and that an interest in neurotoxicology is sparked in current and future neuroscientists. The world will benefit when the young and bright scientists of all countries accept the challenges facing neurotoxicology. Equally important is the interest of nonscientists and scientists in other fields. The challenges facing neurotoxicology will only be addressed when there is a widely held interest in the ways in which toxic agents exert their effects on brain and behavior.

Robert L. Isaacson
Karl F. Jensen

Binghamton, New York
Research Triangle, North Carolina

Index